Expert Consult

Expert Consult とは，エルゼビア・ジャパンで出版している一部のタイトルのコンテンツをオンラインで閲覧するためのサイトです．本サイトをご覧いただくには，書籍ごとに PIN コードが必要となります．

■ Expert Consultのご利用方法

1. ログインしていただき，画面左上の「掲載コンテンツ」よりご覧になりたい書籍をクリックしてください．

2. 初めて登録される方は「新しいユーザー」をクリックします．その後，③以降の手順に従って進んでください．

3. メールアドレス，スクラッチ部分を削ったところに記載された PIN コードを入力し，「送信する」をクリックしてください．

4. ③でご登録いただいたメールアドレスに「Expert Consult ユーザー登録についてのお知らせ」という標題のメールが届きます．メールに記載された URL をクリックしていただくとユーザー登録画面が表示されますので，必要情報をご入力ください．

5. ご登録いただいたログイン ID・パスワードにてログインすると，画面左上に表示されている該当書籍のコンテンツをご覧いただけます．

https://www.expertconsult.jp/

■ Expert Consultの注意点

- 本サービスをご利用になるには，インターネット接続環境が必要になります．購読者ご本人による個人情報の詳細入力と使用条件の承諾後，開始となります．
- 本サービスは書籍をご購入された個人の方にのみ有効なライセンスです．図書館などの施設での共同利用は出来ません．オンラインサービスへのアクセス権は，1つのPINコードに対し，1ユーザーとなっております．登録者以外が使用を試みると該当パスワードが無効となる場合があります．アクセス権を他人と共有すること，転売すること，これらに類似する行為は禁じられています．
- 本サービスは事前の通知をすることなく，内容等に関する一部または全部を変更，追加，停止および終了する場合がありますので予めご了承ください．

※最初にご登録いただくログイン ID とパスワードは，今後ログインしていただく際に必要になりますので，大切に保管してください

詳細な登録方法 はこちらから

https://www.expertconsult.jp/

JN167211

ユーザーサポート Expert Consultに関するお問い合わせはEメールで下記宛にお願いします．
・お問い合わせ先：**support@expertconsult.jp**

Abrahams' and McMinn's
Clinical Atlas of Human Anatomy
8th Edition

人体解剖カラーアトラス

原書第8版
電子書籍付

Peter H. Abrahams
Jonathan D. Spratt
Marios Loukas
Albert N. van Schoor

訳 | 佐藤達夫
　　 秋田恵一

ELSEVIER

南江堂

ELSEVIER

Higashi-Azabu 1-chome Bldg.
1-9-15, Higashi-Azabu,
Minato-ku, Tokyo 106-0044, Japan

ABRAHAMS' AND MCMINN'S CLINICAL ATLAS OF HUMAN ANATOMY

The right of Peter H. Abrahams, Jonathan D. Spratt, Marios Loukas and Albert N. van Schoor to be identified as authors of this work has been asserted by them in accordance with the Copyright, Designs and Patents Act 1988.
All photographs taken by Ralph Hutchings, photographer for Imagingbody.com, remain in his sole copyright.

© 2020, Elsevier Limited. All rights reserved.
First edition 1977 by Wolfe Publishing. Second edition 1988 by Wolfe Publishing. Third edition 1993 by Mosby-Wolfe, an imprint of Times Mirror International Publishers Ltd. Fourth edition 1998 by Mosby, an imprint of Mosby International Ltd. Fifth edition 2003 by Elsevier Science Ltd. Sixth edition 2008 by Elsevier Ltd. Seventh edition 2013 by Elsevier Ltd.

ISBN: 978-0-7020-7332-8

This translation of *Abrahams' and McMinn's Clinical Atlas of Human Anatomy, Eighth Edition* by **Peter H. Abrahams, Jonathan D. Spratt, Marios Loukas** and **Albert N. van Schoor**, was undertaken by Nankodo Co., Ltd. and is published by arrangement with Elsevier Ltd.

本書，Peter H. Abrahams, Jonathan D. Spratt, Marios Loukas and Albert N. van Schoor 著：*Abrahams' and McMinn's Clinical Atlas of Human Anatomy, Eighth Edition* は，Elsevier Ltd. との契約によって出版されている．

人体解剖カラーアトラス 原書第8版（電子書籍付），by Peter H. Abrahams, Jonathan D. Spratt, Marios Loukas and Albert N. van Schoor.
Copyright © 2021 Elsevier Japan KK. Reprinted 2023.
ISBN：978-4-524-22764-8

All rights reserved. No part of this publication may be reproduced or transmitted in any form or by any means, electronic or mechanical, including photocopying, recording, or any information storage and retrieval system, without permission in writing from the publisher. Details on how to seek permission, further information about the Publisher's permissions policies and our arrangements with organizations such as the Copyright Clearance Center and the Copyright Licensing Agency, can be found at our website: www.elsevier.com/permissions.

This book and the individual contributions contained in it are protected under copyright by the Publisher (other than as may be noted herein).

注意

　本翻訳は，エルゼビア・ジャパンがその責任において請け負ったものである．医療従事者と研究者は，ここで述べられている情報，方法，化合物，実験の評価や使用においては，常に自身の経験や知識を基盤とする必要がある．医学は急速に進歩しているため，特に，診断と薬物投与量については独自に検証を行うものとする．法律のおよぶ限り，Elsevier，出版社，著者，編集者，監訳者，翻訳者は，製造物責任，または過失の有無に関係なく人または財産に対する被害および／または損害に関する責任，もしくは本資料に含まれる方法，製品，説明，意見の使用または実施における一切の責任を負わない．

ABRAHAMS' AND MCMINN'S
CLINICAL ATLAS OF HUMAN ANATOMY

EIGHTH EDITION

Peter H. Abrahams, MB BS, FRCS (Ed), FRCR, DO (Hon) FHEA
Professor "Emeritus" of Clinical Anatomy, Warwick Medical School, UK
Professor of Clinical Anatomy, St. George's University, Grenada, W.I.
National Teaching Fellow 2011, UK
Life Fellow, Girton College, Cambridge, UK
Examiner, MRCS, Royal Colleges of Surgeons (UK)
Family Practitioner NHS (retired), Brent, London, UK

Jonathan D. Spratt, MA (Cantab), FRCS (Eng), FRCR
Clinical Director of Radiology, City Hospitals Sunderland, UK
Former Examiner in Anatomy, Royal College of Surgeons of England, UK
Former Examiner in Anatomy, Royal College of Radiologists, UK

Marios Loukas, MD, PhD
Dean of Basic Sciences, Dean of Research,
Professor and Co-Chair, Department of Anatomical Sciences, School of Medicine
St. George's University, Grenada, W.I.

Albert-Neels van Schoor, BSc MedSci, BSc (Hons), MSc, PhD
Associate Professor, Head of Section of Clinical Anatomy, Department of Anatomy, School of Medicine,
Faculty of Health Sciences, University of Pretoria, Pretoria, Gauteng, South Africa

序文と献辞

病に苦しむ人々へ，なかなか会うことのできない忍耐強い家族と伴侶へ，そして会いすぎるほど会っている4大陸から集まった我々の学生たちへ！

1977年にMcMinnによって出版された「人体解剖カラーアトラス」を礎としたこの新しい第8版は，最新の画像解剖学や臨床症例によって，またほとんどの解剖学的構造についての3次元映像によって更新され，補われている．初版から40年の時を経て，これまでの8つの版は次第に変化してきている．英国のRalph Hutchings氏，Bari Logan氏，John Pegington教授，米国のSandy Marks教授，南アフリカ共和国のHanno Boon教授といった，多くの国際的スター解剖学者の技術や専門的知識が活きている．

Peter Abrahamsは，25年以上にわたって，カラー写真による解剖アトラスと，最新の臨床技術や診療情報ならびに多くの画像診断技術とを結びつける原動力となってきた．この版においては，2016年にグレナダのSt. George's Universityで行われた第3回Hanno Boon記念解剖マスタークラスで作製された解剖標本が新たに加えられている（謝辞の写真を参照）．西インド諸島のグレナダのMarios Loukasと南アフリカ共和国のプレトリアのAlbert van Schoorという2人の若い世代の解剖学者が，Jonathan Sprattという放射線科指導医と協働することで，本書を臨床医学と統合した国際的に最先端の解剖学書にしている．

本書の特徴の一つとして，臨床的事項についてのリンクが，それぞれのページの下に示されていることが挙げられる．これらはStudent Consult eBookに，2000枚を超える臨床写真や解説に加え，200本以上の動画が，非常によくまとめられている（注：本翻訳版ではwww.expertconsult.jpにおいて動画のみ閲覧できる）．解剖アトラスと臨床症例とのコラボレーションという素晴らしい特徴は，AbrahamsとSprattに加え，世界中の120人もの臨床家の仲間たちから寄せられた症例によって作られたものである．我々は，70年以上にわたって宝物ともいえる素晴らしい解剖学的情報を6つの大陸から提供し貢献してくれた，献体をしてくださった方々，患者ならびにその医師たちに心より感謝を申し上げる．

この第8版では，25ページにわたる神経解剖学と脳神経についての章を刷新した．脳神経をそのままの位置で確認することができるような，解剖標本や脳の横断標本とそれらに対

応するMR画像を加えたのである．

最後に，言い忘れていた大事なことがある．それは第7章のリンパ系についての改編である．リンパ系は，解剖実習室では見ることが難しいのであるが，病気，特に癌の広がりについての臨床的理解においては不可欠である．この臨床的に最も重要なシステムであるリンパ系について示説するために，ページを増やし，これまでアトラスや教科書においてめったに示されることがなかった色付けしたリンパ系の標本を加えたのである．

私たち著者は，解剖学を学ぶ学生たちならびに臨床医学を学ぶ学生たちを教える中で，臨床の文脈で解剖学的構造を学ぶことが，人体を理解するのに最も効果的であることを感じている．したがって，本書のほとんどすべての解剖標本を示すページに，対応する放射線学的画像，内視鏡写真を示すようにしている．また，臨床的背景がわかることによって正常解剖の理解を深められるような臨床症例を，3次元血管造影画像，断面画像とともに示すようにしている．

学習に役立つ200本以上の動画はwww.expertconsult.jpにおいて閲覧できる（▶マークがあるページ）ので是非とも有効に活用してほしい．

訳者序文

"Abrahams' and McMinn's Clinical Atlas of Human Anatomy, Eighth Edition" の日本語版が出版されることになりました．初版から，教員と学生の方々から多くの支持を受けてきた本書の第8版の翻訳に関わることができましたことを本当に嬉しく思います．

本書は，臨床症例や臨床的事項をもとに，解剖学を学ぶということをコンセプトとして作られています．解剖学を通じて臨床も学ぶというのではないことに注意が必要です．医学の学ぶべき情報量は，年々飛躍的に増加しており，解剖学を解剖学としてじっくりと学ぶという時間がどんどん削減されています．一方で，学生たちにとっては解剖学を学ぶということが，ともすれば無味乾燥にも思えてしまうということが起こります．

本書の編集をリードしてきたPeter Abrahams教授は，臨床解剖学教育に40年以上にわたって貢献してこられました．その中で，症例をもとにして解剖学を語るときに学生たちが示す目の輝きというものを非常に重視されてきました．彼は，最先端の画像診断技術などを臨床解剖学教育に積極的に取り入れることを進めてこられました．また，動画教材の制作にも非常に熱心で，最新のICT（Information and Communication Technology）技術を解剖学教育に積極的に取り入れるということも進めていることは，米国臨床解剖学会や英国臨床解剖学会，欧州臨床解剖学会でのさまざまな活動からもよく知ることができます．一方で，伝統的な解剖学により作られる精緻な標本の重要さも十分にわかっており，その標本の持つ説得力を，さまざまなテクノロジーの力も借りて存分に引き出そうとするところに彼の教育の魅力があります．

本書は，これからの臨床解剖学教育に必要な要素が存分に散りばめられております．多くの美しい標本写真と，放射線学的画像等とのコラボレーションは，ページをめくるたびに，解剖学を学ぼうとする学生たちや，臨床医学を学びながら解剖学的構造の確認や復習をしようという学生たちの学びの心に強く働きかけることは間違いないでしょう．

ロンドンの英国外科協会 The Royal College of Surgens of England の膨大な解剖標本の中に息づく臨床解剖学の伝統から本書の創者者であるMcMinn名誉教授が生み出したものを核として本書はつくられています．本書の「序文と献辞」にあるように，国際的な制作チームによるさまざまな英知が結集した，コラボレーションの賜物であります．

本書が，解剖学という枠組みを超えて，広くさまざまな医学を学ぶ学生に使われることを望んでいます．臨床的事項について触れられている多くの記載が，美しい解剖標本をより際立たせ，その重要さが伝えられるものと確信しております．

本書で用いた解剖学用語は，現在本邦で主に用いられている日本解剖学会監修『解剖学用語　改訂第13版』（医学書院，2007）を参考にしました．それに加えて，臨床で慣習的に用いられている用語や各学会の用語集などを参考にして日本語訳としました．『解剖学用語』にないものについては「＊」を付けております．臨床科ごとに異なる用語が用いられている場合もあり，統一されていないものも多くあることから，できるだけ一般的なものを選択するように努力いたしました．しかしながら，本書には，英語圏の国において慣習的に用いられている用語や表現なども多数みられました．これらについては，学習者の利便性を考慮してできる限り『解剖学用語』に沿った形にいたしました．さらに，原書にて章やページごとに異なる表記法が用いられているところについて統一するように努力はいたしましたが，完全にはできていないところがあることをお詫びいたします．

本書第7版までは，日本語と英語の用語リストを別にして配置してきました．しかしながら，第8版では，新しい試みとして他の多くのアトラスと同様に，日英の併記といたしました．

図内の用語に関しては，下記方針で整理しています．

①部位や上位となる用語の説明が必要なものについては，〔　〕を用いて説明することとする．
　例…回旋枝〔左冠状動脈〕，長頭〔大腿二頭筋〕
　　　Circumflex branch〔Left coronary artery〕, Long head〔Biceps femoris〕

②同義語は「：」を用いて併記する（本文中の英語についてもこの方法を採用する）．
　例…左房室弁：僧帽弁，踵骨腱：Achilles腱
　　　Arch of aorta：Aortic arch

③省略可能な用語は［　］を用いて示す．ただし，脳神経を表すローマ数字についても［　］で囲むこととする（本文中も同様）．
　例…［坐骨］尾骨筋，ラムダ［状］縫合，眼神経［V₁］

④人名については，原語の綴りをできるだけ使用する．

この優れた「人体解剖カラーアトラス　原書第8版」日本語版の出版を企画されたエルゼビア・ジャパン株式会社，株式会社南江堂に感謝いたします．日本語版制作の過程におい

て，特に用語の統一や，本書内での用語の使い方の統一といった非常に困難で複雑な作業がありました．また，版を重ねるごとに増える各ページのさまざまな情報の配置に加えて，日本語と英語を併記することによるレイアウトの難しさがありました．作業においては，"原書の良さをそのまま十分に表現する"ということを中心に取り組みました．このような作業に，忍耐強く，そして創造的に取り組んでいただきました飯塚真一氏，佐藤美里氏をはじめとするエルゼビア・ジャパン株式会社の編集部の方々に心から感謝いたします．一緒に仕事をさせていただいたことを本当に嬉しく感じております．

2020年12月

佐藤達夫・秋田恵一

謝辞

解剖

人類の利益と未来の医学知識に対する，すべての献体者とその御遺族による究極の寄付に心より感謝する．社会の教育と人類の経験に対する最高の贈り物は，明日の臨床医となる今日および次世代の医学生である．

本書の制作には，大きなチームによる5年以上にわたる努力があった．これらは，5大陸から集まった解剖技術者，教授，教育者や学生たちによるものである．我々4人の著者は，この新しい素晴らしい臨床解剖学のアトラスの制作のために貢献してくれたすべての人々に感謝を申し上げる．

解剖標本の作製

Lané Prigge, Soné van der Walt, Nhlanhla Japhta (Sefako Makgatho Health Sciences University, Pretoria, South Africa) に．

Helene Biemond, Levó Beytell, Dylan Calldo, Edwin de Jager, Shavana Govender, Anya König, Lezanne Louw, Ursula Mariani, Thiasha Nadesan, Andiswa Ncube, Siphesihle Sithole, and Daniël van Tonder (University of Pretoria, Pretoria, South Africa) に．

アトラスにおける神経解剖の節の改訂における努力，助言，貢献に深く感謝する．Prof. Marius Bosman, Gerda Venter (University of Pretoria, Pretoria, South Africa) に．

Maira du Plessis, Benjamin Turner, Drs. Theofanis Kollias, Wallisa Roberts (Department of Anatomical Sciences, St. George's University, School of Medicine, Grenada, West Indies) に．

新しい解剖標本の多くは2016年12月のGrenadaでの第3回Hanno Boon記念解剖マスタークラスで作製されたものである．彼らの技術による貢献と，故Hanno Boon教授の国際的な名声に敬意を表する．Vicky Cottrell, Paul Dansie, Maira du Plessis, Richard Tunstall, Erin Fillmore, Shiva Mathurin, James Coey, Natalie Keoughと，彼らを支えてくれたYvonne James に．

写真，技術と研究

・撮影技術について

Marius Loots (Department of Anatomy, University of Pretoria, South Africa) ならびにLaura Jane and Jaco van Schoor (Jack & Jane Photography, South Africa) に．そしてJoanna Loukas (Department of Anatomical Sciences, St. George's University) に．

・技術的支援について

Gert Lewis, Samuel Ngobeni, René Stanley, and Helena Taute (Department of Anatomy, University of Pretoria, South Africa) に．

・このプロジェクト全体の技術的実験の支援について

Rodon Marrast, Shiva Mathurin, Romeo Cox, Seikou Phillip, Marlon Joseph, Nelson Davis, Travis Joseph, Simone Francis, Charlon Charles, Arnelle Gibbs, Sheryce Fraser and Chad Phillip (Department of Anatomical Sciences, St. George's University, School of Medicine, Grenada, West Indies) に．

・第3回Hanno Boon記念解剖マスタークラスにおける非常に有益な支援について

Ryan Jacobs, Nadica Thomas-Dominique, Tracy Shabazz and Yvonne James (St. George's University, School of Medicine, Grenada, West Indies) に．

・解剖学教室のフェローによる多くの貢献について

Drs. Sonja Salandy, Shinelle Whiteman, Rafik Shereen, Mu-Hsiang (Joy) Wang, Mohammad Walid Kassem, Jaspreet Johal. (Department of Anatomical Sciences, St. George's University, School of Medicine, Grenada, West Indies) に．

・解剖学教室の教員による本書全体にわたる多くのイラストと彼らの芸術的才能による貢献について

Jessica Holland, Brandon Holt, David Nahabedian, Charles Price and Katie Yost. (Department of Anatomical Sciences, St. George's University, School of Medicine, Grenada, West Indies) に．

Dr. Lucille Abrahams MBChB, FRCGP, GP, Brent; Mr. Arunmoy Chakravorty MS, FRCS (Ed), Hillingdon Hospital NHS Foundation Trust London; Prof. Paul Finan MD, FRCS Hon, FRCPS (Glas), Hon Professor of Colorectal Surgery, University of Leeds; Mr. Hitesh Lachani BSc, MCOptom, Ashdown & Collins-Optician, Kensal Rise, London; Mark Surgenor BSc RN RNT at Teleflex; Dr. Tom Watson MBChB, FRCR, Consultant Paediatric Radiologist, Great Ormond Street Hospital, London に．

ほとんどないと信じてはいるが，誤りについてのすべての責任は我々著者にある．しかし，以下の方々の校正力と優れた臨床的専門知識によって，誤りを最小とすることができていると考える．

Ang Eng-Tat, PT, PhD; James Chambers FRCR, MRCS（Eng), MBChB, BSc（Hons), MD; Matthew A Boissaud-Cooke BMedSc（Hons), MB ChB（Hons); Erin Fillmore MPH, PhD; Petrut Gogalniceanu MBBS, BSc, MEd, FRCS; Nick Heptonstall MBChB（Hons), PGCert, MAcadMEd; Adam Iqbal, BSc（Hons), MBChB（Hons), MRCP（UK); Ruth Joplin, PhD; Natalie Keough BSc, BSc（Hons), MSc, PhD（UP); Samantha Low, B. Eng（Hons) MBBS MRCS（Eng) FRCR; David A. Magezi MA（Cantab), BM BCh（Oxon), PhD（Notts); David Metcalfe MBChB, LLB, MSc, MRCP, MRCS; Nkhensani Mogale BMedSc, BSc（Hon), MSc Anatomy（UP); Sreenivasulu Reddy Mogali BSc, MSc（med anat), PhD; Tom Paterson BSc（Hons) Anat, MBChB, MRCS, DOHNS; Thomas Peachey BA（Oxon), MBChB（Hons), FRCR; Daryl Ramai MD; Jamie Roebuck MMedEd, MBChB, BSc（Hons), FHEA; Sara Sulaiman PhD; Richard Tunstall BMedSci, PhD, PGCLTHE, FHEA; Zithulele N. Tshabalala BSc（Hons) Macro-anatomy（Cum laude)（UP), MSc Anatomy（Cum laude)（UP) に．

利用ガイド

本書は「頭から足のつまさき」へという一般的な順序で並べられている．頭頸部（脳と脳神経を含む）の章に続いて，脊柱と脊髄，それから上肢，胸部，腹部と骨盤，下肢，そして最後に特に力をいれたリンパ系となる．どの章も，最初に骨格標本を示し，次に解剖標本へと続く．解剖標本の位置等をわかりやすくするために，体表解剖ならびに対応する画像等も合わせて載せてある．すべての構造には番号が付けられており，それぞれの写真の横または下に用語を列挙している．本文はそれぞれの標本の剖出の理解に必要なものにとどめており，詳細に述べることはしていない．

第3回 Hanno Boon 記念解剖マスタークラス．Grenada, 2016

目次

1 頭頸部と脳

頭蓋	1
頭蓋骨（分解骨）	18
頸部	28
頸部の基部	36
顔面	38
側頭窩と側頭下窩	40
側頭下窩	42
側頭下窩の深層	44
咽頭	45
喉頭	48
眼	51
鼻	55
鼻と舌	56
耳	57
頭蓋腔	59
脳	62
脳幹と脳神経	78
脳神経	79

2 脊柱と脊髄

背部と脊柱	87
背部と肩	88
椎骨	89
仙骨	93
仙骨と尾骨	94
骨性骨盤	96
椎骨の骨化	97
脊柱と脊髄	98
背部の体表解剖	104
背部の筋	105
後頭下三角	108
脊椎のX線画像	112

3 上肢

上肢	115
上肢骨	116
肩	132
腋窩	144
上腕	151
肘	153
前腕	157
手	163
手根と手のX線画像	178

4 胸部

胸部	179
胸郭	180
胸壁の体表投影と乳房	184
乳房	185
胸部体表への投影	186
胸壁	187
胸部内臓	190
心臓	196
縦隔	204
縦隔の画像	208
肺	209
上縦隔	217
胸郭上口と上縦隔	218
胸郭上口	220
後縦隔	221
肋間神経と肋骨の関節	223
大動脈と周囲の血管	224
横隔膜	225
食道	226

5 腹部と骨盤

腹部の概観	227
前腹壁	228
鼠径部	233
腹部	236
上腹部	237
肝臓	254
胆嚢	257
［肝］門脈と腸間膜の血管	258
脾臓	259
脾臓と腸	260
腸	261
小腸	262
腎臓と副腎	263
尿管	269
横隔膜と後腹壁	270
後腹壁と骨盤壁	271
骨盤壁	276
男性の鼠径部，外生殖器	278

男性の骨盤	279
骨盤の血管と神経	282
骨盤靱帯	284
女性の骨盤	285
女性の会陰	289
男性の会陰	291

6　下肢

下肢	293
下肢骨	294
足の骨	318
踵と足の骨	320
踵の骨	321
下肢骨の成長	322
殿部	324
大腿	326
大腿前面	328
股関節	333
膝	337
下腿	346
足根と足	354
足	360
足根と足の画像	364

7　リンパ系

リンパ系	365
胸腺	366
頸部	367
胸管	368
後縦隔	369
腋窩	370
腋窩と肘窩	371
後上腹壁	372
骨盤	373
鼠径部	376
和文索引	377
欧文索引	399

断面ならびに位置と方向を示す用語

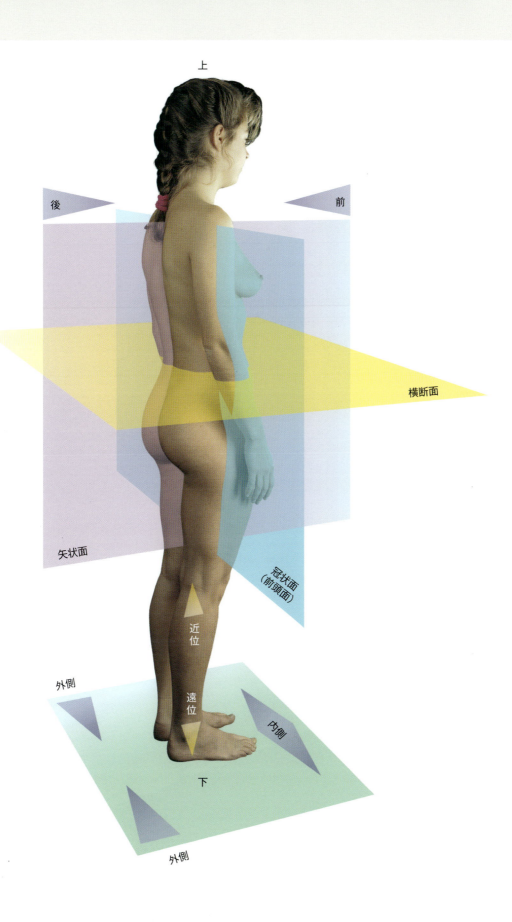

頭頸部と脳

頭蓋

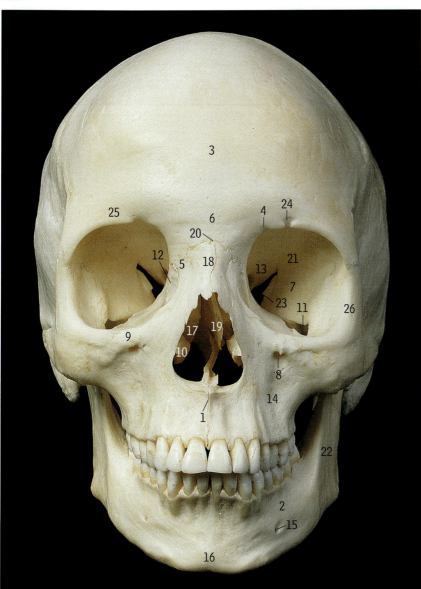

前方から．

1	前鼻棘 Anterior nasal spine	14	上顎骨 Maxilla
2	下顎体 Body of mandible	15	オトガイ孔 Mental foramen
3	前頭骨 Frontal bone	16	オトガイ隆起 Mental protuberance
4	前頭切痕：前頭孔 Frontal notch：Frontal foramen	17	中鼻甲介 Middle nasal concha
5	前頭突起〔上顎骨〕 Frontal process〔Maxilla〕	18	鼻骨 Nasal bone
6	眉間 Glabella	19	鼻中隔 Nasal septum
7	大翼〔蝶形骨〕 Greater wing〔Sphenoid〕	20	ナジオン Nasion
8	眼窩下孔 Infra-orbital foramen	21	眼窩 Orbit：Orbital cavity
9	眼窩下縁 Infra-orbital margin	22	下顎枝 Ramus of mandible
10	下鼻甲介 Inferior nasal concha	23	上眼窩裂 Superior orbital fissure
11	下眼窩裂 Inferior orbital fissure	24	眼窩上孔：眼窩上切痕 Supra-orbital foramen：Supra-orbital notch
12	涙骨 Lacrimal bone	25	眼窩上縁 Supra-orbital margin
13	小翼〔蝶形骨〕 Lesser wing〔Sphenoid〕	26	頬骨 Zygomatic bone

- "頭蓋(skull)"という用語は下顎骨を含み，"頭蓋(cranium)"という用語は下顎骨を含まない．
- 頭蓋冠は頭蓋の円天井のことであり，脳を囲む頭蓋の上部のことである．
- 頭蓋の前部は顔面骨格を形成する．
- 眼窩上孔(24)，眼窩下孔(8)，オトガイ孔(15)の3つの孔はほぼ同じ垂直面に位置する．
- 個々の頭蓋骨の詳細については18〜27頁に，眼窩と鼻腔の構成骨については12頁に，歯については13，16〜19頁に示す．

三脚骨折

頭蓋［筋と靱帯の付着部］

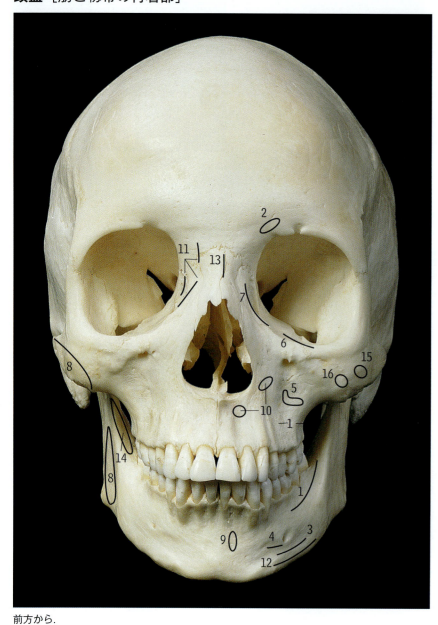

前方から．

1 頬筋 Buccinator
2 皺眉筋 Corrugator supercilii
3 口角下制筋 Depressor anguli oris
4 下唇下制筋 Depressor labii inferioris
5 口角挙筋 Levator anguli oris
6 上唇挙筋 Levator labii superioris
7 上唇鼻翼挙筋 Levator labii superioris alaeque nasi
8 咬筋 Masseter
9 オトガイ筋 Mentalis
10 鼻筋 Nasalis
11 眼輪筋 Orbicularis oculi
12 広頸筋 Platysma
13 鼻根筋 Procerus
14 側頭筋 Temporalis
15 大頬骨筋 Zygomaticus major
16 小頬骨筋 Zygomaticus minor

頭蓋

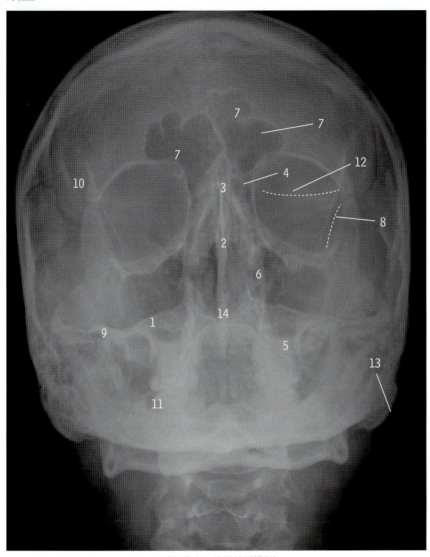

X線画像（15°後頭前頭撮影）

1 底部〔後頭骨〕 Basilar part〔Occipital bone〕
2 蝶形骨体 Body of sphenoid
3 鶏冠 Crista galli
4 篩骨蜂巣 Ethmoidal cells
5 上顎洞底* Floor of maxillary sinus *
6 正円孔 Foramen rotundum
7 前頭洞 Frontal sinus
8 大翼〔蝶形骨〕 Greater wing〔Sphenoid〕
9 内耳道 Internal acoustic meatus
10 ラムダ［状］縫合 Lambdoid suture
11 外側塊〔環椎：第一頸椎〕 Lateral mass〔Atlas：C I〕
12 小翼〔蝶形骨〕 Lesser wing〔Sphenoid〕
13 乳様突起 Mastoid process
14 鼻中隔 Nasal septum

頭蓋

右方から.

1 前涙嚢稜 Anterior lacrimal crest	10 前頭骨 Frontal bone	20 オトガイ孔 Mental foramen	29 プテリオン（○で囲まれた領域） Pterion
2 前鼻棘 Anterior nasal spine	11 前頭突起〔上顎骨〕 Frontal process〔Maxilla〕	21 オトガイ隆起 Mental protuberance	30 下顎枝〔下顎骨〕 Ramus of mandible〔Mandible〕
3 下顎体 Body of mandible	12 前頭頬骨縫合 Frontozygomatic suture	22 鼻骨 Nasal bone	31 鱗部〔側頭骨〕 Squamous part〔Temporal bone〕
4 下顎頭 Head of mandible	13 眉間 Glabella	23 ナジオン Nasion	32 茎状突起〔側頭骨〕 Styloid process〔Temporal bone〕
5 冠状縫合 Coronal suture	14 大翼〔蝶形骨〕 Greater wing〔Sphenoid〕	24 後頭骨 Occipital bone	33 上側頭線 Superior temporal line
6 筋突起〔下顎骨〕 Coronoid process〔Mandible〕	15 下側頭線 Inferior temporal line	25 眼窩板〔篩骨〕 Orbital plate〔Ethmoid〕	34 鼓室部〔側頭骨〕 Tympanic part〔Temporal bone〕
7 外耳道〔側頭骨〕 External acoustic meatus〔Temporal bone〕	16 涙骨 Lacrimal bone	26 頭頂骨 Parietal bone	35 頬骨弓 Zygomatic arch
8 外後頭隆起：イニオン External occipital protuberance：Inion	17 ラムダ〔状〕縫合 Lambdoid suture	27 下垂体窩〔トルコ鞍〕（5頁A参照） Hypophysial fossa〔Sella turcica〕	36 頬骨 Zygomatic bone
9 涙嚢窩 Fossa for lacrimal sac	18 乳様突起〔側頭骨〕 Mastoid process〔Temporal bone〕	28 後涙嚢稜 Posterior lacrimal crest	37 頬骨突起〔側頭骨〕 Zygomatic process〔Temporal bone〕
	19 上顎骨 Maxilla		

- プテリオン（29）は単一の点ではなく，前頭骨（10），頭頂骨（26），側頭骨の鱗部（31）および蝶形骨の大翼（14）が隣接する領域のことである．
- プテリオンは，頭蓋内面を走る中硬膜動脈の前枝の位置を特定する重要な目印となる（17頁）．

硬膜外出血

Ⓐ Ⓑ 頭蓋

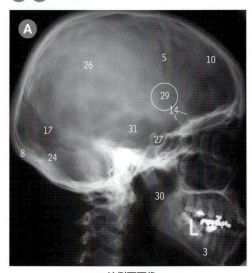

X線側面画像
（番号は前頁の用語表を参照．）

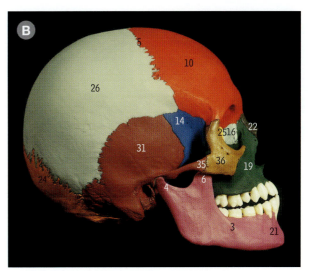

骨に色付けしてある．（番号は前頁の用語表を参照．）

Ⓒ 頭皮

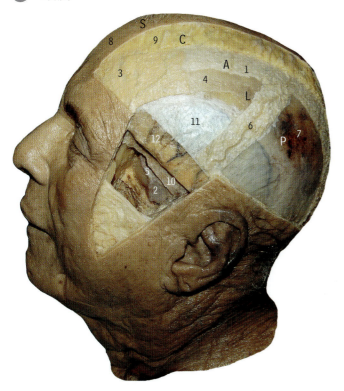

● 皮下の構造物
・S：皮膚，C：結合組織，A：後頭前頭筋の腱膜，L：疎性結合組織，P：骨膜．

1 腱膜〔後頭前頭筋〕
　Aponeurosis〔Occipitofrontalis〕
2 硬膜
　Dura mater
3 前頭筋〔後頭前頭筋〕（疎性結合組織で覆われている）
　Frontal belly〔Occipitofrontalis〕
4 疎性結合組織
　Loose connective tissue
5 硬膜上の中硬膜動脈の痕
6 頭頂枝〔浅側頭動脈〕
　Parietal branch〔Superficial temporal artery〕
7 骨膜
　Periosteum
8 皮膚
　Skin
9 皮下組織
　Subcutaneous tissue
10 側頭骨
　Temporal bone
11 側頭筋膜
　Temporal fascia
12 側頭筋
　Temporalis

頭蓋［筋と靭帯の付着部］

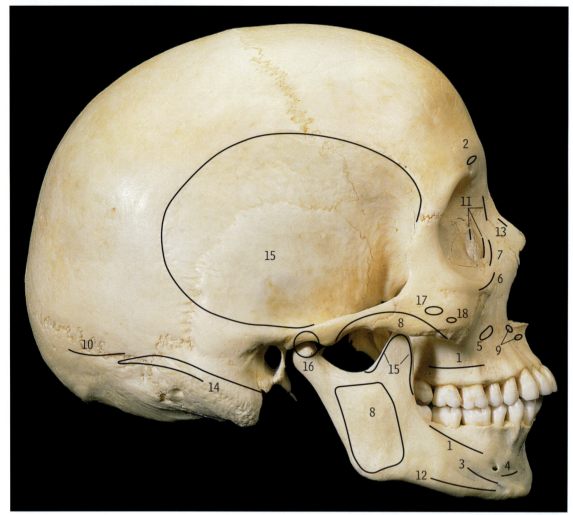

右方から．

1	頬筋 Buccinator	10	後頭筋〔後頭前頭筋〕 Occipital belly〔Occipitofrontalis〕
2	皺眉筋 Corrugator supercilii	11	眼輪筋 Orbicularis oculi
3	口角下制筋 Depressor anguli oris	12	広頸筋 Platysma
4	下唇下制筋 Depressor labii inferioris	13	鼻根筋 Procerus
5	口角挙筋 Levator anguli oris	14	胸鎖乳突筋 Sternocleidomastoid
6	上唇挙筋 Levator labii superioris	15	側頭筋 Temporalis
7	上唇鼻翼挙筋 Levator labii superioris alaeque nasi	16	顎関節 Temporomandibular joint
8	咬筋 Masseter	17	大頬骨筋 Zygomaticus major
9	鼻筋 Nasalis	18	小頬骨筋 Zygomaticus minor

- 頬筋（1）の付着部は，上顎と下顎（上顎骨と下顎骨）の第一〜第三大臼歯の範囲である．（歯の種類については 13 頁参照）．
- 側頭筋の上方付着部（上の 15）は，側頭窩（頬骨弓の上方で頭蓋の側方にある狭い空間）を占める．側頭筋の下方付着部（下の 15）は，下顎切痕の最下部から筋突起を越えて下行し，下顎枝の第三大臼歯の付近にまで達している．
- 咬筋（8）の付着部は，頬骨弓から下顎枝の外側面へ広がっている．

顎関節の脱臼

頭蓋 [B 右側頭下部]

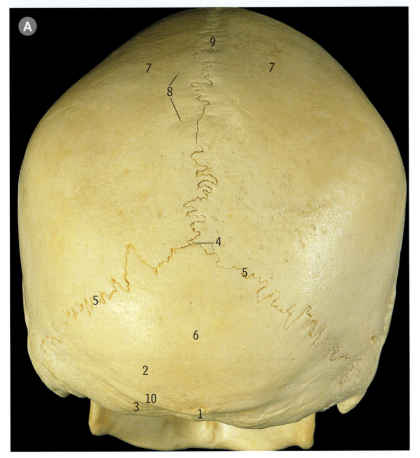

後方から.

1	外後頭隆起：イニオン	External occipital protuberance：Inion
2	最上項線	Highest nuchal line
3	下項線	Inferior nuchal line
4	ラムダ	Lambda
5	ラムダ［状］縫合	Lambdoid suture
6	後頭骨	Occipital bone
7	頭頂骨	Parietal bone
8	頭頂孔	Parietal foramen
9	矢状縫合	Sagittal suture
10	上項線	Superior nuchal line

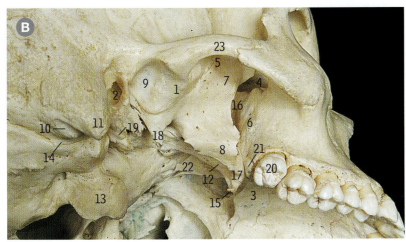

斜め下方から.

1	関節結節	Articular tubercle
2	外耳道	External acoustic meatus
3	水平板〔口蓋骨〕	Horizontal plate〔Palatine bone〕
4	下眼窩裂	Inferior orbital fissure
5	側頭下稜	Infratemporal crest
6	側頭下面〔上顎骨〕	Infratemporal surface〔Maxilla〕
7	側頭下面〔蝶形骨の大翼〕	Infratemporal surface〔Greater wing of Sphenoid〕
8	外側板〔翼状突起〕	Lateral plate〔Pterygoid process〕
9	下顎窩	Mandibular fossa
10	乳突切痕	Mastoid notch
11	乳様突起	Mastoid process
12	内側板〔翼状突起〕	Medial plate〔Pterygoid process〕
13	後頭顆	Occipital condyle
14	後頭動脈溝	Occipital groove
15	翼突鈎	Pterygoid hamulus
16	翼上顎裂と翼口蓋窩	Pterygomaxillary fissure and Pterygopalatine fossa
17	錐体突起〔口蓋骨〕	Pyramidal process〔Palatine bone〕
18	蝶形骨棘	Spine of sphenoid
19	茎状突起と茎状突起鞘	Styloid process and Sheath of styloid process
20	第三大臼歯	3rd molar tooth
21	上顎結節	Maxillary tuberosity
22	鋤骨	Vomer
23	頬骨弓	Zygomatic arch

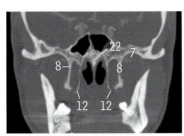

頭部中央のCT冠状断画像

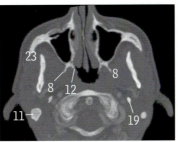

頭部中央のCT横断画像

8　第1章　頭頸部と脳：頭蓋

A B　頭蓋［B 頭蓋冠の内面，中央部］

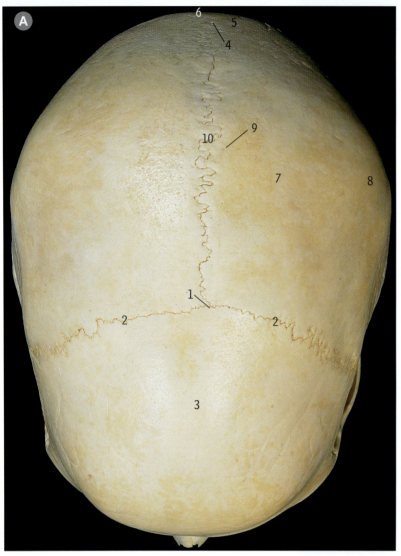
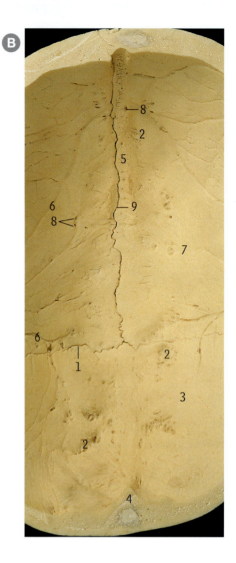

上方から．

1	ブレグマ	Bregma
2	冠状縫合	Coronal suture
3	前頭骨	Frontal bone
4	ラムダ	Lambda
5	ラムダ［状］縫合	Lambdoid suture
6	後頭骨	Occipital bone
7	頭頂骨	Parietal bone
8	頭頂結節	Parietal tuber
9	頭頂孔	Parietal foramen
10	矢状縫合	Sagittal suture

- この頭蓋では，頭頂結節（A8）が発達している．
- 矢状縫合（A10）と冠状縫合（A2）が出合う点をブレグマ（A1）という．出生時には，この領域の前頭骨と頭頂骨がまだ骨化しておらず，膜性の大泉門を形成している（14頁D1）．
- 矢状縫合（A10）とラムダ縫合（A5）の出合う点をラムダ（A4）という．出生時には，この領域の頭頂骨と後頭骨がまだ骨化しておらず，膜性の小泉門を形成している（14頁C13）．
- 前頭骨（A3）の"3"の位置は，胎児の頭蓋に見られる前頭縫合（frontal suture）が走っていた位置を示している（14頁A5）．この前頭縫合は成人にも残存することがある（metopic suture）．
- 脳脊髄液はクモ膜顆粒（62頁B1）を通り抜けて上矢状静脈洞に注ぐ．この顆粒により，静脈洞を覆う前頭骨（B3）と頭頂骨（B7）にクモ膜顆粒小窩（B2．不規則な浅いくぼみ）を生じる．

1	冠状縫合	Coronal suture
2	クモ膜顆粒小窩	Granular foveolae
3	前頭骨	Frontal bone
4	前頭稜	Frontal crest
5	上矢状洞溝	Groove for superior sagittal sinus
6	中硬膜動脈溝	Groove for middle meningeal artery
7	頭頂骨	Parietal bone
8	頭頂孔	Parietal foramen
9	矢状縫合	Sagittal suture

ごましお頭蓋
X線画像

頭蓋［頭蓋底の外面］

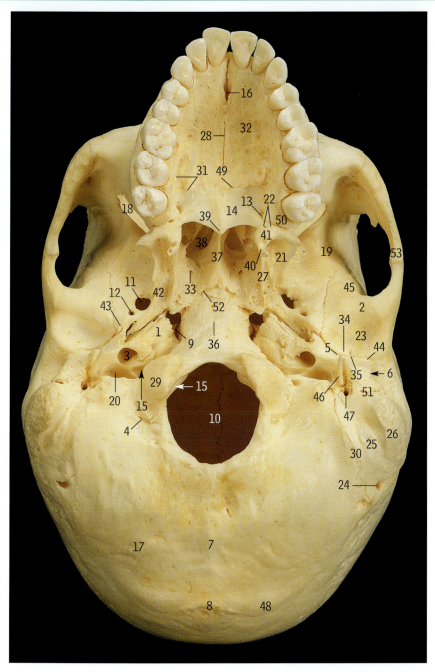

1	錐体尖〔側頭骨〕 Apex of petrous part〔Temporal bone〕	28	正中口蓋縫合：上顎間縫合 Median palatine suture：Intermaxillary suture
2	関節結節 Articular tubercle	29	後頭顆 Occipital condyle
3	頸動脈管 Carotid canal	30	後頭動脈溝 Occipital groove
4	顆管（後方） Condylar canal	31	口蓋溝と口蓋棘 Palatine grooves and Palatine spines
5	鼓室蓋稜* Edge of Tegmen tympani *	32	口蓋突起〔上顎骨〕 Palatine process〔Maxilla〕
6	外耳道 External acoustic meatus	33	口蓋骨鞘突管 Palatovaginal canal
7	外後頭稜 External occipital crest	34	錐体鱗裂 Petrosquamous fissure
8	外後頭隆起 External occipital protuberance	35	錐体鼓室裂 Petrotympanic fissure
9	破裂孔 Foramen lacerum	36	咽頭結節 Pharyngeal tubercle
10	大後頭孔：大孔 Foramen magnum	37	後縁〔鋤骨〕 Posterior border〔Vomer〕
11	卵円孔 Foramen ovale	38	後鼻孔 Choanae：Posterior nasal aperture
12	棘孔 Foramen spinosum	39	後鼻棘 Posterior nasal spine
13	大口蓋孔 Greater palatine foramen	40	翼突鉤 Pterygoid hamulus
14	水平板〔口蓋骨〕 Horizontal plate〔Palatine bone〕	41	錐体突起〔口蓋骨〕 Pyramidal process〔Palatine bone〕
15	舌下神経管 Hypoglossal canal	42	舟状窩 Scaphoid fossa
16	切歯窩 Incisive fossa	43	蝶形骨棘 Spine of sphenoid
17	下項線 Inferior nuchal line	44	鼓室鱗裂 Tympanosquamous fissure
18	下眼窩裂 Inferior orbital fissure	45	鱗部〔側頭骨〕 Squamous part〔Temporal bone〕
19	側頭下稜〔蝶形骨の大翼〕 Infratemporal crest〔Greater wing of Sphenoid〕	46	茎状突起〔側頭骨〕 Styloid process〔Temporal bone〕
20	頸静脈孔 Jugular foramen	47	茎乳突孔 Stylomastoid foramen
21	外側板〔翼状突起〕 Lateral plate〔Pterygoid process〕	48	上項線 Superior nuchal line
22	小口蓋孔 Lesser palatine foramina	49	横口蓋縫合：口蓋上顎縫合 Transverse palatine：Palatomaxillary suture
23	下顎窩 Mandibular fossa	50	上顎結節 Maxillary tuberosity
24	乳突孔 Mastoid foramen	51	鼓室部〔側頭骨〕 Tympanic part〔Temporal bone〕
25	乳突切痕 Mastoid notch	52	鋤骨鞘突管 Vomerovaginal canal
26	乳様突起 Mastoid process	53	頬骨弓 Zygomatic arch
27	内側板〔翼状突起〕 Medial plate〔Pterygoid process〕		

- 上顎骨の口蓋突起(32)と口蓋骨の水平板(14)は硬口蓋を形成する．硬口蓋は口腔の屋根であると同時に鼻腔の床でもある．
- 側頭骨の錐体下面の丸い形から，頸動脈管(3)は識別される．頸動脈管は，上方へまっすぐ走って頭蓋内面に開口するのではない．前内側へ直角に曲がり，錐体内部を通過した後，破裂孔(9)の後ろに開口する．

感染の頭蓋内への拡がり（顔面）

感染の頭蓋内への拡がり（頭皮）

頭蓋 ［外頭蓋底，筋と靱帯の付着部］

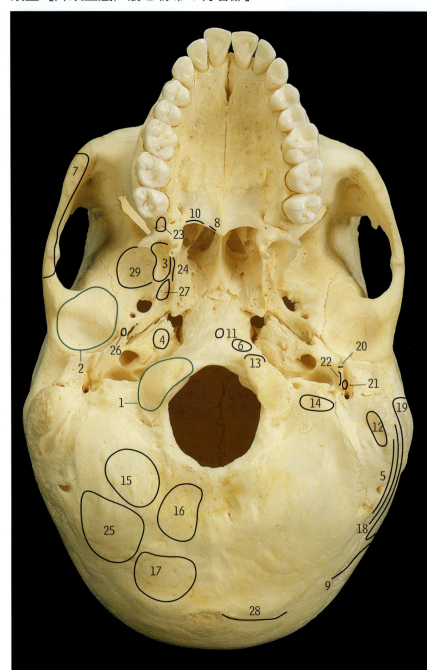

1	環椎後頭関節（関節包付着部）	Atlanto-occipital joint
2	顎関節（関節包付着部）	Temporomandibular joint
3	深頭*〔内側翼突筋〕	Deep head * (Medial pterygoid)
4	口蓋帆挙筋	Levator veli palatini
5	頭最長筋	Longissimus capitis
6	頭長筋	Longus capitis
7	咬筋	Masseter
8	口蓋垂筋	Musculus uvulae
9	後頭筋〔後頭前頭筋〕	Occipital belly (Occipitofrontalis)
10	口蓋咽頭筋	Palatopharyngeus
11	咽頭縫線	Pharyngeal raphe
12	後腹〔顎二腹筋〕	Posterior belly (Digastric)
13	前頭直筋	Rectus capitis anterior
14	外側頭直筋	Rectus capitis lateralis
15	大後頭直筋	Rectus capitis posterior major
16	小後頭直筋	Rectus capitis posterior minor
17	頭半棘筋	Semispinalis capitis
18	頭板状筋	Splenius capitis
19	胸鎖乳突筋	Sternocleidomastoid
20	茎突舌筋	Styloglossus
21	茎突舌骨筋	Stylohyoid
22	茎突咽頭筋	Stylopharyngeus
23	浅頭*〔内側翼突筋〕	Superficial head * (Medial pterygoid)
24	上咽頭収縮筋	Superior constrictor
25	上頭斜筋	Obliquus capitis superior
26	鼓膜張筋	Tensor tympani
27	口蓋帆張筋	Tensor veli palatini
28	僧帽筋	Trapezius
29	上頭〔外側翼突筋〕	Upper head (Lateral pterygoid)

（緑線：環椎後頭関節包と顎関節包の付着部．）

- 翼状突起の内側板に起始する翼突筋はない．内側板は後方へまっすぐに延びており，上咽頭収縮筋(24)の一部が，その下端から起始する．
- 翼状突起の外側板には，内側ならびに外側翼突筋のどちらも起始する．内側翼突筋(3)は外側板の内側面から，外側翼突筋(29)は外側面から起始する．外側板は外側にわずかにねじれている．2つの筋が後外側へ延びて下顎骨へ停止し，絶えず外側板を牽引するためである(18～19頁)．

頭蓋骨骨折

頭蓋 ［内頭蓋底（頭蓋窩）］

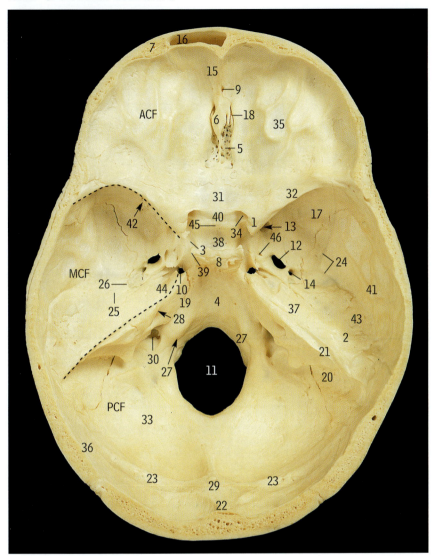

#	日本語	English	#	日本語	English
1	前床突起〔蝶形骨〕	Anterior clinoid process (Sphenoid)	25	大錐体神経管裂孔と大錐体神経溝	Hiatus for greater petrosal nerve and Groove for greater petrosal nerve
2	弓状隆起〔側頭骨の岩様部〕	Arcuate eminence (Petrous part of Temporal bone)	26	小錐体神経管裂孔と小錐体神経溝	Hiatus for lesser petrosal nerve and Groove for lesser petrosal nerve
3	頸動脈溝	Carotid sulcus	27	舌下神経管	Hypoglossal canal
4	斜台	Clivus	28	内耳道	Internal acoustic meatus
5	篩板〔篩骨〕	Cribriform plate (Ethmoid)	29	内後頭隆起	Internal occipital protuberance
6	鶏冠	Crista galli	30	頸静脈孔	Jugular foramen
7	板間層	Diploe	31	蝶形骨隆起	Jugum sphenoidale; Sphenoidal yoke
8	鞍背	Dorsum sellae	32	小翼〔蝶形骨〕	Lesser wing (Sphenoid)
9	盲孔	Foramen cecum	33	小脳窩〔後頭骨〕	Cerebellar fossa (Occipital bone)
10	破裂孔	Foramen lacerum	34	視神経管	Optic canal
11	大後頭孔：大孔	Foramen magnum	35	眼窩部〔前頭骨〕	Orbital part (Frontal bone)
12	卵円孔	Foramen ovale	36	頭頂骨（乳突角のみ）	Parietal bone
13	正円孔	Foramen rotundum	37	岩様部：錐体乳突部〔側頭骨〕	Petrous part (Temporal bone)
14	棘孔	Foramen spinosum	38	下垂体窩〔トルコ鞍〕	Hypophysial fossa (Sella turcica)
15	前頭稜	Frontal crest	39	後床突起〔蝶形骨〕	Posterior clinoid process (Sphenoid)
16	前頭洞	Frontal sinus	40	前視交叉溝	Prechiasmatic sulcus
17	大翼〔蝶形骨〕	Greater wing (Sphenoid)	41	鱗部〔側頭骨〕	Squamous part (Temporal bone)
18	前篩骨動／静脈・神経が通る溝		42	上眼窩裂	Superior orbital fissure
19	下錐体洞溝	Groove for inferior petrosal sinus	43	鼓室蓋	Tegmen tympani
20	S状洞溝	Groove for sigmoid sinus	44	三叉神経圧痕	Trigeminal impression
21	上錐体洞溝	Groove for superior petrosal sinus	45	鞍結節	Tuberculum sellae
22	上矢状洞溝	Groove for superior sagittal sinus	46	導出静脈孔*	Venous foramen*; Emissary foramen*
23	横洞溝	Groove for transverse sinus			
24	中硬膜動脈溝	Groove for middle meningeal artery			

- 前頭蓋窩（ACF）は，左右の蝶形骨小翼（32）の自由縁とその内側端の前床突起（1），中央では前視交叉溝（40）の前縁が，後方の境になる．
- 中頭蓋窩（MCF）は蝶の形をしており，正中部または中心部と，左右の外側部からなる．中心部は，蝶形骨体上面の下垂体窩（トルコ鞍，38），前方は前視交叉溝（40），後方は鞍背（8）と後床突起（39）が含まれる．左右の外側部は，蝶形骨小翼（32）の後縁から側頭骨錐体上縁の上錐体洞溝（21）まで広がる．
- 後頭蓋窩（PCF）で最も顕著なのは，大後頭孔（大孔，11）であり，後方には鞍背（8）ならびに上錐体洞溝（21）がある．
- 脳硬膜の付着部と翻転部については 59～62 頁参照．

無嗅覚症

頭蓋底骨折

A B 頭蓋［眼窩の骨（左）］

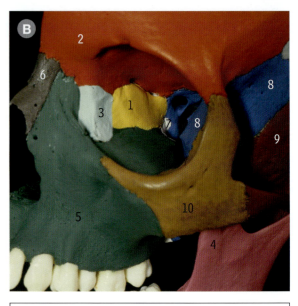

1	前篩骨孔 Anterior ethmoidal foramen	14	上顎骨（下壁を形成する） Maxilla
2	前涙嚢稜 Anterior lacrimal crest	15	鼻涙管 Nasolacrimal duct
3	蝶形骨体（内側壁を形成する） Body of sphenoid	16	視神経管 Optic canal
4	涙嚢窩 Fossa for lacrimal sac	17	眼窩縁〔頬骨〕（下壁を形成する） Orbital margin〔Zygomatic bone〕
5	前頭切痕：前頭孔 Frontal notch：Frontal foramen	18	眼窩部〔前頭骨〕（上壁を形成する） Orbital part〔Frontal bone〕
6	前頭突起〔上顎骨〕（内側壁を形成する） Frontal process〔Maxilla〕	19	眼窩板〔篩骨〕（内側壁を形成する） Orbital plate〔Ethmoid〕
7	大翼〔蝶形骨〕（外側壁を形成する） Greater wing〔Sphenoid〕	20	眼窩突起〔口蓋骨〕（下壁を形成する） Orbital process〔Palatine bone〕
8	下眼窩裂 Inferior orbital fissure	21	後篩骨孔 Posterior ethmoidal foramen
9	眼窩下孔 Infra-orbital foramen	22	後涙嚢稜 Posterior lacrimal crest
10	眼窩下溝 Infra-orbital groove	23	上眼窩裂 Superior orbital fissure
11	涙骨（内側壁を形成する） Lacrimal bone	24	眼窩上孔：眼窩上切痕 Supra-orbital foramen：Supra-orbital notch
12	小翼〔蝶形骨〕（上壁を形成する） Lesser wing〔Sphenoid〕	25	頬骨（外側壁を形成する） Zygomatic bone
13	縁結節 Marginal tubercle	26	頬骨眼窩孔 Zygomatico-orbital foramen

1	篩骨 Ethmoid	5	上顎骨 Maxilla	9	側頭骨 Temporal bone
2	前頭骨 Frontal bone	6	鼻骨 Nasal bone	10	頬骨 Zygomatic bone
3	涙骨 Lacrimal bone	7	口蓋骨 Palatine bone		
4	下顎骨 Mandible	8	蝶形骨 Sphenoid		

- 鼻腔の上壁は，主として篩骨の篩板（C3），後方に蝶形骨洞（C12，C21）を含む蝶形骨体，前方に鼻骨（C14）と前頭骨の鼻棘（C15）からなる．
- 鼻腔の下壁は，上顎骨の口蓋突起（C17）と口蓋骨の水平板（C7）からなる．
- 鼻腔の内側壁は，主として篩骨の垂直板と鋤骨という2つの骨ならびに鼻中隔軟骨からなる．
- 鼻腔の外側壁は，上顎洞と連絡する大きな孔（C16）をもつ上顎骨の内側面でつくられる．この上顎洞口には，上方から篩骨の一部（C1，C5，C24）と涙骨が，後方から口蓋骨の垂直板（C18）が，下方から下鼻甲介（C10）が張り出している．

C 鼻腔［外側壁］

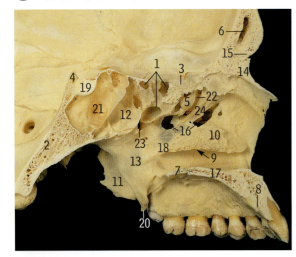

鼻腔の外側壁正中断頭蓋の鼻中隔を取り去り，上・中鼻甲介を剖出して除去し，篩骨洞の蜂巣，とりわけ篩骨胞（5）が見えるようにした．

1	篩骨蜂巣 Ethmoidal cells	13	内側板〔翼状突起〕 Medial plate〔Pterygoid process〕
2	斜台 Clivus	14	鼻骨 Nasal bone
3	篩板〔篩骨〕 Cribriform plate〔Ethmoid〕	15	鼻棘〔前頭骨〕 Nasal spine〔Frontal bone〕
4	鞍背 Dorsum sellae	16	上顎洞口* Opening of maxillary sinus*
5	篩骨胞 Ethmoidal bulla	17	口蓋突起〔上顎骨〕 Palatine process〔Maxilla〕
6	前頭洞 Frontal sinus	18	垂直板〔口蓋骨〕 Perpendicular plate〔Palatine bone〕
7	水平板〔口蓋骨〕 Horizontal plate〔Palatine bone〕	19	下垂体窩〔トルコ鞍〕 Hypophysial fossa〔Sella turcica〕
8	切歯管 Incisive canal	20	翼突鈎 Pterygoid hamulus
9	下鼻道 Inferior nasal meatus	21	（右の）蝶形骨洞 Sphenoidal sinus
10	下鼻甲介 Inferior nasal concha	22	半月裂孔 Semilunar hiatus
11	外側板〔翼状突起〕 Lateral plate〔Pterygoid process〕	23	蝶口蓋孔 Sphenopalatine foramen
12	（左の）蝶形骨洞 Sphenoidal sinus	24	鈎状突起〔篩骨〕 Uncinate process〔Ethmoid〕

副鼻腔の病変

第1章 頭頸部と脳：頭蓋（歯と顎）

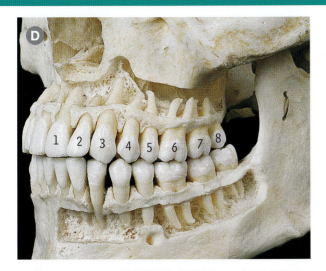

D 永久歯

1	中切歯* 1st incisor * : Central incisor *	5	第二小臼歯 2nd premolar tooth
2	側切歯* 2nd incisor * : Lateral incisor *	6	第一大臼歯 1st molar tooth
3	犬歯 Canine tooth	7	第二大臼歯 2nd molar tooth
4	第一小臼歯 1st premolar tooth	8	第三大臼歯 3rd molar tooth

● 上顎と下顎で対応する歯は，同じ名称でよばれる．歯科の臨床では，歯は名称よりむしろ（図のように）1〜8の番号で同定される．
● 第三大臼歯(8)は，智歯ともよばれる．

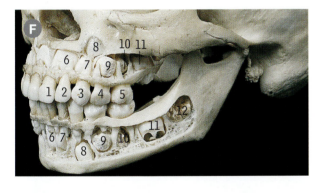

パノラマX線画像

E F 上顎と下顎

1	中切歯*〔乳歯〕 1st incisor * : Central incisor * 〔Deciduous teeth〕	7	側切歯*〔永久歯〕 2nd incisor * : Lateral incisor * 〔Permanent teeth〕
2	側切歯*〔乳歯〕 2nd incisor * : Lateral incisor * 〔Deciduous teeth〕	8	犬歯〔永久歯〕 Canine tooth 〔Permanent teeth〕
3	犬歯〔乳歯〕 Canine tooth 〔Deciduous teeth〕	9	第一小臼歯〔永久歯〕 1st premolar tooth 〔Permanent teeth〕
4	第一臼歯〔乳歯〕 1st molar tooth 〔Deciduous teeth〕	10	第二小臼歯〔永久歯〕 2nd premolar tooth 〔Permanent teeth〕
5	第二臼歯〔乳歯〕 2nd molar tooth 〔Deciduous teeth〕	11	第一大臼歯〔永久歯〕 1st molar tooth 〔Permanent teeth〕
6	中切歯*〔永久歯〕 1st incisor * : Central incisor * 〔Permanent teeth〕	12	第二大臼歯〔永久歯〕 2nd molar tooth 〔Permanent teeth〕

● 乳臼歯は，永久歯列の小臼歯の位置に相当する．

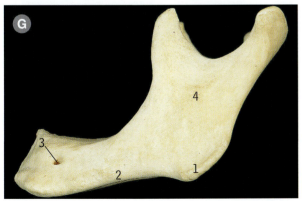

G 無歯下顎骨（左側面）

1	下顎角 Angle of mandible	3	オトガイ孔 Mental foramen
2	下顎体 Body of mandible	4	下顎枝 Ramus of mandible

● 歯の脱落とともに，歯槽骨が吸収され，オトガイ孔(3)と下顎管が下顎骨の上縁に近づく．
● 下顎枝(4)と下顎体(2)がつくる下顎角(1)は，鈍角の度を増し，（図E，Fに示すような）乳幼児の下顎角に似てくる．

D：左前方から．E：6歳児．左前方から．F：4歳児．乳歯は萌出しているが，永久歯が未萌出．左前方から．G：高齢者．左方から．

出生間近の胎児の頭蓋

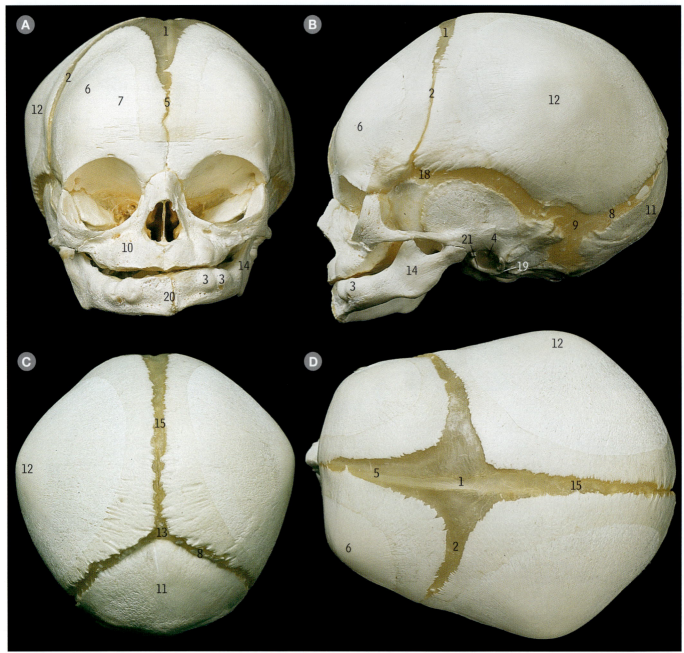

A：前方から．B：左方やや下方から．C：後方から．D：上方から．

1 大泉門 Anterior fontanelle	7 （右半の）前頭骨 Frontal bone	12 頭頂結節 Parietal tuber	17 前骨半規管 Anterior semicircular canal
2 冠状縫合 Coronal suture	8 ラムダ［状］縫合 Lambdoid suture	13 小泉門 Posterior fontanelle	18 前側頭泉門 Sphenoidal fontanelle
3 下顎体の乳歯による隆起	9 後側頭泉門 Mastoid fontanelle	14 下顎枝 Ramus of mandible	19 茎乳突孔 Stylomastoid foramen
4 外耳道 External acoustic meatus	10 上顎骨 Maxilla	15 矢状縫合 Sagittal suture	20 下顎結合 Mandibular symphysis
5 前頭縫合 Frontal suture：Metopic suture	11 後頭骨 Occipital bone	16 トルコ鞍 Sella turcica	21 鼓室輪 Tympanic ring
6 前頭結節 Frontal tuber			

口唇口蓋裂

出生間近の胎児の頭蓋

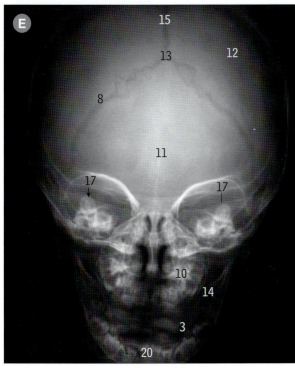

X線画像（前後画像）
（番号は前頁の用語表を参照．）

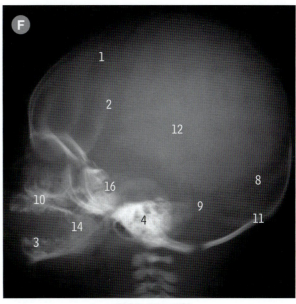

X線画像（側面画像）
（番号は前頁の用語表を参照．）

- 出生時における顔面の頭蓋に占める割合は，成人に比べて小さい（出生時1/8，成人では1/2）．鼻腔と上顎洞が小さく，歯が萌出していないためである．
- 小泉門（C13, E13）は生後約2ヵ月で閉じる．大泉門（A1, D1, F1）は生後2年目に閉鎖する．
- 乳様突起を欠くため（生後2年目まで発達しない），茎乳突孔（B19）とそこから出る顔面神経は比較的表面に近いところにあり，保護されない．

G 出生間近の胎児の頭頸部動脈

この胎児の動脈鋳型標本では，前頸部において甲状腺の動脈分布（G）の密度が高いこと，また，その上の前方において細い血管群（T）が舌の輪郭をつくっていることに注目せよ．

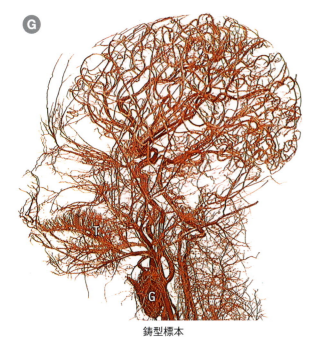

鋳型標本

左方から．

水頭症

頭皮の創傷

頭蓋（左）［A 矢状断面］

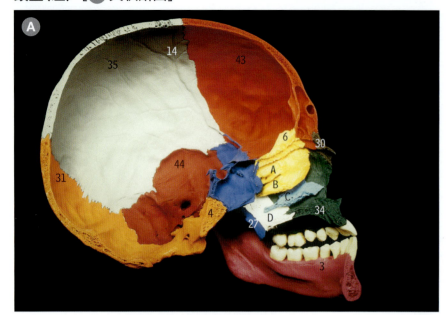

A	上鼻甲介 Superior nasal concha
B	中鼻甲介 Middle nasal concha
C	下鼻甲介 Inferior nasal concha
D	口蓋骨 Palatine bone

骨に色付けしてある．鼻甲介が見えるように，篩骨の垂直板を除去してある．（番号は次頁の用語表を参照．）

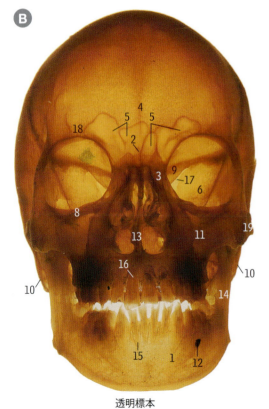

透明標本
前方から（後方から照明を当てている）．

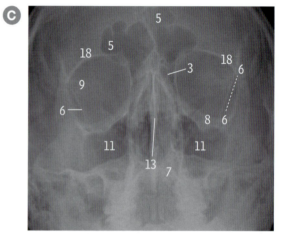

顔面骨のX線画像（後前方向）

1 頁の頭蓋の写真と比較せよ．

1	下顎体 Body of mandible	11	上顎洞 Maxillary sinus
2	鶏冠 Crista galli	12	オトガイ孔 Mental foramen
3	篩骨蜂巣 Ethmoidal cells	13	鼻中隔 Nasal septum
4	前頭稜 Frontal crest	14	下顎枝〔下顎骨〕 Ramus of mandible〔Mandible〕
5	前頭洞 Frontal sinus	15	（下顎の）側切歯*（の根） Root of lower lateral incisor *
6	大翼〔蝶形骨〕 Greater wing〔Sphenoid〕	16	（上顎の）中切歯*（の根） Root of upper central incisor *
7	下鼻甲介 Inferior nasal concha	17	上眼窩裂 Superior orbital fissure
8	眼窩下縁 Infra-orbital margin	18	眼窩上縁 Supra-orbital margin
9	小翼〔蝶形骨〕 Lesser wing〔Sphenoid〕	19	頬骨弓 Zygomatic arch
10	乳様突起 Mastoid process		

眼窩の吹き抜け骨折

乳様突起炎

頭蓋(左)［矢状断面］

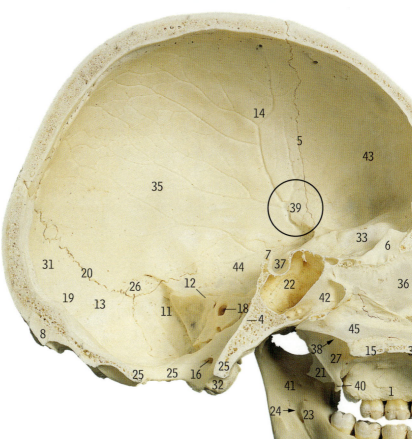

頭蓋の左半の内面を右側から見た．鼻中隔(36, 45)は保たれている．

1	歯槽突起〔上顎骨〕 Alveolar process〔Maxilla〕	24	下顎孔 Mandibular foramen
2	下顎角 Angle of mandible	25	大後頭孔：大孔(の辺縁) Foramen magnum
3	下顎体 Body of mandible	26	乳突角〔頭頂骨〕 Mastoid angle〔Parietal bone〕
4	斜台 Clivus	27	内側板〔翼状突起〕 Medial plate〔Pterygoid process〕
5	冠状縫合 Coronal suture	28	オトガイ隆起 Mental protuberance
6	鶏冠〔篩骨〕 Crista galli〔Ethmoid〕	29	顎舌骨筋線 Mylohyoid line
7	鞍背 Dorsum sellae	30	鼻骨 Nasal bone
8	外後頭隆起 External occipital protuberance	31	後頭骨 Occipital bone
9	前頭洞 Frontal sinus	32	後頭顆 Occipital condyle
10	顎舌骨筋神経溝 Mylohyoid groove	33	眼窩部〔前頭骨〕 Orbital part〔Frontal bone〕
11	S状洞溝 Groove for sigmoid sinus	34	口蓋突起〔上顎骨〕 Palatine process〔Maxilla〕
12	上錐体洞溝 Groove for superior petrosal sinus	35	頭頂骨 Parietal bone
13	横洞溝 Groove for transverse sinus	36	垂直板〔篩骨〕 Perpendicular plate〔Ethmoid〕
14	中硬膜動脈溝(中硬膜動脈の前頭枝) Groove for middle meningeal artery	37	下垂体窩〔トルコ鞍〕 Hypophysial fossa〔Sella turcica〕
15	水平板〔口蓋骨〕 Horizontal plate〔Palatine bone〕	38	後鼻孔 Choanae：Posterior nasal aperture
16	舌下神経管 Hypoglossal canal	39	プテリオン(○で囲まれた領域) Pterion
17	切歯管 Incisive canal	40	翼突鉤〔翼状突起の前側板〕 Pterygoid hamulus〔Medial plate of Pterygoid process〕
18	内耳道(側頭骨錐体の内部にある) Internal acoustic meatus	41	下顎枝 Ramus of mandible
19	内後頭隆起 Internal occipital protuberance	42	(右の)蝶形骨洞 Sphenoidal sinus
20	ラムダ［状］縫合 Lambdoid suture	43	(前頭骨の)前頭鱗 Squamous part of frontal bone
21	外側板〔翼状突起〕 Lateral plate〔Pterygoid process〕	44	鱗部〔側頭骨〕 Squamous part〔Temporal bone〕
22	(左の)蝶形骨洞 Sphenoidal sinus	45	鋤骨 Vomer
23	下顎小舌 Lingula		

- 鼻中隔の骨部は鋤骨(45)と篩骨の垂直板(36)からなる．鼻中隔の前部は鼻中隔軟骨からなる(60，61頁)．
- この標本は蝶形骨洞(22, 42)が大きく，右の蝶形骨洞(42)が，前下方で正中線を越えて左側に広がっている．下垂体窩(トルコ鞍, 37)は左の蝶形骨洞(22)の上に突出している．
- 中硬膜動脈溝(14)は，後上方へ向かって走っている．○は，プテリオン(39)を示しており，4頁に示している頭蓋外面の位置に一致している．

硬膜外出血　　下垂体腫瘍

下顎骨

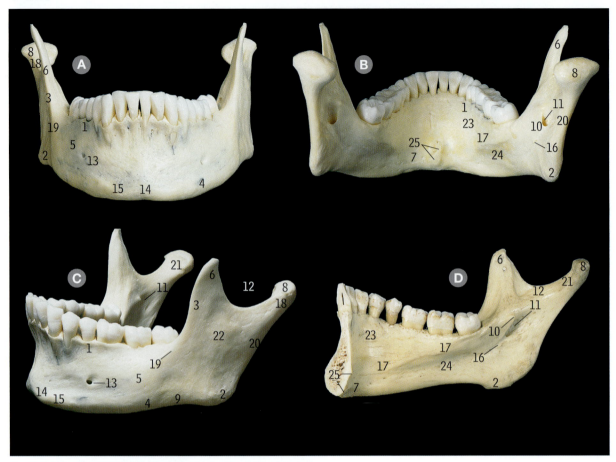

A：前方から．B：後方から．C：左前方から．D：内面．左方から．

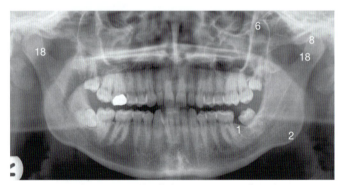

口腔パノラマX線画像（オルソパントモグラム）

1	歯槽部 Alveolar part	14	オトガイ隆起 Mental protuberance
2	下顎角 Angle of mandible	15	オトガイ結節 Mental tubercle
3	前縁〔下顎枝〕 Anterior border〔Ramus of mandible〕	16	顎舌骨筋神経溝 Mylohyoid groove
4	下顎底 Base of mandible	17	顎舌骨筋線 Mylohyoid line
5	下顎体 Body of mandible	18	下顎頸 Neck of mandible
6	筋突起 Coronoid process	19	斜線 Oblique line
7	二腹筋窩 Digastric fossa	20	後縁〔下顎枝〕 Posterior border〔Ramus of mandible〕
8	下顎頭 Head of mandible	21	翼突筋窩 Pterygoid fovea
9	下縁〔下顎枝〕 Inferior border〔Ramus of mandible〕	22	下顎枝 Ramus of mandible
10	下顎小舌 Lingula	23	舌下腺窩 Sublingual fossa
11	下顎孔 Mandibular foramen	24	顎下腺窩 Submandibular fossa
12	下顎切痕 Mandibular notch	25	上オトガイ棘と下オトガイ棘 Superior mental (genial) spine and Inferior mental (genial) spine
13	オトガイ孔 Mental foramen		

- 下顎頭(8)と下顎頸(18．翼突筋窩(21)を含む)が関節突起をつくる．
- 歯槽部(1)には歯槽(歯根をいれるくぼみ)がある．
- 下顎底(4)は下顎体(5)の下縁であり，下顎枝(22)の下縁(9)に続く．

埋状智歯

乳様突起炎

下顎骨［筋と靱帯の付着部］

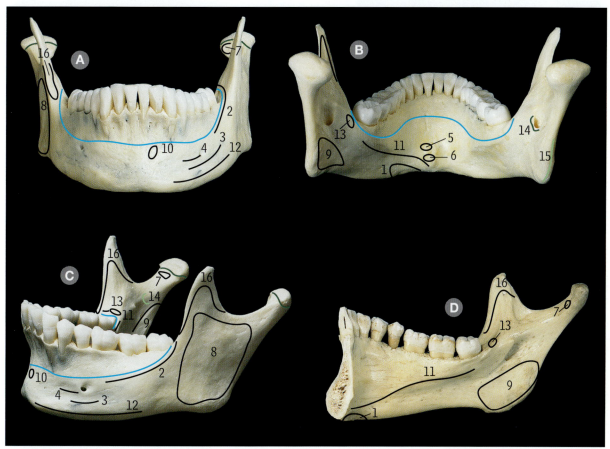

A：前方から．B：後方から．C：左前方から．D：内面．左方から．（緑線：顎関節包の付着線．青線：口腔粘膜付着部の境界線．淡緑線：靱帯の付着部．）

1	前腹〔顎二腹筋〕 Anterior belly〔Digastric〕	9	内側翼突筋 Medial pterygoid
2	頬筋 Buccinator	10	オトガイ筋 Mentalis
3	口角下制筋 Depressor anguli oris	11	顎舌骨筋 Mylohyoid
4	下唇下制筋 Depressor labii inferioris	12	広頸筋 Platysma
5	オトガイ舌筋 Genioglossus	13	翼突下顎縫線と上咽頭収縮筋 Pterygomandibular raphe and Superior constrictor
6	オトガイ舌骨筋 Geniohyoid	14	蝶下顎靱帯 Sphenomandibular ligament
7	外側翼突筋 Lateral pterygoid	15	茎突下顎靱帯 Stylomandibular ligament
8	咬筋 Masseter	16	側頭筋 Temporalis

- 外側翼突筋（A7）は下顎頸の翼突筋窩に停止する（また顎関節包と関節円板にも停止する．42頁 A27, A28参照）．
- 内側翼突筋（B9, C9）は顎舌骨筋神経溝の下方で下顎角の内側面に停止する．
- 咬筋（C8）は下顎枝の外側面に停止する．
- 側頭筋（C16）は筋突起に停止し，さらに後方は下顎切痕の最深部まで，下方は下顎枝の前縁を伝わってほぼ第三大臼歯まで広がっている．
- 頬筋（C2）は第一〜第三大臼歯の範囲，および後方では翼突下顎縫線（C13）に起始する．
- オトガイ舌筋（B5）は上オトガイ棘に，オトガイ舌骨筋（B6）は下オトガイ棘に起始する．
- 顎舌骨筋（B11, D11）は顎舌骨筋線に起始する．
- 顎関節の外側靱帯が，関節突起の下顎頸外側面に付着するところは示されていない．

上顎骨折

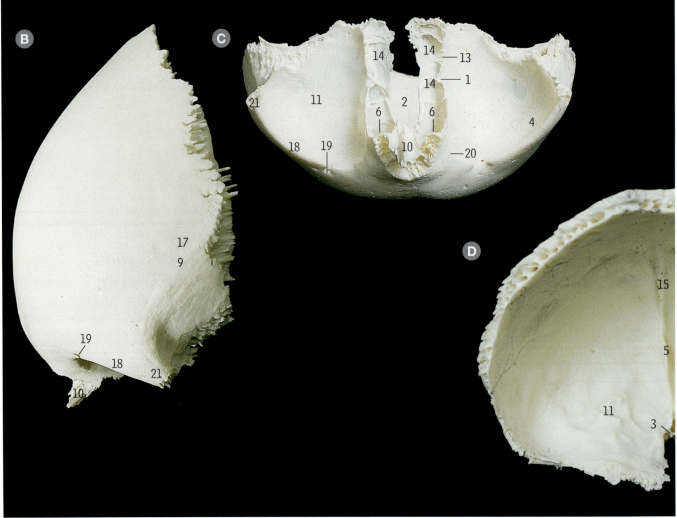

前頭骨

1	前篩骨孔（溝の位置） Anterior ethmoidal foramen	12	前頭切痕（前頭孔）の位置
2	篩骨切痕 Ethmoidal notch	13	後篩骨孔（溝の位置） Posterior ethmoidal foramen
3	盲孔 Foramen cecum	14	上壁*〔篩骨蜂巣〕 Roof*〔Ethmoidal cells〕
4	涙腺窩 Lacrimal fossa	15	矢状稜*（上矢状洞溝の縁をつくる稜） Sagittal crest*
5	前頭稜 Frontal crest	16	眉弓 Superciliary arch
6	前頭洞 Frontal sinus	17	上側頭線 Superior temporal line
7	前頭結節 Frontal tuber	18	眼窩上縁 Supra-orbital margin
8	眉間 Glabella	19	眼窩上切痕：眼窩上孔 Supra-orbital notch：Supra-orbital foramen
9	下側頭線 Inferior temporal line	20	滑車窩（または結節*） Trochlear fovea
10	鼻棘 Nasal spine	21	頬骨突起 Zygomatic process
11	眼窩部 Orbital part		

A：外面．前方から．B：外面．左方から．C：下方から．D：内面．上後方から（右半は見せていない．篩骨切痕が下に見える）．

第1章 頭頸部と脳：頭蓋骨（分解骨）

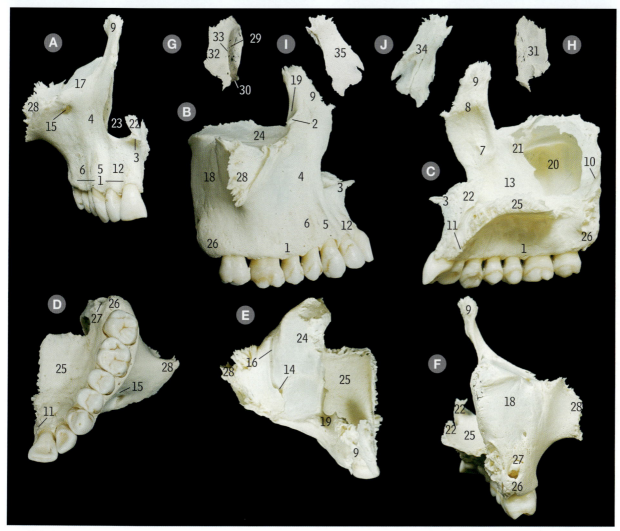

A：前方から．B・I：外側方から．C・J：内側方から．D：下方から．E：上方から．F：後方から．G：外側方から（眼窩側）．H：内側方から（鼻側）．

- Ⓐ～Ⓕ 上顎骨（右）
- Ⓖ～Ⓗ 涙骨（右）
- Ⓘ～Ⓙ 鼻骨（右）

1 歯槽突起 Alveolar process	13 下鼻道 Inferior nasal meatus	25 口蓋突起 Palatine process
2 前涙嚢稜 Anterior lacrimal crest	14 眼窩下管 Infra-orbital canal	26 上顎結節 Maxillary tuberosity
3 前鼻棘 Anterior nasal spine	15 眼窩下孔 Infra-orbital foramen	27 第三大臼歯（未萌出） 3rd molar tooth
4 前面 Anterior surface	16 眼窩下溝 Infra-orbital groove	28 頬骨突起 Zygomatic process
5 犬歯隆起* Canine eminence *	17 眼窩下縁 Infra-orbital margin	29 涙嚢溝 Lacrimal groove
6 犬歯窩 Canine fossa	18 側頭下面 Infratemporal surface	30 涙骨鉤 Lacrimal hamulus
7 鼻甲介稜 Conchal crest	19 涙嚢溝 Lacrimal groove	31 鼻腔面* Nasal surface *
8 篩骨稜 Ethmoidal crest	20 上顎洞裂孔と上顎洞 Maxillary hiatus and Maxillary sinus	32 眼窩面* Orbital surface *
9 前頭突起 Frontal process	21 中鼻道 Middle nasal meatus	33 後涙嚢稜 Posterior lacrimal crest
10 大口蓋溝（管の位置） Greater palatine groove	22 鼻稜 Nasal crest	34 内面*と篩骨神経溝 Internal surface * and Groove for anterior ethmoidal nerve
11 切歯管 Incisive canal	23 鼻切痕 Nasal notch	35 外側面* Lateral surface *
12 切歯窩 Incisive fossa	24 眼窩面 Orbital surface	

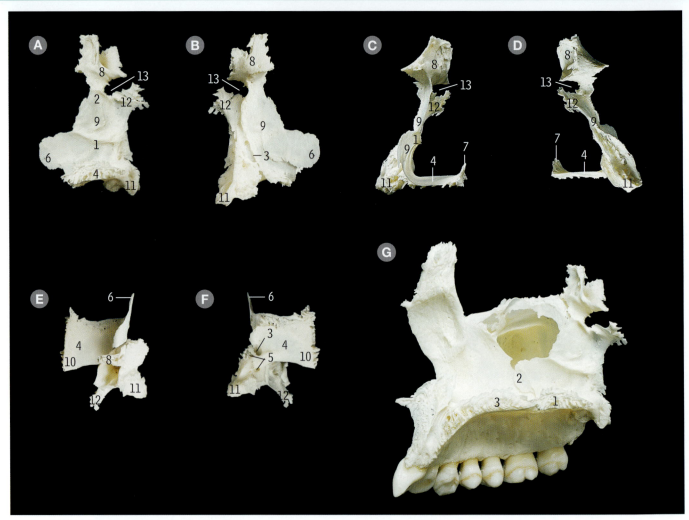

A・G：内側方から．B：外側方から．C：前方から．D：後方から．E：上方から．F：下方から．

A〜F 口蓋骨（右）

1 鼻甲介稜 Conchal crest
2 篩骨稜 Ethmoidal crest
3 大口蓋溝 Greater palatine groove
4 水平板〔口蓋骨〕 Horizontal plate〔Palatine bone〕
5 小口蓋管 Lesser palatine canals
6 上顎突起 Maxillary process
7 鼻稜 Nasal crest
8 眼窩突起 Orbital process
9 垂直板 Perpendicular plate
10 後鼻棘 Posterior nasal spine
11 錐体突起 Pyramidal process
12 蝶形骨突起 Sphenoidal process
13 蝶口蓋切痕 Sphenopalatine notch

G 上顎骨と口蓋骨（右）

1 水平板〔口蓋骨〕 Horizontal plate〔Palatine bone〕
2 上顎突起〔口蓋骨〕 Maxillary process〔Palatine bone〕
3 口蓋突起〔上顎骨〕 Palatine process〔Maxilla〕

側頭骨（右）

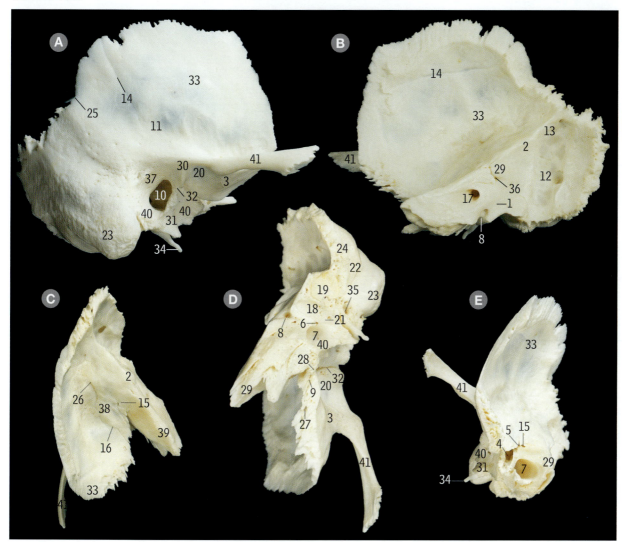

A：外面．B：内面．C：上方から．D：下方から．E：前方から．

1	前庭水管 Aqueduct of vestibule	15	大錐体神経管裂孔と大錐体神経溝 Hiatus for greater petrosal nerve and Groove for greater petrosal nerve
2	弓状隆起 Arcuate eminence	16	小錐体神経管裂孔と小錐体神経溝 Hiatus for lesser petrosal nerve and Groove for lesser petrosal nerve
3	関節結節 Articular tubercle	17	内耳道 Internal acoustic meatus
4	耳管半管：Eustachian 管* Canal for auditory tube：Eustachian tube*	18	頸静脈窩 Jugular fossa
5	鼓膜張筋半管 Canal for tensor tympani	19	頸静脈面* Jugular surface*
6	鼓室神経小管 Tympanic canaliculus	20	下顎窩 Mandibular fossa
7	頸動脈管 Carotid canal	21	乳突小管（迷走神経の耳介枝が通る） Mastoid canaliculus
8	蝸牛小管 Cochlear canaliculus	22	乳突切痕 Mastoid notch
9	鼓室蓋（の辺縁） Tegmen tympani	23	乳様突起 Mastoid process
10	外耳道 External acoustic meatus	24	後頭動脈溝 Occipital groove
11	中側頭動脈溝 Groove for middle temporal artery	25	頭頂切痕 Parietal notch
12	S 状洞溝 Groove for sigmoid sinus	26	錐体鱗裂（上方から） Petrosquamous fissure
13	上錐体洞溝 Groove for superior petrosal sinus	27	錐体鱗裂（下方から） Petrosquamous fissure
14	中硬膜動脈溝 Groove for middle meningeal artery	28	錐体鼓室裂 Petrotympanic fissure
		29	岩様部：錐体乳突部 Petrous part
		30	窩後結節* Postglenoid tubercle*
		31	茎状突起鞘 Sheath of styloid process
		32	鼓室鱗裂 Tympanosquamous fissure
		33	鱗部 Squamous part
		34	茎状突起 Styloid process
		35	茎乳突孔 Stylomastoid foramen
		36	弓下窩 Subarcuate fossa
		37	道上小窩 Suprameatal triangle
		38	鼓室蓋 Tegmen tympani
		39	三叉神経圧痕（錐体尖にある） Trigeminal impression
		40	鼓室部 Tympanic part
		41	頰骨突起 Zygomatic process

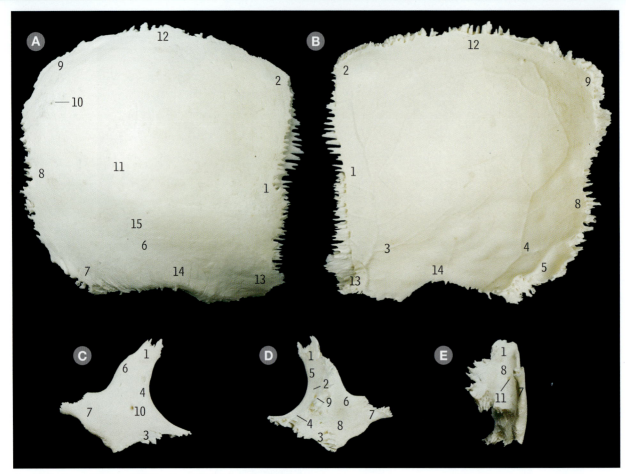

A：外面．B：内面．C：外側面．D：内側方から．E：後方から．

Ⓐ Ⓑ 頭頂骨（右）

1. 前頭縁 Frontal border
2. 前頭角 Frontal angle
3. 中硬膜動脈溝（中硬膜動脈の前頭枝） Groove for middle meningeal artery
4. 中硬膜動脈溝（中硬膜動脈の頭頂枝） Groove for middle meningeal artery
5. S状洞溝（乳突角を通る） Groove for sigmoid sinus
6. 下側頭線 Inferior temporal line
7. 乳突角 Mastoid angle
8. 後頭縁 Occipital border
9. 後頭角 Occipital angle
10. 頭頂孔 Parietal foramen
11. 頭頂結節 Parietal tuber
12. 矢状縁 Sagittal border
13. 蝶形骨角 Sphenoidal angle
14. 鱗縁 Squamosal border
15. 上側頭線 Superior temporal line

Ⓒ～Ⓔ 頬骨（右）

1. 前頭突起 Frontal process
2. 縁結節 Marginal tubercle
3. 上顎縁* Maxillary border*
4. 眼窩縁 Orbital border
5. 眼窩面 Orbital surface
6. 側頭縁* Temporal border*
7. 側頭突起 Temporal process
8. 側頭面 Temporal surface
9. 頬骨眼窩孔 Zygomatico-orbital foramen
10. 頬骨顔面孔 Zygomaticofacial foramen
11. 頬骨側頭孔 Zygomaticotemporal foramen

● 側頭骨の頬骨突起（4頁）と頬骨の側頭突起（C7，D7）が頬骨弓（4頁，38頁）を形成する．

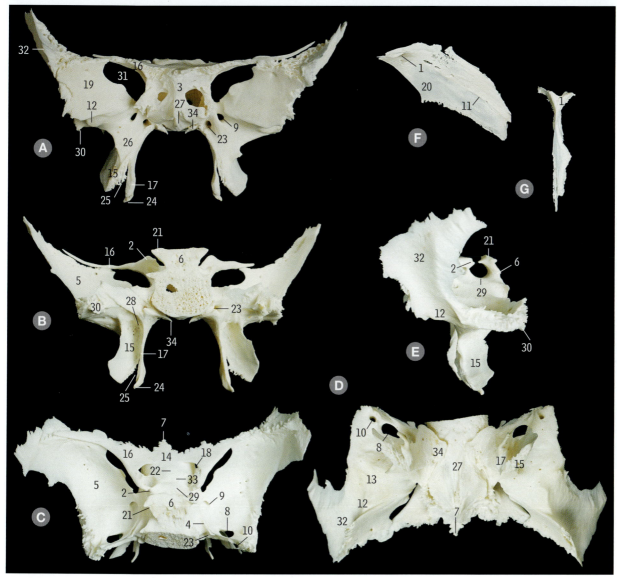

A：前方から．B・G：後方から．C：上後方から．D：下方から．E：左方から．F：右方から．

Ⓐ〜Ⓔ 蝶形骨
ⒻⒼ 鋤骨

1 鋤骨翼 Ala of vomer	12 側頭下稜〔大翼〕 Infratemporal crest (Greater wing)	24 翼突鈎 Pterygoid hamulus
2 前床突起 Anterior clinoid process	13 側頭下面〔大翼〕 Infratemporal surface (Greater wing)	25 翼突切痕 Pterygoid notch
3 蝶形骨体と蝶形骨洞口 Body of sphenoid with Openings of sphenoidal sinuses	14 蝶形骨隆起 Jugum sphenoidale：Sphenoidal yoke	26 翼状突起 Pterygoid process
4 頸動脈溝 Carotid sulcus	15 外側板〔翼状突起〕 Lateral plate (Pterygoid process)	27 蝶形骨吻 Sphenoidal rostrum
5 大脳面〔大翼〕 Cerebral surface (Greater wing)	16 小翼 Lesser wing	28 舟状窩 Scaphoid fossa
6 鞍背 Dorsum sellae	17 内側板〔翼状突起〕 Medial plate (Pterygoid process)	29 下垂体窩〔トルコ鞍〕 Hypophysial fossa (Sella turcica)
7 篩骨棘* Ethmoidal spine *	18 視神経管 Optic canal	30 蝶形骨棘 Spine of sphenoid
8 卵円孔 Foramen ovale	19 眼窩面〔大翼〕 Orbital surface (Greater wing)	31 上眼窩裂 Superior orbital fissure
9 正円孔 Foramen rotundum	20 後縁〔鋤骨〕 Posterior border (Vomer)	32 側頭面〔大翼〕 Temporal surface (Greater wing)
10 棘孔 Foramen spinosum	21 後床突起 Posterior clinoid process	33 鞍結節 Tuberculum sellae
11 鼻口蓋神経と伴行血管が通る溝	22 前視交叉溝 Prechiasmatic sulcus	34 鞘状突起 Vaginal process
	23 翼突管 Pterygoid canal	

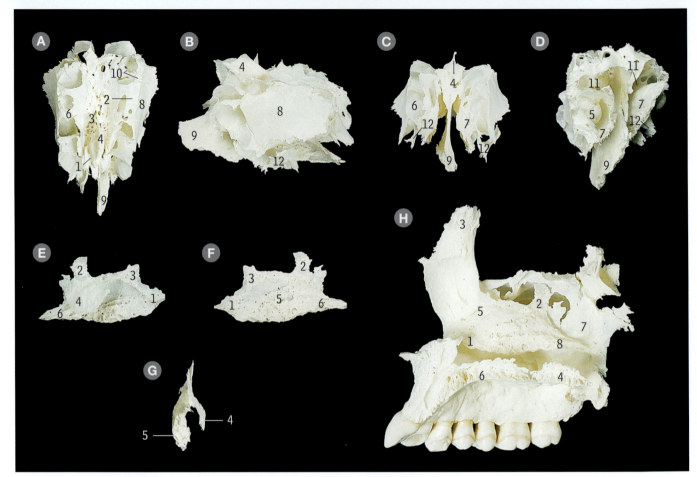

A：上方から．B：左方から．C：前方から．D：左下後方から．E：外側方から．F・H：内側方から．G：後方から．

A〜D 篩骨

1. 鶏冠翼 Ala of crista galli
2. 前篩骨溝* Anterior ethmoidal sulcus*
3. 篩板 Cribriform plate
4. 鶏冠 Crista galli
5. 篩骨胞 Ethmoidal bulla
6. 篩骨迷路（篩骨蜂巣を含む） Ethmoidal labyrinth
7. 中鼻甲介 Middle nasal concha
8. 眼窩板 Orbital plate
9. 垂直板 Perpendicular plate
10. 後篩骨溝* Posterior ethmoidal sulcus*
11. 上鼻甲介と上鼻道 Superior nasal concha and Superior nasal meatus
12. 鉤状突起 Uncinate process

E〜G 下鼻甲介（右）

1. 前端* Anterior end*
2. 篩骨突起 Ethmoidal process
3. 涙骨突起 Lacrimal process
4. 上顎突起 Maxillary process
5. 内側面* Medial surface*
6. 後端* Posterior end*

H 上顎骨
[右の上顎骨，口蓋骨および下鼻甲介の接続]

1. 前端*〔下鼻甲介〕 Anterior end*〔Inferior nasal concha〕
2. 篩骨突起〔下鼻甲介〕 Ethmoidal process〔Inferior nasal concha〕
3. 前頭突起〔上顎骨〕 Frontal process〔Maxilla〕
4. 水平板〔口蓋骨〕 Horizontal plate〔Palatine bone〕
5. 涙骨突起〔下鼻甲介〕 Lacrimal process〔Inferior nasal concha〕
6. 口蓋突起〔上顎骨〕 Palatine process〔Maxilla〕
7. 垂直板〔口蓋骨〕 Perpendicular plate〔Palatine bone〕
8. 後端*〔下鼻甲介〕 Posterior end*〔Inferior nasal concha〕

後頭骨 [D 頭蓋底の骨]

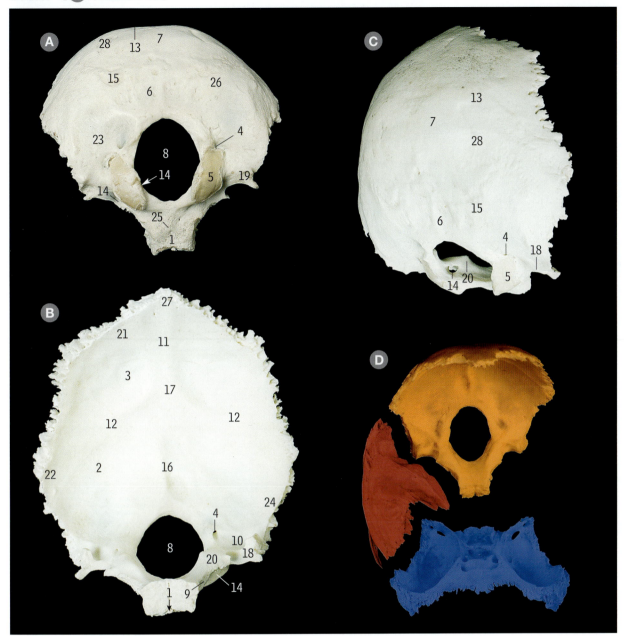

A：外面．下方から．B：内面．C：外面．右下方から．（橙：後頭骨．赤：側頭骨．青：蝶形骨．）

1 底部 Basilar part	11 上矢状洞溝 Groove for superior sagittal sinus	21 ラムダ縁 Lambdoid border
2 小脳窩 Cerebellar fossa	12 横洞溝 Groove for transverse sinus	22 外側角* Lateral angle*
3 大脳窩 Cerebral fossa	13 最上項線 Highest nuchal line	23 外側部 Lateral part
4 顆窩（BとCでは顆管） Condylar fossa	14 舌下神経管 Hypoglossal canal	24 乳突縁 Mastoid border
5 後頭顆 Occipital condyle	15 下項線 Inferior nuchal line	25 咽頭結節 Pharyngeal tubercle
6 外後頭稜 External occipital crest	16 内後頭稜 Internal occipital crest	26 （後頭骨の）後頭鱗 Squamous part of occipital bone
7 外後頭隆起 External occipital protuberance	17 内後頭隆起 Internal occipital protuberance	27 上角* Superior angle*
8 大後頭孔：大孔 Foramen magnum	18 頸静脈切痕 Jugular notch	28 上項線 Superior nuchal line
9 下錐体洞溝 Groove for inferior petrosal sinus	19 頸静脈突起 Jugular process	
10 S状洞溝 Groove for sigmoid sinus	20 頸静脈結節 Jugular tubercle	

頸部［体表解剖］

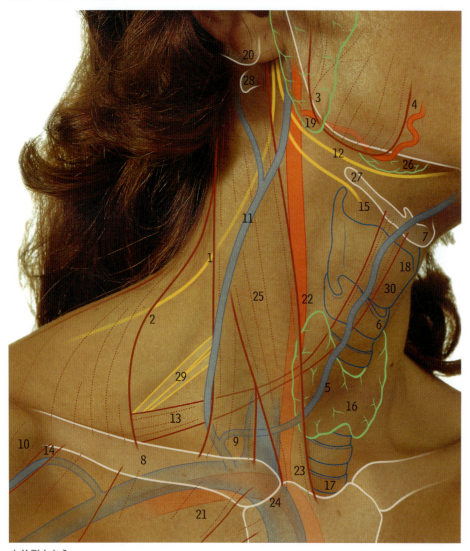

- 総頸動脈（22，次頁の8）の拍動は，胸鎖乳突筋前縁の下部と喉頭ならびに気管の側面との間の角を，後方に向かって圧迫を加えると触知できる．
- 輪状軟骨弓（6）は，胸骨柄の頸切痕（17）の約5 cm上方に位置する．
- 内頸静脈の下端は，前から見ると，胸鎖乳突筋の胸骨頭（23）と鎖骨頭（9）の間隙である小鎖骨上窩の後ろにある．この位置で，内頸静脈と鎖骨下静脈が合して腕頭静脈（24）を形成する．
- 腕神経叢の上神経幹（29）は，後頸三角の下部で索状物として触知できる．

右前側方から．

1 副神経［XI］（胸鎖乳突筋から現れた位置） Accessory nerve [XI]	11 外頸静脈 External jugular vein	21 大胸筋 Pectoralis major
2 副神経［XI］（僧帽筋の前縁の下を通る位置） Accessory nerve [XI]	12 舌下神経［XII］ Hypoglossal nerve [XII]	22 総頸動脈の拍動を触れる位置
3 下顎角 Angle of mandible	13 下腹〔肩甲舌骨筋〕 Inferior belly〔Omohyoid〕	23 胸骨頭〔胸鎖乳突筋〕 Sternal head〔Sternocleidomastoid〕
4 前縁〔咬筋〕と顔面動脈 Anterior border〔Masseter〕and Facial artery	14 鎖骨下窩と橈側皮静脈 Infraclavicular fossa and Cephalic vein	24 胸鎖関節（内頸静脈と鎖骨下静脈が合流して腕頭静脈を形成する位置） Sternoclavicular joint
5 前頸静脈 Anterior jugular vein	15 内枝〔上喉頭神経〕 Internal branch〔Superior laryngeal nerve〕	25 胸鎖乳突筋 Sternocleidomastoid
6 輪状軟骨弓 Arch of cricoid cartilage	16 甲状腺峡部 Isthmus of thyroid gland	26 顎下腺 Submandibular gland
7 （舌骨の）体 Body of hyoid bone	17 頸切痕と気管 Jugular notch and Trachea	27 大角〔舌骨〕（端部） Greater horn〔Hyoid bone〕
8 鎖骨 Clavicle	18 喉頭隆起（Adamのりんご） Laryngeal prominence	28 横突起*〔環椎：第一頸椎〕（端部） Transverse process *〔Atlas : C I〕
9 鎖骨頭*〔胸鎖乳突筋〕 Clavicular head *〔Sternocleidomastoid〕	19 耳下腺（下端部） Parotid gland	29 上神経幹〔腕神経叢〕 Superior trunk : Upper trunk〔Brachial plexus〕
10 三角筋 Deltoid	20 乳様突起 Mastoid process	30 声帯の位置

斜頸

水痘・帯状疱疹ウイルスの感染（頭頸部）

第1章 頭頸部と脳：頸部

側頸部（右）［深層］

- 舌神経(27)は，舌骨舌筋(17)よりも浅層を走り，その下方に顎下腺の深部(10)がある．ここでは，神経は典型的な円柱状ではなく平たくなる．舌神経は，顎下腺管(51)の下方を交叉し，交叉の手前では管の外側を，交叉後は内側を走る．
- 甲状舌骨膜(60)は上喉頭神経の内枝(23)と上喉頭動脈(55)に貫かれている．
- 舌下神経(19)は，舌筋に支配枝を送った後，オトガイ舌骨筋(14)と甲状舌骨筋(59)に支配枝を与え，頸神経ワナの上根(62)の形成に参加する．以上の3枝は第一頸神経(C1)の線維からなり，頸部の上方で舌下神経に合する．したがって，これらの神経線維は舌下神経核から起始したものではない．頸神経ワナの上根に含まれるC1線維は，胸骨舌骨筋(45)と肩甲舌骨筋(21, 54)の支配にも関与する．

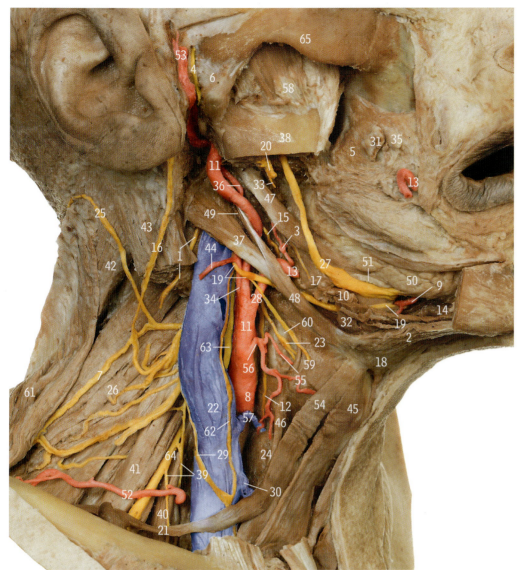

1	副神経［XI］	Accessory nerve [XI]
2	前腹〔顎二腹筋〕と支配神経	Anterior belly (Digastric) and nerve
3	上行口蓋動脈	Ascending palatine artery
4	耳介側頭神経	Auriculotemporal nerve
5	頬筋	Buccinator
6	関節包〔顎関節〕	Articular capsule (Temporomandibular joint)
7	僧帽筋への枝＊〔頸神経〕	Branch to trapezius＊ (Cervical nerves)
8	総頸動脈	Common carotid artery
9	舌深動脈	Deep lingual artery
10	顎下腺（深部）	Submandibular gland
11	外頸動脈	External carotid artery
12	外枝〔上喉頭神経〕	External branch (Superior laryngeal nerve)
13	顔面動脈	Facial artery
14	オトガイ舌骨筋	Geniohyoid
15	舌咽神経［IX］	Glossopharyngeal nerve [IX]
16	大耳介神経	Great auricular nerve
17	舌骨舌筋	Hyoglossus
18	舌骨	Hyoid bone
19	舌下神経［XII］	Hypoglossal nerve [XII]
20	下歯槽神経	Inferior alveolar nerve
21	下腹〔肩甲舌骨筋〕	Inferior belly (Omohyoid)
22	内頸静脈	Internal jugular vein
23	内枝〔上喉頭神経〕	Internal branch (Superior laryngeal nerve)
24	右葉〔甲状腺〕	Right lobe (Thyroid gland)
25	小後頭神経	Lesser occipital nerve
26	肩甲挙筋	Levator scapulae
27	舌神経	Lingual nerve
28	舌顔面動脈幹	Linguofacial trunk
29	下根〔頸神経ワナ〕	Inferior root (Ansa cervicalis)
30	中甲状腺静脈	Middle thyroid vein
31	臼歯腺	Molar salivary glands
32	顎舌骨筋と顎舌骨筋神経	Mylohyoid and Nerve to mylohyoid
33	顎舌骨筋神経	Nerve to mylohyoid
34	後頭動脈	Occipital artery
35	耳下腺管	Parotid duct
36	後耳介動脈	Posterior auricular artery
37	後腹〔顎二腹筋〕	Posterior belly (Digastric)
38	下顎枝	Ramus of mandible
39	横隔神経（の根）	Phrenic nerve
40	前斜角筋	Anterior scalene
41	中斜角筋	Middle scalene
42	頭板状筋	Splenius capitis
43	胸鎖乳突筋（切断してある）	Sternocleidomastoid
44	胸鎖乳突筋枝〔後頭動脈〕	Sternocleidomastoid branches (Occipital artery)
45	胸骨舌骨筋	Sternohyoid
46	胸骨甲状筋	Sternothyroid
47	茎突舌筋	Styloglossus
48	茎突舌骨筋	Stylohyoid
49	茎突舌骨靱帯	Stylohyoid ligament
50	舌下腺	Sublingual gland
51	顎下腺管	Submandibular duct
52	浅頸動脈〔頸横動脈〕	Superficial cervical artery (Transverse cervical artery)
53	浅側頭動脈	Superficial temporal artery
54	上腹〔肩甲舌骨筋〕	Superior belly (Omohyoid)
55	上喉頭動脈	Superior laryngeal artery
56	上甲状腺動脈	Superior thyroid artery
57	上甲状腺静脈	Superior thyroid vein
58	側頭筋	Temporalis
59	甲状舌骨筋と甲状舌骨筋枝	Thyrohyoid and Thyrohyoid branch
60	甲状舌骨膜	Thyrohyoid membrane
61	僧帽筋	Trapezius
62	上根〔頸神経ワナ〕	Superior root (Ansa cervicalis)
63	迷走神経［X］	Vagus nerve [X]
64	前枝〔第五頸神経〕	Ventral ramus (C5)
65	頬骨弓	Zygomatic arch

前頸部［深層］

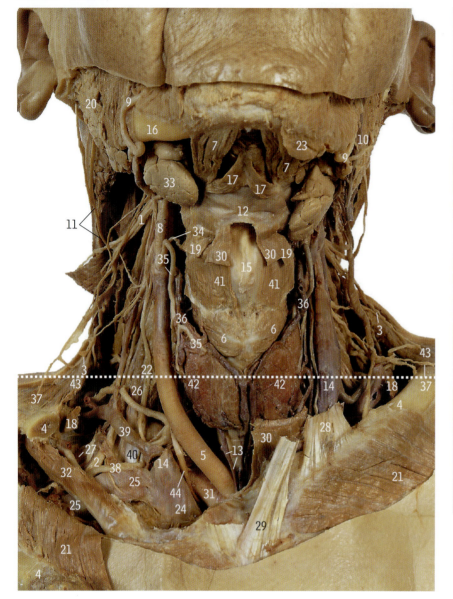

#	日本語	English	#	日本語	English
1	副神経［XI］	Accessory nerve [XI]	24	右腕頭静脈	Right brachiocephalic vein
2	根〔腕神経叢〕	Roots〔Brachial plexus〕	25	（右の）鎖骨下静脈	Subclavian vein
3	僧帽筋への枝*〔頸神経〕	Branch to trapezius *〔Cervical nerves〕	26	前斜角筋	Anterior scalene
4	鎖骨	Clavicle	27	中斜角筋	Middle scalene
5	総頸動脈	Common carotid artery	28	鎖骨頭*〔胸鎖乳突筋〕	Clavicular head *〔Sternocleidomastoid〕
6	輪状甲状筋	Cricothyroid	29	胸骨頭*〔胸鎖乳突筋〕	Sternal head *〔Sternocleidomastoid〕
7	前腹〔顎二腹筋〕	Anterior belly〔Digastric〕	30	胸骨舌骨筋	Sternohyoid
8	外頸動脈	External carotid artery	31	鎖骨下動脈	Subclavian artery
9	顔面動脈	Facial artery	32	鎖骨下筋	Subclavius
10	顔面静脈	Facial vein	33	顎下腺	Submandibular gland
11	大耳介神経	Great auricular nerve	34	上喉頭動脈	Superior laryngeal artery
12	（舌骨の）体	Body of hyoid bone	35	上甲状腺動脈	Superior thyroid artery
13	下甲状腺静脈	Inferior thyroid vein	36	上甲状腺静脈	Superior thyroid vein
14	内頸静脈	Internal jugular vein	37	鎖骨上神経	Supraclavicular nerve
15	喉頭隆起	Laryngeal prominence	38	肩甲上動脈	Suprascapular artery
16	下顎骨	Mandible	39	肩甲上静脈	Suprascapular vein
17	顎舌骨筋（異常筋束）	Mylohyoid	40	前斜角筋（の）腱	Scalenus anterior
18	下腹〔肩甲舌骨筋〕	Inferior belly〔Omohyoid〕	41	甲状舌骨筋	Thyrohyoid
19	上腹〔肩甲舌骨筋〕	Superior belly〔Omohyoid〕	42	右葉と左葉〔甲状腺〕	Right lobe and Left lobe〔Thyroid gland〕
20	耳下腺	Parotid gland	43	僧帽筋	Trapezius
21	大胸筋	Pectoralis major	44	迷走神経［X］	Vagus nerve [X]
22	横隔神経	Phrenic nerve			
23	広頸筋	Platysma			

● 右側は，鎖骨（4）を切断して下方に翻転してあり，鎖骨の下にある鎖骨下筋（32）が見えている．破線は右にあるCTの横断面の高さである．

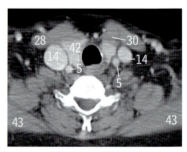

頸部のCT横断画像

副神経麻痺

甲状腺腫

顎下腺腫瘍

側頸部（右）

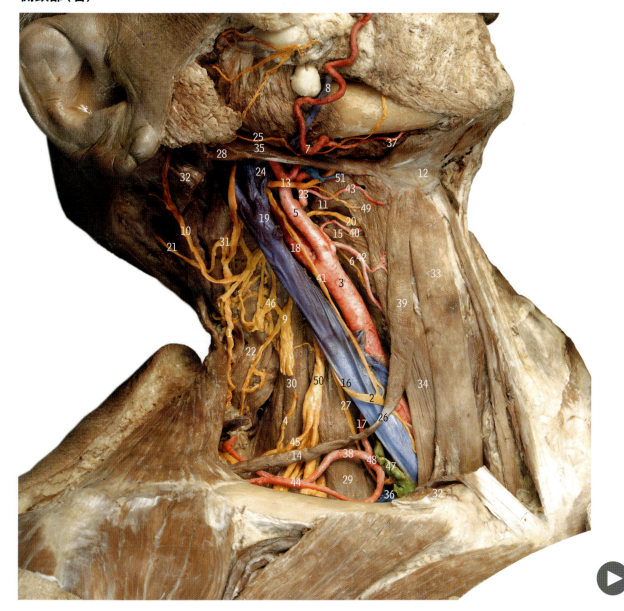

1	副神経［XI］	Accessory nerve [XI]
2	頸神経ワナ	Ansa cervicalis
3	総頸動脈	Common carotid artery
4	肩甲背神経	Dorsal scapular nerve
5	外頸動脈	External carotid artery
6	外枝〔上喉頭神経〕	External branch (Superior laryngeal nerve)
7	顔面動脈	Facial artery
8	顔面静脈	Facial vein
9	前枝〔第四頸神経〕	Ventral ramus (C4)
10	大耳介神経	Great auricular nerve
11	大角〔舌骨〕	Greater horn (Hyoid bone)
12	舌骨	Hyoid bone
13	舌下神経［XII］	Hypoglossal nerve [XII]
14	下腹〔肩甲舌骨筋〕	Inferior belly (Omohyoid)
15	下咽頭収縮筋	Inferior constrictor
16	下根〔頸神経ワナ〕	Inferior root (Ansa cervicalis)
17	下甲状腺動脈	Inferior thyroid artery
18	内頸動脈	Internal carotid artery
19	内頸静脈（上端は二本になっている）	Internal jugular vein
20	内枝〔上喉頭神経〕（甲状舌骨筋を貫く）	Internal branch (Superior laryngeal nerve)
21	小後頭神経	Lesser occipital nerve
22	肩甲挙筋	Levator scapulae
23	舌動脈	Lingual artery
24	舌静脈	Lingual vein
25	下顎縁枝〔顔面神経［VII］〕	Marginal mandibular branch (Facial nerve [VII])
26	肩甲舌骨筋（の中間腱）	Omohyoid
27	横隔神経	Phrenic nerve
28	後腹〔顎二腹筋〕	Posterior belly (Digastric)
29	前斜角筋	Anterior scalene
30	中斜角筋	Middle scalene
31	前枝〔第二頸神経〕	Ventral ramus (C2)
32	胸鎖乳突筋（切断してある）	Sternocleidomastoid
33	胸骨舌骨筋	Sternohyoid
34	胸骨甲状筋	Sternothyroid
35	茎突舌骨筋	Stylohyoid
36	鎖骨下静脈	Subclavian vein
37	オトガイ下動脈	Submental artery
38	浅頸動脈〔頸横動脈〕	Superficial cervical artery (Transverse cervical artery)
39	上腹〔肩甲舌骨筋〕	Superior belly (Omohyoid)
40	上喉頭動脈	Superior laryngeal artery
41	上根〔頸神経ワナ〕	Superior root (Ansa cervicalis)
42	上甲状腺動脈	Superior thyroid artery
43	舌骨上枝〔舌動脈〕（甲状舌骨筋の表面を走る）	Suprahyoid branch (Lingual artery)
44	肩甲上動脈	Suprascapular artery
45	肩甲上神経	Suprascapular nerve
46	前枝〔第三頸神経〕	Ventral ramus (C3)
47	右リンパ本幹（終末部）	Right lymphatic duct
48	甲状頸動脈	Thyrocervical trunk
49	甲状舌骨筋と甲状舌骨筋枝	Thyrohyoid and Thyrohyoid branch
50	上神経幹〔腕神経叢〕	Superior trunk: Upper trunk (Brachial plexus)
51	舌下神経伴行静脈	Vena comitans of hypoglossal nerve

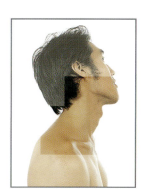

鰓性嚢胞

頸動脈の狭窄

側頭部

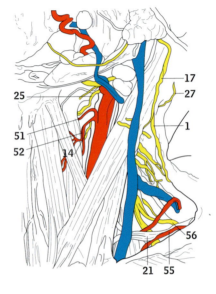

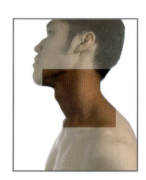

●本例のように，顔面神経の下顎縁枝(30)が顔面から少し下方に外れて弓状に走り，20％の例においては，顎下腺(46)の表面を通過する．

左前方から．広頸筋と頸筋膜を除去してある．

1	副神経 [XI]	Accessory nerve [XI]
2	前腹〔顎二腹筋〕	Anterior belly (Digastric)
3	前頸静脈	Anterior jugular vein
4	(舌骨の)体	Body of hyoid bone
5	下顎体	Body of mandible
6	頰脂肪体	Buccal fat pad
7	頸枝〔顔面神経 [VII]〕	Cervical branch (Facial nerve [VII])
8	僧帽筋への枝*〔頸神経〕	Branch to trapezius * (Cervical nerves)
9	鎖骨頭*〔胸鎖乳突筋〕	Clavicular head * (Sternocleidomastoid)
10	総頸動脈	Common carotid artery
11	肩甲背神経	Dorsal scapular nerve
12	外頸動脈	External carotid artery
13	外頸静脈	External jugular vein
14	外枝〔上喉頭神経〕	External branch (Superior laryngeal nerve)
15	顔面動脈	Facial artery
16	顔面静脈	Facial vein
17	大耳介神経	Great auricular nerve
18	大角〔舌骨〕(25 より奥にある)	Greater horn (Hyoid bone)
19	舌骨舌筋	Hyoglossus
20	舌下神経 [XII]	Hypoglossal nerve [XII]
21	下腹〔肩甲舌骨筋〕	Inferior belly (Omohyoid)
22	下咽頭収縮筋	Inferior constrictor
23	下甲状腺静脈	Inferior thyroid vein
24	内頸動脈と上根〔頸神経ワナ〕	Internal carotid artery and Superior root (Ansa cervicalis)
25	内枝〔上喉頭神経〕	Internal branch (Superior laryngeal nerve)
26	頸静脈二腹筋リンパ節	Jugulodigastric nodes
27	小後頭神経	Lesser occipital nerve
28	舌動脈	Lingual artery
29	舌静脈	Lingual vein
30	下顎縁枝〔顔面神経 [VII]〕	Marginal mandibular branch (Facial nerve [VII])
31	咬筋	Masseter
32	顎舌骨筋	Mylohyoid
33	甲状舌骨筋枝（神経）	Thyrohyoid branch
34	耳下腺	Parotid gland
35	横隔神経(前斜角筋の前を通る)	Phrenic nerve
36	後耳介静脈	Posterior auricular vein
37	後腹〔顎二腹筋〕	Posterior belly (Digastric)
38	下顎後静脈	Retromandibular vein
39	前斜角筋	Anterior scalene
40	中斜角筋	Middle scalene
41	胸骨頭*〔胸鎖乳突筋〕	Sternal head * (Sternocleidomastoid)
42	胸鎖乳突筋	Sternocleidomastoid
43	胸骨舌骨筋	Sternohyoid
44	胸骨甲状筋	Sternothyroid
45	茎突舌骨筋	Stylohyoid
46	顎下腺	Submandibular gland
47	オトガイ下動／静脈	Submental artery/vein
48	浅頸動脈〔頸横動脈〕	Superficial cervical artery (Transverse cervical artery)
49	浅頸静脈*〔頸横静脈〕	Superficial cervical vein * (Transverse cervical vein)
50	上腹〔肩甲舌骨筋〕	Superior belly (Omohyoid)
51	上喉頭動脈	Superior laryngeal artery
52	上甲状腺動脈	Superior thyroid artery
53	鎖骨上神経(上端部で切断)	Supraclavicular nerve
54	舌骨上枝〔舌動脈〕	Suprahyoid branch (Lingual artery)
55	肩甲上動脈	Suprascapular artery
56	肩甲上神経	Suprascapular nerve
57	甲状舌骨筋	Thyrohyoid
58	甲状舌骨膜	Thyrohyoid membrane
59	左葉〔甲状腺〕	Left lobe (Thyroid gland)
60	僧帽筋	Trapezius
61	上神経幹〔腕神経叢〕	Superior trunk：Upper trunk (Brachial plexus)

頸動脈の雑音

頸動脈の異常

頸リンパ節の腫脹

顔面下部と上頸部（右）[Ⓐ 耳下腺部と上頸部, Ⓑ 顎下部]

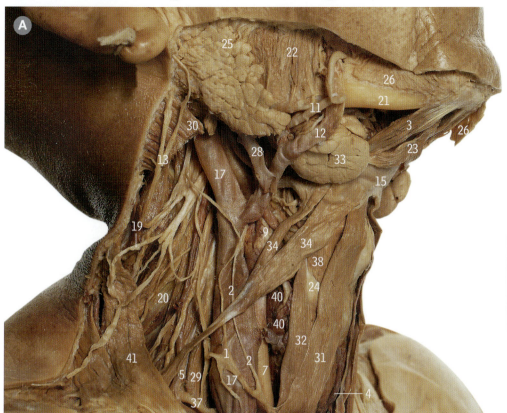
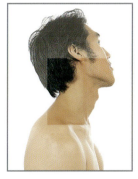
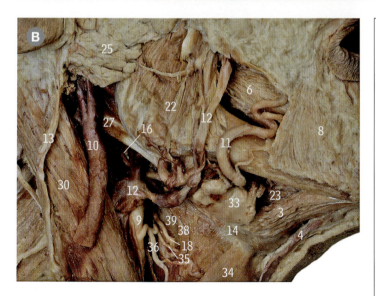

1	下根〔頸神経ワナ〕 Inferior root〔Ansa cervicalis〕	15	舌骨 Hyoid bone	28	下顎後静脈 Retromandibular vein
2	上根〔頸神経ワナ〕 Superior root〔Ansa cervicalis〕	16	舌下神経［XII］ Hypoglossal nerve［XII］	29	前斜角筋 Anterior scalene
3	前腹〔顎二腹筋〕 Anterior belly〔Digastric〕	17	内頸静脈 Internal jugular vein	30	胸鎖乳突筋 Sternocleidomastoid
4	前頸静脈 Anterior jugular vein	18	内枝〔上喉頭神経〕 Internal branch〔Superior laryngeal nerve〕	31	胸骨舌骨筋 Sternohyoid
5	根〔腕神経叢〕 Roots〔Brachial plexus〕	19	小後頭神経 Lesser occipital nerve	32	胸骨甲状筋 Sternothyroid
6	頬筋 Buccinator	20	肩甲挙筋 Levator scapulae	33	顎下腺 Submandibular gland
7	総頸動脈 Common carotid artery	21	下顎骨 Mandible	34	上腹〔肩甲舌骨筋〕（2分している変異） Superior belly〔Omohyoid〕
8	口角下制筋 Depressor anguli oris	22	咬筋 Masseter	35	上喉頭動脈 Superior laryngeal artery
9	外頸動脈 External carotid artery	23	顎舌骨筋 Mylohyoid	36	上甲状腺動脈 Superior thyroid artery
10	外頸静脈 External jugular vein	24	斜線〔甲状軟骨〕 Oblique line〔Thyroid cartilage〕	37	肩甲上動脈 Suprascapular artery
11	顔面動脈 Facial artery	25	耳下腺と顔面神経（耳下腺の前縁から現れる枝） Parotid gland and Facial nerve	38	甲状舌骨筋 Thyrohyoid
12	顔面静脈 Facial vein	26	広頸筋 Platysma	39	甲状舌骨膜 Thyrohyoid membrane
13	大耳介神経 Great auricular nerve	27	後腹〔顎二腹筋〕 Posterior belly〔Digastric〕	40	右葉〔甲状腺〕 Right lobe〔Thyroid gland〕
14	大角〔舌骨〕 Greater horn〔Hyoid bone〕			41	僧帽筋 Trapezius

流行性耳下腺炎（おたふくかぜ）

耳下腺摘出術

耳下腺腫瘍

顔面下部と上頸部（左）

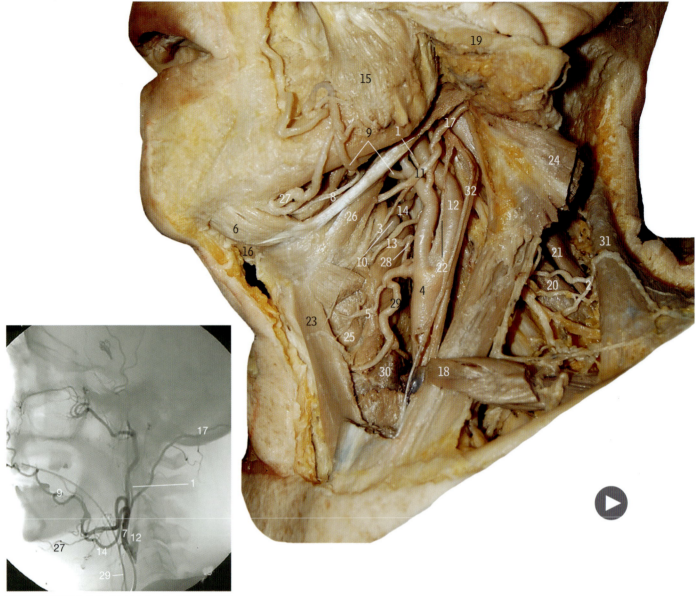

外頸動脈のデジタルサブトラクション血管造影画像

1 上行咽頭動脈 Ascending pharyngeal artery	9 顔面動脈 Facial artery	17 後頭動脈 Occipital artery	25 甲状舌骨筋 Thyrohyoid
2 頸神経叢の枝 Branches of Cervical plexus	10 大角〔舌骨〕 Greater horn (Hyoid bone)	18 肩甲舌骨筋（翻転してある） Omohyoid	26 茎突舌骨筋 Stylohyoid
3 第一頸神経注 1st cervical nerve (C1)	11 舌下神経〔XII〕 Hypoglossal nerve [XII]	19 耳下腺（翻転してある） Parotid gland	27 オトガイ下動脈 Submental artery
4 総頸動脈 Common carotid artery	12 内頸動脈 Internal carotid artery	20 後斜角筋 Posterior scalene	28 上喉頭動脈 Superior laryngeal artery
5 輪状甲状枝 Cricothyroid branch	13 内枝〔上喉頭神経〕 Internal branch (Superior laryngeal nerve)	21 中斜角筋 Middle scalene	29 上甲状腺動脈 Superior thyroid artery
6 前腹〔顎二腹筋〕 Anterior belly (Digastric)	14 舌動脈 Lingual artery	22 頸動脈洞枝と頸動脈小体への枝 Carotid branch and Branches to carotid body	30 左葉〔甲状腺〕 Left lobe (Thyroid gland)
7 外頸動脈 External carotid artery	15 咬筋 Masseter	23 胸骨舌骨筋 Sternohyoid	31 僧帽筋 Trapezius
8 下顎縁枝〔顔面神経〔VII〕〕 Marginal mandibular branch (Facial nerve [VII])	16 顎舌骨筋 Mylohyoid	24 胸鎖乳突筋（翻転してある） Sternocleidomastoid	32 迷走神経〔X〕 Vagus nerve [X]

注：舌下神経の下行枝のように見えるが，C1 に由来する線維である．

頸部の動脈内膜切除術

側頸部（右）［深層］

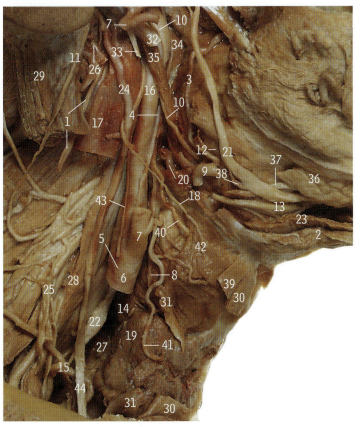
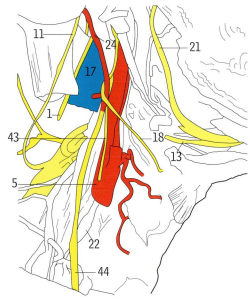
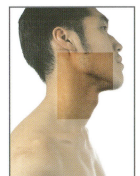

- 舌下神経(13)は下行し，後頭動脈(24)を回り込んで，外頸動脈(7)と舌動脈(20)の浅層を横切る．
- 舌咽神経(10)は下前方へ走り，茎突咽頭筋(35)の外側を回り込む．
- 胸骨舌骨筋(30)，肩甲舌骨筋(39)，胸骨甲状筋(31)を部分的に取り去り，甲状腺(19)を剖出している．甲状腺の左・右葉の下部の後ろを下甲状腺動脈(15)が通ることに注意せよ．また，ループ状の走行をとるこの動脈より深層を反回神経(27)が通過し，下咽頭収縮筋(14)の下層で咽頭に進入することに注意せよ．

1 副神経［XI］（切断してある） Accessory nerve [XI]	16 内頸動脈 Internal carotid artery	31 胸骨甲状筋 Sternothyroid
2 前腹〔顎二腹筋〕 Anterior belly〔Digastric〕	17 内頸静脈 Internal jugular vein	32 茎突舌筋 Styloglossus
3 上行口蓋動脈 Ascending palatine artery	18 内枝〔上喉頭神経〕 Internal branch〔Superior laryngeal nerve〕	33 茎突舌筋（切断端を内側へ転位） Stylohyoid
4 上行咽頭動脈 Ascending pharyngeal artery	19 右葉〔甲状腺〕 Right lobe〔Thyroid gland〕	34 茎突舌骨靱帯 Stylohyoid ligament
5 頸動脈洞 Carotid sinus	20 舌動脈 Lingual artery	35 茎突咽頭筋 Stylopharyngeus
6 総頸動脈 Common carotid artery	21 舌神経 Lingual nerve	36 舌下腺 Sublingual gland
7 外頸動脈 External carotid artery	22 中頸神経節（交感神経） Middle cervical ganglion	37 顎下腺管 Submandibular duct
8 外枝〔上喉頭神経〕 External branch〔Superior laryngeal nerve〕	23 顎舌骨筋 Mylohyoid	38 顎下神経節 Submandibular ganglion
9 顔面動脈 Facial artery	24 後頭動脈 Occipital artery	39 上腹〔肩甲舌骨筋〕 Superior belly〔Omohyoid〕
10 舌咽神経［IX］ Glossopharyngeal nerve [IX]	25 横隔神経 Phrenic nerve	40 上喉頭動脈 Superior laryngeal artery
11 大耳介神経 Great auricular nerve	26 後腹〔顎二腹筋〕（切断縁） Posterior belly〔Digastric〕	41 上甲状腺動脈 Superior thyroid artery
12 舌骨舌筋 Hyoglossus	27 反回神経 Recurrent laryngeal nerve	42 甲状舌骨筋と甲状舌骨筋枝（神経） Thyrohyoid and Thyrohyoid branch
13 舌下神経［XII］（切断してある） Hypoglossal nerve [XII]	28 前斜角筋 Anterior scalene	43 上根〔頸神経ワナ〕 Superior root〔Ansa cervicalis〕
14 下咽頭収縮筋 Inferior constrictor	29 胸鎖乳突筋 Sternocleidomastoid	44 迷走神経［X］ Vagus nerve [X]
15 下甲状腺動脈 Inferior thyroid artery	30 胸骨舌骨筋 Sternohyoid	

頸部の基部

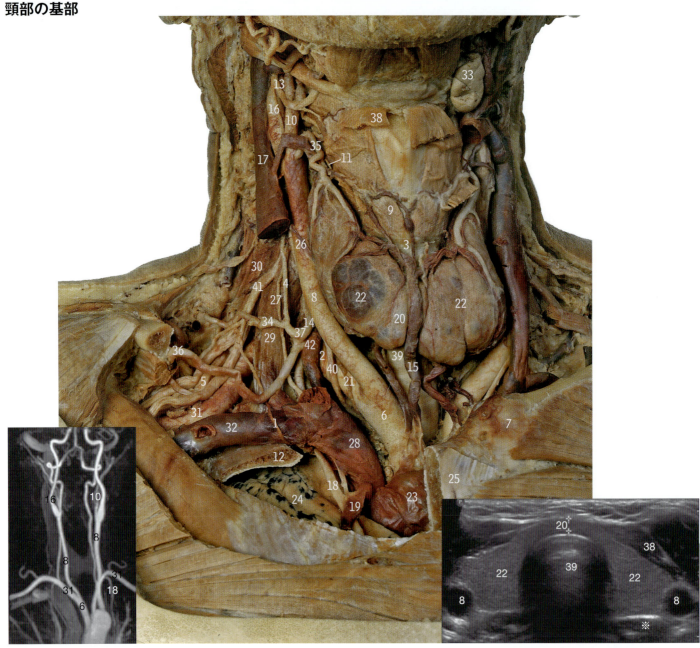

頸部のMR血管造影画像

甲状腺の超音波画像(横断面)
(※:甲状腺の左葉の背側に頸長筋が見られる.)

内頸静脈穿刺

鎖骨下静脈穿刺

1	副横隔神経	Accessory phrenic nerve
2	鎖骨下ワナ	Ansa subclavia
3	輪状軟骨弓	Arch of cricoid cartilage
4	上行頸動脈	Ascending cervical artery
5	腕神経叢	Brachial plexus
6	腕頭動脈	Brachiocephalic trunk
7	胸鎖関節(の関節包)	Sternoclavicular joint
8	総頸動脈	Common carotid artery
9	輪状甲状筋	Cricothyroid
10	外頸動脈	External carotid artery
11	外枝〔上喉頭神経〕	External branch (Superior laryngeal nerve)
12	第一肋骨(切断してある)	1st rib: Rib I
13	舌下神経 [XII]	Hypoglossal nerve [XII]
14	下甲状腺動脈	Inferior thyroid artery
15	下甲状腺静脈	Inferior thyroid vein
16	内頸動脈	Internal carotid artery
17	内頸静脈	Internal jugular vein
18	内胸動脈	Internal thoracic artery
19	内胸静脈	Internal thoracic vein
20	甲状腺峡部	Isthmus of thyroid gland
21	頸リンパ本幹	Jugular trunk
22	右葉と左葉〔甲状腺〕	Right lobe and Left lobe (Thyroid gland)
23	左腕頭静脈	Left brachiocephalic vein
24	肺尖	Apex of lung
25	胸骨柄	Manubrium of sternum
26	中甲状腺静脈	Middle thyroid vein
27	横隔神経	Phrenic nerve
28	右腕頭静脈	Right brachiocephalic vein
29	前斜角筋	Anterior scalene
30	中斜角筋	Middle scalene
31	鎖骨下動脈	Subclavian artery
32	鎖骨下静脈	Subclavian vein
33	顎下腺	Submandibular gland
34	浅頸動脈〔頸横動脈〕	Superficial cervical artery (Transverse cervical artery)
35	上甲状腺動/静脈	Superior thyroid artery/vein
36	肩甲上動脈	Suprascapular artery
37	甲状頸動脈	Thyrocervical trunk
38	胸骨舌骨筋	Sternohyoid
39	気管	Trachea
40	迷走神経 [X]	Vagus nerve [X]
41	前枝〔第五頸神経〕	Ventral ramus (C5)
42	椎骨静脈	Vertebral vein

椎前部

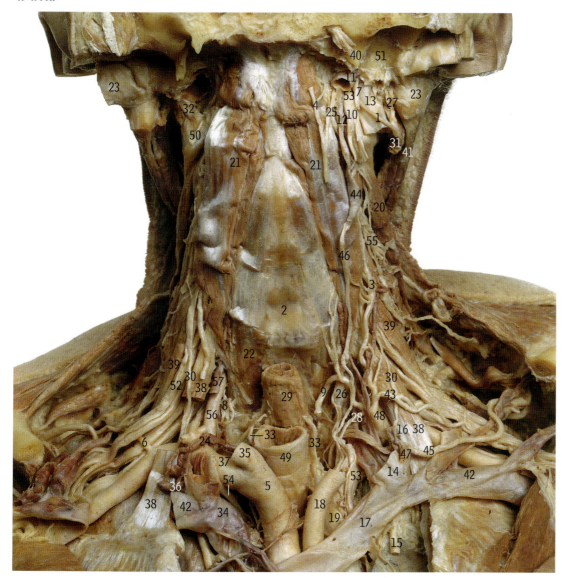

1	脊髄根〔副神経［XI］〕	Spinal root (Accessory nerve [XI])
2	前縦靱帯	Anterior longitudinal ligament
3	上行頸動脈とその伴行静脈	Ascending cervical artery and venae comitantes
4	上行咽頭動脈	Ascending pharyngeal artery
5	腕頭動脈	Brachiocephalic trunk
6	肩甲背動脈	Dorsal scapular artery
7	舌咽神経［IX］	Glossopharyngeal nerve [IX]
8	下頸神経節	Inferior cervical ganglion
9	下甲状腺動脈	Inferior thyroid artery
10	下神経節〔迷走神経［X］〕	Inferior ganglion (Vagus nerve [X])
11	内頸動脈	Internal carotid artery
12	内頸動脈神経	Internal carotid nerve
13	内頸静脈（上端部）	Internal jugular vein
14	内頸静脈（下端部）	Internal jugular vein
15	内胸動脈	Internal thoracic artery
16	頸リンパ本幹	Jugular trunk
17	左腕頭静脈	Left brachiocephalic vein
18	（左の）総頸動脈	Common carotid artery
19	（左の）鎖骨下動脈	Subclavian artery
20	肩甲挙筋	Levator scapulae
21	頭長筋	Longus capitis
22	頸長筋	Longus colli
23	乳様突起	Mastoid process
24	気管支縦隔リンパ本幹	Bronchomediastinal trunk
25	後硬膜動脈〔上行咽頭動脈〕	Posterior meningeal artery (Ascending pharyngeal artery)
26	中頸神経節	Middle cervical ganglion
27	後頭動脈	Occipital artery
28	食道枝〔下甲状腺動脈〕	Esophageal branch (Inferior thyroid artery)
29	食道	Esophagus
30	横隔神経	Phrenic nerve
31	後腹〔顎二腹筋〕	Posterior belly (Digastric)
32	外側頭直筋	Rectus capitis lateralis
33	反回神経	Recurrent laryngeal nerve
34	右腕頭静脈	Right brachiocephalic vein
35	（右の）総頸動脈	Common carotid artery
36	右リンパ本幹	Right lymphatic duct
37	（右の）鎖骨下動脈	Subclavian artery
38	前斜角筋	Anterior scalene
39	中斜角筋	Middle scalene
40	蝶形骨棘	Spine of sphenoid
41	胸鎖乳突筋	Sternocleidomastoid
42	鎖骨下静脈	Subclavian vein
43	浅頸動脈	Superficial cervical artery
44	上頸神経節	Superior cervical ganglion
45	肩甲上動脈	Suprascapular artery
46	交感神経幹	Sympathetic trunk
47	胸管	Thoracic duct
48	甲状頸動脈	Thyrocervical trunk
49	気管	Trachea
50	横突起*〔環椎：第一頸椎〕	Transverse process * (Atlas: C I)
51	鼓室部〔側頭骨〕	Tympanic part (Temporal bone)
52	上神経幹〔腕神経叢〕	Superior trunk : Upper trunk (Brachial plexus)
53	（左の）迷走神経［X］	Vagus nerve [X]
54	（右の）迷走神経［X］	Vagus nerve [X]
55	前枝〔第三頸神経〕	Ventral ramus (C3)
56	椎骨動脈	Vertebral artery
57	椎骨静脈	Vertebral vein

Horner 症候群

顔面［右前面の表面構造］

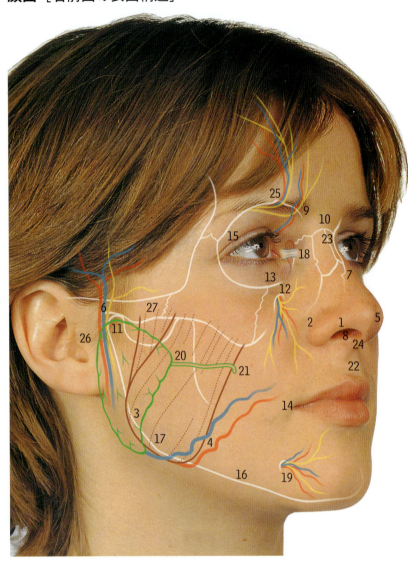

1 鼻翼 Ala of nose
2 鼻唇溝 Nasolabial sulcus
3 下顎角 Angle of mandible
4 前縁〔咬筋〕と顔面動／静脈 Anterior border〔Masseter〕and Facial artery/vein
5 鼻尖 Apex of nose
6 耳介側頭神経と浅側頭動／静脈 Auriculotemporal nerve and Superficial temporal artery/veins
7 鼻背 Dorsum of nose
8 外鼻孔 Nares：Nostrils
9 前頭切痕と滑車上神経・動／静脈 Frontal notch and Supratrochlear nerve and artery/veins
10 眉間 Glabella
11 下顎頭 Head of mandible
12 眼窩下孔，眼窩下神経・眼窩下動／静脈* Infra-orbital foramen, Infra-orbital nerve and Infra-orbital artery/vein*
13 眼窩下縁 Infra-orbital margin
14 口角 Angle of mouth
15 眼窩上縁（外側部） Supra-orbital margin
16 下縁〔下顎体〕 Inferior border〔Body of mandible〕
17 下縁〔下顎枝〕 Inferior border〔Ramus of mandible〕
18 内側眼瞼靱帯（涙嚢の前にある） Medial palpebral ligament
19 オトガイ孔，オトガイ神経・オトガイ動／静脈* Mental foramen, Mental nerve and Mental artery/vein*
20 耳下腺管（耳下腺から出る位置） Parotid duct
21 耳下腺管（咬筋の前縁で内側に屈曲する位置） Parotid duct
22 人中 Philtrum
23 鼻根 Root of nose
24 鼻中隔 Nasal septum
25 眼窩上切痕（または孔），眼窩上神経・動／静脈 Supra-orbital notch：Supra-orbital foramen, nerve and artery/vein
26 耳珠 Tragus
27 頬骨弓 Zygomatic arch

- 耳珠(26)の前で，浅側頭動脈(6)の拍動を触れることができる．
- 耳下腺管(20, 21)は，耳珠(26)と人中(22)の中点を結ぶ線の，中間1/3の下を走る．
- 咬筋の前縁で下顎骨下縁を横切るところで，顔面動脈(4)の拍動を触れることができる．その位置は下顎角(3)の約2.5 cm前方である．

眼の周囲の帯状疱疹

顔面［浅層］

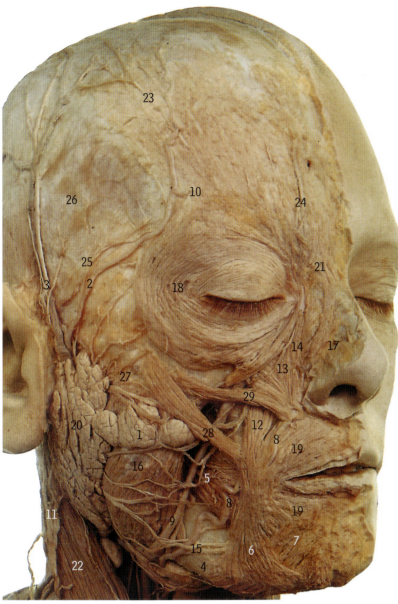
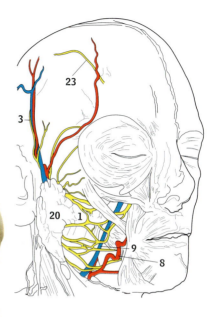

右前方から．

1	副耳下腺（耳下腺管の表面に延びている） Accessory parotid gland	6	口角下制筋 Depressor anguli oris	14	上唇鼻翼挙筋 Levator labii superioris alaeque nasi	22	胸鎖乳突筋 Sternocleidomastoid
2	前頭枝〔浅側頭動脈〕 Frontal branch*〔Superficial temporal artery〕	7	下唇下制筋 Depressor labii inferioris	15	下顎縁枝〔顔面神経［Ⅶ］〕 Marginal mandibular branch〔Facial nerve［Ⅶ］〕	23	眼窩上神経 Supra-orbital nerve
3	耳介側頭神経と浅側頭動／静脈 Auriculotemporal nerve and Superficial temporal artery/veins	8	顔面動脈 Facial artery	16	咬筋 Masseter	24	滑車上神経 Supratrochlear nerve
4	下顎体 Body of mandible	9	顔面静脈 Facial vein	17	鼻筋 Nasalis	25	側頭枝〔顔面神経［Ⅶ］〕 Temporal branch〔Facial nerve［Ⅶ］〕
5	頬筋と頬筋枝〔顔面神経［Ⅶ］〕 Buccinator and Buccal branches〔Facial nerve［Ⅶ］〕	10	前頭筋〔後頭前頭筋〕 Frontal belly〔Occipitofrontalis〕	18	眼輪筋 Orbicularis oculi	26	側頭筋（側頭筋膜の下層にある） Temporalis
		11	大耳介神経 Great auricular nerve	19	口輪筋 Orbicularis oris	27	頬骨枝〔顔面神経［Ⅶ］〕 Zygomatic branch〔Facial nerve［Ⅶ］〕
		12	口角挙筋 Levator anguli oris	20	耳下腺 Parotid gland	28	大頬骨筋 Zygomaticus major
		13	上唇挙筋 Levator labii superioris	21	鼻根筋 Procerus	29	小頬骨筋 Zygomaticus minor

顔面神経麻痺（Bell麻痺）

感染の頭蓋内への拡がり（顔面）

感染の頭蓋内への拡がり（頭皮）

頭皮の外科的皮弁

顔面（右）[浅層]

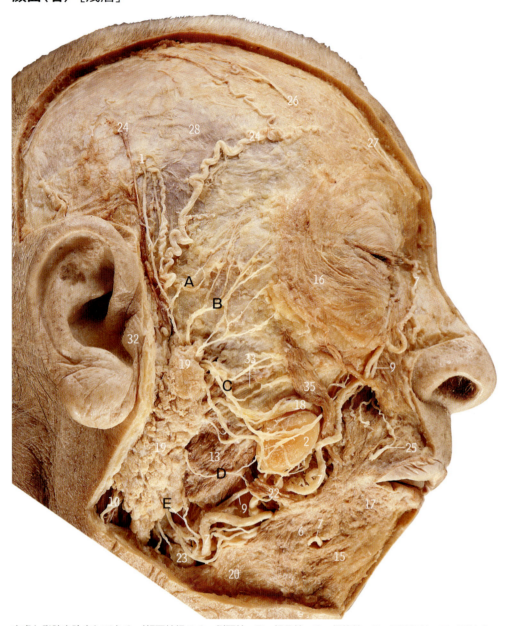

皮膚と脂肪を除去してある．（顔面神経の A：側頭枝，B：頬骨枝，C：頬筋枝，D：下顎縁枝，E：頸枝．）

1 耳介側頭神経 Auriculotemporal nerve	10 大耳介神経 Great auricular nerve	19 耳下腺 Parotid gland	27 滑車上神経 Supratrochlear nerve
2 頬脂肪体 Buccal fat pad	11 眼窩下神経 Infra-orbital nerve	20 広頸筋 Platysma	28 側頭筋膜 Temporal fascia
3 頬神経〔下顎神経［V₃］〕 Buccal nerve〔Mandibular nerve［V₃］〕	12 下顎体 Body of mandible	21 下顎後静脈 Retromandibular vein	29 下側頭線 Inferior temporal line
4 頬筋 Buccinator	13 咬筋 Masseter	22 笑筋（顔面動／静脈の表面にある） Risorius	30 上側頭線 Superior temporal line
5 関節包〔顎関節〕 Articular capsule（Temporomandibular joint）	14 オトガイ神経 Mental nerve	23 顎下腺 Submandibular gland	31 側頭筋 Temporalis
6 口角下制筋 Depressor anguli oris	15 オトガイ筋 Mentalis	24 浅側頭動／静脈 Superficial temporal artery/veins	32 耳珠 Tragus
7 顔面動脈 Facial artery	16 眼輪筋 Orbicularis oculi	25 上唇動脈 Superior labial branch	33 顔面横動脈 Transverse facial artery
8 顔面神経［Ⅶ］（A～E は枝） Facial nerve［Ⅶ］	17 口輪筋 Orbicularis oris	26 眼窩上神経 Supra-orbital nerve	34 頬骨弓 Zygomatic arch
9 顔面静脈 Facial vein	18 耳下腺管 Parotid duct		35 大頬骨筋 Zygomaticus major

側頭窩(右)

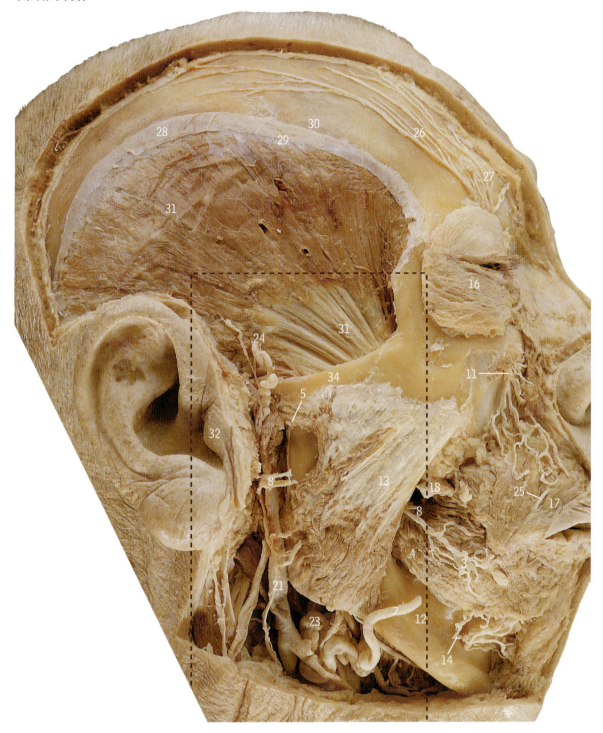

側頭筋膜，耳下腺ならびに顔面神経の枝の大半を取り除いてある．点線は次頁に示す深層の剖出領域を表す．(番号は前頁の用語表を参照．)

側頭下窩

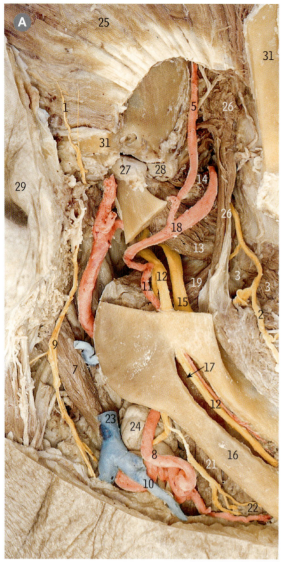
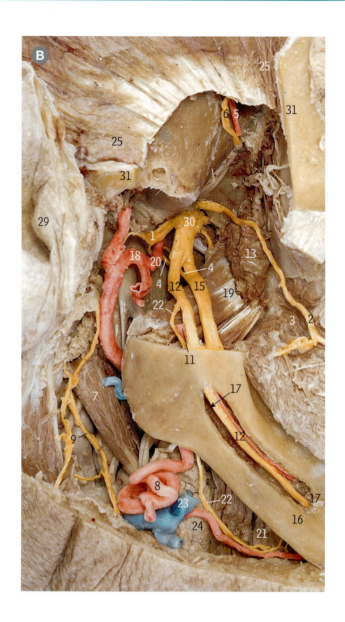

A・B：深層を段階的に示す．

咬筋，頬骨弓の一部，側頭筋の浅層と下部の大半，下顎枝の上半分（下顎頸と関節突起は残す），翼突筋静脈叢を取り除き，側頭下窩の浅部を解剖した．

側頭筋の深頭，外側翼突筋，下顎頸と関節突起を取り除き，側頭下窩の最深部を解剖した．

1 耳介側頭神経 Auriculotemporal nerve	12 下歯槽神経 Inferior alveolar nerve	23 下顎後静脈 Retromandibular vein
2 頬神経〔下顎神経［V₃］〕 Buccal nerve (Mandibular nerve [V₃])	13 下頭（外側翼突筋） Inferior head (Lateral pterygoid)	24 顎下腺 Submandibular gland
3 頬筋 Buccinator	14 上頭（外側翼突筋） Upper head (Lateral pterygoid)	25 側頭筋 Temporalis
4 鼓索神経 Chorda tympani	15 舌神経 Lingual nerve	26 深頭*（側頭筋）：蝶下顎筋* Deep head * (Temporalis): Sphenomandibularis *
5 前深側頭動脈 Anterior deep temporal artery	16 下顎体 Body of mandible	27 関節包（顎関節） Articular capsule (Temporomandibular joint)
6 深側頭神経 Deep temporal nerve	17 下顎管（開放してある） Mandibular canal	28 関節円板（顎関節） Articular disc (Temporomandibular joint)
7 後腹（顎二腹筋） Posterior belly (Digastric)	18 顎動脈 Maxillary artery	29 耳珠 Tragus
8 顔面動脈 Facial artery	19 内側翼突筋 Medial pterygoid	30 下顎神経［V₃］〔三叉神経［V］〕 Mandibular nerve [V₃] (Trigeminal nerve [V])
9 頸枝〔顔面神経［VII］〕 Cervical branch (Facial nerve [VII])	20 中硬膜動脈 Middle meningeal artery	31 頬骨弓 Zygomatic arch
10 顔面静脈 Facial vein	21 顎舌骨筋 Mylohyoid	
11 下歯槽動脈 Inferior alveolar artery	22 顎舌骨筋神経 Nerve to mylohyoid	

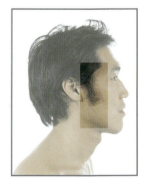

A 顔面［冠状断面］

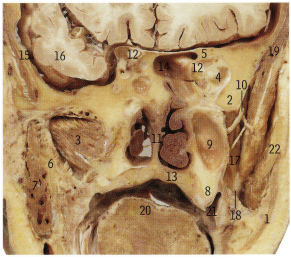

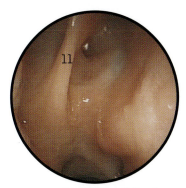

鼻中隔（後鼻孔）の内視鏡写真

側頭筋の浅頭と深頭を示す．

1	頬筋 Buccinator	7	咬筋 Masseter	13	口蓋 Palate	18	側頭筋（の停止部） Temporalis
2	大翼〔蝶形骨〕 Greater wing (Sphenoid)	8	上顎骨 Maxilla	14	蝶形骨洞 Sphenoidal sinus	19	浅頭*〔側頭筋〕 Superficial head* (Temporalis)
3	外側翼突筋 Lateral pterygoid	9	上顎洞〔副鼻腔〕 Maxillary sinus (Paranasal sinuses)	15	側頭骨 Temporal bone	20	舌 Tongue
4	外側直筋 Lateral rectus	10	翼突筋枝〔顎動脈〕 Pterygoid branches (Maxillary artery)	16	側頭葉〔大脳〕 Temporal lobe (Cerebrum)	21	口腔前庭 Oral vestibule
5	小翼〔蝶形骨〕 Lesser wing (Sphenoid)	11	鼻中隔 Nasal septum	17	深頭*〔側頭筋〕：蝶下顎筋* Deep head* (Temporalis): Sphenomandibularis*	22	頬骨 Zygomatic bone
6	下顎骨 Mandible	12	視神経〔Ⅱ〕 Optic nerve [Ⅱ]				

B 咀嚼筋

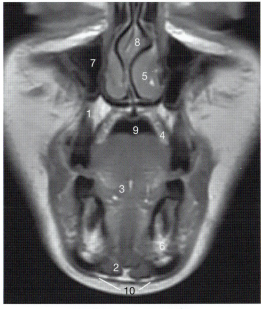

顔面後部のMR冠状断画像

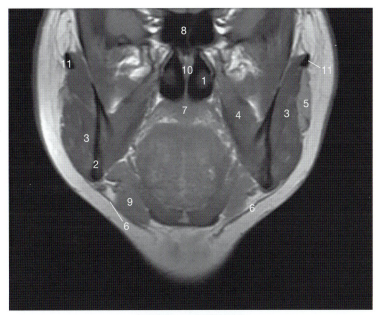

顔面部のMR冠状断画像

1	歯茎*〔上顎骨〕 Alveolarridge* (Maxilla)	6	下顎骨 Mandible
2	前腹〔顎二腹筋〕 Anterior belly (Digastric)	7	上顎洞 Maxillary sinus
3	オトガイ舌筋 Genioglossus	8	鼻中隔 Nasal septum
4	硬口蓋 Hard palate	9	口腔 Oral cavity
5	下鼻甲介 Inferior nasal concha	10	広頸筋 Platysma

1	下鼻甲介 Inferior nasal concha	7	軟口蓋 Soft palate
2	下顎骨 Mandible	8	蝶形骨洞 Sphenoidal sinus
3	咬筋 Masseter	9	顎下腺 Submandibular gland
4	内側翼突筋 Medial pterygoid	10	鋤骨 Vomer
5	耳下腺 Parotid gland	11	頬骨弓 Zygomatic arch
6	広頸筋 Platysma		

下歯槽神経ブロック

三叉神経，顔面神経，錐体神経および関連する神経節

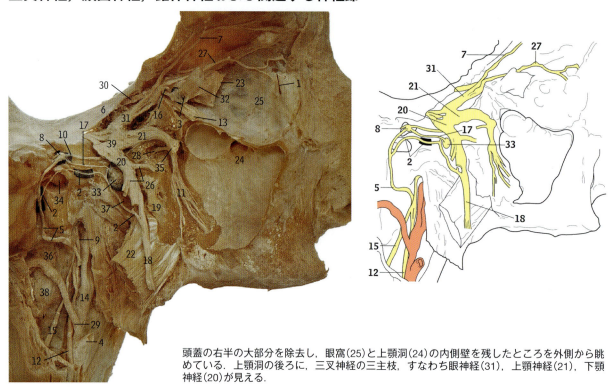

頭蓋の右半の大部分を除去し，眼窩(25)と上顎洞(24)の内側壁を残したところを外側から眺めている．上顎洞の後ろに，三叉神経の三主枝，すなわち眼神経(31)，上顎神経(21)，下顎神経(20)が見える．

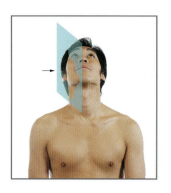

1	涙小管（管にマーカーを挿入して示す） Lacrimal canaliculus	14	内頸動脈 Internal carotid artery	26	筋枝〔下顎神経［V₃］〕 Muscular branches〔Mandibular nerve [V₃]〕
2	鼓索神経 Chorda tympani	15	内頸静脈と副神経［XI］ Internal jugular vein and Accessory nerve [XI]	27	鼻毛様体神経 Nasociliary nerve
3	毛様体神経節 Ciliary ganglion	16	涙腺神経 Lacrimal nerve	28	翼突管神経 Nerve of pterygoid canal
4	外頸動脈 External carotid artery	17	小錐体神経 Lesser petrosal nerve	29	後頭動脈 Occipital artery
5	顔面神経［VII］ Facial nerve [VII]	18	舌神経 Lingual nerve	30	動眼神経［III］ Oculomotor nerve [III]
6	小脳テント（自由縁） Tentorium cerebelli	19	下頭〔外側翼突筋〕と外側板〔翼状突起〕 Inferior head (Lateral pterygoid) and Lateral plate (Pterygoid process)	31	眼神経［V₁］ Ophthalmic nerve [V₁]
7	前頭神経 Frontal nerve	20	下顎神経［V₃］ Mandibular nerve [V₃]	32	視神経［II］ Optic nerve [II]
8	膝神経節〔顔面神経［VII］〕 Geniculate ganglion (Facial nerve [VII])	21	上顎神経［V₂］ Maxillary nerve [V₂]	33	耳神経節 Otic ganglion
9	舌咽神経［IX］ Glossopharyngeal nerve [IX]	22	内側翼突筋 Medial pterygoid	34	鼓膜のある位置
10	大錐体神経 Greater petrosal nerve	23	内側直筋 Medial rectus	35	翼口蓋神経節 Pterygopalatine ganglion
11	大口蓋神経と小口蓋神経 Greater palatine nerve and Lesser palatine nerves	24	上顎洞（内側壁と開口部） Maxillary sinus	36	外側頭直筋 Rectus capitis lateralis
12	舌下神経［XII］ Hypoglossal nerve [XII]	25	内側壁（眼窩） Medial wall (Orbit)	37	口蓋帆張筋 Tensor veli palatini
13	下直筋 Inferior rectus			38	横突起*〔環椎：第一頸椎〕 Transverse process*(Atlas：C I)
				39	三叉神経節 Trigeminal ganglion

- 大錐体神経(10)は顔面神経の膝神経節(8)の枝であり，（鼻腺にも分布しているが）涙の分泌神経と記憶しておくとよい．この神経の節前線維は，橋の上唾液核から中頭蓋窩の床にある溝を走り(11頁25)，破裂孔を通って翼突管神経(28)となって翼口蓋神経節(35)に合する．節後線維は，翼口蓋神経節を出て上顎神経に加わり，その枝である頬骨神経を経て眼窩に入り，涙腺神経と交通して涙腺を支配する．
- 小錐体神経(17)は，顔面神経とも交通しているが，舌咽神経の枝である．この神経は，鼓室神経叢をつくって(57頁C19)，中耳の粘膜に分布する鼓室神経から分かれる．小錐体神経(17)の線維は橋の下唾液核に起こり，中耳を出て中頭蓋窩の床の溝(11頁26)を走り，卵円孔を経て耳神経節(33)に達する．この神経節から出た分泌運動線維は下顎神経(20)に加わり，耳介側頭神経の線維を介して耳下腺に分布する．
- 鼓索神経(2)は，顔面神経(5)が茎乳突孔を抜ける位置(5の水平の引き出し線が示すところ)の手前で，この神経から起こる．鼓索神経は鼓膜(34)の上部を粘膜に覆われて横切り，側頭骨を通過して錐体鼓室裂(9頁35)から出て，舌神経(18)に合する．鼓索神経は，顎下神経節(56頁C35)に節前線維を運び，顎下腺と舌下腺を支配する．また舌の前2/3へ味覚線維を与える．
- 耳神経節(33)は，正常では下顎神経(20)の深側面に付着しているが，神経から引き離し，後ろに黒色マーカーを置いて示している．

咽頭

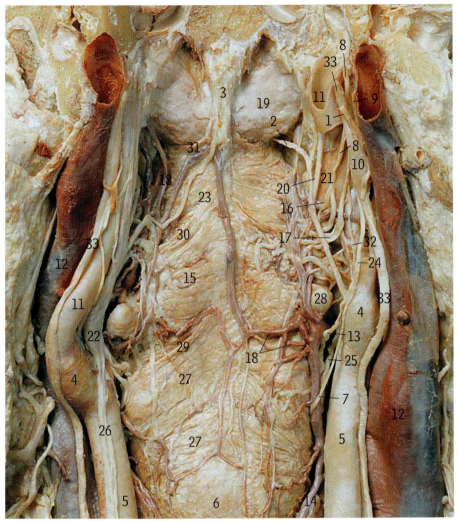

後面．後方から．

1	副神経〔XI〕 Accessory nerve〔XI〕	18	咽頭静脈 Pharyngeal veins
2	上行咽頭動脈 Ascending pharyngeal artery	19	咽頭底板 Pharyngobasilar fascia
3	咽頭縫線（頭蓋底の咽頭結節への付着部） Pharyngeal raphe	20	後硬膜動脈 Posterior meningeal artery
4	頸動脈洞 Carotid sinus	21	茎突咽頭筋 Stylopharyngeus
5	総頸動脈 Common carotid artery	22	上頸神経節〔交感神経〕 Superior cervical ganglion〔Sympathetic part〕
6	輪状咽頭部〔下咽頭収縮筋〕 Cricopharyngeal part〔Inferior constrictor〕	23	上咽頭収縮筋 Superior constrictor
7	外枝〔上喉頭神経〕 External branch〔Superior laryngeal nerve〕	24	上喉頭神経〔迷走神経〔X〕〕 Superior laryngeal nerve〔Vagus nerve〔X〕〕
8	舌咽神経〔IX〕 Glossopharyngeal nerve〔IX〕	25	上甲状腺動脈 Superior thyroid artery
9	舌下神経〔XII〕 Hypoglossal nerve〔XII〕	26	交感神経幹 Sympathetic trunk
10	下神経節〔迷走神経〔X〕〕 Inferior ganglion〔Vagus nerve〔X〕〕	27	甲状咽頭部〔下咽頭収縮筋〕 Thyropharyngeal part〔Inferior constrictor〕
11	内頸動脈 Internal carotid artery	28	大角の先端〔舌骨〕 Tip of greater horn〔Hyoid bone〕
12	内頸静脈 Internal jugular vein	29	下咽頭収縮筋（の上縁） Inferior constrictor
13	内枝〔上喉頭神経〕 Internal branch〔Superior laryngeal nerve〕	30	中咽頭収縮筋（の上縁） Middle constrictor
14	右葉〔甲状腺〕 Right lobe〔Thyroid gland〕	31	上咽頭収縮筋（の上縁） Superior constrictor
15	中咽頭収縮筋 Middle constrictor	32	頸動脈小体枝*〔迷走神経〔X〕〕 Branch to carotid body*〔Vagus nerve〔X〕〕
16	咽頭枝〔舌咽神経〔IX〕〕 Pharyngeal branches〔Glossopharyngeal nerve〔IX〕〕	33	迷走神経〔X〕 Vagus nerve〔X〕
17	咽頭枝〔迷走神経〔X〕〕 Pharyngeal branch〔Vagus nerve〔X〕〕		

脊柱を取り外し，頸動脈鞘と咽頭収縮筋を明らかにした．

咽頭反射

A 咽頭の後壁

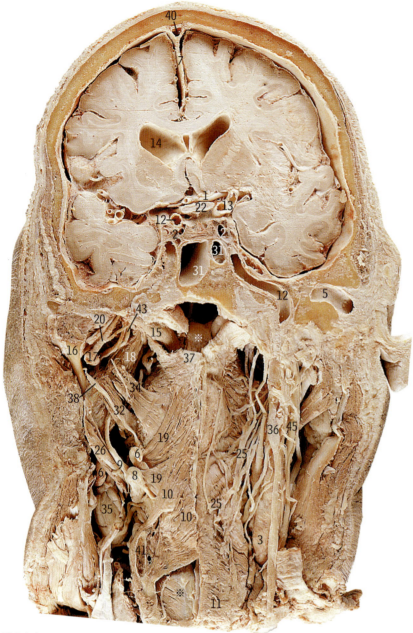

咽頭の後壁を通る頭頸部の冠状断標本である．右側が左側のわずかに後ろにくるようにやや斜めに切ってある．
咽頭の後壁の一部は除去されており，それぞれ咽頭鼻部と咽頭喉頭部が見えている（※：上方は咽頭頭底板，下方は下咽頭収縮筋の下縁を示している）．
（番号は次頁の用語表を参照．）

後方から．

咽頭嚢胞

扁桃切除術

第1章 頭頸部と脳：咽頭　47

B 咽頭の後壁（開かれている）

咽頭下部の拡大．咽頭後壁を切って翻転してある．左咽頭壁の粘膜は取り除いてある．

後方から．

後鼻孔と鼻中隔の内視鏡写真（後部）
注：鼻腔栄養チューブ（経鼻胃管）が通っている

1	前大脳動脈	Anterior cerebral artery
2	海綿静脈洞	Cavernous sinus
3	総頸動脈	Common carotid artery
4	喉頭蓋	Epiglottis
5	外耳道	External acoustic meatus
6	顔面動脈	Facial artery
7	大脳鎌	Falx cerebri：Cerebral falx
8	大角の先端〔舌骨〕	Tip of greater horn（Hyoid bone）
9	舌下神経［XII］	Hypoglossal nerve [XII]
10	下咽頭収縮筋	Inferior constrictor
11	輪状咽頭部〔下咽頭収縮筋〕	Cricopharyngeal part（Inferior constrictor）
12	内頸動脈	Internal carotid artery
13	内頸動脈が中大脳動脈を分枝するところ	
14	側脳室	Lateral ventricle
15	口蓋帆挙筋	Levator veli palatini
16	下顎頸	Neck of mandible
17	顎動脈	Maxillary artery
18	内側翼突筋	Medial pterygoid
19	中咽頭収縮筋	Middle constrictor
20	中硬膜動脈	Middle meningeal artery
21	斜披裂筋	Oblique arytenoid
22	視神経交叉：視交叉	Optic chiasm：Optic chiasma
23	口蓋咽頭筋	Palatopharyngeus
24	耳下腺	Parotid gland
25	咽頭静脈叢	Pharyngeal plexus of veins
26	後腹〔顎二腹筋〕	Posterior belly（Digastric）
27	後輪状披裂筋	Posterior crico-arytenoid
28	梨状陥凹	Piriform fossa：Piriform recess
29	反回神経	Recurrent laryngeal nerve
30	軟口蓋（の鼻腔面）	Soft palate
31	蝶形骨洞	Sphenoidal sinus
32	茎突舌筋	Styloglossus
33	茎突舌骨筋	Stylohyoid
34	茎突咽頭筋，舌咽神経［IX］	Stylopharyngeus, Glossopharyngeal nerve [IX]
35	顎下腺	Submandibular gland
36	上頸神経節	Superior cervical ganglion
37	上咽頭収縮筋	Superior constrictor
38	上咽頭枝*〔迷走神経［X］〕	Superior pharyngeal branch *（Vagus nerve [X]）
39	内枝〔上喉頭神経〕	Internal branch（Superior laryngeal nerve）
40	上矢状静脈洞	Superior sagittal sinus
41	左板〔甲状軟骨〕（断面）	Left lamina（Thyroid cartilage）
42	舌背（後ろ1/3）	Dorsum of tongue
43	下顎神経［V₃〕〔三叉神経［V〕〕	Mandibular nerve [V₃]（Trigeminal nerve [V]）
44	口蓋垂	Uvula
45	迷走神経［X］	Vagus nerve [X]
46	喉頭蓋谷	Epiglottic vallecula

咽頭炎

A B 舌骨 [B 筋と靭帯の付着部]

1 (舌骨の)体 Body of hyoid bone
2 オトガイ舌筋 Genioglossus
3 オトガイ舌骨筋 Geniohyoid
4 大角 Greater horn
5 舌骨舌筋 Hyoglossus
6 小角 Lesser horn
7 中咽頭収縮筋 Middle constrictor
8 顎舌骨筋 Mylohyoid
9 肩甲舌骨筋 Omohyoid
10 胸骨舌骨筋 Sternohyoid
11 茎突舌筋 Stylohyoid
12 茎突舌骨靭帯 Stylohyoid ligament
13 甲状舌骨筋 Thyrohyoid

C 喉頭蓋軟骨
D E 甲状軟骨 [E 右側面と筋と靭帯の付着部]

1 輪状甲状筋 Cricothyroid
2 下咽頭収縮筋 Inferior constrictor
3 下角 Inferior horn
4 下甲状結節 Inferior thyroid tubercle
5 右板 Right lamina
6 喉頭隆起(Adamのりんご) Laryngeal prominence
7 胸骨甲状筋 Sternothyroid
8 上角 Superior horn
9 上甲状結節 Superior thyroid tubercle
10 甲状舌骨筋 Thyrohyoid
11 上甲状切痕 Superior thyroid notch

F 披裂軟骨

1 [披裂軟骨]尖 Apex of arytenoid cartilage
2 関節面(輪状軟骨と関節を営む) Articular surface
3 筋突起 Muscular process
4 声帯突起 Vocal process

G H 輪状軟骨 [筋と靭帯の付着部]

1 輪状軟骨弓 Arch of cricoid cartilage
2 披裂関節面 Arytenoid articular surface
3 甲状関節面(甲状軟骨下角と関節をつくる) Thyroid articular surface
4 輪状甲状筋 Cricothyroid
5 下咽頭収縮筋 Inferior constrictor
6 輪状軟骨板 Lamina of cricoid cartilage
7 後輪状披裂筋 Posterior crico-arytenoid
8 食道(の腱) Esophagus

A・B：上前方から．C・D：前方から．E・H：右側方から．F：後方から．G：後下方から．I：側面．J：前面．

気管切開術

I J 喉頭 [体表解剖]

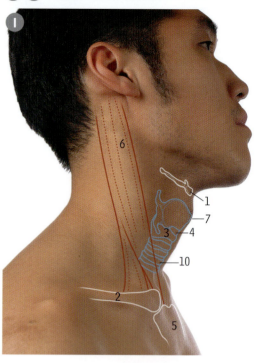

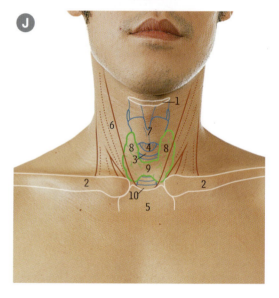

1 (舌骨の)体 Body of hyoid bone
2 鎖骨 Clavicle
3 輪状軟骨 Cricoid cartilage
4 正中輪状甲状靭帯 Median cricothyroid ligament
5 胸骨柄 Manubrium of sternum
6 胸鎖乳突筋 Sternocleidomastoid
7 喉頭隆起〔甲状軟骨〕 Laryngeal prominence〔Thyroid cartilage〕
8 右葉と左葉〔甲状腺〕 Right lobe and Left lobe〔Thyroid gland〕
9 甲状腺峡部 Isthmus of thyroid gland
10 気管軟骨 Tracheal cartilages

A 舌と喉頭口

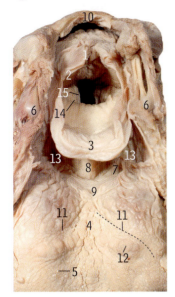

上方から．

1	小角軟骨（披裂喉頭蓋ヒダに含まれる） Corniculate cartilage	
2	楔状軟骨（披裂喉頭蓋ヒダに含まれる） Cuneiform cartilage	
3	喉頭蓋 Epiglottis	
4	盲孔 Foramen cecum	
5	茸状乳頭 Fungiform papilla	
6	大角〔舌骨〕 Greater horn (Hyoid bone)	
7	外側舌喉頭蓋ヒダ Lateral glosso-epiglottic fold	
8	正中舌喉頭蓋ヒダ Median glosso-epiglottic fold	
9	舌背（咽頭部） Dorsum of tongue	
10	咽頭の後壁	
11	分界溝（片側のみ破線で示した） Terminal sulcus of tongue	
12	有郭乳頭 Vallate papillae	
13	喉頭蓋谷 Epiglottic vallecula	
14	［喉頭］前庭ヒダ（仮声帯） Vestibular fold	
15	声帯ヒダ（真の声帯） Vocal fold	

B 喉頭

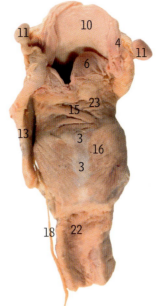

後方から．

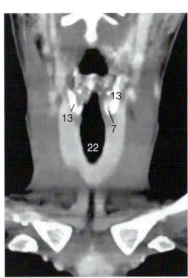

頸部中央のCT冠状断画像

Bの番号は左下の用語表を参照．

喉頭筋

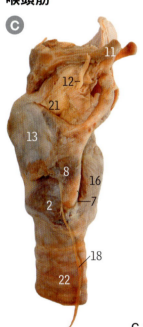

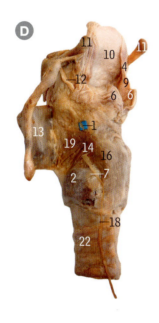

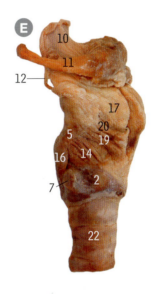

C：左側方から．　D：斜め後方から．　E：右側方から．

Dでは甲状軟骨を前方へ翻転してある．Eでは甲状軟骨の右板を取り除いてある．

1	内枝〔上喉頭神経〕と反回神経との交通枝（Galenの吻合）	9	楔状軟骨 Cuneiform cartilage	17	四角膜 Quadrangular membrane
2	輪状軟骨弓 Arch of cricoid cartilage	10	喉頭蓋 Epiglottis	18	反回神経 Recurrent laryngeal nerve
3	輪状軟骨板に食道の腱が着く領域	11	大角〔舌骨〕 Greater horn (Hyoid bone)	19	甲状披裂筋 Thyro-arytenoid
4	披裂喉頭蓋ヒダ Ary-epiglottic fold	12	内枝〔上喉頭神経〕 Internal branch (Superior laryngeal nerve)	20	甲状喉頭蓋筋 Thyro-epiglotticus
5	披裂喉頭蓋筋 Ary-epiglotticus	13	左板〔甲状軟骨〕 Left lamina (Thyroid cartilage)	21	甲状舌骨膜 Thyrohyoid membrane
6	小角軟骨 Corniculate cartilage	14	外側輪状披裂筋 Lateral crico-arytenoid	22	気管 Trachea
7	輪状甲状関節 Cricothyroid joint	15	斜披裂筋 Oblique arytenoid	23	横披裂筋 Transverse arytenoid
8	輪状甲状筋（甲状軟骨から起こる） Cricothyroid	16	後輪状披裂筋 Posterior crico-arytenoid		

気管内挿管

反回神経麻痺

喉頭（Ⓐ 左，Ⓑ 右）

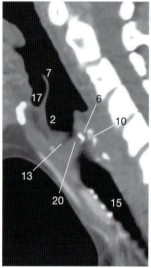

矢状断面．左側を内側方から．

声帯ヒダ（声帯，20）は前庭ヒダ（仮声帯，18）の下方に位置する．

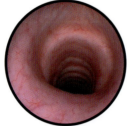

輪状軟骨と気管軟骨の内視鏡写真

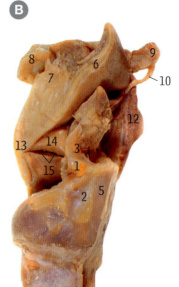

頸部中央のCT矢状断画像

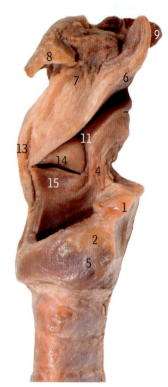

喉頭の右側を内側方から．左の披裂軟骨を残して輪状軟骨より上方の，喉頭の左側を除去してある．

喉頭の右側を内側方から．輪状軟骨より上方の，喉頭の左側を除去してある．

1	輪状軟骨弓	Arch of cricoid cartilage
2	披裂喉頭蓋ヒダと喉頭口	Ary-epiglottic fold and Laryngeal inlet
3	（舌骨の）体	Body of hyoid bone
4	内枝〔上喉頭神経〕と反回神経との交通枝	
5	神経枝〔反回神経〕	Branches〔Recurrent laryngeal nerve〕
6	小角軟骨と〔披裂軟骨〕尖	Corniculate cartilage and Apex of arytenoid cartilage
7	喉頭蓋	Epiglottis
8	内枝〔上喉頭神経〕（梨状陥凹に進入する）	Internal branch〔Superior laryngeal nerve〕
9	甲状腺峡部	Isthmus of thyroid gland
10	輪状軟骨板	Lamina of cricoid cartilage
11	左板〔甲状軟骨〕（断面）	Left lamina〔Thyroid cartilage〕
12	咽頭の壁	
13	喉頭室	Laryngeal ventricle
14	舌	Tongue
15	気管	Trachea
16	横披裂筋	Transverse arytenoid
17	喉頭蓋谷	Epiglottic vallecula
18	［喉頭］前庭ヒダ（仮声帯）	Vestibular fold
19	喉頭前庭	Laryngeal vestibule
20	声帯ヒダ	Vocal fold

1	関節面〔（左の）輪状披裂関節〕 Articular surfaces〔Crico-arytenoid joint〕		8	（舌骨の）体（断面） Body of hyoid bone
2	甲状関節面〔輪状軟骨〕 Thyroid articular surface〔Cricoid cartilage〕		9	大角〔舌骨〕 Greater horn〔Hyoid bone〕
3	前外側面〔（左の）披裂軟骨〕 Anterolateral surface〔Arytenoid cartilage〕		10	内枝〔上喉頭神経〕 Internal branch〔Superior laryngeal nerve〕
4	内側面〔（右の）披裂軟骨〕 Medial surface〔Arytenoid cartilage〕		11	四角膜 Quadrangular membrane
5	輪状軟骨板 Lamina of cricoid cartilage		12	甲状舌骨膜 Thyrohyoid membrane
6	喉頭蓋 Epiglottis		13	右板〔甲状軟骨〕（断面） Right lamina〔Thyroid cartilage〕
7	舌骨喉頭蓋靱帯 Hyo-epiglottic ligament		14	［喉頭］前庭ヒダ（仮声帯） Vestibular fold
			15	声帯ヒダ（真の声帯ヒダ） Vocal fold

- 前庭ヒダと声帯ヒダの間の空隙が喉頭室（A13）である．喉頭室は，喉頭小嚢という前庭ヒダと甲状披裂筋内面の間を数mm上方にのびた小さな袋に続いている．
- 左右の前庭ヒダ（A18）の間の裂隙を前庭裂という．左右の声帯ヒダの間の裂隙を声門裂という．
- 前庭ヒダは，仮声帯とよばれることがある．
- 喉頭筋の支配神経は，輪状甲状筋（49頁C8）が上喉頭神経外枝（29頁12）に支配されることを除き，他はすべて反回神経である．

A 眼（左）

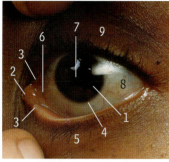

眼の表面構造．

眼瞼を通常の開眼状態にすると上眼瞼(9)の下縁が虹彩(1)の上半にほぼ重なる．下眼瞼(5)の辺縁は，虹彩(1)の下縁の高さに位置する．

1	虹彩（角膜の後ろ） Iris	6	結膜半月ヒダ Plica semilunaris
2	涙丘 Lacrimal caruncle	7	瞳孔（角膜の後ろにある） Pupil
3	涙乳頭 Lacrimal papilla	8	強膜 Sclera
4	角膜縁 Corneal limbus： Corneoscleral junction	9	上眼瞼 Superior eyelid
5	下眼瞼 Inferior eyelid		

- 角膜は眼球外膜の前方にある透明な部分で，角膜縁(A4)で強膜(A8)に連なる．
- 瞳孔(A7)は，水晶体の前にある色素を含んだ輪状の隔膜である虹彩(A1)の中央に開いた孔である．
- 上下の涙乳頭(A3)には，小さな涙小管(B8)の開口部である涙点がある．涙小管は内側へ走り，内側眼瞼靱帯(B10)の深部で涙嚢に開く．涙嚢は，骨性の鼻涙管の中を粘膜性の鼻涙管(B12)として下行する．

B 鼻涙管

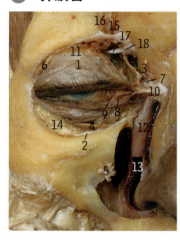

Bでは，顔面筋と頭蓋の一部を除去し，鼻涙管(12)が下鼻道(13の番号が付けられているところ)に開口する様子を示している．

1	腱膜〔上眼瞼挙筋〕 Aponeurosis〔Levator palpebrae superioris〕	10	内側眼瞼靱帯 Medial palpebral ligament
2	眼窩隔膜と骨膜（切断縁） Orbital septum and Periosteum	11	上眼瞼挙筋（筋線維） Levator palpebrae superioris
3	鼻背動脈 Dorsal nasal artery	12	鼻涙管 Nasolacrimal duct
4	下斜筋 Inferior oblique	13	鼻涙管（下鼻道への開口部．骨性の前壁を取り除いてある） Nasolacrimal duct
5	眼窩下神経 Infra-orbital nerve	14	眼窩脂肪体 Retrobulbar fat：Orbital fat body
6	涙腺 Lacrimal gland	15	眼窩上動脈 Supra-orbital artery
7	涙嚢（上端） Lacrimal sac	16	眼窩上神経 Supra-orbital nerve
8	（下の）涙小管 Lacrimal canaliculus	17	上斜筋（の腱） Superior oblique
9	（下の）涙乳頭と涙点 Lacrimal papilla and Lacrimal punctum	18	滑車 Trochlea

C 涙嚢

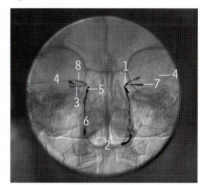

涙嚢造影画像

1	総涙小管＊（上下の涙小管が合したもの） Common lacrimal canaliculus＊
2	硬口蓋 Hard palate
3	（下の）涙小管 Lacrimal canaliculus
4	涙管カテーテル＊ Lacrimal catheters＊
5	涙嚢 Lacrimal sac
6	鼻涙管 Nasolacrimal duct
7	涙点の位置
8	（上の）涙小管 Lacrimal canaliculus

D 眼窩

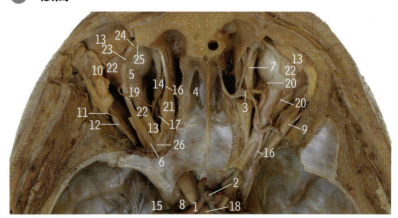

上方から．

1	前大脳動脈 Anterior cerebral artery	14	内側直筋 Medial rectus
2	前交通動脈 Anterior communicating artery	15	中大脳動脈 Middle cerebral artery
3	前篩骨動脈と前篩骨神経 Anterior ethmoidal artery and Anterior ethmoidal nerve	16	鼻毛様体神経 Nasociliary nerve
4	篩板〔篩骨〕 Cribriform plate〔Ethmoid〕	17	眼動脈 Ophthalmic artery
5	眼球 Eyeball	18	視神経交叉：視交叉 Optic chiasm：Optic chiasma
6	前頭神経 Frontal nerve	19	視神経［II］（左では上方を伴行する短毛様体神経も示している） Optic nerve［II］
7	滑車下神経と滑車上動脈 Infratrochlear nerve and Supratrochlear artery	20	後毛様体動脈 Posterior ciliary artery
8	内頸動脈 Internal carotid artery	21	上斜筋 Superior oblique
9	涙腺動脈 Lacrimal artery	22	上直筋（切断してある） Superior rectus
10	涙腺 Lacrimal gland	23	眼窩上動脈 Supra-orbital artery
11	涙腺神経 Lacrimal nerve	24	眼窩上神経 Supra-orbital nerve
12	外側直筋 Lateral rectus	25	滑車上神経 Supratrochlear nerve
13	上眼瞼挙筋（切断してある） Levator palpebrae superioris	26	滑車神経［IV］ Trochlear nerve［IV］

網膜中心動脈閉塞症

角膜環（老人環）

角膜反射

霰粒腫

眼底検査

瞳孔反射

眼窩の内面（左）

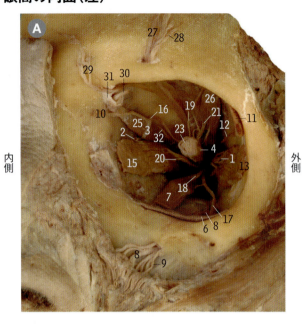
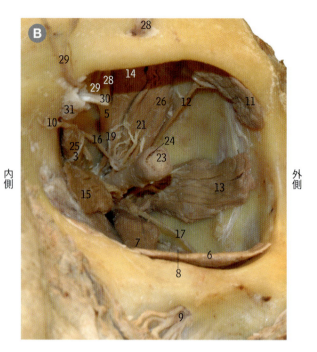
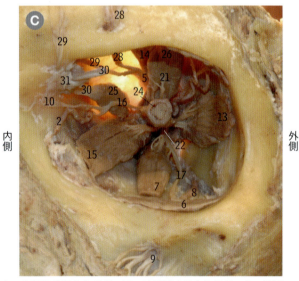
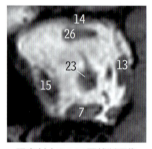

眼窩（左）のMR冠状断画像

A：内側壁を見たところ．B：外側壁を見たところ．C：前面から見たところ．

1	外転神経［Ⅵ］ Abducent nerve [VI]	17	下斜筋の支配神経〔動眼神経［Ⅲ］〕
2	前篩骨動脈 Anterior ethmoidal artery	18	下直筋の支配神経〔動眼神経［Ⅲ］〕
3	前篩骨神経 Anterior ethmoidal nerve	19	上眼瞼挙筋の支配神経〔動眼神経［Ⅲ］〕
4	視神経外鞘 Outer sheath；Dural sheath of optic nerve *	20	内側直筋の支配神経〔動眼神経［Ⅲ］〕
5	前頭神経 Frontal nerve	21	上直筋の支配神経〔動眼神経［Ⅲ］〕
6	下斜筋 Inferior oblique	22	動眼神経［Ⅲ］ Oculomotor nerve [III]
7	下直筋 Inferior rectus	23	視神経［Ⅱ］と網膜中心動脈 Optic nerve [II] and Central retinal artery
8	眼窩下動脈 Infra-orbital artery	24	クモ膜下腔 Subarachnoid space
9	眼窩下神経 Infra-orbital nerve	25	上斜筋 Superior oblique
10	滑車下神経 Infratrochlear nerve	26	上直筋 Superior rectus
11	涙腺 Lacrimal gland	27	眼窩上動脈 Supra-orbital artery
12	涙腺神経 Lacrimal nerve	28	眼窩上神経 Supra-orbital nerve
13	外側直筋 Lateral rectus	29	滑車上神経 Supratrochlear nerve
14	上眼瞼挙筋 Levator palpebrae superioris	30	上斜筋（の腱） Superior oblique
15	内側直筋 Medial rectus	31	滑車 Trochlea
16	鼻毛様体神経 Nasociliary nerve	32	滑車神経［Ⅳ］ Trochlear nerve [IV]

霰粒腫

眼窩周囲出血と結膜下出血

緑内障

Ⓐ Ⓑ 眼窩（右）［Ⓐ 浅層，Ⓑ 深層］

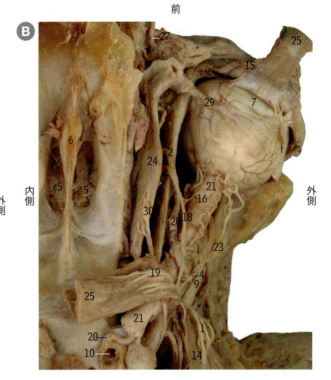

上方から．Ｂ：眼筋は翻転してある．

1	外転神経［Ⅵ］ Abducent nerve [Ⅵ]	15	上眼瞼挙筋 Levator palpebrae superioris
2	前篩骨動脈と前篩骨神経 Anterior ethmoidal artery and Anterior ethmoidal nerve	16	長毛様体神経 Long ciliary nerves
3	毛様体動脈 Ciliary arteries	17	内側直筋 Medial rectus
4	毛様体神経節 Ciliary ganglion	18	鼻毛様体神経 Nasociliary nerve
5	篩板〔篩骨〕 Cribriform plate〔Ethmoid〕	19	上直筋の支配神経〔動眼神経［Ⅲ］〕
6	鶏冠 Crista galli	20	眼動脈 Ophthalmic artery
7	眼球 Eyeball	21	視神経［Ⅱ］ Optic nerve [Ⅱ]
8	前頭神経 Frontal nerve	22	後毛様体動脈 Posterior ciliary artery
9	眼窩下神経 Infra-orbital nerve	23	短毛様体神経 Short ciliary nerves
10	内頸動脈 Internal carotid artery	24	上斜筋 Superior oblique
11	涙腺動脈 Lacrimal artery	25	上直筋 Superior rectus
12	涙腺 Lacrimal gland	26	眼窩上神経 Supra-orbital nerve
13	涙腺神経 Lacrimal nerve	27	滑車上動脈 Supratrochlear artery
14	外側直筋（翻転してある） Lateral rectus	28	滑車上神経 Supratrochlear nerve
		29	上斜筋（の腱） Superior oblique
		30	滑車神経［Ⅳ］ Trochlear nerve [Ⅳ]

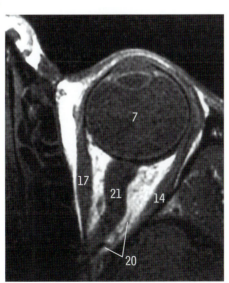

眼窩の MR 横断画像

Ⓒ 眼底

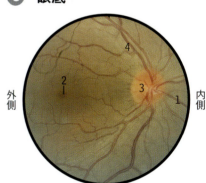

網膜の検眼鏡写真

1	下内側動／静脈〔網膜中心動／静脈〕 Inferior nasal retinal arteriole/venule (Central retinal artery/vein)
2	中心窩〔黄斑〕 Fovea centralis (Macula)
3	視神経円板：視神経乳頭 Optic disc
4	上外側動／静脈〔網膜中心動／静脈〕 Superior temporal arteriole/venule (Central retinal artery/vein)

外転神経麻痺

動眼神経麻痺

眼窩蜂巣炎

滑車神経麻痺

眼窩（右）［A 浅層，B 深層］

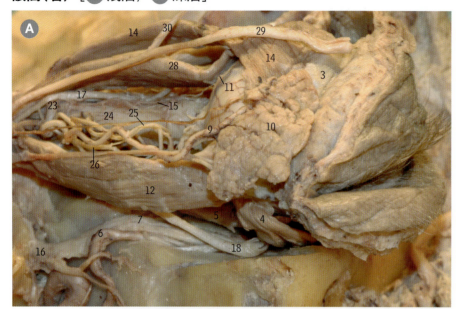

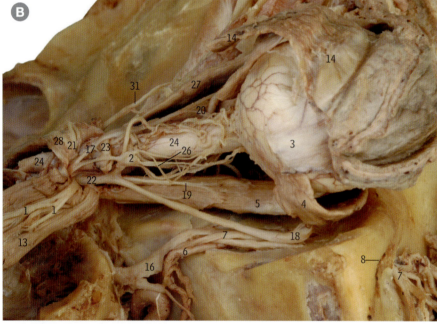

外側方から．

1	外転神経［Ⅵ］	Abducent nerve [VI]
2	毛様体神経節	Ciliary ganglion
3	眼球	Eyeball
4	下斜筋	Inferior oblique
5	下直筋	Inferior rectus
6	眼窩下動脈	Infra-orbital artery
7	眼窩下神経	Infra-orbital nerve
8	眼窩下孔	Infra-orbital foramen
9	涙腺動脈	Lacrimal artery
10	涙腺	Lacrimal gland
11	涙腺神経	Lacrimal nerve
12	外側直筋	Lateral rectus
13	外側直筋（後方へ翻転してある）	Lateral rectus
14	上眼瞼挙筋	Levator palpebrae superioris
15	長毛様体神経	Long ciliary nerves
16	上顎神経［V₂］〔三叉神経［Ⅴ］〕	Maxillary nerve [V₂] 〔Trigeminal nerve [V]〕
17	鼻毛様体神経	Nasociliary nerve
18	下斜筋の支配神経〔動眼神経［Ⅲ］〕	
19	下直筋の支配神経〔動眼神経［Ⅲ］〕	
20	内側直筋の支配神経〔動眼神経［Ⅲ］〕	
21	上直筋の支配神経〔動眼神経［Ⅲ］〕	
22	下枝〔動眼神経［Ⅲ］〕	Inferior branch〔Oculomotor nerve [III]〕
23	眼動脈	Ophthalmic artery
24	視神経［Ⅱ］	Optic nerve [II]
25	短毛様体動脈	Short ciliary artery
26	短毛様体神経	Short ciliary nerves
27	上斜筋	Superior oblique
28	上直筋	Superior rectus
29	眼窩上神経	Supra-orbital nerve
30	滑車上神経	Supratrochlear nerve
31	滑車神経［Ⅳ］	Trochlear nerve [IV]

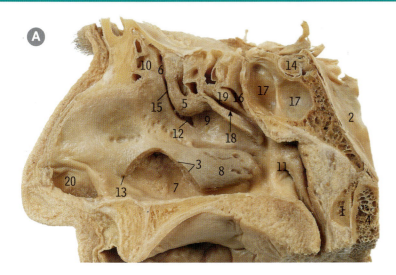

A 鼻腔の外側壁（右）

1	前弓〔環椎：第一頸椎〕 Anterior arch〔Atlas：C I〕	11	耳管咽頭口 Pharyngeal opening of auditory tube
2	斜台 Clivus	12	上顎洞（開口部） Maxillary sinus
3	下鼻甲介（切断縁） Inferior nasal concha	13	鼻涙管（開口部） Nasolacrimal duct
4	歯突起〔軸椎：第二頸椎〕 Dens〔Axis：C II〕	14	下垂体 Pituitary gland
5	篩骨胞 Ethmoidal bulla	15	半月裂孔 Semilunar hiatus
6	篩骨漏斗 Ethmoidal infundibulum	16	蝶篩陥凹 Spheno-ethmoidal recess
7	下鼻道 Inferior nasal meatus	17	蝶形骨洞 Sphenoidal sinus
8	下鼻甲介 Inferior nasal concha	18	上鼻道 Superior nasal meatus
9	中鼻道 Middle nasal meatus	19	上鼻甲介 Superior nasal concha
10	前篩骨洞（開口部） Anterior ethmoidal cells	20	鼻前庭 Nasal vestibule

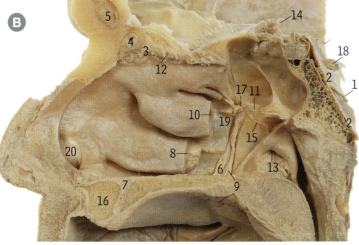

B 鼻腔と翼口蓋神経節（右）

1	外転神経［VI］ Abducent nerve [VI]	11	翼突管神経 Nerve of pterygoid canal
2	斜台 Clivus	12	嗅神経糸 Olfactory nerves
3	篩板〔篩骨〕 Cribriform plate〔Ethmoid〕	13	耳管咽頭口 Pharyngeal opening of auditory tube
4	前篩骨洞 Anterior ethmoidal cells	14	視神経［II］ Optic nerve [II]
5	前頭洞 Frontal sinus	15	咽頭枝 Pharyngeal nerve
6	大口蓋神経 Greater palatine nerve	16	切歯骨 Incisive bone：Premaxilla
7	切歯孔 Incisive foramina	17	翼口蓋神経節 Pterygopalatine ganglion
8	下鼻甲介（粘膜と骨膜の切断縁） Inferior nasal concha	18	三叉神経［V］ Trigeminal nerve [V]
9	小口蓋神経 Lesser palatine nerves	19	垂直板〔篩骨〕 Perpendicular plate〔Ethmoid〕
10	中鼻甲介（切断縁） Middle nasal concha	20	鼻前庭 Nasal vestibule

A・B：内側方から．

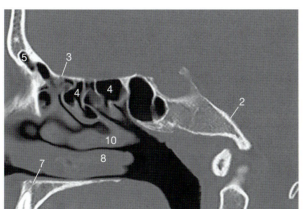

鼻腔のCT矢状断画像

中耳の均圧化

鼻ポリープ（鼻茸）

経鼻胃管の挿管

三叉神経の枝（右）

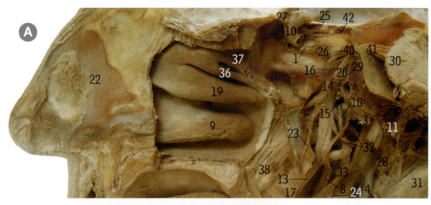
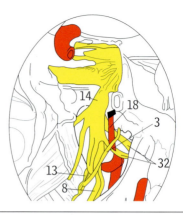

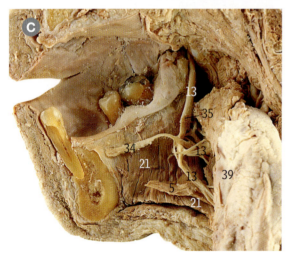

1	外転神経［VI］	Abducent nerve [VI]
2	（舌骨の）体	Body of hyoid bone
3	鼓索神経	Chorda tympani
4	外頸動脈	External carotid artery
5	オトガイ舌骨筋	Geniohyoid
6	舌骨舌筋	Hyoglossus
7	舌下神経［XII］	Hypoglossal nerve [XII]
8	下歯槽神経	Inferior alveolar nerve
9	下鼻甲介	Inferior nasal concha
10	内頸動脈	Internal carotid artery
11	頸静脈上球	Superior bulb of jugular vein
12	舌動脈	Lingual artery
13	舌神経	Lingual nerve
14	下顎神経［V₃］〔三叉神経［V］〕	Mandibular nerve [V₃] (Trigeminal nerve [V])
15	耳管（マーカーを挿入して示す）	Auditory tube：Pharyngotympanic tube
16	上顎神経［V₂］〔三叉神経［V］〕	Maxillary nerve [V₂] (Trigeminal nerve [V])
17	内側翼突筋	Medial pterygoid
18	中硬膜動脈	Middle meningeal artery
19	中鼻甲介	Middle nasal concha
20	運動根〔三叉神経［V］〕	Motor root (Trigeminal nerve [V])
21	顎舌骨筋	Mylohyoid
22	鼻中隔（耳管軟骨部）	Nasal septum
23	内側翼突筋神経	Nerve to medial pterygoid
24	顎舌骨筋神経	Nerve to mylohyoid
25	動眼神経［III］	Oculomotor nerve [III]
26	眼神経［V₁］〔三叉神経［V］〕	Ophthalmic nerve [V₁] (Trigeminal nerve [V])
27	視神経［II］	Optic nerve [II]
28	耳下腺	Parotid gland
29	岩様部：錐体乳突部〔側頭骨〕	Petrous part (Temporal bone)
30	橋	Pons
31	後腹〔顎二腹筋〕	Posterior belly (Digastric)
32	耳介側頭神経（の根）	Auriculotemporal nerve
33	蝶下顎靱帯と顎動脈	Sphenomandibular ligament and Maxillary artery
34	顎下腺管	Submandibular duct
35	顎下神経節	Submandibular ganglion
36	上鼻甲介	Superior nasal concha
37	最上鼻甲介	Higest nasal concha
38	口蓋帆張筋	Tensor veli palatini
39	舌	Tongue
40	三叉神経節	Trigeminal ganglion
41	三叉神経［V］	Trigeminal nerve [V]
42	滑車神経［IV］	Trochlear nerve [IV]

正中面から．**A**：正中面のすぐ左を通る矢状断面．**B・C**：正中面のすぐ右を通る矢状断面．オトガイ舌骨筋，舌下腺，口腔粘膜を取り除いてある．**C**では舌を内側に翻転してある．

舌下神経麻痺

口腔内病変

舌癌

A 外耳（右）

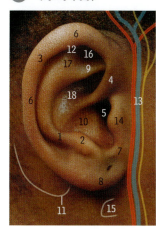

#	日本語	English
1	対輪	Antihelix
2	対珠	Antitragus
3	耳介結節	Auricular tubercle
4	耳輪脚	Crus of helix
5	外耳道	External acoustic meatus
6	耳輪	Helix
7	珠間切痕	Intertragic incisure：Intertragic notch
8	耳垂	Lobule of auricle
9	下脚*〔対輪脚〕	Lower crus *〔Antihelix〕
10	耳甲介（の下部、18とともに耳甲介のくぼみを形成する）	Concha
11	乳様突起	Mastoid process
12	舟状窩	Scaphoid fossa
13	浅側頭動／静脈と耳介側頭神経	Superficial temporal artery/veins and Auriculotemporal nerve
14	耳珠	Tragus
15	横突起*〔環椎：第一頚椎〕	Transverse process *〔Atlas：C I〕
16	三角窩	Triangular fossa
17	上脚*〔対輪脚〕	Upper crus *〔Antihelix〕
18	耳甲介（の上部、10とともに耳甲介のくぼみを形成する）	Concha

B 鼓膜（右）

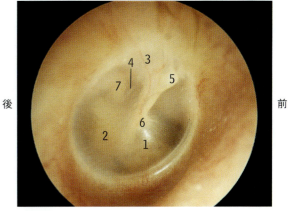

後 — 前

耳鏡写真

#	日本語	English
1	光錐*	Cone of light *：Llight reflex *
2	緊張部	Pars tensa
3	弛緩部	Pars flaccida
4	鼓索神経	Chorda tympani
5	外側突起〔ツチ骨〕	Lateral process（Malleus）
6	鼓膜臍	Umbo of tympanic membrane
7	長脚〔キヌタ骨〕	Long limb〔Incus〕

C 側頭骨と耳（右）

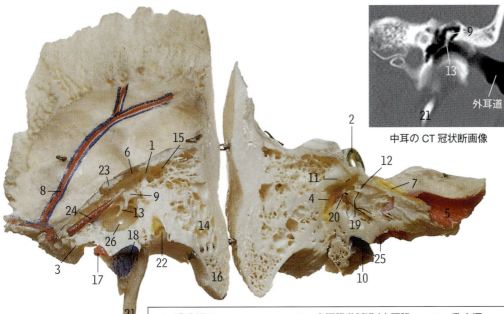

中耳のCT冠状断画像

側頭骨を2つに切り、本のように開いている。錐体の上部は一部除去してある。切断により、鼓室（中耳）が開放されている。図の左側には鼓膜（26）を含む中耳の外側壁が内側から見えており、右側には内側壁の主な構造物が見えている。

#	日本語	English
1	乳突洞口	Aditus to mastoid antrum
2	前骨半規管	Anterior semicircular canal
3	骨部〔耳管〕	Bony part〔Auditory tube：Pharyngotympanic tube〕
4	顔面神経管（黄）	Facial canal
5	頸動脈管（赤）	Carotid canal
6	鼓索上陥凹	Epitympanic recess
7	大錐体神経溝（黄）	Groove for greater petrosal nerve
8	中硬膜動脈溝（中硬膜動／静脈が通る）	Groove for middle meningeal artery
9	キヌタ骨	Incus
10	頸静脈上球（青）	Superior bulb of jugular vein
11	外側骨半規管	Lateral semicircular canal
12	小錐体神経	Lesser petrosal nerve
13	ツチ骨	Malleus
14	乳突蜂巣	Mastoid cells
15	乳突洞	Mastoid antrum
16	乳様突起	Mastoid process
17	頸動脈管（の一部、赤）	Carotid canal
18	頸静脈上球（の一部、青）	Superior bulb of jugular vein
19	岬角（鼓室神経叢に覆われている）	Promontory
20	アブミ骨（前庭窓にはまっている）とアブミ骨筋	Stapes and Stapedius
21	茎状突起〔側頭骨〕	Styloid process〔Temporal bone〕
22	茎乳突孔	Stylomastoid foramen
23	鼓室蓋	Tegmen tympani
24	鼓膜張筋（鼓膜張筋半管の中にある）	Tensor tympani
25	鼓室神経〔舌咽神経〕（鼓室神経小管を走る）	Tympanic nerve〔Glossopharyngeal nerve [IX]〕
26	鼓膜	Tympanic membrane

聴覚過敏

鼓膜穿孔

耳痛（関連痛）

A〜C 耳
[側頭骨（右）．**A** **B** 中耳および顔面神経とその枝，**C** 中耳と内耳]

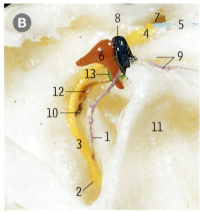

B：A1 の拡大図．

中耳を剖出して，右上方から見ている．ツチ骨(8)とキヌタ骨(6)の上部を示すために一部の骨を除去している．通常，2つの耳小骨は鼓室上陥凹に突出している．顔面神経管(2)を開放し，顔面神経(3)が鼓索神経(1)とアブミ骨筋神経(10)を分枝することを示している．顔面神経の膝神経節(4)から大錐体神経(5)が起こっている．

1	鼓索神経 Chorda tympani
2	顔面神経管（茎乳突孔に通じる） Facial canal
3	顔面神経［VII］ Facial nerve［VII］
4	膝神経節〔顔面神経［VII］〕 Geniculate ganglion〔Facial nerve［VII］〕
5	大錐体神経 Greater petrosal nerve
6	キヌタ骨 Incus
7	内耳道 Internal acoustic meatus
8	ツチ骨 Malleus
9	耳管（の縁） Auditory tube：Pharyngotympanic tube
10	アブミ骨筋神経 Nerve to stapedius
11	鼓膜（パラフィンで覆い支持している） Tympanic membrane
12	アブミ骨筋 Stapedius
13	アブミ骨 Stapes

● アブミ骨筋(12)の腱は，鼓室の後壁の錐体隆起（ここでは取り除いてある）という小さな円錐形の突起から起こる．

中耳と内耳の拡大．

中耳と内耳を上方から培出し，後外側から見たところである．中耳腔の内部に3つの耳小骨，つまりツチ骨(12)，キヌタ骨(9)，アブミ骨(17)が見える．鼓膜と外耳道は，番号7の下方に位置する．蝸牛は，骨構造(3，5，13，14)を開放して示している．

1	前骨半規管 Anterior semicircular canal
2	耳管 Auditory tube：Pharyngotympanic tube
3	骨性の蝸牛管* Bony canal of cochlea*
4	鼓索神経 Chorda tympani
5	蝸牛頂 Cochlear cupula
6	アブミ骨底（前庭窓にはまっている） Base of stapes
7	キヌタ・ツチ関節 Incudomallealar joint
8	キヌタ・アブミ関節 Incudostapedial joint
9	キヌタ骨 Incus
10	内耳道 Internal acoustic meatus
11	外側骨半規管 Lateral semicircular canal
12	ツチ骨 Malleus
13	蝸牛軸 Modiolus
14	骨ラセン板〔蝸牛〕 Osseous spiral lamina〔Cochlea〕
15	後骨半規管 Posterior semicircular canal
16	アブミ骨筋（の腱） Stapedius
17	アブミ骨 Stapes

D 耳（右）

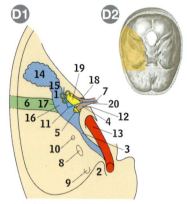

上方から．

1	乳突洞口 Aditus to mastoid antrum
2	前床突起〔蝶形骨〕 Anterior clinoid process〔Sphenoid〕
3	耳管 Auditory tube：Pharyngotympanic tube
4	蝸牛神経 Cochlear nerve
5	蝸牛〔内耳〕 Cochlea〔Inner ear〕
6	外耳道 External acoustic meatus
7	顔面神経［VII］ Facial nerve［VII］
8	卵円孔 Foramen ovale
9	正円孔 Foramen rotundum
10	棘孔 Foramen spinosum
11	膝神経節〔顔面神経［VII］〕 Geniculate ganglion〔Facial nerve［VII］〕
12	内耳道 Internal acoustic meatus
13	内頸動脈（破裂孔から現れたところ） Internal carotid artery
14	乳突蜂巣 Mastoid cells
15	乳突洞 Mastoid antrum
16	中耳（鼓室） Middle ear
17	鼓膜 Tympanic membrane
18	前庭神経 Vestibular nerve
19	前庭〔内耳〕 Vestibule〔Inner ear〕
20	内耳神経：前庭蝸牛神経［VIII］ Vestibulocochlear nerve［VIII］

E 内耳

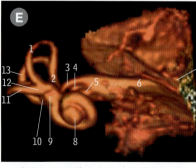

内耳のCT画像からの三次元構築画像

1	前骨半規管 Anterior semicircular canal	7	外転神経［VI］ Abducent nerve［VI］
2	骨総脚 Common bony limb	8	蝸牛 Cochlea
3	顔面神経［VII］（迷路通過部） Facial nerve［VII］	9	前庭 Vestibule
4	上部〔前庭神経〕 Superior part〔Vestibular nerve〕	10	前庭窓 Oval window
5	蝸牛神経 Cochlear nerve	11	外側骨半規管 Lateral semicircular canal
6	内耳神経：前庭蝸牛神経［VIII］ Vestibulocochlear nerve［VIII］	12	外側骨膨大部 Lateral bony ampulla
		13	後骨半規管 Posterior semicircular canal

頭蓋窩

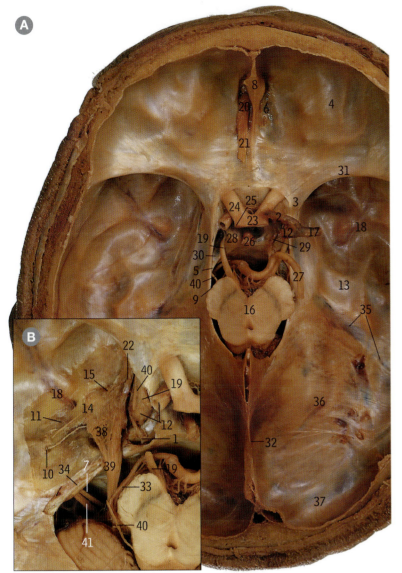
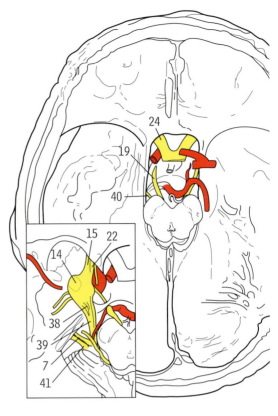

A：硬膜はそのままにしてある．B：硬膜の一部を除去してある．

#	日本語	English
1	外転神経［Ⅵ］	Abducent nerve [VI]
2	前大脳動脈	Anterior cerebral artery
3	前床突起〔蝶形骨〕	Anterior clinoid process〔Sphenoid〕
4	前頭蓋窩	Anterior cranial fossa
5	小脳テント（の付着縁）	Tentorium cerebelli
6	篩板〔篩骨〕	Cribriform plate〔Ethmoid〕
7	顔面神経［Ⅶ］	Facial nerve [VII]
8	大脳鎌（鶏冠に付着している）	Falx cerebri : Cerebral falx
9	小脳テント（自由縁）	Tentorium cerebelli
10	大錐体神経管裂孔	Hiatus for greater petrosal nerve
11	小錐体神経管裂孔	Hiatus for lesser petrosal nerve
12	内頸動脈	Internal carotid artery
13	中頭蓋窩（外側部）	Middle cranial fossa
14	下顎神経［V₃］	Mandibular nerve [V₃]
15	上顎神経［V₂］	Maxillary nerve [V₂]
16	中脳（上丘の高さ）	Midbrain：Mesencephalon
17	中大脳動脈	Middle cerebral artery
18	中硬膜動／静脈	Middle meningeal artery/veins
19	動眼神経［Ⅲ］（切断してある）	Oculomotor nerve [III]
20	嗅球	Olfactory bulb
21	嗅索	Olfactory tract
22	眼神経［V₁］	Ophthalmic nerve [V₁]
23	視神経交叉：視交叉	Optic chiasm：Optic chiasma
24	視神経［Ⅱ］	Optic nerve [II]
25	視索	Optic tract
26	下垂体茎*	Pituitary stalk*
27	後大脳動脈	Posterior cerebral artery
28	後床突起〔蝶形骨〕	Posterior clinoid process〔Sphenoid〕
29	後交通動脈	Posterior communicating artery
30	海綿静脈洞（の上壁）	Cavernous sinus
31	蝶形〔骨〕頭頂静脈洞（蝶形骨小翼の後縁にある）	Sphenoparietal sinus
32	直静脈洞（大脳鎌と小脳鎌の結合部に含まれる）	Straight sinus
33	上小脳動脈	Superior cerebellar artery
34	上錐体静脈洞	Superior petrosal sinus
35	上錐体静脈洞（小脳テントの付着縁に含まれる）	Superior petrosal sinus
36	小脳テント	Tentorium cerebelli
37	横静脈洞（小脳テントの付着縁に含まれる）	Transverse sinus
38	三叉神経節	Trigeminal ganglion
39	三叉神経［Ⅴ］	Trigeminal nerve [V]
40	滑車神経［Ⅳ］	Trochlear nerve [IV]
41	内耳神経：前庭蝸牛神経［Ⅷ］	Vestibulocochlear nerve [VIII]

海綿静脈洞血栓症

A 脳

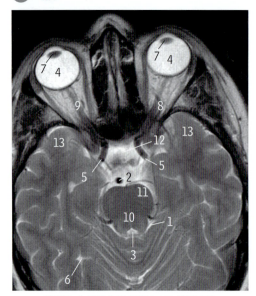

脳槽および橋上部を通る MR 横断画像

1	迂回槽 Ambient cistern	
2	脳底動脈（橋前槽*を走る） Basilar artery	
3	第四脳室 4th ventricle	
4	眼球 Eyeball	
5	内頸動脈 Internal carotid artery	
6	側脳室 Lateral ventricle	
7	水晶体 Lens	
8	眼動脈 Ophthalmic artery	
9	視神経［Ⅱ］ Optic nerve [Ⅱ]	
10	橋 Pons	
11	橋被蓋：橋背側部 Tegmentum of pons	
12	鞍上槽*：視交叉槽 Suprasellar cistern * : Chiasmatic cistern	
13	側頭葉 Temporal lobe	

B 頭部矢状断面（右）

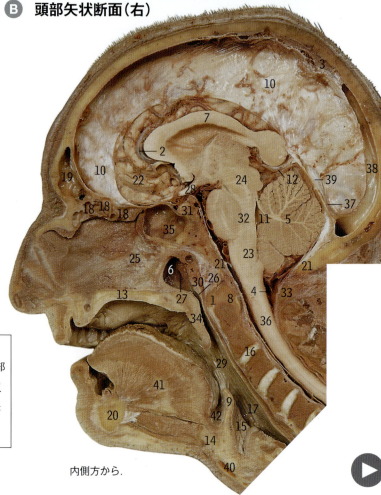

内側方から．

C 下垂体窩

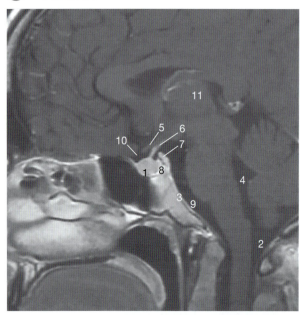

下垂体窩の MR 矢状断画像（ガドリニウム造影剤投与後）

1	前葉〔下垂体〕 Anterior lobe〔Pituitary gland〕	7	鞍背 Dorsum sellae	
2	後小脳延髄槽：大槽 Posterior cerebellomedullary cistern : Cisterna magna	8	後葉〔下垂体〕 Posterior lobe〔Pituitary gland〕	
3	斜台 Clivus	9	橋前槽* Prepontine cistern *	
4	第四脳室 4th ventricle	10	鞍上槽*：視交叉槽 Suprasellar cistern * : Chiasmatic cistern	
5	視神経交叉：視交叉 Optic chiasm : Optic chiasma	11	視床 Thalamus	
6	下垂体茎* Pituitary stalk *			

1	前弓〔環椎：第一頸椎〕 Anterior arch〔Atlas : C Ⅰ〕	15	喉頭口 Laryngeal inlet	28	視神経交叉：視交叉 Optic chiasm : Optic chiasma
2	前大脳動脈 Anterior cerebral artery	16	椎間円板（第二・第三頸椎間） Intervertebral disc	29	［咽頭］口部 Oropharynx
3	クモ膜顆粒 Arachnoid granulations	17	［咽頭］喉頭部 Laryngopharynx : Hypopharynx	30	咽頭扁桃 Pharyngeal tonsil
4	後小脳延髄槽：大槽 Posterior cerebellomedullary cistern : Cisterna magna	18	（左の）篩骨蜂巣 Ethmoidal cells	31	下垂体 Pituitary gland
5	小脳 Cerebellum	19	（左の）前頭洞 Frontal sinus	32	橋 Pons
6	後鼻孔 Choanae : Posterior nasal apertures	20	下顎骨 Mandible	33	後弓〔環椎：第一頸椎〕 Posterior arch〔Atlas : C Ⅰ〕
7	脳梁 Corpus callosum	21	大後頭孔：大孔（の辺縁） Foramen magnum	34	軟口蓋 Soft palate
8	歯突起〔軸椎：第二頸椎〕 Dens〔Axis : C Ⅱ〕	22	（右の）大脳半球内側面 Medial surface of cerebral hemisphere	35	蝶形骨洞 Sphenoidal sinus
9	喉頭蓋 Epiglottis	23	延髄 Medulla oblongata	36	脊髄 Spinal cord
10	大脳鎌 Falx cerebri : Cerebral falx	24	中脳 Midbrain : Mesencephalon	37	直静脈洞 Straight sinus
11	第四脳室 4th ventricle	25	鼻中隔（骨部） Nasal septum	38	上矢状静脈洞 Superior sagittal sinus
12	大大脳静脈：Galen 静脈* Great cerebral vein : Vein of Galen *	26	［咽頭］鼻部 Nasopharynx	39	小脳テント Tentorium cerebelli
13	硬口蓋 Hard palate	27	耳管咽頭口 Pharyngeal opening of auditory tube	40	甲状軟骨 Thyroid cartilage
14	舌骨 Hyoid bone			41	舌 Tongue
				42	喉頭蓋谷 Epiglottic vallecula

アデノイド（咽頭扁桃）肥大

下垂体卒中

A 脳硬膜と脳神経

標本は左後方から斜めに見たものである。脳を除去し、大脳鎌（7）の後部を切除して小脳テント（29）の上面が見える。

1	外転神経〔Ⅵ〕 Abducent nerve [VI]	18	視神経〔Ⅱ〕 Optic nerve [II]
2	クモ膜顆粒 Arachnoid granulations	19	下垂体 Pituitary gland
3	小脳テント（の付着縁） Tentorium cerebelli	20	後弓〔環椎：第一頸椎〕 Posterior arch (Atlas: C I)
4	後鼻孔 Choanae: Posterior nasal apertures	21	舌下神経〔Ⅻ〕（の根糸） Hypoglossal nerve [XII]
5	斜台 Clivus	22	中間神経〔顔面神経 Ⅶ〕 Intermediate nerve (Facial nerve [VII])
6	歯突起〔軸椎：第二頸椎〕 Dens (Axis: C II)	23	蝶形骨洞 Sphenoidal sinus
7	大脳鎌 Falx cerebri: Cerebral falx	24	蝶形〔骨〕頭頂静脈洞 Sphenoparietal sinus
8	小脳テント（自由縁） Tentorium cerebelli	25	脊髄 Spinal cord
9	舌咽神経〔Ⅸ〕，迷走神経〔Ⅹ〕，副神経〔Ⅺ〕 Glossopharyngeal nerve [IX], Vagus nerve [X], Accessory nerve [XI]	26	脊髄根〔副神経 Ⅺ〕 Spinal root (Accessory nerve [XI])
10	下矢状静脈洞 Inferior sagittal sinus	27	直静脈洞 Straight sinus
11	内頸動脈 Internal carotid artery	28	上矢状静脈洞 Superior sagittal sinus
12	大後頭孔：大孔（の辺縁） Foramen magnum	29	小脳テント Tentorium cerebelli
13	延髄 Medulla oblongata	30	横静脈洞 Transverse sinus
14	運動根〔顔面神経 Ⅶ〕 Motor root (Facial nerve [VII])	31	三叉神経〔Ⅴ〕 Trigeminal nerve [V]
15	鼻中隔 Nasal septum	32	滑車神経〔Ⅳ〕 Trochlear nerve [IV]
16	動眼神経〔Ⅲ〕 Oculomotor nerve [III]	33	椎骨動脈 Vertebral artery
17	嗅索 Olfactory tract	34	内耳神経：前庭蝸牛神経〔Ⅷ〕 Vestibulocochlear nerve [VIII]

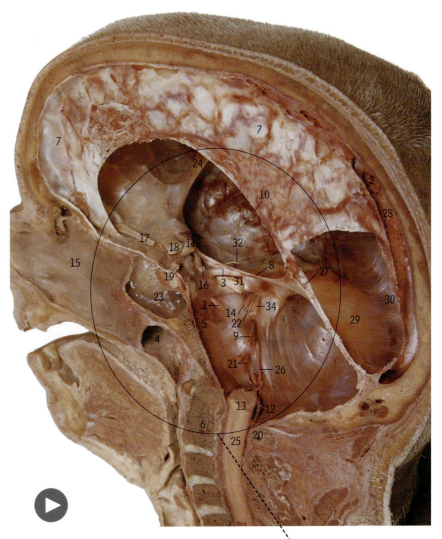

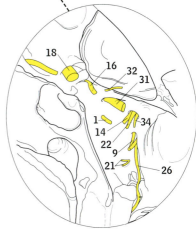

B 後頭蓋窩（右）

頭蓋の後部，硬膜，上位頸椎の椎弓，右では小脳半球のすべて，左では小脳半球のかなりの部分を除去し，第四脳室底（菱形窩※）を示してある．

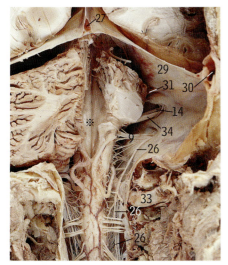

後方から．

開頭術

硬膜下出血

A 頭蓋冠と大脳鎌

B〜D 脳［右の大脳半球］

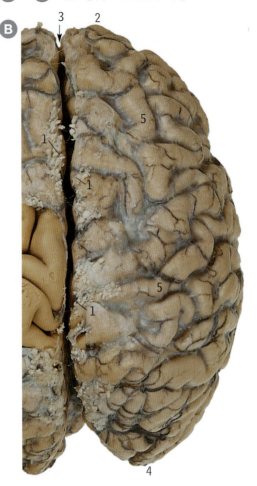

A：下方から．**B・C**：上方から．

頭蓋冠の内面を下から見上げると，頭蓋冠の内面全体を裏打ちした硬膜(2)に大脳鎌(3)が続いていることがわかる．小脳テントと接続する大脳鎌の後方部(1)を切断してある．

1	大脳鎌（後方部の切断縁） Falx cerebri：Cerebral falx
2	硬膜（頭蓋冠を裏打ちしている） Dura mater
3	大脳鎌 Falx cerebri：Cerebral falx
4	上大脳静脈 Superior cerebral veins
5	上矢状静脈洞 Superior sagittal sinus

右の大脳半球は，クモ膜をかぶったままの状態であり，大脳縦裂(3)のそばにクモ膜顆粒(1)が見える．左の大脳半球では，クモ膜の一部を切開してあるので，クモ膜下腔が見える．

1	クモ膜顆粒 Arachnoid granulations
2	前頭極 Frontal pole
3	大脳縦裂 Longitudinal cerebral fissure
4	後頭極 Occipital pole
5	大脳上外側面 Superolateral face of cerebral hemisphere

クモ膜とその下層の血管を取り去り，大脳回と大脳溝を明らかにしている．図内には最小限の用語を付すにとどめてある．ここで最も重要なのは，中心溝(1)，中心前回(5)ならびに中心後回(3)である．

1	中心溝 Central sulcus	5	中心前回 Precentral gyrus
2	頭頂後頭溝 Parieto-occipital sulcus	6	中心前溝 Precentral sulcus
3	中心後回 Postcentral gyrus	7	上前頭回 Superior frontal gyrus
4	中心後溝 Postcentral sulcus		

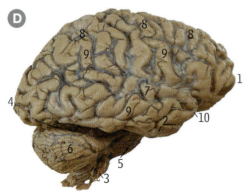

Bのように，クモ膜をそのまま残してある．クモ膜の下に，浅中大脳静脈(7)のような静脈が太い血管として見えている．

1	前頭極 Frontal pole	7	浅中大脳静脈（外側溝を覆う） Superficial middle cerebral vein
2	下大脳静脈 Inferior cerebral veins	8	上大脳静脈 Superior cerebral veins
3	延髄と椎骨動脈 Medulla oblongata and vertebral artery	9	（右の）大脳上外側面 Superolateral face of cerebral hemisphere
4	後頭極 Occipital pole	10	側頭極 Temporal pole
5	橋と脳底動脈 Pons and Basilar artery		
6	（右の）小脳半球 Hemisphere of cerebellum		

側方から．

クモ膜下出血

A〜D 大脳葉と大脳の表面 [D 島：島葉]

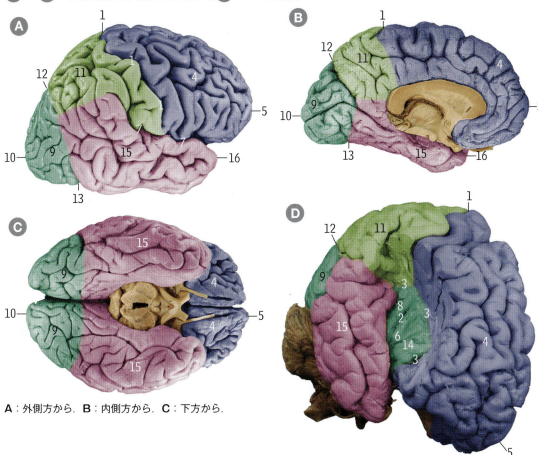

A：外側方から．B：内側方から．C：下方から．

1	中心溝 Central sulcus	9	後頭葉 Occipital lobe
2	島中心溝 Central sulcus of insula	10	後頭極 Occipital pole
3	島輪状溝 Circular sulcus of insula	11	頭頂葉 Parietal lobe
4	前頭葉 Frontal lobe	12	頭頂後頭溝 Parieto-occipital sulcus
5	前頭極 Frontal pole	13	後頭前切痕 Preoccipital notch
6	島：島葉 Insula：Insular lobe	14	島短回 Short gyri of insula
7	外側溝 Lateral sulcus	15	側頭葉 Temporal lobe
8	島長回 Long gyrus of insula	16	側頭極 Temporal pole

E 大脳の表面

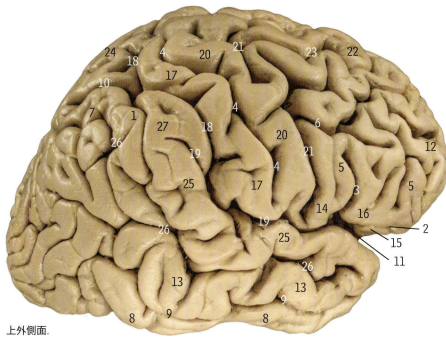

上外側面．

1	角回 Angular gyrus
2	前枝〔外側溝〕 Anterior ramus〔Lateral sulcus〕
3	上行枝〔外側溝〕 Ascending ramus〔Lateral sulcus〕
4	中心溝 Central sulcus
5	下前頭回 Inferior frontal gyrus
6	下前頭溝 Inferior frontal sulcus
7	下頭頂小葉 Inferior parietal lobule
8	下側頭回 Inferior temporal gyrus
9	下側頭溝 Inferior temporal sulcus
10	頭頂内溝：頭頂間溝 Intraparietal sulcus
11	島限 Limen insulae：Insular
12	中前頭回 Middle frontal gyrus
13	中側頭回 Middle temporal gyrus
14	弁蓋部：前頭弁蓋〔下前頭回〕 Opercular part〔Inferior frontal gyrus〕
15	眼窩部〔下前頭回〕 Orbital part〔Inferior frontal gyrus〕
16	三角部〔下前頭回〕 Triangular part〔Inferior frontal gyrus〕
17	中心後回 Postcentral gyrus
18	中心後溝 Postcentral sulcus
19	後枝〔外側溝〕 Posterior ramus〔Lateral sulcus〕
20	中心前回 Precentral gyrus
21	中心前溝 Precentral sulcus
22	上前頭回 Superior frontal gyrus
23	上前頭溝 Superior frontal sulcus
24	上頭頂小葉 Superior parietal lobule
25	上側頭回 Superior temporal gyrus
26	上側頭溝 Superior temporal sulcus
27	縁上回 Supramarginal gyrus

F G 大脳の表面

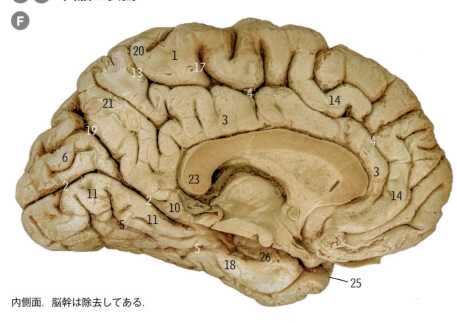

内側面．脳幹は除去してある．

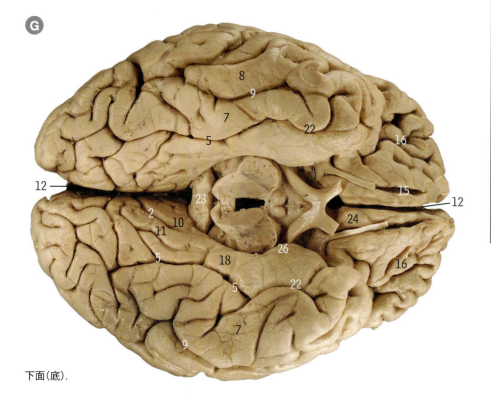

下面（底）．

1	前中心傍回〔中心傍小葉〕 Anterior paracentral gyrus〔Paracentral lobule〕
2	鳥距溝 Calcarine sulcus
3	帯状回 Cingulate gyrus
4	帯状溝 Cingulate sulcus
5	側副溝 Collateral sulcus
6	楔部 Cuneus
7	紡錘状回＊：外側後頭側頭回 Fusiform gyrus＊：Lateral occipito-temporal gyrus
8	下側頭回 Inferior temporal gyrus
9	下側頭溝 Inferior temporal sulcus
10	帯状回峡 Isthmus of cingulate gyrus
11	舌状回 Lingual gyrus
12	大脳縦裂 Longitudinal cerebral fissure
13	縁枝：縁溝〔帯状溝〕 Marginal branch：Marginal sulcus〔Cingulate sulcus〕
14	内側前頭回 Medial frontal gyrus
15	嗅溝 Olfactory sulcus
16	眼窩溝と眼窩回 Orbital sulci and Orbital gyri
17	中心傍枝＊〔帯状溝〕 Paracentral rami＊〔Cingulate sulcus〕
18	海馬傍回 Parahippocampal gyrus
19	頭頂後頭溝 Parieto-occipital sulcus
20	後中心傍回〔中心傍小葉〕 Posterior paracentral gyrus〔Paracentral lobule〕
21	楔前部 Precuneus
22	嗅脳溝 Rhinal sulcus
23	脳梁膨大 Splenium of corpus callosum
24	直回 Straight gyrus
25	側頭極 Temporal pole
26	鉤 Uncus

大脳の機能領野

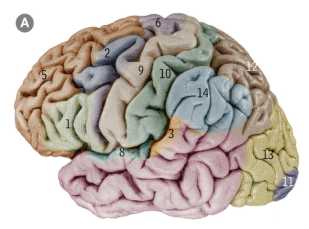
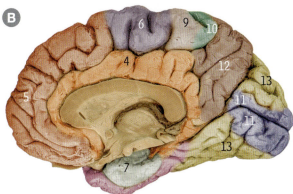
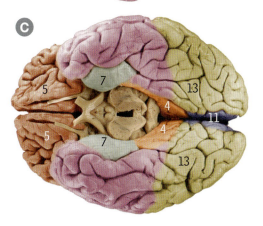
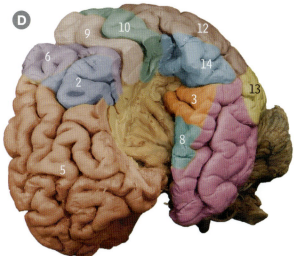

大脳の主な機能領野を，大脳の外側面(A)，内側面(B)，下面(C)に投影している．(D)は，前頭弁蓋と頭頂弁蓋を除去し，上側頭回を明らかにしている．

1	Broca 運動性言語野(Broadmann44，45 野)
2	前頭眼野(Broadmann8 野)
3	聴覚連合野(Broadmann22 野)
4	大脳辺縁系
5	前頭前野(Broadmann9，10，11，46，47 野)
6	運動前野または補足運動野(Broadmann6 野)
7	嗅内野(Broadmann28 野)
8	一次聴覚野(Broadmann41，42 野)
9	一次運動野(Broadmann4 野)
10	一次体性感覚野(Broadmann1，2，3 野)
11	一次視覚野(Broadmann17 野)
12	体性感覚連合野(Broadmann5，7 野)
13	視覚連合野(Broadmann18，19 野)
14	Wernicke（聴覚連合）野(Broadmann39，40 野)

- 一次運動野は，大脳の上外側面と内側面(中心傍小葉の前面)にある中心前回からなる．
- 運動前野または補足運動野は，主に中心傍小葉の前部の内側表面，ならびに上前頭回と中前頭回，下前頭回上部の中心前回のすぐ前にある細い領域からなる．
- 前頭眼野は，中前頭回の後端に位置する．
- **Broca 運動性言語野**は，下前頭回の弁蓋部と三角部にある．
- 前頭前野は，これまでに述べた運動野を除く前頭葉の全体からなる．
- 一次体性感覚野は，大脳の上外側面と内側面(中心傍小葉の後面)にある中心後回からなる．
- 体性感覚連合野は，上頭頂小葉にある．
- 一次聴覚野は，外側裂の中にある短い前横側頭回(Heschl 回)にあり，上側頭回の近くである．**聴覚連合野**は，一次聴覚野のすぐ尾方の長い後横側頭回(側頭平面)にある．
- **Wernicke（聴覚連合）野**は，上側頭回と下頭頂小葉の大部分(縁上回と角回)にある．
- 一次視覚野は，後頭葉の内側面の鳥距溝に隣接した領域にある．一方，**視覚連合野**は，後頭葉の残りの部分，ならびに側頭葉や頭頂葉にも広がっている．

脳

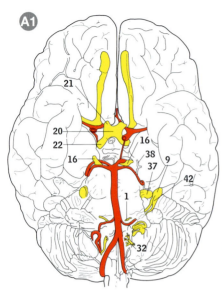

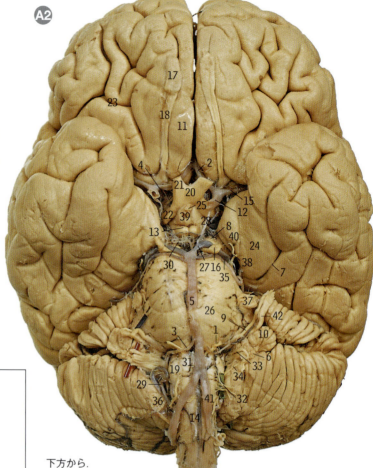

下方から.

1	外転神経［VI］ Abducent nerve [VI]	23	眼窩溝 Orbital sulci
2	前大脳動脈 Anterior cerebral artery	24	海馬傍回 Parahippocampal gyrus
3	前下小脳動脈 Anterior inferior cerebellar artery	25	下垂体茎* Pituitary stalk *
4	前有孔質 Anterior perforated substance	26	橋 Pons
5	脳底動脈 Basilar artery	27	後大脳動脈 Posterior cerebral artery
6	脈絡叢（第四脳室外側陥凹から出ている） Choroid plexus	28	後交通動脈 Posterior communicating artery
7	側副溝 Collateral sulcus	29	後下小脳動脈 Posterior inferior cerebellar artery
8	［狭義の］大脳脚〔［広義の］大脳脚〕 Cerebral crus (Cerebral peduncle)	30	後有孔質 Posterior perforated substance
9	顔面神経［VII］ Facial nerve [VII]	31	延髄錐体 Pyramid
10	片葉〔小脳〕 Flocculus〔Cerebellum〕	32	舌下神経［XII］（の根．マーカーを挿入して示す） Hypoglossal nerve [XII]
11	直回 Straight gyrus	33	根〔舌咽神経［IX］，迷走神経［X］，副神経［XI］〕 Roots（Glossopharyngeal nerve [IX], Vagus nerve [X] and Accessory nerve [XI]）
12	内頚動脈 Internal carotid artery	34	脊髄根〔副神経［XI］〕 Spinal root〔Accessory nerve [XI]〕
13	乳頭体 Mamillary body	35	上小脳動脈 Superior cerebellar artery
14	延髄 Medulla oblongata	36	小脳扁桃：腹側傍片葉 Tonsil of cerebellum：Ventral paraflocculus
15	中大脳動脈 Middle cerebral artery	37	三叉神経［V］ Trigeminal nerve [V]
16	動眼神経［III］ Oculomotor nerve [III]	38	滑車神経［IV］ Trochlear nerve [IV]
17	嗅球 Olfactory bulb	39	灰白隆起と正中隆起 Tuber cinereum and Median eminence
18	嗅索 Olfactory tract	40	鈎 Uncus
19	オリーブ〔延髄：髄脳〕 Inferior olive〔Medulla oblongata：Myelencephalon〕	41	椎骨動脈 Vertebral artery
20	視神経交叉：視交叉 Optic chiasm：Optic chiasma	42	内耳神経：前庭蝸牛神経［VIII］ Vestibulocochlear nerve [VIII]
21	視神経［II］ Optic nerve [II]		
22	視索 Optic tract		

脳底の内視鏡写真

- 動眼神経(16)は［広義の］大脳脚(8)の内側面に現れるが，滑車神経(38)は外側面を迂回する．2つの神経は，後大脳動脈(27)と上小脳動脈(35)の間を通過する．
- 滑車神経(38)は，脳幹の背側面から現れる唯一の脳神経である．
- 三叉神経(37)は橋(26)の外側面から現れる．
- 外転神経(1)は橋(26)と延髄錐体(31)の間から現れる．
- 顔面神経(9)と内耳神経(42)は橋と延髄の境界の外側部から現れる．
- 舌咽神経，迷走神経(33)ならびに副神経の延髄根は，延髄のオリーブ(19)の外側から現れる．
- 舌下神経(32)は，延髄錐体(31)と延髄のオリーブ(19)の間から，2列の根糸として現れる．
- 副神経の脊髄根は，歯状靱帯の背側で脊髄の上位五ないし六頚髄節から現れる(71頁E5)．

脳底の動脈　[Ⓑ 大脳動脈輪（Willis動脈輪）と脳底動脈，Ⓒ 大脳動脈輪（Willis動脈輪），Ⓓ 脳底]

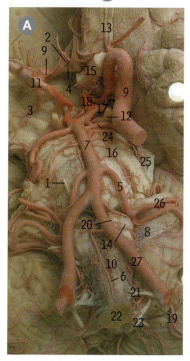
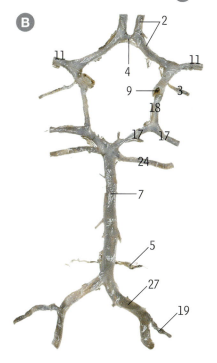
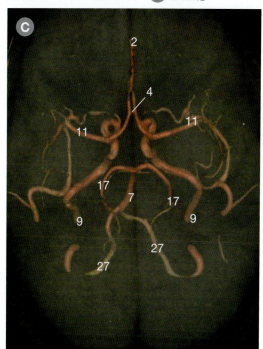

A：注入標本．
右の大脳半球（図の左側）の一部を除去し，右中大脳動脈（11）を示している．

吻合血管を脳底から除去し，位置関係を変えずに広げてある．

大脳動脈輪（Willis動脈輪）の三次元CT血管造影画像

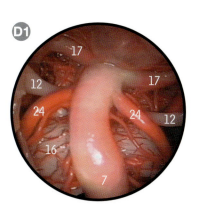

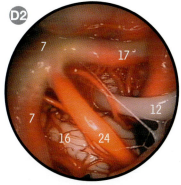

脳底の頭蓋内内視鏡写真

脳底の頭蓋内内視鏡写真

1	外転神経［Ⅵ］ Abducent nerve［Ⅵ］	8	根糸〔舌咽神経［Ⅸ］，迷走神経［Ⅹ］，副神経［Ⅺ］〕 Rootlets〔Glossopharyngeal nerve［Ⅸ］, Vagus nerve［Ⅹ］and Accessory nerve［Ⅺ］〕	14	オリーブ Olive	21	根糸〔第一頸神経〕 Rootlets〔C1〕
2	前大脳動脈 Anterior cerebral artery			15	視神経［Ⅱ］ Optic nerve［Ⅱ］	22	脊髄 Spinal cord
3	前脈絡叢動脈 Anterior choroidal artery			16	橋 Pons	23	脊髄根〔副神経［Ⅺ］〕 Spinal root〔Accessory nerve［Ⅺ］〕
4	前交通動脈 Anterior communicating artery	9	内頸動脈 Internal carotid artery	17	後大脳動脈 Posterior cerebral artery	24	上小脳動脈 Superior cerebellar artery
5	前下小脳動脈 Anterior inferior cerebellar artery	10	延髄 Medulla oblongata	18	後交通動脈 Posterior communicating artery	25	三叉神経［Ⅴ］ Trigeminal nerve［Ⅴ］
6	前脊髄動脈 Anterior spinal artery	11	中大脳動脈 Middle cerebral artery	19	後下小脳動脈 Posterior inferior cerebellar artery	26	前下小脳動脈の太い異常枝（顔面神経と内耳神経を覆っている）
7	橋枝〔脳底動脈〕 Pontine arteries〔Basilar artery〕	12	動眼神経［Ⅲ］ Oculomotor nerve［Ⅲ］	20	延髄錐体 Pyramid	27	椎骨動脈 Vertebral artery
		13	嗅索 Olfactory tract				

嚢状動脈瘤

A 脳（右半）

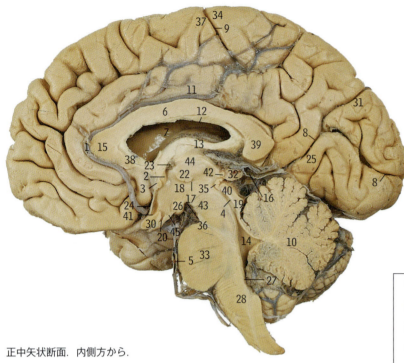

正中矢状断面．内側方から．

この脳の正中断標本では，右大脳半球の内側面と脳幹（中脳 4, 19, 40, 43．橋 33．延髄 28）の断面が見える．側脳室の中心部（7 の番号が付けられているところ）の内景を示すため，透明中隔を除去してある．この中隔の切断縁（12）が，脳梁幹（6）の下に見えている．第三脳室の側壁に視床（44）と視床下部（18）があり，床には前から後ろに視神経交叉（30），下垂体茎の基部（20 の番号が付けられているところ），内側隆起（45 の番号が付けられているところ），乳頭体（26）および後有孔質（36）が順に並んでいる．

- 第三脳室の腔の外側壁に視床（44）と視床下部（18）がある．
- 第四脳室（14）の大部分は，橋（33）と小脳（10）の間に位置する．しかし，その下端は延髄（28）の上部の後ろにある（61頁 B 参照）．
- 中脳水道（4）は，第三脳室と第四脳室を連絡している．正常では，脳脊髄液は第三脳室から中脳水道を経て第四脳室へ流れる．
- 室間孔（23）は，第三脳室と側脳室を連絡しており，前方は脳弓柱（2）により，後方は視床（44）と接する．

1	前大脳動脈 Anterior cerebral artery	23	室間孔と脈絡叢 Interventricular foramen and Choroid plexus
2	脳弓柱 Column of fornix	24	終板 Lamina terminalis
3	前交連 Anterior commissure	25	舌状回 Lingual gyrus
4	中脳水道 Aqueduct of midbrain：Cerebral aqueduct	26	乳頭体 Mamillary body
5	脳底動脈 Basilar artery	27	第四脳室正中口：Magendie 孔* Median aperture of 4th ventricle：Foramen of Magendie *
6	脳梁幹 Trunk of corpus callosum：Body of corpus callosum	28	延髄 Medulla oblongata
7	尾状核体（側脳室内に突出している） Body of Caudate nucleus	29	中大脳動脈 Middle cerebral artery
8	鳥距溝 Calcarine sulcus	30	視神経交叉：視交叉 Optic chiasm：Optic chiasma
9	中心溝 Central sulcus	31	頭頂後頭溝 Parieto-occipital sulcus
10	小脳 Cerebellum	32	松果体 Pineal body *：Pineal gland
11	帯状回 Cingulate gyrus	33	橋 Pons
12	透明中隔（切断縁） Septum pellucidum	34	中心後回 Postcentral gyrus
13	脳弓体 Body of fornix	35	後交連 Posterior commissure
14	第四脳室 4th ventricle	36	後有孔質 Posterior perforated substance
15	脳梁膝 Genu of corpus callosum	37	中心前回 Precentral gyrus
16	大大脳静脈：Galen 静脈* Great cerebral vein：Vein of Galen *	38	脳梁吻 Rostrum of corpus callosum
17	視床下溝 Hypothalamic sulcus	39	脳梁膨大 Splenium of corpus callosum
18	視床下部 Hypothalamus	40	上丘〔中脳〕 Superior colliculus〔Midbrain〕
19	下丘〔中脳〕 Inferior colliculus〔Midbrain〕	41	視索上陥凹 Supra-optic recess
20	漏斗陥凹 Infundibular recess	42	松果体上陥凹 Suprapineal recess
21	内頸動脈 Internal carotid artery	43	中脳被蓋 Tegmentum of midbrain
22	視床間橋：中間質 Interthalamic adhesion：Massa intermedia	44	視床 Thalamus
		45	灰白隆起と正中隆起 Tuber cinereum and Median eminence

B 脳の動脈

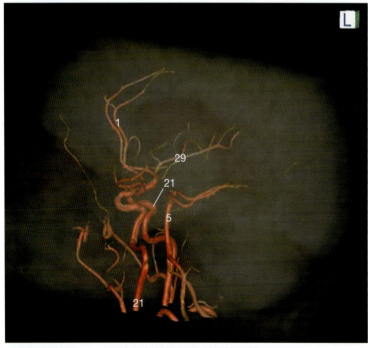

三次元血管造影画像（左側方から）

皮質流域［大脳の血液供給］

動脈の分布を，大脳の(A)上外側面，(B)内側面，(C)下面に投影している．

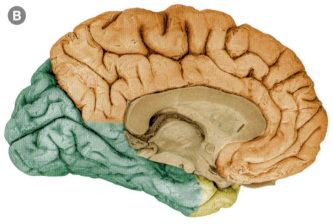

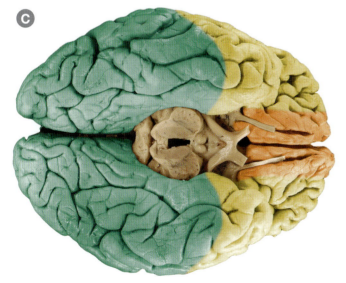

- 大脳半球の表面の血管や基底部の血管は吻合しないので，前大脳動脈，中大脳動脈，後大脳動脈の血管は，独自の供給領域をもつということを認識することが重要である．これらが，いわゆる皮質流域である．
- 前大脳動脈（オレンジ色）は，前頭葉および頭頂葉の内側面に供給するが，後頭葉の内側面には供給しない．この動脈は，内側面の辺縁を越えて約一横指幅の分だけ，前頭葉および頭頂葉の大脳の上外側面ならびに前頭葉の下面に供給する．
- 中大脳動脈（黄色）は，島と，前頭葉と頭頂葉の外側面（前大脳動脈によって供給される領域を除く）に供給する．また，側頭葉の前部と上部に供給するが，後頭葉には供給しない．
- 後大脳動脈（緑色）は，頭頂後頭溝までの後頭葉全体ならびに側頭葉の残りの領域に供給する．

Ⓐ~Ⓒ 脳幹と小脳

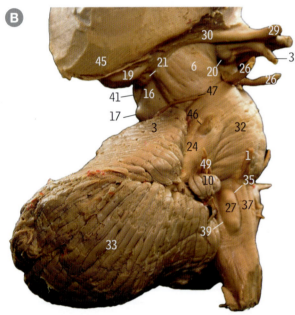

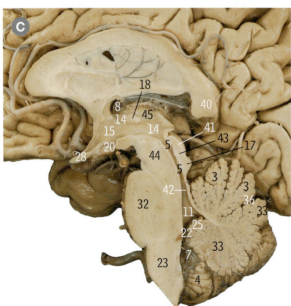

1	外転神経［Ⅵ］ Abducent nerve [VI]	25	小節：虫部小節 Nodule
2	副神経［Ⅺ］ Accessory nerve [XI]	26	動眼神経［Ⅲ］ Oculomotor nerve [III]
3	小脳前葉 Anterior lobe of cerebellum	27	オリーブ Olive
4	小脳扁桃 Tonsil of cerebellum	28	視神経交叉：視交叉 Optic chiasm：Optic chiasma
5	中脳水道：Sylvius 水道* Cerebral aqueduct：Aqueduct of midbrain：Aqueduct of Sylvius *	29	視神経［Ⅱ］ Optic nerve [II]
6	［広義の］大脳脚 Cerebral peduncle	30	視索 Optic tract
7	第四脳室脈絡叢 Choroid plexus of 4th ventricle	31	下垂体茎* Pituitary stalk *
8	第三脳室脈絡叢 Choroid plexus of 3rd ventricle	32	橋 Pons
9	顔面神経［Ⅶ］ Facial nerve [VII]	33	小脳後葉 Posterior lobe of cerebellum
10	片葉 Flocculus	34	後有孔質 Posterior perforated substance
11	第四脳室 4th ventricle	35	オリーブ前溝 Pre-olivary groove
12	舌咽神経［Ⅸ］ Glossopharyngeal nerve [IX]	36	第一裂：山腹前裂 Primary fissure：Preclival fissure
13	水平裂：脚間裂〔小脳〕 Horizontal fissure：Intercrural fissure〔Cerebellum〕	37	延髄錐体 Pyramid
14	視床下溝 Hypothalamic sulcus	38	錐体交叉 Decussation of pyramids：Motor decussat10n
15	視床下部 Hypothalamus	39	オリーブ後溝 Retro-olivary groove
16	下丘腕 Brachium of inferior colliculus	40	脳梁膨大 Splenium of corpus callosum
17	下丘 Inferior colliculus	41	上丘 Superior colliculus
18	視床間橋：中間質 Interthalamic adhesion：Massa intermedia	42	上髄帆 Superior medullary velum
19	外側膝状体 Lateral geniculate body	43	中脳蓋 Tectum of midbrain
20	乳頭体 Mammillary body	44	中脳被蓋 Tegmentum of midbrain
21	内側膝状体 Medial geniculate body	45	視床 Thalamus
22	第四脳室正中口：Magendie 孔* Median aperture of 4th ventricle：Foramen of Magendie *	46	三叉神経［Ⅴ］ Trigeminal nerve [V]
23	延髄 Medulla oblongata	47	滑車神経［Ⅳ］ Trochlear nerve [IV]
24	中小脳脚 Middle cerebellar peduncle	48	迷走神経［Ⅹ］ Vagus nerve [X]
		49	内耳神経：前庭蝸牛神経［Ⅷ］ Vestibulocochlear nerve [VIII]

Ⓐ：前方から．Ⓑ：右側方から．Ⓒ：正中矢状断面．

D 脳幹と第四脳室底

中脳上部にある上丘のすぐ下で，脳の他の部分から切り離し，脳幹の背側を見ている．小脳の虫部と，小脳半球の内側部を除去し，第四脳室底を明らかにしている．

1	楔状束結節 Cuneate tubercle	9	正中溝 Median sulcus
2	上髄帆（切断縁） Superior medullary velum	10	第四脳室髄条 Medullary striae of 4th ventricle
3	後正中溝 Dorsal median sulcus	11	閂（カンヌキ） Obex
4	顔面神経丘 Facial colliculus	12	境界溝 Sulcus limitans
5	薄束結節 Gracile tubercle	13	上窩 Superior fovea
6	舌下神経三角 Hypoglossal trigone : Trigone of hypoglossal nerve	14	迷走神経三角：灰白翼 Vagal trigone : Trigone of vagus nerve
7	下丘 Inferior colliculus	15	前庭神経野 Vestibular area
8	内側隆起 Medial eminence		

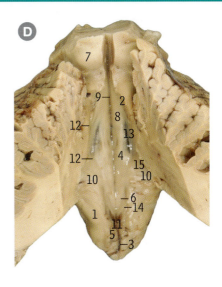

E 脳幹と脊髄の上部

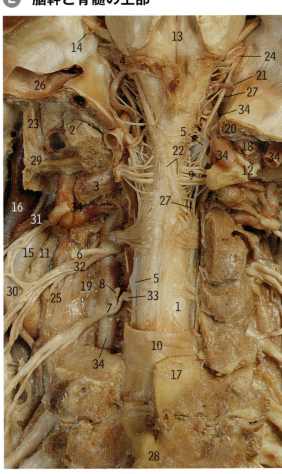

頭蓋の後部と上方の椎弓を除去し，（9に示されるように）脊髄神経の後根の根糸が現れる脳幹と脊髄の接続部を示してある．副神経の脊髄根（27）は，大後頭孔（20）を通り抜けて上行し，頸静脈孔（24）で延髄根と合する．（33に示されるように）脊髄神経の前根の根糸群は，歯状靱帯（5）より腹側で起こり，合流して脊髄神経の前根を形づくる．前根は，脊髄神経節（7）を越えたところで後根（8）と合体して脊髄神経を形成する（歯状靱帯の背側を通る後根の根糸群を脊髄から切り取り，前根が見えるようにしてある）．脊髄神経は，（6，32に示すように）ただちに前枝と後枝に分岐する．

1	クモ膜 Arachnoid mater	18	外側塊〔環椎：第一頸椎〕 Lateral mass〔Atlas：C I〕
2	環椎後頭関節 Atlanto-occipital joint	19	頭長筋 Longus capitis
3	外側環軸関節（の関節包） Lateral atlanto-axial joint	20	大後頭孔：大孔（の辺縁） Foramen magnum
4	脈絡叢（第四脳室外側陥凹から出ている） Choroid plexus	21	後下小脳動脈 Posterior inferior cerebellar artery
5	歯状靱帯 Denticulate ligament	22	後脊髄動脈 Posterior spinal artery
6	後枝〔第三頸神経〕 Dorsal ramus〔C3〕	23	外側頭直筋 Rectus capitis lateralis
7	脊髄神経節〔第四頸神経〕 Spinal ganglion : Dorsal root ganglion〔C4〕	24	舌咽神経・迷走神経の根，副神経の延髄根，頸静脈孔 Roots of glossopharyngeal nerve and vagus nerve, Cranial root of accessory nerve, Jugular foramen
8	後根〔第四頸神経〕 Dorsal root〔C4〕	25	前斜角筋 Anterior scalene
9	後根の根糸*〔第二頸神経〕 Dorsal rootlets *〔C2〕	26	S状静脈洞 Sigmoid sinus
10	硬膜 Dura mater	27	脊髄根〔副神経〔XI〕〕 Spinal root〔Accessory nerve〔XI〕〕
11	外頸動脈 External carotid artery	28	棘突起〔隆椎：第七頸椎〕 Spinous process〔Vertebra prominens : C VII〕
12	第一頸神経と後弓〔環椎：第一頸椎〕 C1 and Posterior arch〔Atlas：C I〕	29	横突起*〔環椎：第一頸椎〕 Transverse process *〔Atlas：C I〕
13	菱形窩：第四脳室底 Rhomboid fossa : Floor of 4th ventricle	30	迷走神経〔X〕 Vagus nerve〔X〕
14	内耳道（顔面神経，内耳神経，迷路動脈を伴う） Internal acoustic meatus	31	椎骨静脈叢からの静脈
15	内頸動脈 Internal carotid artery	32	前枝〔第三頸神経〕 Ventral ramus〔C3〕
16	内頸静脈 Internal jugular vein	33	前根の根糸*〔第四頸神経〕 Ventral rootlets *〔C4〕
17	椎弓板〔第六頸神経〕 Lamina〔C VI〕	34	椎骨動脈 Vertebral artery

椎弓を除去して後方から見たところ．

- 菱形である第四脳室底の下部は延髄の一部であり，舌下神経三角（D6）と迷走神経三角（D14）を含む．第四脳室底の残りは橋の一部に属する．
- 薄束結節（D5）と楔状束結節（D1）は，下層にある薄束核と楔状束核によってつくられる．そこは，薄束と楔状束（後柱）の線維が核の細胞とシナプスをつくるところである．これらの細胞から起こった神経線維は，内側毛帯をつくり，脳幹を通り抜けて視床に達する．
- 顔面神経丘（D4）は，第四脳室底の内側隆起（D8）の下端に位置し，外転神経核を覆うように走る顔面神経線維によってつくられる．顔面神経核は，橋において，より深部に位置するため，顔面神経丘の形成には関係していない．
- 環椎の横突孔から出た椎骨動脈（E34）は環椎の外側塊（E18）の後方を回り，大後頭孔より頭蓋内に進入する．

A B 脳室

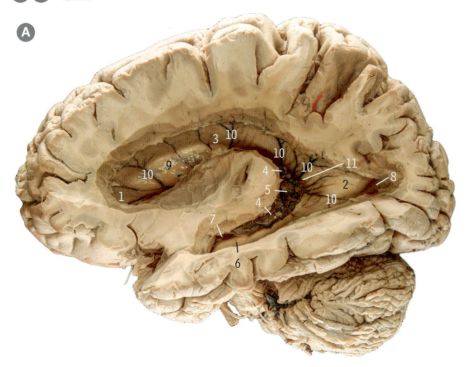

1	前［頭］角〔側脳室〕 Anterior horn : Frontal horn〔Lateral ventricle〕
2	鳥距 Calcarine spur
3	中心部〔側脳室〕 Central part〔Lateral ventricle〕
4	脈絡叢 Choroid plexus
5	脈絡糸球 Choroid enlargement
6	海馬 Hippocampus
7	下角：側頭角〔側脳室〕 Inferior horn : Tempolar horn〔Lateral ventricle〕
8	後［頭］角〔側脳室〕 Posterior horn : Occipital horn〔Lateral ventricle〕
9	透明中隔 Septum pellucidum
10	視床線条体静脈*に流入する静脈
11	（側脳室の）房：三角領域*（側副三角が突出しているところ） Atrium : Trigone area* : Antrum*

左の大脳半球の側脳室を左側方から見たところ．

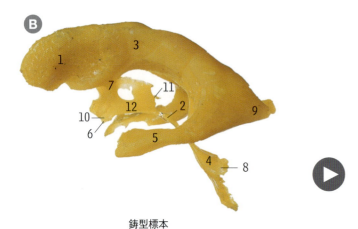

鋳型標本
左側方から．

この標本では，左側脳室が右側脳室の大部分を覆っている．

1	前［頭］角〔側脳室〕 Anterior horn : Frontal horn〔Lateral ventricle〕	7	室間孔 Interventricular foramen
2	中脳水道 Aqueduct of midbrain : Cerebral aqueduct	8	第四脳室外側陥凹 Lateral recess
3	中心部〔側脳室〕 Central part : Body〔Lateral ventricle〕	9	後［頭］角〔側脳室〕 Posterior horn : Occipital horn〔Lateral ventricle〕
4	第四脳室 4th ventricle	10	視索上陥凹〔第三脳室〕 Supra-optic recess〔3rd ventricle〕
5	下角：側頭角〔側脳室〕 Inferior horn : Tempolar horn〔Lateral ventricle〕	11	松果体上陥凹〔第三脳室〕 Suprapineal recess〔3rd ventricle〕
6	漏斗陥凹〔第三脳室〕 Infundibular recess〔3rd ventricle〕	12	第三脳室（その上に視床間橋が通る間隙が見える） 3rd ventricle

● 第三脳室(B12)は，上前部にある室間孔(B7)を通じて左右の側脳室と交通する．側脳室の主たる部は，中心部(A3, B3)である．室間孔(B7)の前方の部分は前角(A1, B1)であり，大脳の前頭葉の内部に広がっている．中心部の後端は，後方へ延びて後頭葉の内部に広がる後角(後頭角, A8, B9)と，下前方へ向かい側頭葉の内部に広がる下角(側頭角, A7, B 5)に分かれる．第三脳室(B12)の下後部は，中脳水道(B2)を通って第四脳室(B4)と交通する．下角(側頭角)の底は，内側は海馬(A6, 73頁C11)によって，外側は側副隆起(73頁C4)によってつくられている．後角(後頭角, A8, B9, 73頁C12)との接合部で，側副隆起は幅を広げ，側副三角(73頁C5)となる．側副隆起(73頁C4)は，側副溝が内方に突出することによってつくられる．後角(後頭角)の内側壁には，脳梁の線維群でつくられた後角球と，鳥距溝が内方に突出することによってつくられる鳥距(A2)が認められる．

脳室と海馬 ［側脳室の下角（右）］

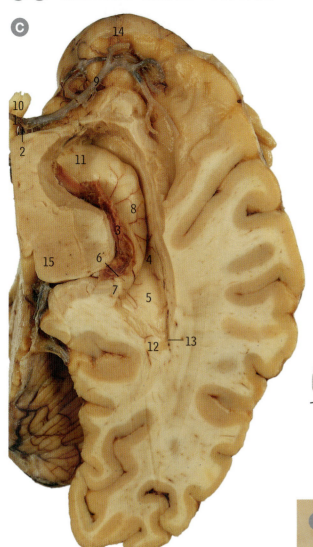

外側溝の前部より上方の脳の実質を除去し，中大脳動脈(9)が側頭葉の前部(14)の上面を越えて外側に走行するのを明らかにしている．側頭葉の一部を上方から開き，側脳室の下角（側頭角）の底にある海馬(11, 8)を示している．

1	前大脳動脈 Anterior cerebral artery	9	中大脳動脈 Middle cerebral artery
2	前脈絡叢動脈 Anterior choroidal artery	10	視神経［Ⅱ］ Optic nerve [Ⅱ]
3	脈絡叢 Choroid plexus	11	海馬足〔海馬〕 Pes (Hippocampus)
4	側副隆起 Collateral eminence	12	後角：後頭角 Posterior horn
5	側副三角 Collateral trigone	13	壁板〔脳梁放線〕 Tapetum (Radiation of corpus callosum)
6	海馬采 Fimbria	14	側頭極〔側頭葉〕 Temporal pole (Temporal lobe)
7	脳弓 Fornix	15	視床 Thalamus
8	海馬 Hippocampus		

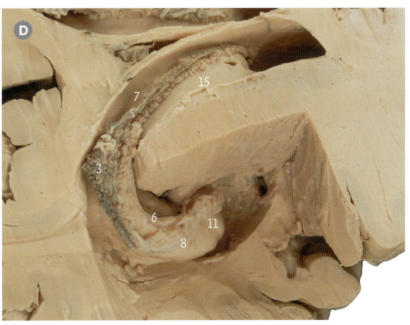

大脳半球

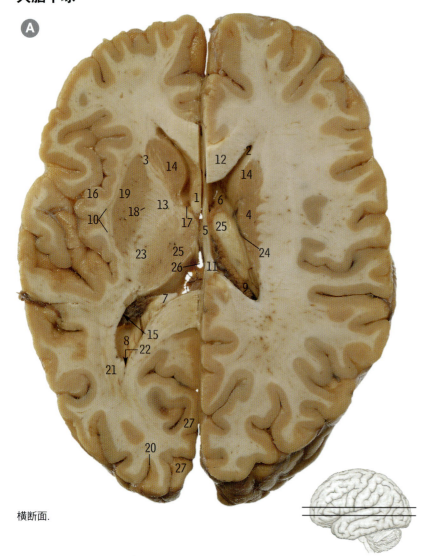

横断面．

左大脳半球は室間孔(17)の高さで，また右大脳半球は左より1.5cm高いところで切断し，上方から見た．左大脳半球では，最も重要な構造物である内包(3, 13, 23)が，尾状核(14)，レンズ核(18, 19)，視床(25)の間に位置しているのが見える．右側では，脳梁(11)を広く除去してあるため，側脳室(6)が開放されており，尾状核(14, 4)が視床(25)を越えて弧を描きながら後方へのびることがわかる．また，両者の間の浅い溝に収まった視床線条体静脈(24)と脈絡叢(9)が見えている．

1	前部＊〔脳弓柱〕 Anterior column＊〔Fornix〕
2	前〔頭〕角〔側脳室〕 Anterior horn：Frontal horn〔Lateral ventricle〕
3	前脚：内包前脚〔内包〕 Anterior limb〔Internal capsule〕
4	尾状核体 Body of caudate nucleus
5	脳弓体 Body of fornix
6	中心部〔側脳室〕 Central part：Body〔Lateral ventricle〕
7	後角球：後頭角球 Bulb of occipital horn
8	鳥距 Calcarine spur
9	脈絡叢 Choroid plexus
10	前障 Claustrum
11	脳梁 Corpus callosum
12	小鉗子〔脳梁〕 Minor forceps：Occipital forceps〔Corpus callosum〕
13	内包膝 Genu of internal capsule
14	尾状核頭 Head of caudate nucleus
15	下角：側頭角〔側脳室〕 Inferior horn：Tempoal horn〔Lateral ventricle〕
16	島：島葉 Insula：Insular lobe
17	室間孔 Interventricular foramen
18	淡蒼球：古線条体〔レンズ核〕 Pallidum：Paleostriatum〔Lentiform nucleus〕
19	被殻〔レンズ核〕 Putamen〔Lentiform nucleus〕
20	月状溝 Lunate sulcus
21	視放線 Optic radiation：Geniculocalcarine fibers
22	後〔頭〕角〔側脳室〕 Posterior horn：Occipital horn〔Lateral ventricle〕
23	後脚：内包後脚〔内包〕 Posterior limb〔Internal capsule〕
24	視床線条体静脈＊ Thalamostriate vein＊
25	視床 Thalamus
26	第三脳室 3rd ventricle
27	視覚野 Visual cortex

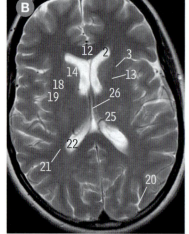

大脳半球のMR横断画像

- 内包前脚(3)は，内側では尾状核頭(14)と，外側ではレンズ核(被殻19と淡蒼球18)と接している．
- 内包膝(13)は，淡蒼球(18)の最内側と接する．
- 内包後脚(23)は，内側では視床(25)と，外側ではレンズ核(被殻19と淡蒼球18)と接している．
- 皮質核線維(大脳皮質から脳神経の運動神経核に至る運動神経線維群)は，内包膝(13)を通過する．
- 皮質脊髄線維(大脳皮質から脊髄の前角細胞に至る運動神経線維群)は，内包後脚(23)の前2/3を通過する．
- 内包膝と内包後脚は，前・中大脳動脈の線条体枝と前脈絡叢動脈の支配を受ける．この領域は，脳出血や脳血栓(卒中)の好発部位なので，臨床上最も重要である．

脳［横断標本］

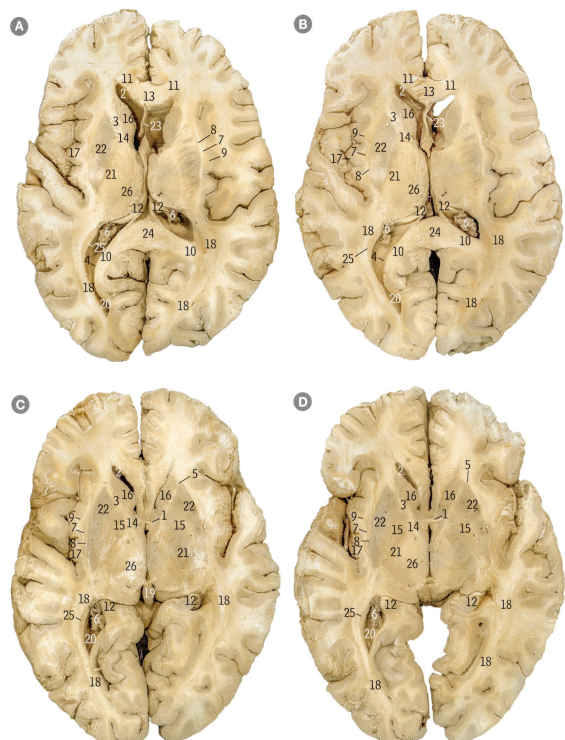

Aから順に，上方から下方に並べてある．

1 前交連 Anterior commissure	8 外包 External capsule	15 淡蒼球：古線条体 Pallidum : Paleostriatum	22 被殻〔レンズ核〕 Putamen〔Lentiform nucleus〕
2 前［頭］角〔側脳室〕 Anterior horn : Frontal horn〔Lateral ventricle〕	9 最外包 Extreme capsule	16 尾状核頭 Head of caudate nucleus	23 透明中隔 Septum pellucidum
3 前脚：内包前脚〔内包〕 Anterior limb〔Internal capsule〕	10 大鉗子〔脳梁放線〕 Major forceps : Occipital forceps〔Radiation of corpus callosum〕	17 島：島葉 Insula : Insular lobe	24 脳梁膨大 Splenium of corpus callosum
4 鳥距 Calcarine spur	11 小鉗子〔脳梁放線〕 Minor forceps : Frontal forceps〔Radiation of corpus callosum〕	18 視放線 Optic radiation : Geniculocalcarine fibers	25 壁板〔脳梁放線〕 Tapetum〔Radiation of corpus callosum〕
5 尾状核と被殻をつなぐ灰白質の細胞間橋（線条）	12 脳弓脚 Crus of fornix	19 松果体 Pineal body* : Pineal gland	26 視床 Thalamus
6 側脳室脈絡叢 Choroid plexus of lateral ventricle	13 脳梁膝 Genu of corpus callosum	20 後［頭］角〔側脳室〕 Posterior horn : Occipital horn〔Lateral ventricle〕	
7 前障 Claustrum	14 内包膝〔内包〕 Genu〔Internal capsule〕	21 後脚：内包後脚〔内包〕 Posterior limb〔Internal capsule〕	

A B 脳

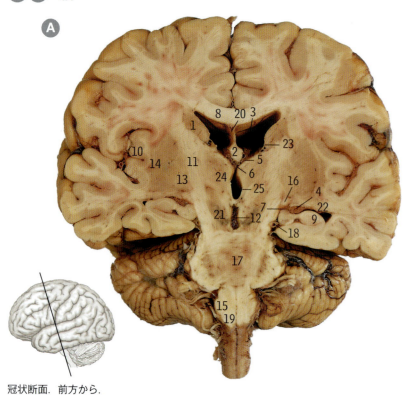

冠状断面．前方から．

この冠状断標本は，完全な垂直ではなく，わずかに後方に傾いている．室間孔の0.5cm後方で第三脳室(25)と側脳室の中心部(3)を通過し，さらに下方で橋(17)と延髄錐体(19)を通る．このように切断すると，重要な皮質脊髄線維（運動線維）が，内包(11)と橋(17)を下行し，延髄錐体(19)を形成することがわかる．MR画像と比較せよ．

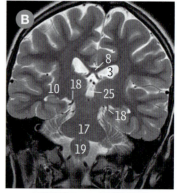

大脳半球のMR冠状断画像

1 尾状核体 Body of caudate nucleus	5 側脳室脈絡叢 Choroid plexus of lateral ventricle	10 島：島葉 Insula：Insular lobe
2 脳弓体 Body of fornix	6 第三脳室脈絡叢 Choroid plexus of 3rd ventricle	11 内包 Internal capsule
3 中心部〔側脳室〕 Central part：Body（Lateral ventricle）	7 脈絡裂 Choroidal fissure	12 脚間槽 Interpeduncular cistern
4 脈絡叢：側脳室脈絡叢〔下角：側頭角（側脳室）〕 Choroid plexus（Inferior horn：Temporal horn（Lateral ventricle））	8 脳梁 Corpus callosum	13 淡蒼球：古線条体〔レンズ核〕 Pallidum：Paleostriatum（Lentiform nucleus）
	9 海馬 Hippocampus	14 被殻〔レンズ核〕 Putamen（Lentiform nucleus）

15 オリーブ〔延髄：髄脳〕 Inferior olive（Medulla oblongata：Myelencephalon）	21 黒質 Substantia nigra
16 視索 Optic tract	22 尾状核尾 Tail of caudate nucleus
17 橋 Pons	23 視床線条体静脈* Thalamostriate vein*
18 後大脳動脈 Posterior cerebral artery	24 視床 Thalamus
19 延髄錐体 Pyramid	25 第三脳室 3rd ventricle
20 透明中隔 Septum pellucidum	

C 大脳半球と脳幹

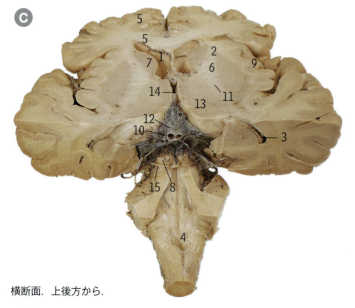

横断面．上後方から．

動静脈瘻

大脳半球と脳幹を，室間孔のすぐ上方で横断した．大脳半球の後部を小脳全体とともに取り除いてあるので，第三脳室上壁の後部の脈絡組織(12)とその下を通る内大脳静脈(10)が見える．

1 前〔頭〕角〔側脳室〕 Anterior horn：Frontal horn（Lateral ventricle）	8 下丘 Inferior colliculus
2 前脚：内包前脚〔内包〕 Anterior limb（Internal capsule）	9 島：島葉 Insula：Insular lobe
3 脈絡叢および下角（側頭角）と後角（後頭角）の移行部	10 内大脳静脈 Internal cerebral veins
4 菱形窩：第四脳室底 Rhomboid fossa：Floor of 4th ventricle	11 後脚：内包後脚〔内包〕 Posterior limb（Internal capsule）
5 小鉗子 Minor forceps：Occipital forceps	12 第三脳室脈絡組織 Tela choroidea of 3rd ventricle
6 内包膝 Genu of internal capsule	13 視床 Thalamus
7 尾状核頭 Head of caudate nucleus	14 第三脳室 3rd ventricle
	15 滑車神経〔IV〕 Trochlear nerve〔IV〕

脳［冠状断標本］

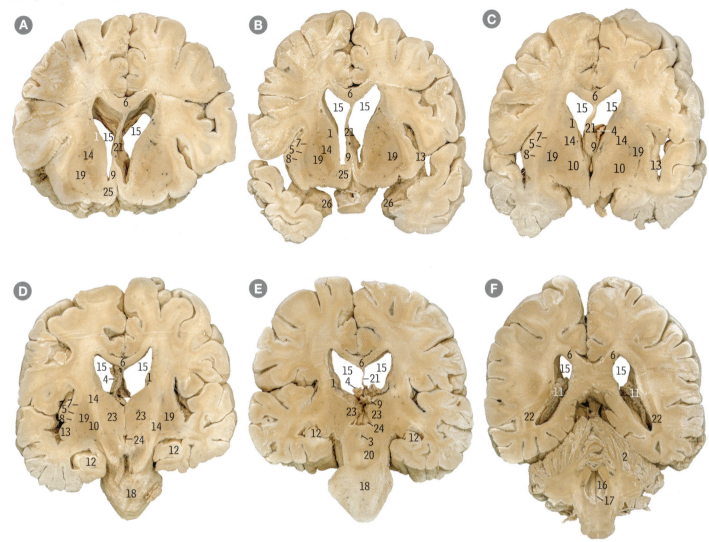

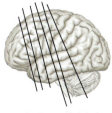

Aから順に，前方から後方に並べてある．

1 尾状核 Caudate nucleus	10 淡蒼球：古線条体 Pallidum：Paleostriatum	19 被殻 Putamen
2 小脳 Cerebellum	11 脈絡糸球 Choroid enlargement	20 赤核 Red nucleus
3 中脳水道 Aqueduct of midbrain：Cerebral aqueduct	12 海馬 Hippocampus	21 透明中隔 Septum pellucidum
4 側脳室脈絡叢 Choroid plexus of lateral ventricle	13 島：島葉 Insula：Insular lobe	22 壁板〔脳梁放線〕 Tapetum（Radiation of corpus callosum）
5 前障 Claustrum	14 内包 Internal capsule	23 視床 Thalamus
6 脳梁 Corpus callosum	15 側脳室 Lateral ventricle	24 第三脳室 3rd ventricle
7 外包 External capsule	16 内側隆起〔第四脳室〕 Medial eminence（4th ventricle）	25 腹側淡蒼球 Ventral pallidum
8 最外包 Extreme capsule	17 正中溝〔第四脳室〕 Median sulcus（4th ventricle）	26 鈎 Uncus
9 脳弓 Fornix	18 橋 Pons	

脳神経

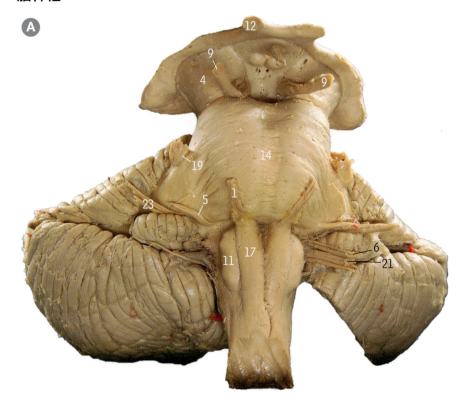

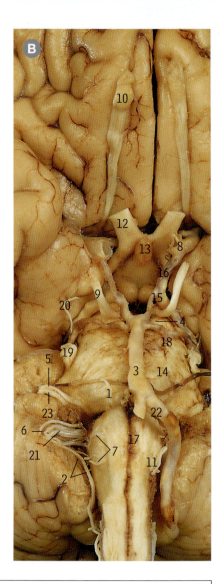

腹側から脳の中心部を見ており，右の椎骨動脈を左の椎骨動脈(B22)との合流部付近で切断してある(図Bの左側)．嗅球(B10)に入る第一脳神経(嗅神経)の線維群は，脳を摘出したときに切れたため見えない．舌咽神経(6)，迷走神経(21)および副神経(B2)の構成根は互いに明確に区別がつくわけではない．しかし副神経の脊髄根(B2)は，延髄のわきを上行して副神経の延髄根に合しているので，認識することができる．

1 外転神経 [Ⅵ] Abducent nerve [VI]	9 動眼神経 [Ⅲ] Oculomotor nerve [III]	17 延髄錐体 Pyramid
2 脊髄根〔副神経 [Ⅺ]〕 Spinal root (Accessory nerve [XI])	10 嗅球 Olfactory bulb	18 上小脳動脈 Superior cerebellar artery
3 脳底動脈 Basilar artery	11 オリーブ〔延髄：髄脳〕 Inferior olive (Medulla oblongata：Myelencephalon)	19 三叉神経 [Ⅴ] Trigeminal nerve [V]
4 [狭義の] 大脳脚 Cerebral crus (Midbrain：Mesencephalon)	12 視神経 [Ⅱ] Optic nerve [II]	20 滑車神経 [Ⅳ] Trochlear nerve [IV]
5 顔面神経 [Ⅶ] Facial nerve [VII]	13 下垂体茎* Pituitary stalk *	21 迷走神経 [Ⅹ] Vagus nerve [X]
6 舌咽神経 [Ⅸ] Glossopharyngeal nerve [IX]	14 橋 Pons	22 椎骨動脈 Vertebral artery
7 舌下神経 [Ⅻ] Hypoglossal nerve [XII]	15 後大脳動脈 Posterior cerebral artery	23 内耳神経：前庭蝸牛神経 [Ⅷ] Vestibulocochlear nerve [VIII]
8 内頸動脈 Internal carotid artery	16 後交通動脈 Posterior communicating artery	

A 第一脳神経［Ⅰ］：嗅神経

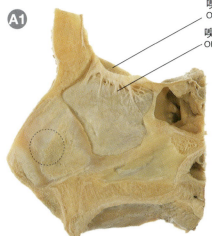

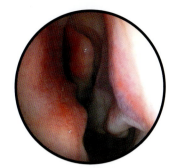

嗅球 Olfactory bulbs
嗅神経 Olfactory nerves
中鼻甲介 Middle concha
下鼻甲介 Inferior concha

嗅粘膜の内視鏡写真

（破線円は Kiesselbach 部位を示す（Little 部位）．55，66，78 頁参照．）

1	前弓〔環椎：第一頸椎〕 Anterior arch（Atlas：C Ⅰ）	4	［咽頭］鼻部：鼻咽頭* Nasopharynx
2	斜台 Clivus	5	蝶形骨洞 Sphenoidal sinus
3	篩板 Cribriform plate	6	鋤骨 Vomer

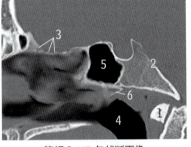

篩板の MR 矢状断画像

B 視索と膝状体

1	前有孔質 Anterior perforated substance
2	中脳水道 Aqueduct of midbrain：Cerebral aqueduct
3	［狭義の］大脳脚 Cerebral crus（Midbrain：Mesencephalon）
4	外側膝状体 Lateral geniculate body
5	乳頭体 Mamillary body
6	内側膝状体 Medial geniculate body
7	嗅索 Olfactory tract
8	視神経交叉：視交叉 Optic chiasm：Optic chiasma
9	視神経［Ⅱ］ Optic nerve［Ⅱ］
10	視索 Optic tract
11	下垂体茎* Pituitary stalk*
12	後有孔質 Posterior perforated substance
13	視床枕 Pulvinar
14	脳梁膨大 Splenium of corpus callosum
15	黒質（中脳） Substantia nigra
16	中脳蓋 Tectum of midbrain
17	中脳被蓋 Tegmentum of midbrain
18	灰白隆起 Tuber cinereum

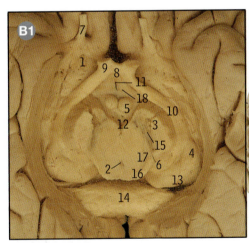

下方から．

脳幹の大部分を除去し，中脳のみを残してある．大脳半球の最内側部も除去している．視床の後部（視床枕，13）の下面にある膝状体（B1 の 4，6）を見出すため，視神経交叉（B1 の 8，B2 の 4）を同定してから，視索（B1 の 10，B2 の 7）を中脳の側面（3 の番号が付けられているところ）に沿って後方へたどるとよい．

1	外側膝状体 Lateral geniculate body	4	視神経交叉：視交叉 Optic chiasm：Optic chiasma
2	Meyer［の］ループ* （視放線下部の前方に張り出して側頭葉を走る線維） Meyer's loop*	5	視神経［Ⅱ］ Optic nerve［Ⅱ］
3	後頭葉と一次視覚野* Occipital lobe and Primary visual area*	6	視放線 Optic radiation
		7	視索 Optic tract

嗅覚障害

鼻出血

眼底検査

扁桃炎

第三脳神経［Ⅲ］：動眼神経，第四脳神経［Ⅳ］：滑車神経，第六脳神経［Ⅵ］：外転神経

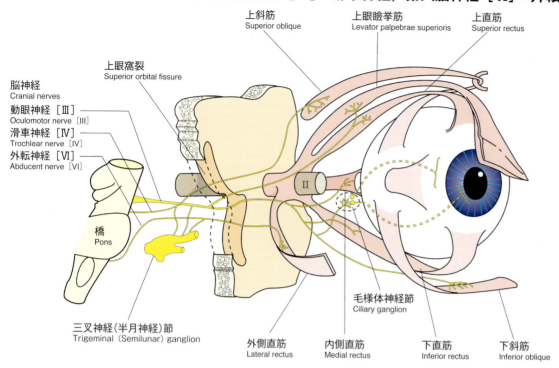

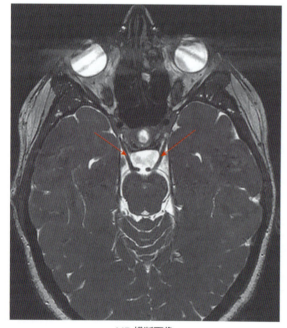

MR 横断画像
動眼神経［Ⅲ］が中脳から出ている（赤矢印）．

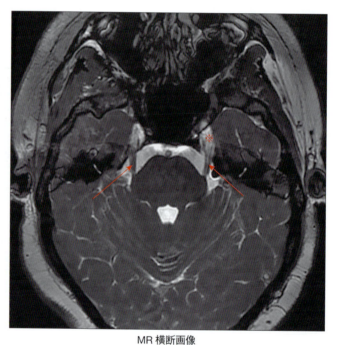

MR 横断画像
三叉神経［Ⅴ］が橋から出ており（赤矢印），Meckel 腔（※）で三叉神経節を形成する．（81 頁参照．）

外転神経麻痺

輻輳反射

動眼神経麻痺

滑車神経麻痺

A 第五脳神経［V］：三叉神経（全体図）

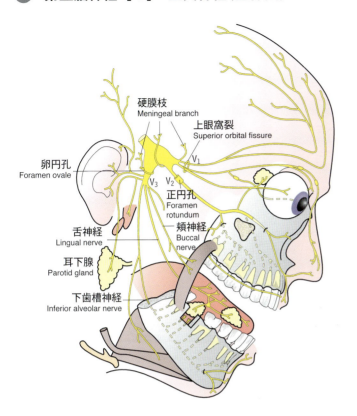

B 三叉神経第一枝［V₁］：眼神経

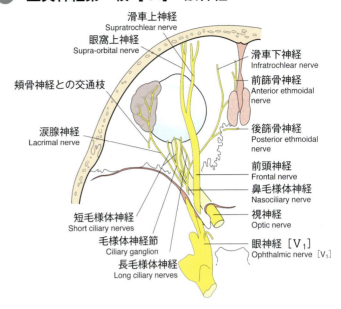

C 三叉神経第二枝［V₂］：上顎神経

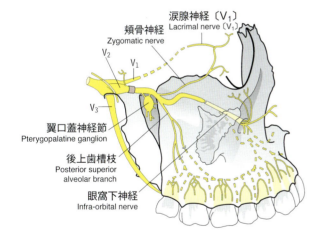

D 三叉神経第三枝［V₃］：下顎神経

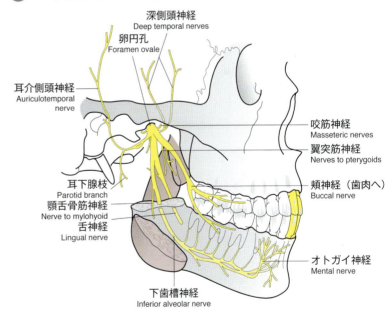

三叉神経［V］については56，82頁参照．
眼神経［V₁］については52〜54，59頁参照．
上顎神経［V₂］については44，55頁参照．
下顎神経［V₃］については29，35，40，42頁参照．

三叉神経［隣接する副交感神経の神経節］

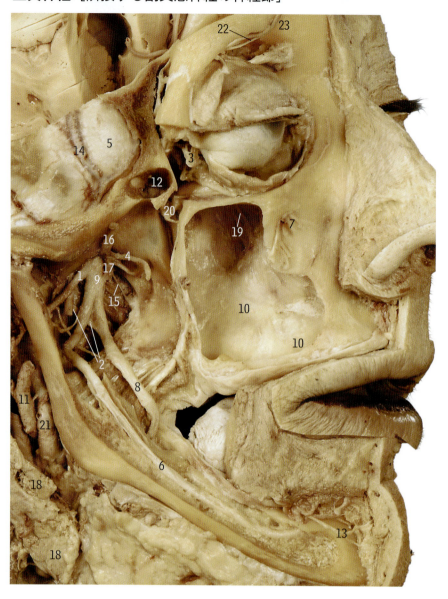

1	耳介側頭神経 Auriculotemporal nerve	13	オトガイ神経 Mental nerve
2	鼓索神経 Chorda tympani	14	中硬膜動脈 Middle meningeal artery
3	毛様体神経節 Ciliary ganglion	15	外側翼突筋神経 Nerve to lateral pterygoid
4	深側頭神経 Deep temporal nerves	16	咬筋神経 Masseteric nerve
5	硬膜 Dura mater	17	耳神経節 Otic ganglion
6	下歯槽神経（下顎管の中にある） Inferior alveolar nerve	18	耳下腺 Parotid gland
7	眼窩下神経 Infra-orbital nerve	19	後上歯槽神経 Posterior superior alveolar nerves
8	舌神経 Lingual nerve	20	翼口蓋神経節 Pterygopalatine ganglion
9	下顎神経［V_3］ Mandibular nerve [V_3]	21	下顎後静脈 Retromandibular vein
10	上顎洞（開けてある） Maxillary air sinus	22	眼窩上神経 Supra-orbital nerve
11	顎動脈 Maxillary artery	23	滑車上神経 Supratrochlear nerve
12	上顎神経［V_2］ Maxillary nerve [V_2]		

三叉神経［隣接する副交感神経の神経節］

A 第七脳神経［VII］：顔面神経

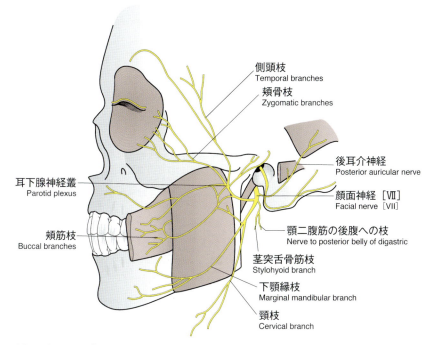

39, 40, 44 頁参照.

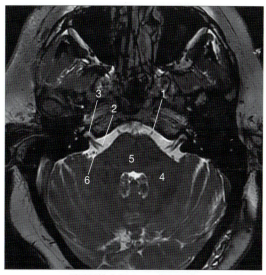

橋延髄接合部の MR 横断画像

1	外転神経［VI］ Abducent nerve [VI]	
2	顔面神経［VII］ Facial nerve [VII]	
3	内耳道 Internal acoustic meatus	
4	中小脳脚 Middle cerebellar peduncle	
5	橋 Pons	
6	内耳神経：前庭蝸牛神経［VIII］ Vestibulocochlear nerve [VIII]	

B 第八脳神経［VIII］：内耳神経

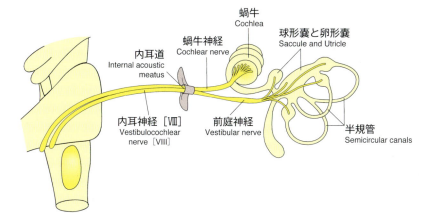

66, 70, 71, 78 頁参照.

聴神経腫

顔面神経麻痺
（Bell 麻痺）

聴覚過敏

耳痛（関連痛）

A 第九脳神経［IX］：舌咽神経

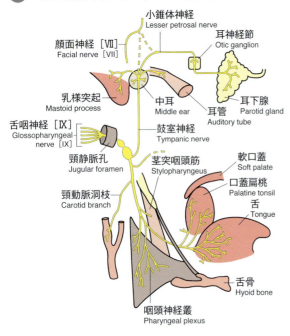

B 第十脳神経［X］：迷走神経

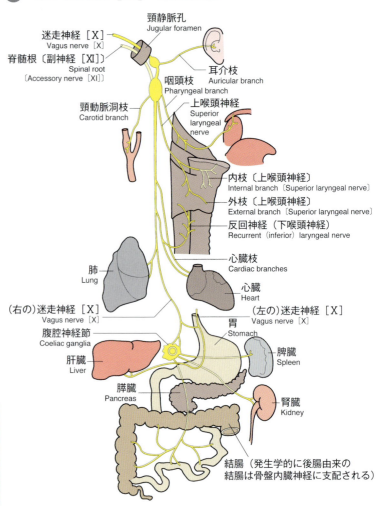

29, 35, 44〜46, 78 頁参照.

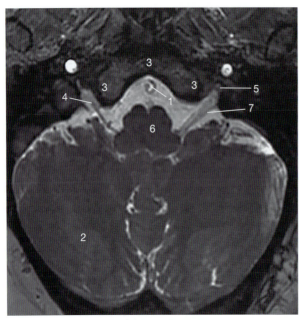

上部延髄の MR 横断画像

1	脳底動脈	Basilar artery
2	小脳半球	Hemisphere of cerebellum
3	斜台	Clivus
4	舌咽神経［IX］	Glossopharyngeal nerve [IX]
5	頸静脈孔	Jugular foramen
6	延髄	Medulla
7	迷走神経［X］	Vagus nerve [X]

耳下腺腫瘍

反回神経麻痺

A 第十一脳神経［XI］：副神経

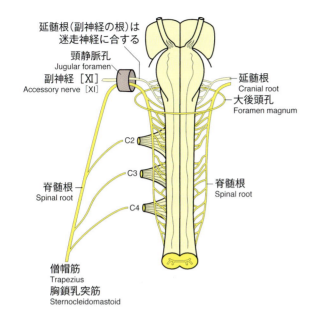

37, 61頁参照.

B 第十二脳神経［XII］：舌下神経

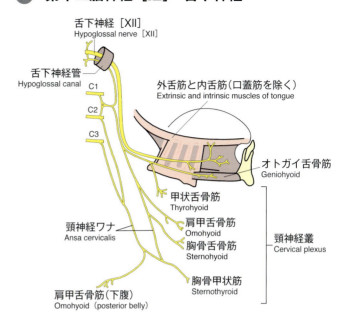

45, 47, 56頁参照.

C

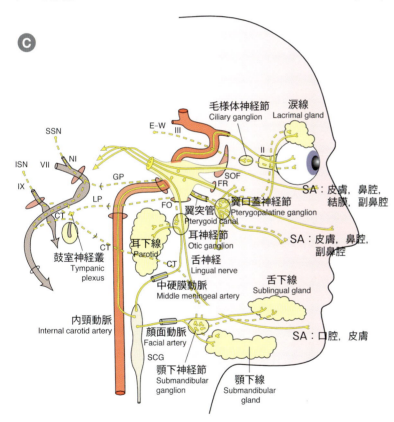

C 頭部の自律神経系

CT	鼓索神経 Chorda tympani	
E-W	Edinger-Westphal 核＊：動眼神経副核 Edinger-Westphal nucleus＊：Accessory nuclei of oculomotor nerve	
FO	卵円孔 Foramen ovale	
FR	正円孔 Foramen rotundum	
GP	大錐体神経 Greater petrosal nerve	
ISN	下唾液核 Inferior salivatory nucleus	
LP	小錐体神経 Lesser petrosal nerve	
NI	中間神経 Intermediate nerve	
SA	体性求心性線維 Somatic afferent fiber	
SCG	上頸神経節 Superior cervical ganglion	
SOF	上眼窩裂 Superior orbital fissure	
SSN	上唾液核 Superior salivatory nucleus	

副神経麻痺

咽頭反射

舌下神経麻痺

脊柱と脊髄

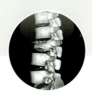

背部と脊柱　[Ⓐ 体表解剖，Ⓑ 軸骨格，Ⓒ 脊柱]

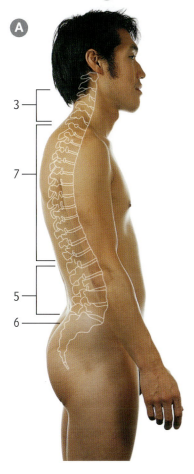
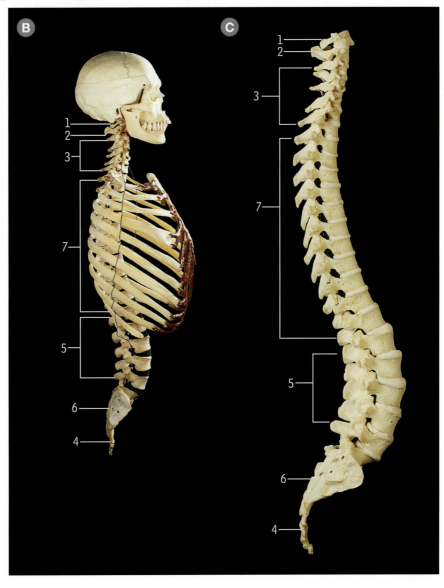

1. 環椎：第一頸椎
   Atlas：1st cervical vertebra（C I）
2. 軸椎：第二頸椎
   Axis：2nd cervical vertebra（C II）
3. 頸椎，前弯
   Cervical vertebrae, Lordosis
4. 尾骨：第一〜第四尾椎
   Coccyx：Coccygeal vertebrae（Co I–IV）
5. 腰椎，前弯
   Lumbar vertebrae, Lordosis
6. 仙骨
   Sacrum
7. 胸椎，後弯
   Thoracic vertebrae, Kyphosis

背部と肩 [Ⓐ 体表解剖, Ⓑ 筋]

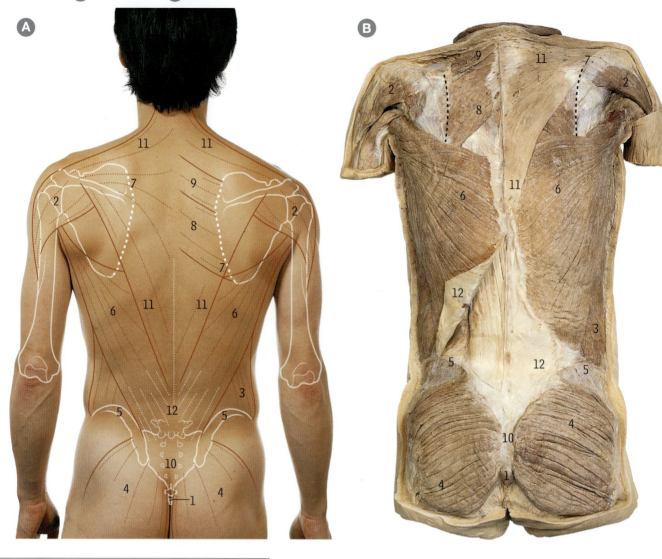

1	尾骨 Coccyx	7	内側縁〔肩甲骨〕(破線) Medial border (Scapula)
2	三角筋 Deltoid	8	大菱形筋 Rhomboid major
3	外腹斜筋 External oblique	9	小菱形筋 Rhomboid minor
4	大殿筋 Gluteus maximus	10	仙骨 Sacrum
5	腸骨稜 Iliac crest	11	僧帽筋 Trapezius
6	広背筋 Latissimus dorsi	12	胸腰筋膜 Thoracolumbar fascia

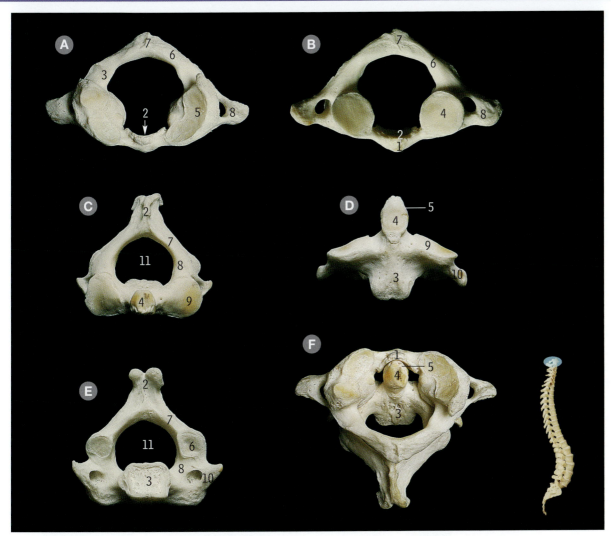

A：上方から．B：下方から．C：上面．D：前面．E：下面．F：上方から．環椎（第一頸椎）と組み合わせてある．

Ⓐ Ⓑ 環椎：第一頸椎

1	前弓と前結節 Anterior arch and Anterior tubercle	5	上関節面〔外側塊〕 Superior articular surface〔Lateral mass〕
2	歯突起窩 Facet for dens	6	後弓 Posterior arch
3	椎骨動脈溝 Groove for vertebral artery	7	後結節 Posterior tubercle
4	下関節面〔外側塊〕 Inferior articular surface〔Lateral mass〕	8	横突起と横突孔 Transverse process and Foramen transversarium

Ⓒ～Ⓕ 軸椎：第二頸椎

1	前弓〔環椎：第一頸椎〕 Anterior arch〔Atlas：CⅠ〕	7	椎弓板 Lamina
2	棘突起（二又になっている） Spinous process	8	椎弓根 Pedicle
3	椎体 Vertebral body	9	上関節面 Superior articular facet
4	歯突起 Dens：Odontoid peg *	10	横突起と横突孔 Transverse process and Foramen transversarium
5	翼状靱帯による圧痕	11	椎孔 Vertebral foramen
6	下関節面 Inferior articular facet		

- 上関節面(5)は，腎臓形でくぼんでいる．
- 下関節面(4)は，円形でほとんど平らである．
- 前弓(1)は，後弓(6)に比べてまっすぐで短い．前弓の後面には，軸椎（第二頸椎）の歯突起と対面する関節面（歯突起窩，2）がある．
- 環椎は，椎体を欠く唯一の椎骨である．

- 軸椎（第二頸椎）は，椎体から上方に突出した歯突起(4)をもつ，独特な椎骨である．歯突起は環椎（第一頸椎）の椎体に相当する．

歯突起骨折

A〜C 第五頸椎（典型的な頸椎）

1. 前結節〔横突起〕 Anterior tubercle (Transverse process)
2. 棘突起（二又になっている） Spinous process
3. 椎体 Vertebral body
4. 横突孔 Foramen transversarium
5. 下関節突起 Inferior articular process
6. 結節間板*〔横突起〕 Intertubercular lamella* 〔Transverse process〕
7. 椎弓板 Lamina
8. 椎弓根 Pedicle
9. 後結節〔横突起〕 Posterior tubercle (Transverse process)
10. 体鈎：鈎状突起 Uncus of body : Uncinate process
11. 上関節突起 Superior articular process
12. 椎孔 Vertebral foramen

D 隆椎：第七頸椎

1. 前結節〔横突起〕 Anterior tubercle (Transverse process)
2. 椎体 Vertebral body
3. 横突孔 Foramen transversarium
4. 結節間板*〔横突起〕 Intertubercular lamella* 〔Transverse process〕
5. 椎弓板 Lamina
6. 椎弓根 Pedicle
7. 後結節〔横突起〕 Posterior tubercle (Transverse process)
8. 体鈎：鈎状突起 Uncus of body : Uncinate process
9. 棘突起（とその側面の結節） Spinous process
10. 上関節突起 Superior articular process
11. 椎孔 Vertebral foramen

- すべての頸椎（第一〜第七頸椎）には，横突起に横突孔（A4）が空いている．
- 典型的な頸椎（第三〜第六頸椎）の特徴は，①上関節突起（A11，C11）の関節面が後上方を向いていること，②椎体上面に鈎状突起（A10）があること，③椎孔（A12）が三角形であること，④棘突起（A2）が二又になっていることである．
- 第六頸椎の横突起の前結節は大きく，頸動脈結節とよばれている．
- 隆椎（第七頸椎）の棘突起（D9）の先端は，二又にならず，一つの結節に終わる．
- 横突孔の前脚，前結節（D1），結節間板（D4，脊髄神経前枝の通る溝を含む）および後結節（D7）の前部は，本来，肋骨要素である．

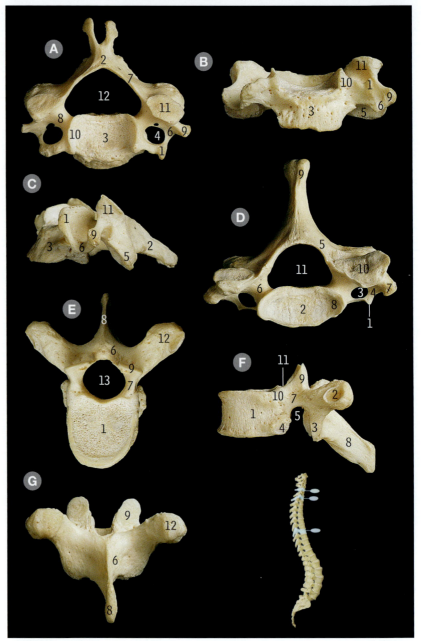

A・D・E：上方から．B：前方から．C・F：左側方から．G：後方から．

E〜G 第七胸椎（典型的な胸椎）

1. 椎体 Vertebral body
2. 横突肋骨窩 Transverse costal facet
3. 下関節突起 Inferior articular process
4. 下肋骨窩 Inferior costal facet
5. 下椎切痕 Inferior vertebral notch
6. 椎弓板 Lamina
7. 椎弓根 Pedicle
8. 棘突起 Spinous process
9. 上関節突起 Superior articular process
10. 上肋骨窩 Superior costal facet
11. 上椎切痕 Superior vertebral notch
12. 横突起 Transverse process
13. 椎孔 Vertebral foramen

- 典型的な胸椎（第二〜第九胸椎）の特徴は，①椎体と横突起に肋骨窩（F10, F4）があること，②椎孔（E13）が丸いこと，③棘突起（F8, G8）が後方のみならず下方にも向かって突き出していること，④上関節突起（E9, F9, G9）が垂直かつ平らであり，かつ関節面が後外側に向いていることである．

強直性脊椎炎

A B 第一胸椎

1. 椎体 Vertebral body
2. 下関節突起 Inferior articular process
3. 下肋骨窩 Inferior costal facet
4. 椎弓板 Lamina
5. 椎弓根 Pedicle
6. 体鉤：鉤状突起 Uncus of body：Uncinate process
7. 棘突起 Spinous process
8. 上関節突起 Superior articular process
9. 上肋骨窩 Superior costal facet
10. 横突肋骨窩〔横突起〕 Transverse costal facet〔Transverse process〕
11. 椎孔 Vertebral foramen

C 第十胸椎
D 第十一胸椎

1. 椎体 Vertebral body
2. 上肋骨窩 Superior costal facet
3. 下関節突起 Inferior articular process
4. 下椎切痕 Inferior vertebral notch
5. 椎弓根 Pedicle
6. 棘突起 Spinous process
7. 上関節突起 Superior articular process
8. 横突起 Transverse process

E〜G 第十二胸椎

1. 椎体 Vertebral body
2. 上肋骨窩 Superior costal facet
3. 下関節突起 Inferior articular process
4. 下結節*（副突起） Inferior tubercle*
5. 外側結節*（横突起） Lateral tubercle*
6. 椎弓根 Pedicle
7. 棘突起 Spinous process
8. 上関節突起 Superior articular process
9. 上結節*（乳頭突起） Superior tubercle*

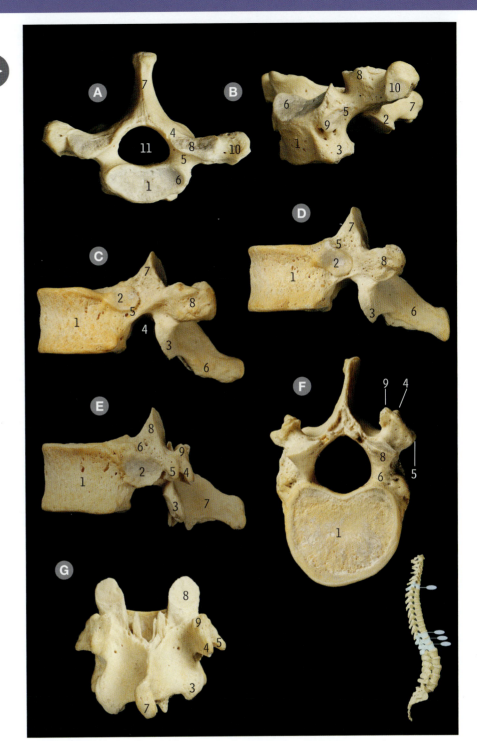

A・F：上方から．B：前左方から．C・D・E：左側方から．G：後方から．

- 第一・第十・第十一・第十二胸椎は，典型的な胸椎ではない．
- 第一胸椎は，椎孔が三角形であり，椎体上面の両側に鉤状突起（A6，B6）がある（これらは，典型的な頸椎に見られる特徴である）．椎体の側面にある上肋骨窩（B9）は，完全な円形である．
- 第十・第十一・第十二胸椎の特徴は，①椎体の側面に単一の完全な肋骨窩があること，②下位の肋骨の肋骨窩（C2，D2，E2）ほど椎体上面から離れて椎弓根のほうへ近づいていくことである．また，これらの胸椎には，横突肋骨窩がない．

脊椎分離症・脊椎分離すべり症

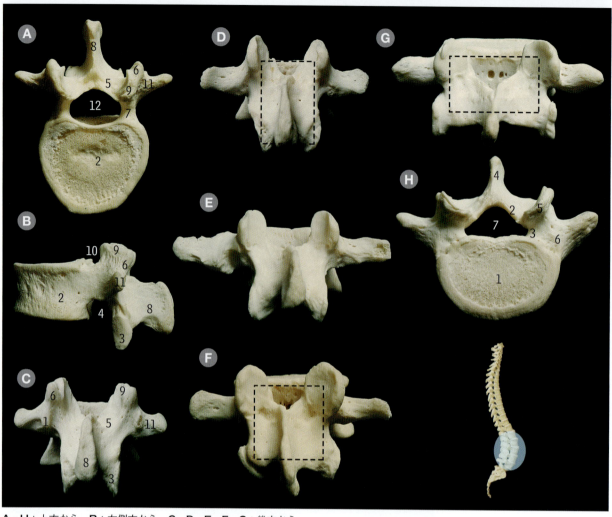

A・H：上方から．B：左側方から．C・D・E・F・G：後方から．

A〜C 第一腰椎

1 副突起 Accessory process	7 椎弓根 Pedicle
2 椎体 Vertebral body	8 棘突起 Spinous process
3 下関節突起 Inferior articular process	9 上関節突起 Superior articular process
4 下椎切痕 Inferior vertebral notch	10 上椎切痕 Superior vertebral notch
5 椎弓板 Lamina	11 肋骨突起 Costal process
6 乳頭突起 Mamillary process	12 椎孔 Vertebral foramen

- D 第二腰椎
- E 第三腰椎
- F 第四腰椎
- G・H 第五腰椎

1 椎体 Vertebral body
2 椎弓板 Lamina
3 椎弓根 Pedicle
4 棘突起 Spinous process
5 上関節突起 Superior articular process
6 肋骨突起（椎弓根および椎体と癒合している） Costal process
7 椎孔 Vertebral foramen

- 腰椎の特徴は，①椎体が大きいこと，②椎体と肋骨突起に肋骨窩がないこと，③椎孔(A12)が三角形であること，④棘突起(B8)がまっすぐ後方を向いていること，⑤側面は四角形もしくは斧のような形をしていること，⑥上関節突起(A9)が垂直で，関節面が弯曲して後内側を向いていること，⑦上関節突起の後縁に乳頭突起(A6)があることである．
- 腰椎の肋骨要素は，肋骨突起(A11)である．
- 胸椎と腰椎の関節突起の関節面が向く方向には違いがあるが，この向きが変化する高さには個体差がある．

- 後方から見て，4つの関節突起を結んだ四角形（D，F，Gは破線で示している）は，第一・第二腰椎では縦長の長方形，第三・第四腰椎では正方形，第五腰椎では横長の長方形である．
- 第五腰椎は，肋骨突起(H6)が椎弓根(H3)にのみならず椎体(H1)の側面にも直接癒合している点が特徴である．

椎弓切除術

腰部脊柱管狭窄症

椎体骨折

腰椎椎体骨折

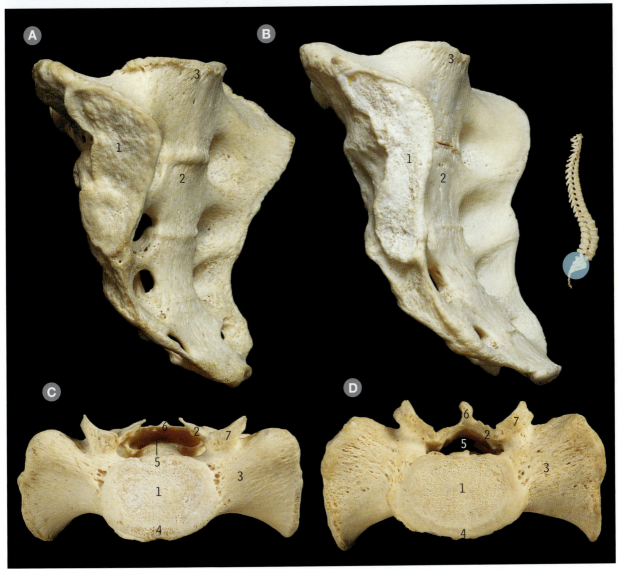

A：右前方から．女性．B：右前方から．男性．C：上面．女性．D：上面．男性．

A B 仙骨

1. 耳状面 Auricular surface
2. 前面 Pelvic surface
3. 岬角 Promontory

C D 仙骨底

1. 椎体〔第一仙椎〕 Vertebral body〔S I〕
2. 椎弓板 Lamina
3. 外側部（仙骨翼） Lateral part (Ala of sacrum : Wing of sacrum)
4. 岬角 Promontory
5. 仙骨管 Sacral canal
6. 棘結節＊（正中仙骨稜） Spinous tubercle＊(Median sacral crest)
7. 上関節突起 Superior articular process

- 女性では，第一〜第三仙椎では仙骨前面が比較的まっすぐであるが，第四・第五仙椎では弯曲が強くなる．男性では，仙骨前面は，女性に比べて一様に弯曲している．
- 仙腸関節の関節包は，耳状面（関節面，A1，B1）の辺縁に付着している．

- 仙骨底に占める第一仙椎の椎体の割合は，（横径から判断すると）女性に比べて男性が大きい（D1 を C1 と比較せよ）．
- C では，第一仙椎の左右の椎弓板（C2）が癒合していない，軽度の二分脊椎が見られる．完全な椎弓が形成されている D と比較するとよい．

腰椎の仙骨化

仙骨と尾骨

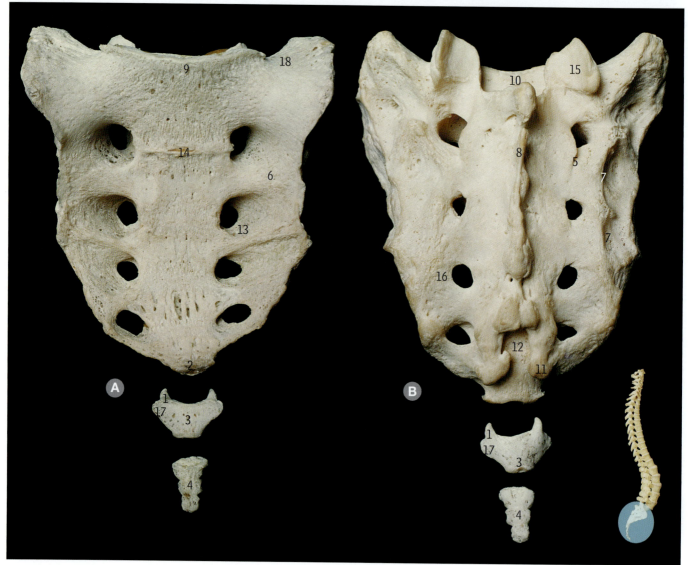

A：前面．B：後面．

1	尾骨角	Coccygeal cornu
2	仙骨尖（尾骨との関節面をもつ）	Apex of sacrum
3	第一尾椎	1st coccygeal vertebra (Co I)
4	癒合した第二〜第四尾椎	
5	中間仙骨稜	Intermediate sacral crest
6	外側部	Lateral part
7	外側仙骨稜	Lateral sacral crest
8	正中仙骨稜	Median sacral crest
9	岬角	Promontory
10	仙骨管	Sacral canal
11	仙骨角	Sacral cornu：Sacral horn
12	仙骨裂孔	Sacral hiatus
13	第二前仙骨孔	2nd anterior sacral foramen
14	横線（第一・第二仙椎の癒合位置）	Transverse ridge
15	上関節突起	Superior articular process
16	第三後仙骨孔	3rd posterior sacral foramen
17	横突起	Transverse process
18	外側部（仙骨翼）	Lateral part (Ala of sacrum：Wing of sacrum)

- 仙骨は，5つの仙椎が癒合して形成される．正中仙骨稜（B8）は癒合した棘突起を，中間仙骨稜（B5）は癒合した関節突起を，外側仙骨稜（B7）は癒合した横突起をそれぞれ示す．
- 仙骨裂孔（B12）は，仙骨管（B10）の下口である．
- 尾骨は，通常4つの痕跡的椎骨が癒合して形成されるが，その数は3〜5個の範囲で変動する．この標本では，第一尾椎（3）は，第二以下の尾椎（4）と癒合していない．

尾骨痛

仙骨（腰仙移行椎）

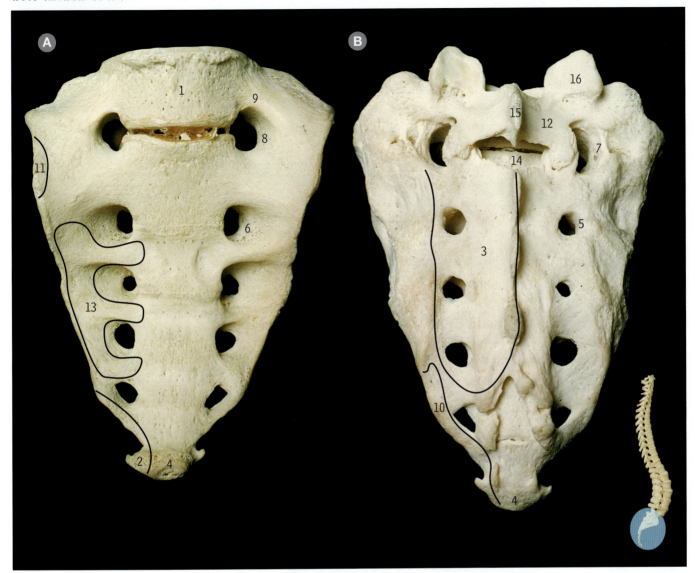

第五腰椎が仙骨化している．A：前面．筋と靱帯の付着部を示す．B：後面．筋と靱帯の付着部を示す．

1	椎体〔第五腰椎〕 Vertebral body〔L V〕	9	肋骨突起と仙骨の外側部の癒合
2	〔坐骨〕尾骨筋 [Ischio] coccygeus	10	大殿筋 Gluteus maximus
3	脊柱起立筋 Erector spinae	11	腸骨筋 Iliacus
4	第一尾椎（仙骨尖と癒合している） 1st coccygeal vertebra (Co I)	12	椎弓板 Lamina
5	第一後仙骨孔 1st posterior sacral foramen	13	梨状筋 Piriformis
6	第一前仙骨孔 1st anterior sacral foramen	14	仙骨管 Sacral canal
7	第五腰神経後枝が通過する孔	15	棘突起〔第五腰椎〕 Spinous process〔L V〕
8	第五腰神経前枝が通過する孔	16	上関節突起〔第五腰椎〕 Superior articular process〔L V〕

- 第五腰椎(A1)の仙骨化は，腰椎が仙骨と癒合することをいう（通常は不完全癒合である）．これよりまれではあるが，第一仙椎の腰椎化は（図に示されていない），第一仙椎と他の仙椎との癒合が不完全なことをいう．
- この標本では，第五腰椎と仙骨上部との癒合に加えて，第一尾椎の体(4)が仙骨尖と癒合している．

仙骨麻酔

骨性骨盤 [A 女性，B 男性]

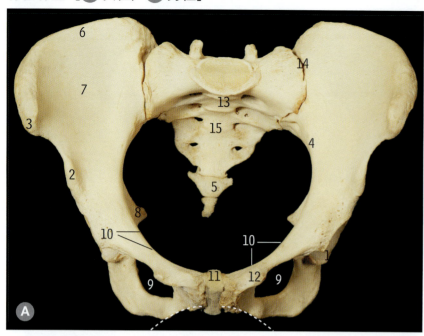

1	寛骨臼 Acetabulum
2	下前腸骨棘 Anterior inferior iliac spine
3	上前腸骨棘 Anterior superior iliac spine
4	弓状線 Arcuate line
5	尾骨 Coccyx
6	腸骨稜 Iliac crest
7	腸骨窩 Iliac fossa
8	坐骨棘 Ischial spine
9	閉鎖孔 Obturator foramen
10	恥骨櫛 Pecten pubis
11	恥骨結合 Pubic symphysis
12	恥骨結節 Pubic tubercle
13	岬角〔仙骨〕 Promontory〔Sacrum〕
14	仙腸関節 Sacro-iliac joint
15	仙骨 Sacrum

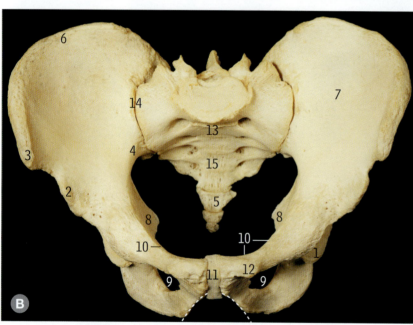

- 骨盤上口（骨盤縁*）は，岬角（13），弓状線（4），恥骨櫛（10），恥骨稜，前方では恥骨結合（11）によってつくられる．
- 骨盤上口の形は，女性ではより円形に近く，男性ではよりハート形に近い．
- 女性の仙骨（15）は，男性に比べて幅が広く，短く，弯曲が少ない．
- 女性の坐骨棘（8）は，男性に比べて左右が離れている．
- 女性の恥骨下角（Aの白い破線）は90〜120°と広い．一方，男性の恥骨下角（Bの白い破線）はわずか60〜90°しかない．

A・B：前上方から．

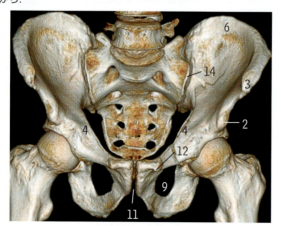

三次元CT立体画像
前方から．

A〜H 椎骨，肋骨および胸骨の骨化

- 典型的な椎骨は，はじめ軟骨性であるが，胎時期の早い段階で3つの一次骨化中心から骨化しはじめる．骨化中心の1つは椎体の大半をつくり（椎心，A2），他の2つは椎弓の右半と左半をつくる（A1）．成人の椎体のうち椎弓根が付く部分（B4）は，椎弓の骨化中心の一部に属している．発生途上の椎骨において椎弓と椎心が出会うところが椎弓椎心接合部（B5）である．左右の椎弓の癒合ならびに椎弓と椎心の癒合が起こる時期には個体差があり，出生から6歳までの間である．骨化は，椎弓から延び出した横突起と棘突起に広がる．思春期には，先端に二次骨化中心（B3）が現れ，ほぼ25歳までに癒合する（腰椎では二次骨化中心が乳頭突起に付加的に現れる）．また椎体の上面と下面の周縁に輪状の骨端が現れる（C6, D6）．
- 環椎（第一頸椎）では，一次骨化中心が，左右の外側塊とそれに隣接した後弓に（E7），そして前弓に1個（E8）現れる．癒合は約8歳までに完了する．
- 軸椎（第二頸椎）に，一次骨化中心が5個ある．椎体の大部分をつくるもの（F10），左右の外側塊とそれに隣接した後弓をつくるもの（F9），ならびに左右の歯突起とそれに隣接した椎体の一部をつくるもの（F8）である．以上はすべて，ほぼ3歳までに癒合する．二次骨化中心は，歯突起の先端（F12，約2歳までに現れ，12歳で癒合する）と，椎体の下面（F11．思春期に現れ約25歳で癒合する）に出現する．

- 仙骨は，5個の仙椎が癒合して形成される．仙骨には骨化中心が多数ある．それらは各椎の椎心，椎弓，肋骨要素ならびに椎体と関節面の輪状骨端に相当する．大半は20歳頃までに癒合するが，中年以降も癒合しないことがある．
- 典型的な肋骨では，一次骨化中心は肋骨体にある．二次骨化中心は，肋骨頭（G13）ならびに肋骨結節の関節部（G14）と非関節部（G15）にできる．これらは思春期に現れ，20歳頃に癒合する．
- 胸骨の一次骨化中心（H16）の数は不定であるが，胸骨柄に1ないし2個，胸骨体に左右4個ずつが普通である．癒合は，思春期から25歳の間に行われる．癒合が不完全であると，胸に弾丸が貫通したような孔（胸骨孔）が残ることがある．

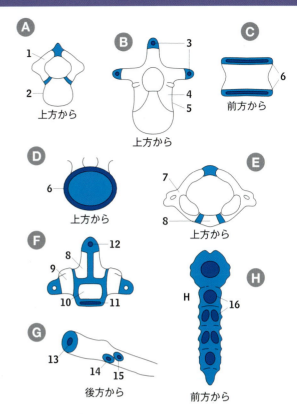

A：6ヵ月の胎児の典型的な椎骨．B：4歳児の典型的な椎骨．C・D：思春期の典型的な椎骨．E：4歳児の環椎（第一頸椎）．F：軸椎（第二頸椎）の一次および二次骨化中心．G：典型的な肋骨の二次骨化中心．H：出生時の胸骨の一次骨化中心．

I 椎骨の要素の発生由来

胸椎と関節をつくる肋骨要素は，頸椎，腰椎および仙椎の一部として取り込まれている．これらの肋骨要素は，ここでは赤で示されている．
- 頸椎：前結節，後結節および前後両結節間の連絡部．
- 胸椎：胸椎と関節をつくる真肋．
- 腰椎：横突起の前部．
- 仙骨：外側部（耳状面を含む）．

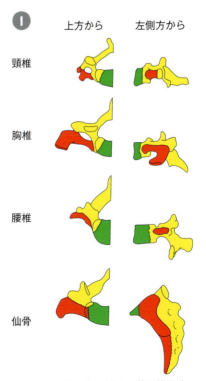

（赤：肋骨要素．緑：椎心．黄：椎弓．）

A〜E 脊柱と脊髄 ［A B D 頸部，C 頸部と上位胸部，E 下位頸部と上位胸部］

A：前方から．B：後方から．

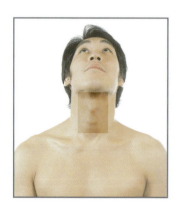

椎骨動脈（14）が頸椎の横突孔を通っているのが見える．

1	前縦靱帯	Anterior longitudinal ligament
2	前結節〔横突起〕	Anterior tubercle〔Transverse process〕
3	軸椎：第二頸椎	Axis：2nd cervical vertebra（C II）
4	椎体〔第五頸椎〕	Vertebral body（C V）
5	胸膜〔切断縁〕	Pleura
6	結節間板*〔横突起〕	Intertubercular lamella *〔Transverse process〕
7	椎間円板	Intervertebral disc
8	肋骨頭関節〔第一肋骨〕	Joint of head of rib〔Rib I〕
9	外側塊〔環椎：第一頸椎〕	Lateral mass（Atlas：C I）
10	後結節〔横突起〕	Posterior tubercle〔Transverse process〕
11	前斜角筋	Anterior scalene
12	横突起*〔環椎：第一頸椎〕	Transverse process *〔Atlas：C I〕
13	前枝〔第四頸神経〕	Ventral ramus〔C4〕
14	椎骨動脈	Vertebral artery

頭蓋の大部分，椎弓，脳幹および脊髄の上部を除去し，環椎十字靱帯（10, 19），環椎横靱帯（21），翼状靱帯（1）を剖出してある．下方では，クモ膜と硬膜（2）を翻転し，後根と前根の根糸（6, 22）を示してある．

1	翼状靱帯 Alar ligament		12	椎弓根〔軸椎：第二頸椎〕 Pedicle（Axis：C II）
2	クモ膜と硬膜（翻転してある） Arachnoid mater and Dura mater		13	後弓〔環椎：第一頸椎〕 Posterior arch（Atlas：C I）
3	環椎後頭関節 Atlanto-occipital joint		14	後縦靱帯 Posterior longitudinal ligament
4	底部〔後頭骨〕と蓋膜（の付着部） Basilar part（Occipital bone）and Tectorial membrane		15	後脊髄動脈 Posterior spinal artery
			16	根動脈 Radicular artery
5	歯状靱帯 Denticulate ligament		17	脊髄 Spinal cord
6	根糸〔脊髄神経の後根〕 Rootlets（Dorsal root of Spinal nerve）		18	上関節面〔軸椎：第二頸椎〕 Superior articular facet（Axis：C II）
7	硬膜 Dura mater		19	縦束〔環椎十字靱帯〕（上部） Longitudinal bands〔Cruciate ligament of atlas〕
8	硬膜鞘*〔脊髄神経節〕 Dural sheath *〔Spinal ganglion〕		20	蓋膜 Tectorial membrane
9	舌下神経［XII］と舌下神経管 Hypoglossal nerve [XII] and Hypoglossal canal		21	環椎横靱帯〔環椎十字靱帯〕 Transverse ligament of atlas（Cruciate ligament of atlas）
10	縦束〔環椎十字靱帯〕（下部） Longitudinal bands〔Cruciate ligament of atlas〕		22	根糸〔脊髄神経の前根〕 Rootlets（Ventral root of Spinal nerve）
11	外側環軸関節 Lateral atlanto-axial joint		23	椎骨動脈 Vertebral artery

脊髄神経の前枝(16)と後枝(4)が，椎間孔(7)から現れるところがわかる．

1	前結節〔第五頸椎の横突起〕 Anterior tubercle〔Transverse process of C V〕	10	後弓〔環椎：第一頸椎〕 Posterior arch〔Atlas：C I〕
2	椎体〔第一胸椎〕 Vertebral body〔T I〕	11	第八頸神経 8th cervical nerve (C8)
3	椎体〔隆椎：第七頸椎〕 Vertebral body〔Vertebra prominens：C VII〕	12	棘突起〔軸椎：第二頸椎〕 Spinous process〔Axis：C II〕
4	後枝〔第一頸神経〕 Dorsal ramus〔C1〕	13	棘突起〔隆椎：第七頸椎〕 Spinous process〔Vertebra prominens：C VII〕
5	第一頸神経 1st cervical nerve (C1)	14	横突起*〔環椎：第一頸椎〕 Transverse process *〔Atlas：C I〕
6	第一肋骨 1st rib：Rib I	15	第一肋骨結節 Tubercle of 1st rib
7	椎間孔 Intervertebral foramen	16	前枝〔第六頸神経〕 Ventral ramus〔C6〕
8	外側環軸関節 Lateral atlanto-axial joint	17	椎骨動脈 Vertebral artery
9	外側塊〔環椎：第一頸椎〕 Lateral mass〔Atlas：C I〕	18	椎間関節 Zygapophysial joint

● 第一頸神経と第二頸神経は，それぞれ環椎（第一頸椎）の後弓の上方と下方を通る．

右側方から．

軟組織を除去し，椎間孔(5)の輪郭を示している．胸椎の透明標本（102頁A）と比較するとよい．

1	前結節〔第五頸椎の横突起〕 Anterior tubercle〔Transverse process of C V〕	3	結節間板*〔第五頸椎の横突起〕 Intertubercular lamella *〔Transverse process of C V〕	6	椎弓根 Pedicle
2	椎体〔第三頸椎〕 Vertebral body〔C III〕	4	椎間円板 Intervertebral disc	7	後結節〔第五頸椎の横突起〕 Posterior tubercle〔Transverse process of C V〕
		5	椎間孔 Intervertebral foramen	8	椎間関節 Zygapophysial joint

● 椎間孔(5)の輪郭は，前方は椎体(2)および椎間円板(4)，上方および下方は椎弓根(6)，後方は椎間関節(8)によってつくられている．
● 胸部および腰部では，椎骨の数（12個の胸椎と5個の腰椎）と同数の脊髄神経が対を成して存在し，神経の番号は，その神経の上の椎弓根が属する椎骨の番号が付けられている．頸部では，7つの頸椎と8つの頸神経がある．第一頸神経は後頭骨と環椎（第一頸椎）の間から現れ，第八頸神経は隆椎（第七頸椎）の椎弓根の下から現れる．

左側方から．

椎弓ならびに硬膜とクモ膜の大部分を除去し，脊髄(9)の後外側部から現れた根糸(5)が合して後根をつくり，硬膜鞘(7)に進入する様子を示している．前根も，脊髄の前面から同様に現れるが，後根に隠れていて，この標本では見えない．

1	脊髄神経根が硬膜鞘*に入るところに生じた屈曲	6	硬膜 Dura mater
2	後枝〔第五胸神経〕 Dorsal ramus〔T5〕	7	硬膜鞘*〔第二胸神経〕 Dural sheath *〔T2〕
3	脊髄神経節〔第八頸神経〕 Spinal ganglion〔C8〕	8	椎弓根〔第一胸椎〕 Pedicle〔T I〕
4	脊髄神経節〔第二胸神経〕 Spinal ganglion〔T2〕	9	脊髄と後脊髄動／静脈 Spinal cord and Posterior spinal artery/veins
5	根糸〔第八頸神経の後根〕 Rootlets〔Dorsal root of C8〕	10	前枝〔第五胸神経〕 Ventral ramus〔T5〕

後方から．

左側方から.

A 脊柱と脊髄 [頸部と上位胸部]

椎弓と髄膜の一部を除去して歯状靱帯(3)を示した．後根を形成する根糸(7)は歯状靱帯の後ろに，前根の根糸(19)は靱帯の前に位置する(この標本では，前根の根糸の大部分は後根の陰に隠れて見えない)．

1	クモ膜 Arachnoid mater	11	後頭骨 Occipital bone
2	椎体〔第一胸椎〕 Vertebral body〔T I〕	12	後弓〔環椎：第一頸椎〕 Posterior arch〔Atlas：C I〕
3	歯状靱帯 Denticulate ligament	13	脊髄 Spinal cord
4	後枝〔第五頸神経〕 Dorsal ramus〔C5〕	14	脊髄根〔副神経〔XI〕〕 Spinal root〔Accessory nerve〔XI〕〕
5	脊髄神経節〔第八頸神経〕 Spinal ganglion〔C8〕	15	棘突起〔軸椎：第二頸椎〕(異常に大きい) Spinous process〔Axis：C II〕
6	脊髄神経節〔第五頸神経〕 Spinal ganglion〔C5〕	16	棘突起〔隆椎：第七頸椎〕 Spinous process〔Vertebra prominens：C VII〕
7	根糸〔第五頸神経の後根〕 Rootlets〔Dorsal root of C5〕	17	交感神経幹 Sympathetic trunk
8	硬膜 Dura mater	18	前枝〔第五頸神経(C5)〕 Ventral ramus〔5th cervical nerve(C5)〕
9	大後頭孔 Foramen magnum	19	根糸〔第五頸神経の前根〕 Rootlets〔Ventral root of C5〕
10	延髄 Medulla oblongata		

- 脊髄神経は，前根と後根が合して形成される．
- 前根と後根は，それぞれ数本の根糸(7)から形成される．
- 前根と後根が合して脊髄神経をつくる位置は，脊髄神経節(6)のすぐ遠位，すなわち椎間孔の内部である．こうしてつくられた脊髄神経は，ただちに前枝(18)と後枝(4)に分岐する．脊髄神経固有の長さは1～2mmにすぎない．このように非常に短いため，脊髄神経節そのものから前枝と後枝が出ているように見えることがある．
- 最下位の頸神経と上位の胸神経の根は，硬膜鞘に進入するため急角度に屈曲している．

上方から.

B 脊髄 [頸部(前面)]

脊髄(6)の上部を腹側から見たこの標本では，クモ膜と硬膜(2)を縦に切開して観音開きとし，前根糸と前根(7)が歯状靱帯(3)の前を外側方へ走り，後根(4)とともに硬膜鞘に入って脊髄神経を形成している様が見られる．根動静脈(5)が前根に沿って走り，前脊髄動静脈(1)と吻合を形成している．

1	前脊髄動／静脈 Anterior spinal artery/veins	5	根動／静脈 Radicular artery/vein
2	クモ膜と硬膜 Arachnoid mater and Dura mater	6	脊髄 Spinal cord
3	歯状靱帯 Denticulate ligament	7	前根〔第五頸神経〕(硬膜鞘*に入るところ) Ventral root〔C5〕
4	後根〔第六頸神経〕 Dorsal root〔C6〕		

- 歯状靱帯(3)は，軟膜でつくられている．前根と後根は，歯状靱帯の前方と後方をそれぞれ通過する．この靱帯は脊髄の側面から外側へ延び，尖った歯状靱帯(3)としてクモ膜を貫き，硬膜下腔を通って硬膜に付着する．最も高い歯状靱帯は第一頸神経の上方にあり，最も低いものは第十二胸神経の下方に見られる．

横断性脊髄炎

C〜E 脊柱と脊髄 [C 腰部と仙骨部, D 腰神経の脊髄神経根, E 下位胸部と上位腰部]

椎弓と髄膜の一部を除去し，馬尾(1)と神経根(11)が髄膜鞘に進入する様子を示してある．髄膜鞘は，神経根撮影では造影剤により帯状に見える．

1	馬尾 Cauda equina	8	椎間円板(第四・第五腰椎間) Intervertebral disc
2	脊髄円錐 Conus medullaris：Medullary cone	9	外側部(仙骨) Lateral part (Sacrum)
3	脊髄神経節〔第五腰神経〕 Spinal ganglion (L5)	10	椎弓根〔第五胸椎〕 Pedicle (T V)
4	硬膜 Dura mater	11	根糸〔第五腰神経の後根〕 Rootlets (Dorsal root of L5)
5	硬膜鞘＊〔第一仙骨神経の根〕 Dural sheath * (Root of S1)	12	第二仙椎 2nd sacral vertebra (S II)
6	椎間円板(第五腰椎・第一仙椎間) Intervertebral disc	13	上関節突起〔第三腰椎〕 Superior articular process (L III)
7	終糸 Filum terminale：Terminal filum	14	髄膜嚢＊ Thecal sac *

- 脊髄は，通常第一腰椎の高さで終わる．
- クモ膜下腔は，第二仙椎の高さで終わる．
- 脊髄円錐(2)は，脊髄の下端にある尖っている部分である．
- 馬尾(1)を構成するものは，腰神経，仙骨神経，尾骨神経の前根と後根である．馬尾の形成に関与するのは前根と後根であって，脊髄神経ではないことに注意せよ．脊髄神経は，前根と後根が脊髄神経節(3)のすぐ遠位で，すなわち椎間孔の内部で合して形成される．

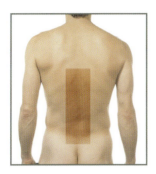

後方から．

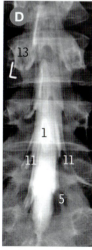

脊髄神経根造影画像

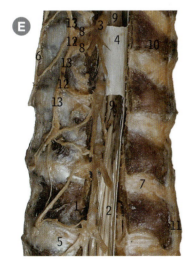

椎弓と髄膜の一部を除去し，左側方から見たところである．前方では，椎体の表面を走る交感神経幹(13)の一部，後方では棘間靱帯(7)，棘上靱帯(11)が見えている．

1	椎体〔第一腰椎〕 Vertebral body (L I)	8	交通枝 Rami communicantes
2	馬尾 Cauda equina	9	脊髄 Spinal cord
3	脊髄神経節〔第十胸神経〕 Spinal ganglion (T10)	10	棘突起〔第十胸椎〕 Spinous process (T X)
4	硬膜 Dura mater	11	棘上靱帯 Supraspinous ligament
5	椎間円板(第一・第二腰椎間) Intervertebral disc	12	幹神経節：交感神経幹神経節 Ganglion of sympathetic trunk
6	大内臓神経 Greater splanchnic nerve	13	交感神経幹 Sympathetic trunk
7	棘間靱帯 Interspinous ligament		

硬膜外麻酔

脊髄麻酔

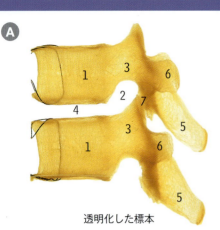

A 胸椎

2つの椎骨を組み合わせて側方から見て，椎間孔(2)の輪郭を示してある．

1	椎体 Vertebral body	5	棘突起 Spinous process
2	椎間孔 Intervertebral foramen	6	横突起 Transverse process
3	椎弓根 Pedicle	7	椎間関節 Zygapophysial joint
4	椎間円板による間隙		

- 椎間孔(A2)の輪郭は，前方は椎体(A1)の下部および椎間円板(A4)，上方および下方は椎弓根(A3)，後方は椎間関節(A7)によってつくられる．
- 後縦靱帯は，椎間円板には幅広く堅く付着するが，椎体にはそれほど堅くは付着せず，狭い．椎体後面には血管の通過孔が開いており，ここで椎体静脈が椎体外に出て，内椎骨静脈叢に入るのである．
- 前縦靱帯(B1)は，椎間円板および椎体に，一様に幅広く，堅く付着している．

透明化した標本

B C 脊柱 [B 下位腰部，C 上位腰部]

図の上部では，前縦靱帯(1)の後ろにマーカーを挿入してある．それより下方では，2つの椎体(2, 3)とその間にある椎間円板(4)の範囲の前縦靱帯の一部を切って翻転している．

1	前縦靱帯 Anterior longitudinal ligament	4	椎間円板（第四・第五腰椎間） Intervertebral disc
2	椎体〔第五腰椎〕 Vertebral body (L V)	5	外側部〔仙骨〕 Lateral part (Sacrum)
3	椎体〔第四腰椎〕 Vertebral body (L IV)	6	前枝〔第五腰神経〕 Ventral ramus (L5)

前方から．

横から見ているので，椎間孔から腰神経が現れる様子(5)がわかる．

1	前縦靱帯 Anterior longitudinal ligament	9	棘突起〔第二腰椎〕 Spinous process (L II)
2	後枝〔第一腰神経〕 Dorsal ramus (L1)	10	棘上靱帯 Supraspinous ligament
3	後枝〔第二腰神経〕 Dorsal ramus (L2)	11	交感神経幹神経節 Ganglion of sympathetic trunk
4	椎間円板（第一・第二腰椎間） Intervertebral disc	12	第十二肋骨 12th rib：Rib XII
5	第一腰神経（椎間孔から現れるところ） 1st lumbar nerve (L1)	13	前枝〔第一腰神経〕 Ventral ramus (L1)
6	第一腰椎 1st lumbar vertebra (L I)	14	前枝〔第二腰神経〕 Ventral ramus (L2)
7	棘間靱帯 Interspinous ligament	15	椎間関節 Zygapophysial joint
8	交通枝 Rami communicantes		

右側方から．

脊髄神経の圧迫　椎骨静脈叢

A 脊柱［腰部］

右の腰椎を後外側方から見て，黄色靱帯を示してある．この靱帯(4)は，上下の椎弓板(2, 3)を結んでいる．

1 棘間靱帯
  Interspinous ligament
2 椎弓板〔第二腰椎〕
  Lamina (L II)
3 椎弓板〔第三腰椎〕
  Lamina (L III)
4 黄色靱帯
  Ligamentum flava
5 棘突起〔第二腰椎〕
  Spinous process (L II)
6 棘上靱帯
  Supraspinous ligament
7 肋骨突起〔第三腰椎〕
  Costal process (L III)
8 椎間関節
  Zygapophysial joint

B 腰椎の椎間円板

1 線維輪
  Anulus fibrosus
2 大動脈
  Aorta
3 腹膜外脂肪*
  Extraperitoneal fat *
4 下大静脈
  Inferior vena cava
5 線維輪の層板構造
6 髄核
  Nucleus pulposus
7 性腺動脈*
  Gonadal artery *
8 左精巣(卵巣)静脈
  Left testicular (ovarian) vein
9 腹膜
  Peritoneum
10 大腰筋
  Psoas major
11 前葉〔胸腰筋膜〕
  Anterior layer (Thoracolumbar fascia)
12 尿管
  Ureter

● 椎間円板の髄核は，脊索の遺残物である．
● 椎間円板の線維輪は，隣接する上下2椎体の間葉に由来する．

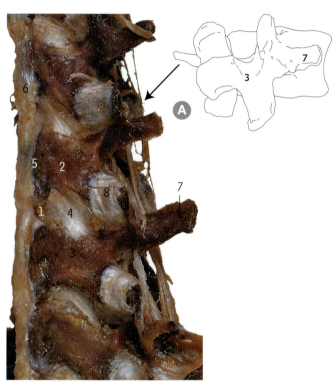

右後方から．

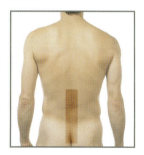

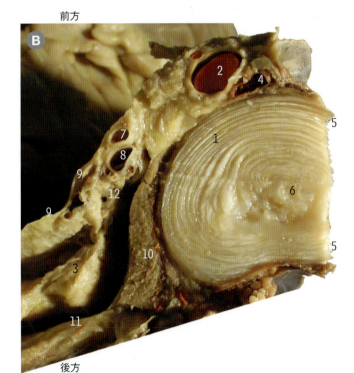

上方から．原位置のまま．

腰椎穿刺

髄膜瘤

背部［体表解剖］

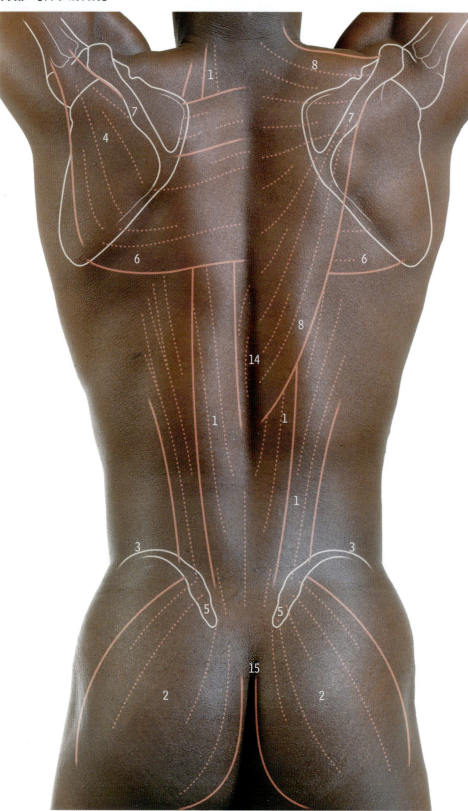

1	脊柱起立筋 Erector spinae
2	大殿筋 Gluteus maximus
3	腸骨稜 Iliac crest
4	棘下筋 Infraspinatus
5	上後腸骨棘 Posterior superior iliac spine
6	菱形筋 Rhomboids
7	肩甲棘 Spine of scapula
8	僧帽筋 Trapezius

（14．15 は次頁の用語表を参照．）

背部［浅層の筋（左），深層の筋（右）］

1	聴診三角	Auscultatory triangle
2	三角筋	Deltoid
3	脊柱起立筋	Erector spinae
4	脊柱起立筋（の腱）	Erector spinae
5	外腹斜筋	External oblique
6	大殿筋	Gluteus maximus
7	腸骨稜	Iliac crest
8	腸肋筋	Iliocostalis
9	棘下筋	Infraspinatus
10	棘下筋膜	Infraspinous fascia
11	広背筋	Latissimus dorsi
12	最長筋	Longissimus
13	腰三角：Petit 腰三角*	Lumbar triangle：Petit's triangle*
14	正中溝*（104 頁を参照）	Median furrow*
15	殿裂（104 頁を参照）	Intergluteal cleft：Natal cleft
16	上後腸骨棘	Posterior superior iliac spine
17	大菱形筋	Rhomboid major
18	仙骨	Sacrum
19	棘筋	Spinalis
20	肩甲棘	Spine of scapula
21	大円筋	Teres major
22	胸腰筋膜	Thoracolumbar fascia
23	上行部〔僧帽筋〕	Ascending part：Inferior part〔Trapezius〕
24	水平部：横行部〔僧帽筋〕	Transverse part：Middle part〔Trapezius〕
25	下行部〔僧帽筋〕	Descending part：Superior part〔Trapezius〕

背部

A：拡大図（左）．B：拡大図（右）．

Bでは，広背筋と僧帽筋の一部を切除して，背部の筋の深層を見せている．

1	聴診三角 Auscultatory triangle	14	大菱形筋 Rhomboid major
2	三角筋 Deltoid	15	小菱形筋 Rhomboid minor
3	後枝〔腰神経〕 Dorsal ramus〔Lumbar nerves〕	16	前鋸筋 Serratus anterior
4	脊柱起立筋 Erector spinae	17	棘筋 Spinalis
5	脊柱起立筋（の腱） Erector spinae	18	肩甲棘 Spine of scapula
6	外腹斜筋 External oblique	19	大円筋 Teres major
7	外肋間筋 External intercostal muscle	20	小円筋 Teres minor
8	腸肋筋 Iliocostalis	21	胸腰筋膜 Thoracolumbar fascia
9	棘下筋 Infraspinatus	22	上行部〔僧帽筋〕 Ascending part：Inferior part〔Trapezius〕
10	広背筋 Latissimus dorsi	23	水平部：横行部〔僧帽筋〕 Transverse part：Middle part〔Trapezius〕
11	肩甲挙筋 Levator scapulae	24	下行部〔僧帽筋〕 Descending part：Superior part〔Trapezius〕
12	最長筋 Longissimus	25	長頭〔上腕三頭筋〕 Long head〔Triceps brachii〕
13	腰三角 Lumbar triangle		

背部

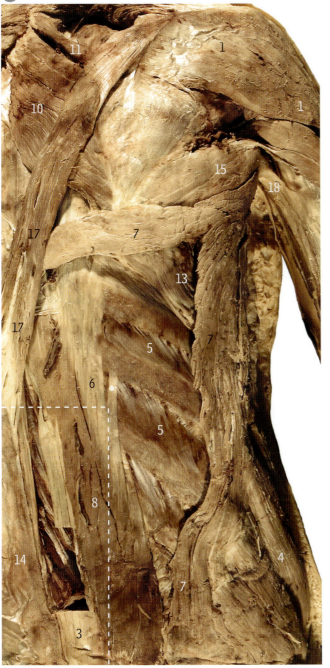

拡大図（右）．

広背筋と僧帽筋の一部を切除してあることに注意せよ．

Aの破線の範囲．

下胸部と上腰部の棘筋と最長筋の一部を除去し，脊柱起立筋の最深部の横突棘筋を見せている．

1	三角筋 Deltoid	7	広背筋 Latissimus dorsi
2	後枝〔胸神経〕 Posterior ramus：Dorsal ramus（Thoracic nerve）	8	最長筋 Longissimus
3	脊柱起立筋（の腱） Erector spinae	9	多裂筋 Multifidus
4	外腹斜筋 External oblique	10	大菱形筋 Rhomboid major
5	外肋間筋 External intercostal muscle	11	小菱形筋 Rhomboid minor
6	腸肋筋 Iliocostalis	12	半棘筋 Semispinalis
13	前鋸筋 Serratus anterior		
14	棘筋 Spinalis		
15	大円筋 Teres major		
16	胸腰筋膜 Thoracolumbar fascia		
17	上行部〔僧帽筋〕 Ascending part：Inferior part（Trapezius）		
18	長頭〔上腕三頭筋〕 Long head（Triceps brachii）		

Ⓐ Ⓑ 後頭下三角 [Ⓐ 浅層, Ⓑ 深層]

Ⓐ

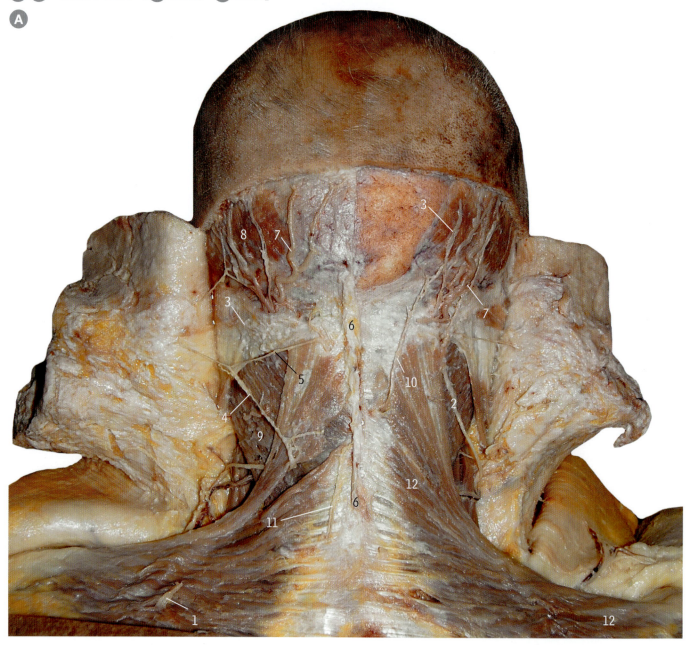

1	皮枝〔脊髄神経の後枝〕 Cutaneous branch〔Dorsal ramus of Spinal nerve〕	7	後頭動脈 Occipital artery
2	大耳介神経 Great auricular nerve	8	後頭筋〔後頭前頭筋〕 Occipital belly〔Occipitofrontalis〕
3	大後頭神経 Greater occipital nerve	9	頭板状筋 Splenius capitis
4	小後頭神経 Lesser occipital nerve	10	第三後頭神経 3rd occipital nerve
5	小後頭神経（第三後頭神経との交通） Lesser occipital nerve	11	第三後頭神経（下方へ翻転してある） 3rd occipital nerve
6	項靱帯 Nuchal ligament	12	僧帽筋 Trapezius

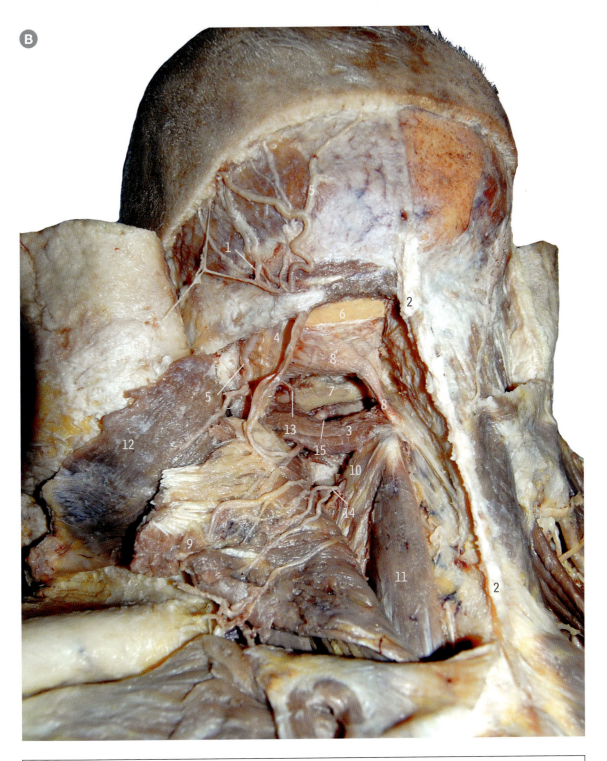

1	大後頭神経 Greater occipital nerve	9	頭半棘筋（外側へ翻転してある） Semispinalis capitis
2	項靱帯 Nuchal ligament	10	頸半棘筋 Semispinalis cervicis
3	下頭斜筋 Obliquus capitis inferior	11	頸棘筋 Spinalis cervicis
4	上頭斜筋 Obliquus capitis superior	12	頭板状筋（外側へ翻転してある） Splenius capitis
5	後頭動脈 Occipital artery	13	後頭下神経 Suboccipital nerve
6	後頭骨 Occipital bone	14	第三後頭神経 3rd occipital nerve
7	後弓〔環椎：第一頸椎〕 Posterior arch〔Atlas：C I〕	15	椎骨動脈 Vertebral artery
8	大後頭直筋 Rectus capitis posterior major		

Ⓐ～Ⓓ 後頭下三角 ［Ⓐ 浅層，Ⓑ 深層，Ⓒ 上位の頸神経，Ⓓ 環椎（第一頸椎）と軸椎（第二頸椎）］

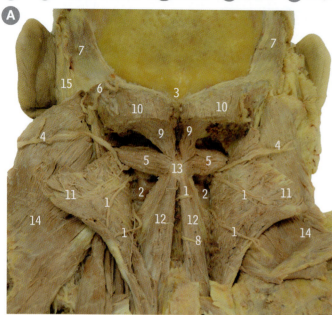

1	第三後頭神経の枝	Branches of 3rd occipital nerve
2	第三頸椎	3rd cervical vertebra (C III)
3	外後頭隆起	External occipital protuberance
4	大後頭神経	Greater occipital nerve
5	下頭斜筋	Obliquus capitis inferior
6	後頭動脈	Occipital artery
7	後頭筋〔後頭前頭筋〕	Occipital belly〔Occipitofrontalis〕
8	皮枝〔第四頸神経の後枝〕	Cutaneous branch〔Dorsal ramus of C4〕
9	大後頭直筋	Rectus capitis posterior major
10	頭半棘筋(切断してある)	Semispinalis capitis
11	頭半棘筋(外側へ翻転してある)	Semispinalis capitis
12	頸半棘筋	Semispinalis cervicis
13	棘突起〔軸椎：第二頸椎〕	Spinous process〔Axis：C II〕
14	頭板状筋(翻転してある)	Splenius capitis
15	胸鎖乳突筋	Sternocleidomastoid

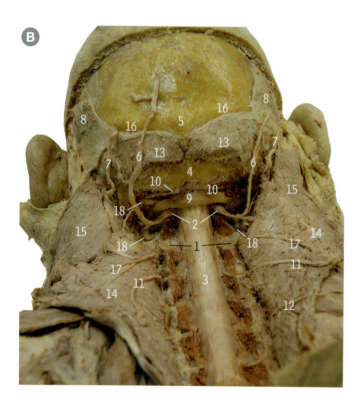

1	軸椎：第二頸椎(切断縁)	Axis：2nd cervical vertebra (C II)
2	脊髄神経節〔第二頸神経〕	Spinal ganglion〔C2〕
3	硬膜	Dura mater
4	外後頭稜	External occipital crest
5	外後頭隆起	External occipital protuberance
6	大後頭神経	Greater occipital nerve
7	後頭動脈	Occipital artery
8	後頭筋〔後頭前頭筋〕	Occipital belly〔Occipitofrontalis〕
9	後弓〔環椎：第一頸椎〕	Posterior arch〔Atlas：C I〕
10	後環椎後頭膜	Posterior atlanto-occipital membrane
11	皮枝〔第四頸神経の後枝〕	Cutaneous branch〔Dorsal ramus of C4〕
12	皮枝〔第六頸神経の後枝〕	Cutaneous branch〔Dorsal ramus of C6〕
13	頭半棘筋(切断してある)	Semispinalis capitis
14	頭半棘筋(外側へ翻転してある)	Semispinalis capitis
15	頭板状筋(翻転してある)	Splenius capitis
16	上項線	Superior nuchal line
17	第三後頭神経	3rd occipital nerve
18	椎骨動脈	Vertebral artery

第 2 章　脊柱と脊髄：後頭下三角　111

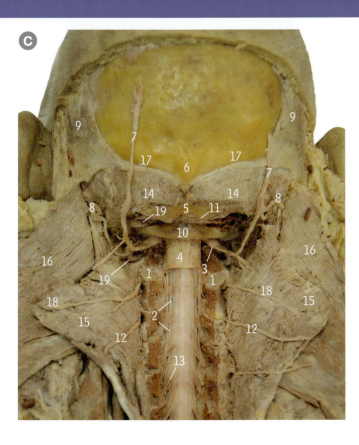

1	軸椎：第二頸椎（切断してある）	Axis: 2nd cervical vertebra（C II）
2	歯状靱帯	Denticulate ligament
3	脊髄神経節〔第二頸神経〕	Spinal ganglion（C2）
4	硬膜	Dura mater
5	外後頭稜	External occipital crest
6	外後頭隆起	External occipital protuberance
7	大後頭神経	Greater occipital nerve
8	後頭動脈	Occipital artery
9	後頭筋〔後頭前頭筋〕	Occipital belly〔Occipitofrontalis〕
10	後弓〔環椎：第一頸椎〕	Posterior arch〔Atlas：C I〕
11	後環椎後頭膜	Posterior atlanto-occipital membrane
12	後皮枝〔第四頸神経〕	Posterior cutaneous branches〔C4〕
13	根糸〔後根〕	Rootlets〔Dorsal root〕
14	頭半棘筋（切断してある）	Semispinalis capitis
15	頭半棘筋（外側へ翻転してある）	Semispinalis capitis
16	頭板状筋（翻転してある）	Splenius capitis
17	上項線	Superior nuchal line
18	第三後頭神経	3rd occipital nerve
19	椎骨動脈	Vertebral artery

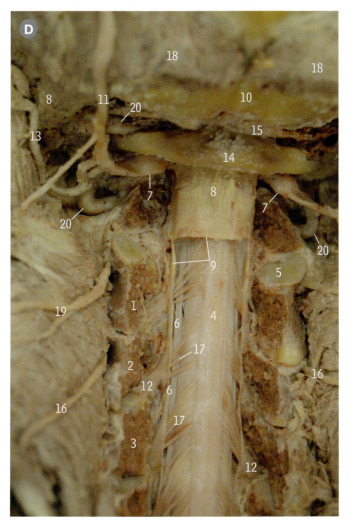

1	第三頸椎（切断してある）	3rd cervical vertebra（C III）
2	第四頸椎（切断してある）	4th cervical vertebra（C IV）
3	第五頸椎（切断してある）	5th cervical vertebra（C V）
4	クモ膜	Arachnoid mater
5	軸椎：第二頸椎（切断してある）	Axis: 2nd cervical vertebra（C II）
6	歯状靱帯	Denticulate ligament
7	脊髄神経節〔第二頸神経〕	Spinal ganglion（C2）
8	硬膜	Dura mater
9	硬膜（切離してある）	Dura mater
10	外後頭稜	External occipital crest
11	大後頭神経	Greater occipital nerve
12	髄膜鞘＊（脊髄神経節を覆う）	Meningeal sheath＊
13	後頭動脈	Occipital artery
14	後弓〔環椎：第一頸椎〕	Posterior arch〔Atlas：C I〕
15	後環椎後頭膜	Posterior atlanto-occipital membrane
16	皮枝〔第四頸神経の後枝〕	Cutaneous branch〔Dorsal ramus of C4〕
17	根糸〔後根〕	Rootlets〔Dorsal root〕
18	頭半棘筋（切断してある）	Semispinalis capitis
19	第三後頭神経	3rd occipital nerve
20	椎骨動脈	Vertebral artery

上位頸椎

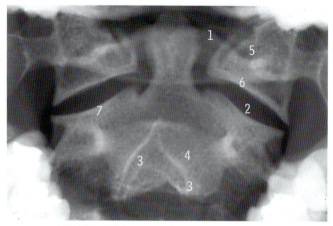

軸椎（第二頸椎）とその歯突起の標準的な X 線画像
口腔内から見たところ．

歯列と上下顎の陰影が重なるのを避けるため，口を開け，適切な角度を選んで撮影しなければならない．外側環軸関節の関節面(6, 7)が適合していないように見えるが，それは骨の関節面を覆う硝子軟骨が X 線透過性であるためである（このことはすべての滑膜性の関節に当てはまる）．環椎（第一頸椎）の前弓および後弓の輪郭は，歯突起の陰影の両側にある環椎（第一頸椎）の外側塊(5)の陰影との間にかすかに見えている．

1	前弓と後弓〔環椎：第一頸椎〕 Anterior arch and Posterior arch〔Atlas：C I〕
2	外側環軸関節 Lateral atlanto-axial joint
3	棘突起〔軸椎：第二頸椎〕(2 分岐性) Spinous process〔Axis：C II〕
4	椎体〔軸椎：第二頸椎〕 Vertebral body〔Axis：C II〕
5	外側塊〔環椎：第一頸椎〕 Lateral mass〔Atlas：C I〕
6	下関節面〔環椎：第一頸椎〕 Inferior articular surface〔Atlas：C I〕
7	上関節面〔軸椎：第二頸椎〕 Superior articular facet〔Axis：C II〕

下位頸椎と上位胸椎

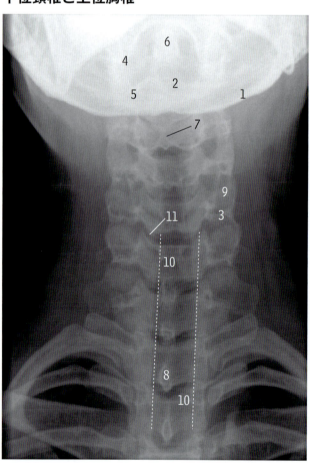

気管は空気を含んでいるため，X 線の高い透過性を示すことに注意せよ．

1	底部〔後頭骨〕 Basilar part〔Occipital bone〕
2	椎体〔軸椎：第二頸椎〕 Vertebral body〔Axis：C II〕
3	下関節突起 Inferior articular process
4	外側塊〔環椎：第一頸椎〕 Lateral mass〔Atlas：C I〕
5	外側部*〔軸椎：第二頸椎〕 Lateral part*〔Axis：C II〕
6	歯突起〔軸椎：第二頸椎〕 Dens〔Axis：C II〕
7	棘突起〔第三頸椎〕 Spinous process〔C III〕
8	棘突起〔第一胸椎〕 Spinous process〔T I〕
9	上関節突起 Superior articular process
10	気管 Trachea
11	鉤椎関節*：Luschka 関節* Uncovertebral joint*：Luschka's joint*

環軸椎亜脱臼

頸椎の固定

脊柱 [AB 頸椎, CD 腰椎]

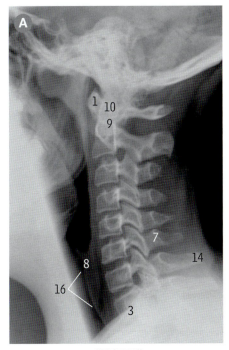

X線側面画像

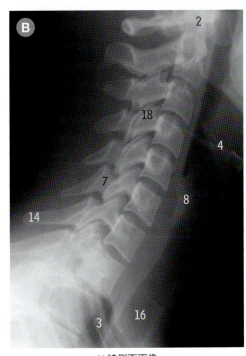

X線側面画像

1	前弓〔環椎：第一頸椎〕 Anterior arch〔Atlas：C I〕	
2	歯突起〔軸椎：第二頸椎〕 Dens〔Axis：C II〕	
3	第一肋骨 1st rib：Rib I	
4	舌骨 Hyoid bone	
5	下関節突起〔第一腰椎〕 Inferior articular process〔L I〕	
6	椎間円板の間隙＊（第二・第三腰椎間） Intervertebral disc space＊	
7	椎弓板〔第六頸椎〕 Lamina〔C VI〕	
8	喉頭 Larynx	
9	外側環軸関節 Lateral atlanto-axial joint	
10	外側塊〔環椎：第一頸椎〕 Lateral mass〔Atlas：C I〕	
11	関節間部＊〔第二腰椎〕 Pars interarticularis＊〔L II〕	
12	椎弓根〔第三腰椎〕 Pedicle〔L III〕	
13	棘突起〔第二腰椎〕 Spinous process〔L II〕	
14	棘突起〔隆椎：第七頸椎〕 Spinous process〔Vertebra prominens：C VII〕	
15	上関節突起〔第二腰椎〕 Superior articular process〔L II〕	
16	気管 Trachea	
17	肋骨突起〔第三腰椎〕 Costal process〔L III〕	
18	椎間関節 Zygapophysial joint	

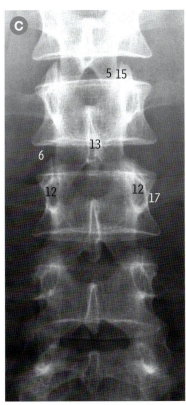

X線前後画像

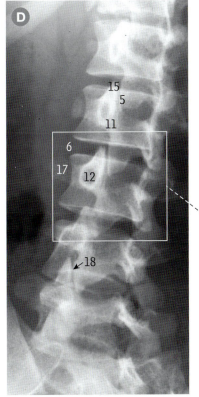

X線斜方向画像

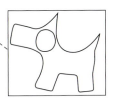

● 腰椎のX線斜方向画像には，スコッチテリアが見られる．鼻が肋骨突起(17)，耳が上関節突起(15)，そして眼が椎弓根(12)である．そして首は，脊椎分離症では癒合が不完全となる関節間部(11)である．

椎体骨折

3

上肢

上肢 [Ⓐ 体表解剖, Ⓑ 筋, Ⓒ 骨]

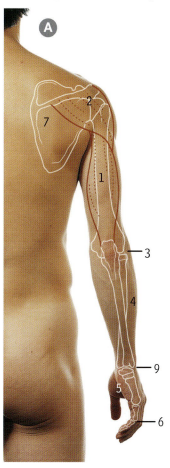  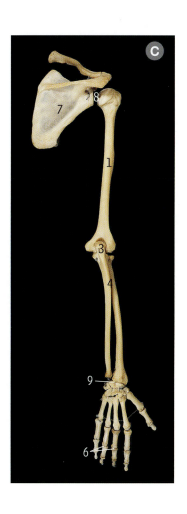

1	上腕 Arm	6	(手の)指節間関節 Interphalangeal joint of hand
2	三角筋 Deltoid	7	肩甲骨 Scapula
3	肘関節 Elbow joint	8	肩関節 Glenohumeral joint：Shoulder joint
4	前腕 Forearm	9	橈骨手根関節 Wrist joint
5	手 Hand		

副小骨

肩甲骨（左）

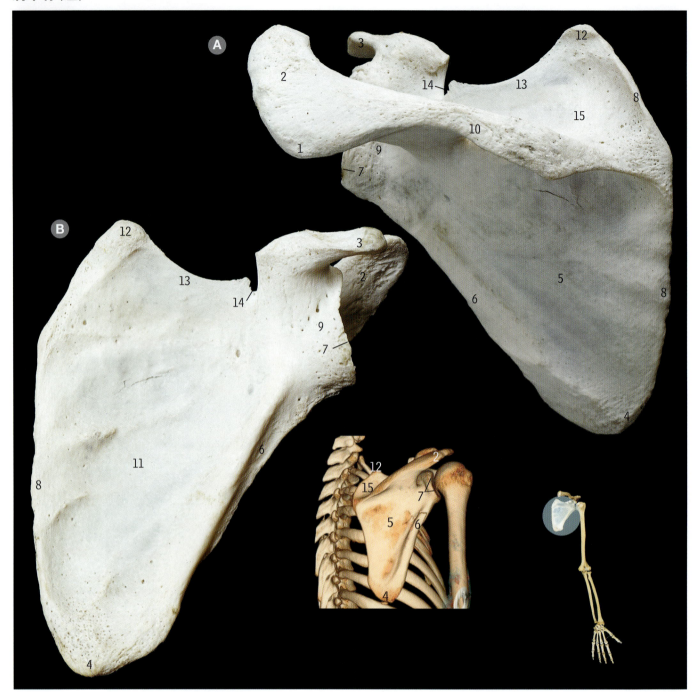

A：背側面．B：肋骨面．

1 肩峰角 Acromial angle	6 外側縁 Lateral border	11 肩甲下窩 Subscapular fossa
2 肩峰 Acromion	7 関節窩（の辺縁） Glenoid cavity	12 上角 Superior angle
3 烏口突起 Coracoid process	8 内側縁 Medial border	13 上縁 Superior border
4 下角 Inferior angle	9 肩甲頸（および棘窩切痕*（Aのみ）） Neck of scapula	14 肩甲切痕 Suprascapular notch
5 棘下窩 Infraspinous fossa	10 肩甲棘 Spine of scapula	15 棘上窩 Supraspinous fossa

● 肩甲棘（A10）は，肩甲骨の背側面から突出しており，その外側端に肩峰（A2）がある．

肩甲骨（左）［筋と靱帯の付着部］

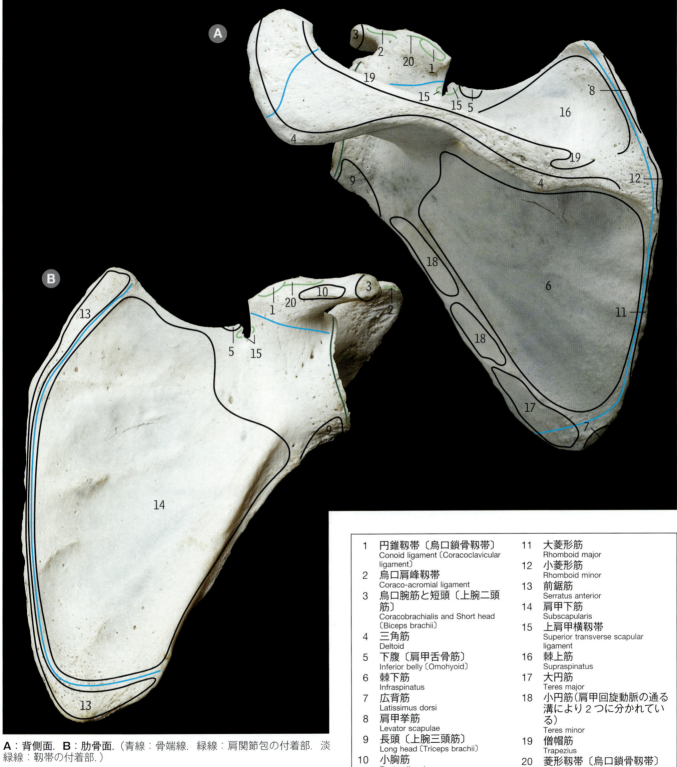

A：背側面. B：肋骨面.（青線：骨端線. 緑線：肩関節包の付着部. 淡緑線：靱帯の付着部.）

1	円錐靱帯〔烏口鎖骨靱帯〕 Conoid ligament〔Coracoclavicular ligament〕	11	大菱形筋 Rhomboid major
2	烏口肩峰靱帯 Coraco-acromial ligament	12	小菱形筋 Rhomboid minor
3	烏口腕筋と短頭〔上腕二頭筋〕 Coracobrachialis and Short head〔Biceps brachii〕	13	前鋸筋 Serratus anterior
4	三角筋 Deltoid	14	肩甲下筋 Subscapularis
5	下腹〔肩甲舌骨筋〕 Inferior belly〔Omohyoid〕	15	上肩甲横靱帯 Superior transverse scapular ligament
6	棘下筋 Infraspinatus	16	棘上筋 Supraspinatus
7	広背筋 Latissimus dorsi	17	大円筋 Teres major
8	肩甲挙筋 Levator scapulae	18	小円筋（肩甲回旋動脈の通る溝により2つに分かれている） Teres minor
9	長頭〔上腕三頭筋〕 Long head〔Triceps brachii〕	19	僧帽筋 Trapezius
10	小胸筋 Pectoralis minor	20	菱形靱帯〔烏口鎖骨靱帯〕 Trapezoid ligament〔Coracoclavicular ligament〕

- 肩甲切痕には，上肩甲横靱帯(15)が張っている.
- 円錐靱帯(1)と菱形靱帯(20)を合わせて烏口鎖骨靱帯といい，肩甲骨の烏口突起を鎖骨外側端の下面へと結び付けている.
- 烏口肩峰靱帯(2)は，烏口突起と肩峰の間に張り，これらの2つの骨部とともに肩関節の上にアーチを形成している.

A 肩甲骨（左）

1 肩峰 Acromion	5 関節下結節 Infraglenoid tubercle	9 関節上結節 Supraglenoid tubercle
2 烏口突起 Coracoid process	6 棘下窩 Infraspinous fossa	10 棘上窩 Supraspinous fossa
3 関節窩 Glenoid cavity	7 外側縁 Lateral border	
4 下角 Inferior angle	8 肩甲棘 Spine of scapula	

B 肩甲骨と鎖骨（左）［肩鎖関節］

1 肩峰端〔鎖骨〕 Acromial end (Clavicle)	4 烏口突起 Coracoid process	7 胸骨端〔鎖骨〕 Sternal end (Clavicle)
2 肩鎖関節 Acromioclavicular joint	5 鎖骨体 Body of clavicle	8 棘上窩 Supraspinous fossa
3 肩峰 Acromion	6 肩甲棘 Spine of scapula	

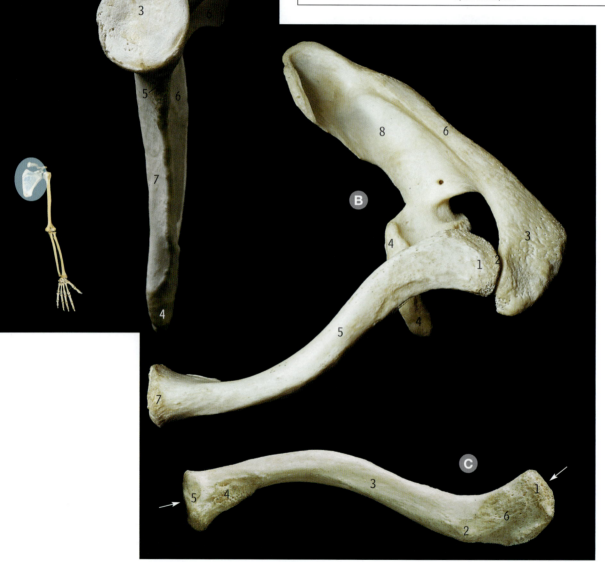

A：外側方から．B：上方から．C：下方から．

C 鎖骨（左）

1 肩峰関節面〔肩峰端〕（矢印） Acromial facet (Acromial end)
2 円錐靱帯結節 Conoid tubercle
3 鎖骨下筋溝 Groove for subclavius
4 肋鎖靱帯圧痕 Impression for costoclavicular ligament
5 胸骨関節面〔胸骨端〕（矢印） Sternal facet (Sternal end)
6 菱形靱帯線 Trapezoid line

● 鎖骨の胸骨端（B7，C5）は球状で，肩峰端（B1，C1）は扁平である．鎖骨体の内側2/3は前方に凸に弯曲し，下面には鎖骨下筋溝（C3）が見られる．

肩鎖関節脱臼

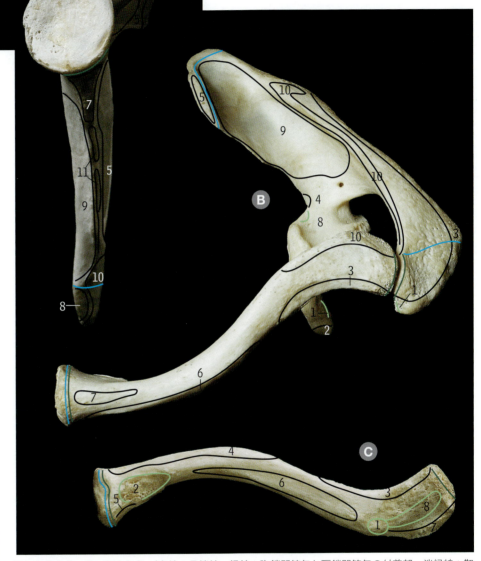

A 肩甲骨（左）[筋と靱帯の付着部]

1	烏口肩峰靱帯 Coraco-acromial ligament	7	長頭〔上腕三頭筋〕 Long head (Triceps brachii)
2	烏口腕筋と短頭〔上腕二頭筋〕 Coracobrachialis and Short head (Biceps brachii)	8	前鋸筋 Serratus anterior
3	烏口上腕靱帯 Coracohumeral ligament	9	肩甲下筋 Subscapularis
4	三角筋 Deltoid	10	大円筋 Teres major
5	棘下筋 Infraspinatus	11	小円筋（肩甲回旋動脈の通る溝により2つに分かれている） Teres minor
6	長頭〔上腕二頭筋〕 Long head (Biceps brachii)		

A：外側方から．（青線：骨端線．緑線：肩関節包の付着部．淡緑線：靱帯の付着部．）

B 肩甲骨と鎖骨（左）[肩鎖関節]

1. 烏口肩峰靱帯 Coraco-acromial ligament
2. 烏口腕筋と短頭〔上腕二頭筋〕 Coracobrachialis and Short head (Biceps brachii)
3. 三角筋 Deltoid
4. 下腹〔肩甲舌骨筋〕 Inferior belly (Omohyoid)
5. 肩甲挙筋 Levator scapulae
6. 大胸筋 Pectoralis major
7. 胸鎖乳突筋 Sternocleidomastoid
8. 上肩甲横靱帯 Superior transverse scapular ligament
9. 棘上筋 Supraspinatus
10. 僧帽筋 Trapezius

C 鎖骨（左）[筋と靱帯の付着部]

1. 円錐靱帯 Conoid ligament
2. 肋鎖靱帯 Costoclavicular ligament
3. 三角筋 Deltoid
4. 大胸筋 Pectoralis major
5. 胸骨舌骨筋 Sternohyoid
6. 鎖骨下筋と鎖骨胸筋筋膜 Subclavius and Clavipectoral fascia
7. 僧帽筋 Trapezius
8. 菱形靱帯 Trapezoid ligament

B：上方から．**C**：下方から．（青線：骨端線．緑線：胸鎖関節包と肩鎖関節包の付着部．淡緑線：靱帯の付着部．）

鎖骨骨折

肩甲骨骨折

上腕骨(右)［上端］

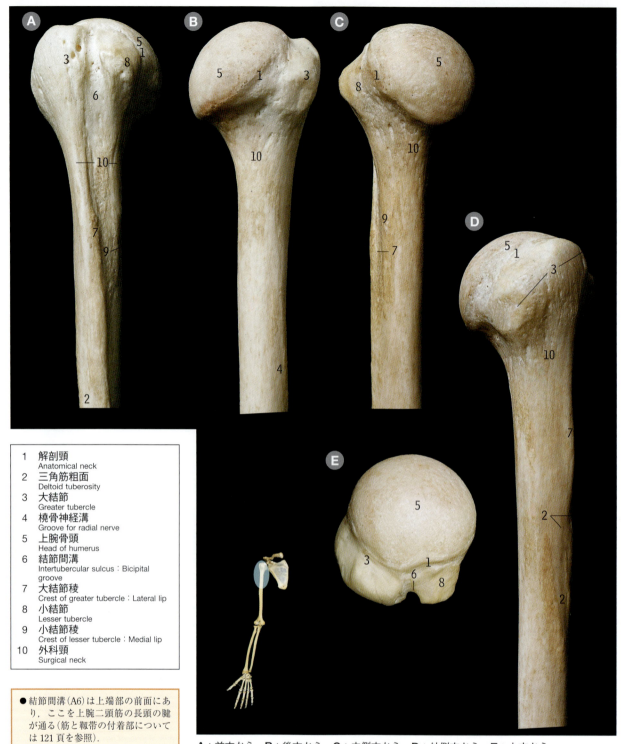

1	解剖頸 Anatomical neck
2	三角筋粗面 Deltoid tuberosity
3	大結節 Greater tubercle
4	橈骨神経溝 Groove for radial nerve
5	上腕骨頭 Head of humerus
6	結節間溝 Intertubercular sulcus；Bicipital groove
7	大結節稜 Crest of greater tubercle；Lateral lip
8	小結節 Lesser tubercle
9	小結節稜 Crest of lesser tubercle；Medial lip
10	外科頸 Surgical neck

● 結節間溝(A6)は上端部の前面にあり，ここを上腕二頭筋の長頭の腱が通る(筋と靱帯の付着部については121頁を参照).

A：前方から．B：後方から．C：内側方から．D：外側方から．E：上方から．

肩関節の脱臼

上腕骨（右）［上端，筋と靱帯の付着部］

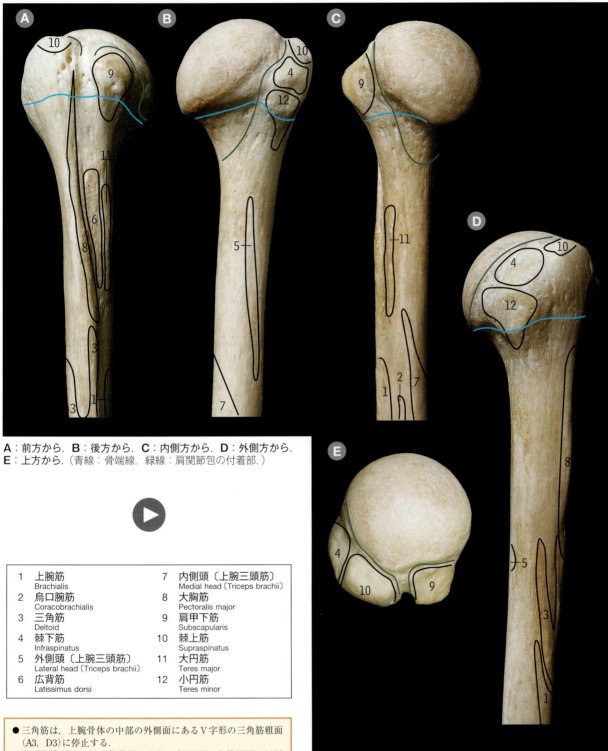

A：前方から．B：後方から．C：内側方から．D：外側方から．
E：上方から．（青線：骨端線．緑線：肩関節包の付着部．）

1	上腕筋 Brachialis	7	内側頭〔上腕三頭筋〕 Medial head〔Triceps brachii〕
2	烏口腕筋 Coracobrachialis	8	大胸筋 Pectoralis major
3	三角筋 Deltoid	9	肩甲下筋 Subscapularis
4	棘下筋 Infraspinatus	10	棘上筋 Supraspinatus
5	外側頭〔上腕三頭筋〕 Lateral head〔Triceps brachii〕	11	大円筋 Teres major
6	広背筋 Latissimus dorsi	12	小円筋 Teres minor

- 三角筋は，上腕骨体の中部の外側面にあるV字形の三角筋粗面（A3，D3）に停止する．
- 烏口腕筋（C2）は，上腕骨体の中部の内側面（三角筋粗面の反対側）に停止する．
- 骨端線と，関節包の付着線の相互位置関係に注意せよ．上腕骨上端部の骨端線は，一部が関節包の内部に，一部がその外部になる．

骨髄内注射

上腕骨（右）［下端］

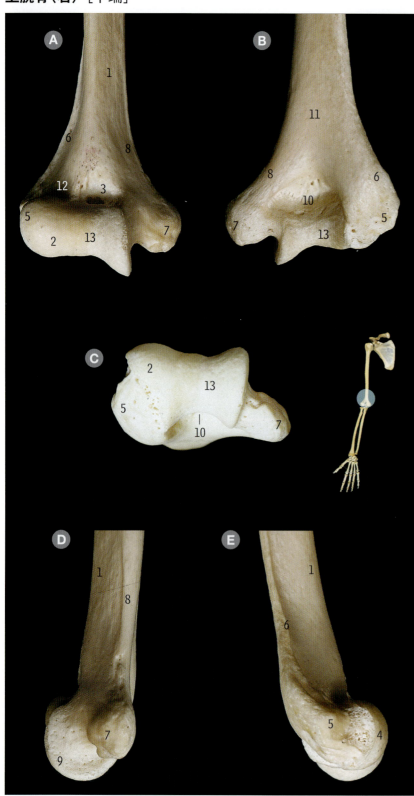

1	前面 Anterior surface
2	上腕骨小頭 Capitulum of humerus
3	鈎突窩 Coronoid fossa
4	上腕骨小頭（の外側縁） Capitulum of humerus
5	外側上顆 Lateral epicondyle
6	外側顆上稜 Lateral supracondylar ridge
7	内側上顆 Medial epicondyle
8	内側顆上稜 Medial supracondylar ridge
9	上腕骨滑車（の内側面） Trochlea of humerus
10	肘頭窩 Olecranon fossa
11	後面 Posterior surface
12	橈骨窩 Radial fossa
13	上腕骨滑車 Trochlea of humerus

- 内側上顆(7)は，外側上顆(5)より突出している．
- 上腕骨滑車(13)の内側部は，外側部より突出している．
- 後面にある肘頭窩(10)は前面の鈎突窩(3)や橈骨窩(12)より深い．

A：前方から．B：後方から．C：下方から．D：内側方から．E：外側方から．

内側上顆の剥離

顆上突起

上腕骨（右）［下端，筋と靱帯の付着部］

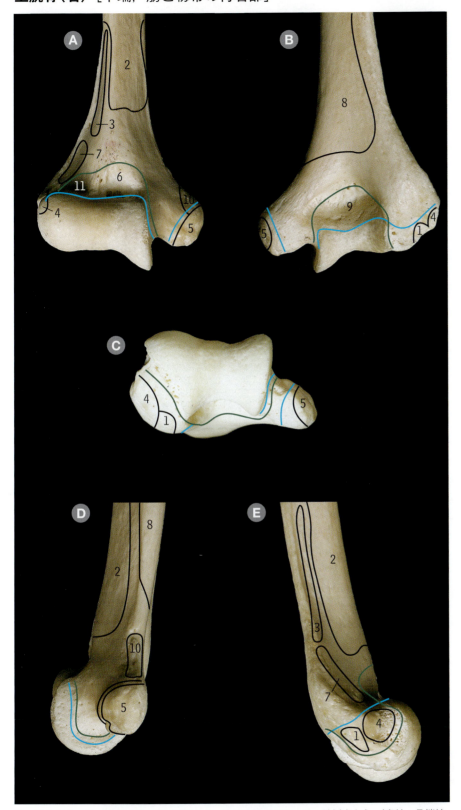

1	肘筋 Anconeus
2	上腕筋 Brachialis
3	腕橈骨筋 Brachioradialis
4	前腕伸筋群の共同起始部
5	前腕屈筋群の共同起始部
6	鈎突窩 Coronoid fossa
7	長橈側手根伸筋 Extensor carpi radialis longus
8	内側頭〔上腕三頭筋〕 Medial head〔Triceps brachii〕
9	肘頭窩 Olecranon fossa
10	上腕頭〔円回内筋〕 Humeral head〔Pronator teres〕
11	橈骨窩 Radial fossa

A：前方から．B：後方から．C：下方から．D：内側方から．E：外側方から．（青線：骨端線．緑線：肘関節包の付着部．）

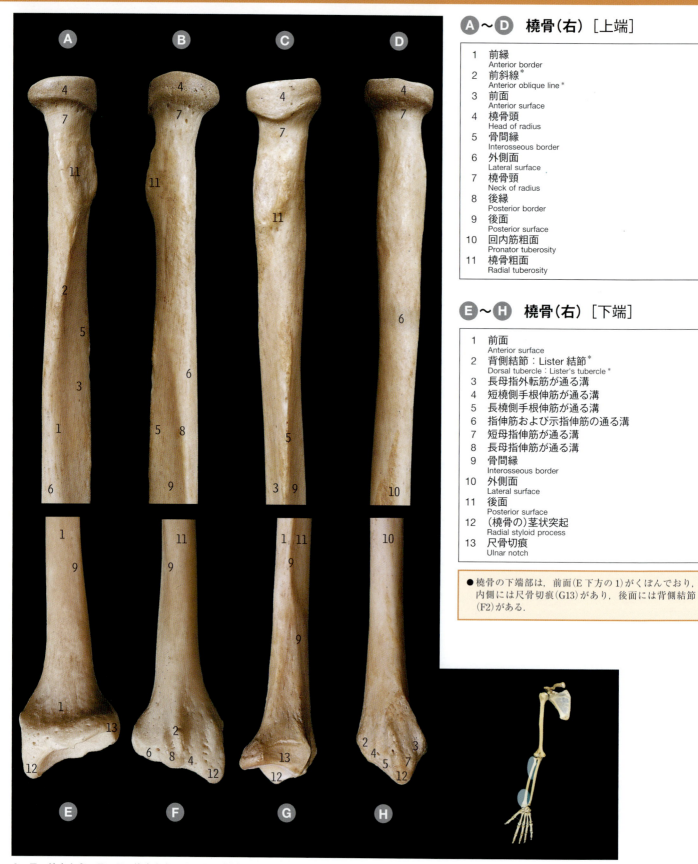

A〜D 橈骨（右）[上端]

1 前縁 Anterior border
2 前斜線* Anterior oblique line *
3 前面 Anterior surface
4 橈骨頭 Head of radius
5 骨間縁 Interosseous border
6 外側面 Lateral surface
7 橈骨頸 Neck of radius
8 後縁 Posterior border
9 後面 Posterior surface
10 回内筋粗面 Pronator tuberosity
11 橈骨粗面 Radial tuberosity

E〜H 橈骨（右）[下端]

1 前面 Anterior surface
2 背側結節：Lister 結節* Dorsal tubercle：Lister's tubercle *
3 長母指外転筋が通る溝
4 短橈側手根伸筋が通る溝
5 長橈側手根伸筋が通る溝
6 指伸筋および示指伸筋の通る溝
7 短母指伸筋が通る溝
8 長母指伸筋が通る溝
9 骨間縁 Interosseous border
10 外側面 Lateral surface
11 後面 Posterior surface
12 （橈骨の）茎状突起 Radial styloid process
13 尺骨切痕 Ulnar notch

● 橈骨の下端部は，前面（E下方の1）がくぼんでおり，内側には尺骨切痕（G13）があり，後面には背側結節（F2）がある．

A・E：前方から．B・F：後方から．C・G：内側方から．D・H：外側方から．

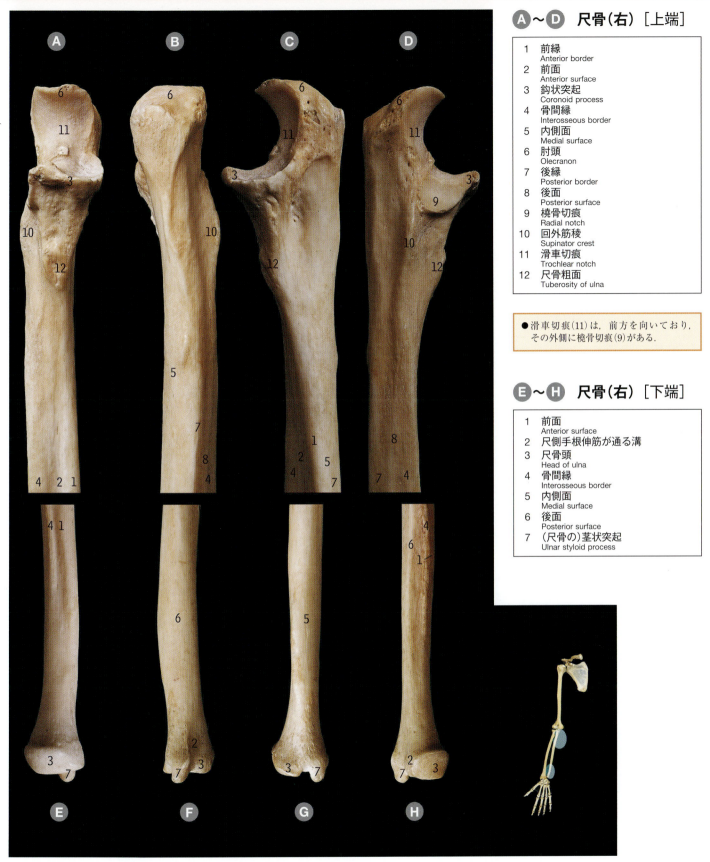

A 橈骨と尺骨（右）［上端］

1. 鉤状突起〔尺骨〕
   Coronoid process〔Ulna〕
2. 橈骨頭
   Head of radius
3. 橈骨頸
   Neck of radius
4. 肘頭〔尺骨〕
   Olecranon〔Ulna〕
5. 滑車切痕〔尺骨〕
   Trochlear notch〔Ulna〕
6. 橈骨粗面
   Radial tuberosity
7. 尺骨粗面
   Tuberosity of ulna

B 橈骨と尺骨（右）［下端］

1. 関節円板の付着部
2. 背側結節：Lister 結節*
   Dorsal tubercle：Lister's tubercle*
3. 短橈側手根伸筋が通る溝
4. 長橈側手根伸筋が通る溝
5. 尺側手根伸筋が通る溝
6. 指伸筋および示指伸筋が通る溝
7. 長母指伸筋が通る溝
8. （橈骨の）茎状突起
   Radial styloid process
9. （尺骨の）茎状突起
   Ulnar styloid process
10. 関節円板のための面
11. 月状骨との関節面
12. 舟状骨との関節面

C D 上腕骨，橈骨および尺骨（右）

1. 上腕骨小頭
   Capitulum of humerus
2. 鉤状突起〔尺骨〕
   Coronoid process〔Ulna〕
3. 橈骨頭
   Head of radius
4. 外側上顆〔上腕骨〕
   Lateral epicondyle〔Humerus〕
5. 内側上顆〔上腕骨〕
   Medial epicondyle〔Humerus〕
6. 肘頭〔尺骨〕
   Olecranon〔Ulna〕
7. 橈骨切痕〔尺骨〕
   Radial notch〔Ulna〕
8. 上腕骨滑車
   Trochlea of humerus

● 腕尺関節，腕橈関節，上橈尺関節は，同じ関節腔を共有している．

A：上前方から．B：下方から．C：前方から（肘関節における位置関係に合わせてある）．D：後方から（肘関節における位置関係に合わせてある）．

肘関節脱臼

上腕骨顆上骨折

橈骨と尺骨（右）［筋と靱帯の付着部］

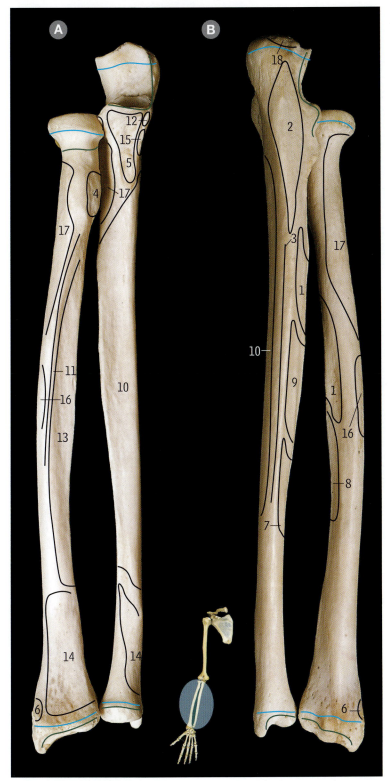

1	長母指外転筋	Abductor pollicis longus
2	肘筋	Anconeus
3	深指屈筋，尺側手根屈筋および尺側手根伸筋（の腱膜性付着部）	Flexor digitorum profundus, Flexor carpi ulnaris and Extensor carpi ulnaris
4	上腕二頭筋	Biceps brachii
5	上腕筋	Brachialis
6	腕橈骨筋	Brachioradialis
7	示指伸筋	Extensor indicis
8	短母指伸筋	Extensor pollicis brevis
9	長母指伸筋	Extensor pollicis longus
10	深指屈筋	Flexor digitorum profundus
11	橈骨頭〔浅指屈筋〕	Radial head〔Flexor digitorum superficialis〕
12	上腕尺骨頭〔浅指屈筋〕	Humero-ulnar head〔Flexor digitorum superficialis〕
13	長母指屈筋	Flexor pollicis longus
14	方形回内筋	Pronator quadratus
15	尺骨頭〔円回内筋〕	Ulnar head〔Pronator teres〕
16	円回内筋	Pronator teres
17	回外筋	Supinator
18	上腕三頭筋	Triceps brachii

● 長母指外転筋（1）と短母指伸筋（8）の2筋だけが，橈骨の後面に起始部をもつ（2筋とも骨間膜の表面に広がっており，長母指外転筋は尺骨の後面からも起始する）．これらの2筋は並走し，橈骨の外側部（161頁）をまわり，解剖学的嗅ぎタバコ入れ（163, 174頁）の橈側の境界をつくる．

● 若年者では，橈骨の骨折は，時として橈骨下部の骨端線を横切るようにして起こる．成人では，Colles骨折（129頁）とよばれる，骨折線が橈骨下端より約2.5cm以内で横走する骨折が起こる．尺骨の茎状突起もしばしば骨折する．

A：前方から．B：後方から．（青線：骨端線．緑線：肘関節および橈骨手根関節の関節包の付着部．）

前腕の骨折の牽引整復

手の骨（右）［C 舟状骨，D 有鈎骨］

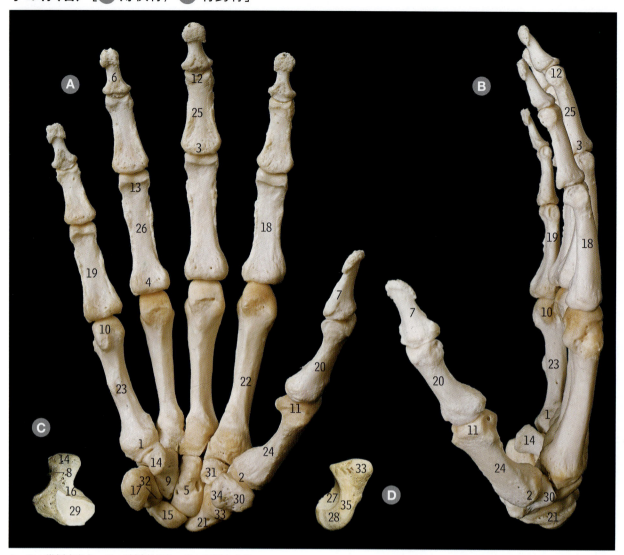

A・D：掌側方から．B：外側方から．C：内側方から．

- 舟状骨，月状骨，三角骨ならびに豆状骨は，近位手根骨を構成する．
- 大菱形骨，小菱形骨，有頭骨ならびに有鈎骨は，遠位手根骨を構成する．
- 舟状骨結節(33)と舟状骨の峡部(35)は，非関節部であるため，栄養孔が認められる．したがって，峡部を横切るような骨折では，舟状骨の近位極の血液供給が障害され，虚血性壊死となる（173頁参照）．舟状骨の峡部の位置は，体表では解剖学的嗅ぎタバコ入れの中にある．舟状骨結節は，この嗅ぎタバコ入れの橈側の境界の前に触れることができる．

1	第五中手骨底	Base of 5th metacarpal bone
2	第一中手骨底	Base of 1st metatarsal bone
3	中節骨底〔中指（第三指）〕	Base of middle phalanx〔Middle finger〕
4	基節骨底〔薬指（第四指）〕	Base of proximal phalanx〔Ring finger〕
5	有頭骨	Capitate
6	末節骨〔薬指（第四指）〕	Distal phalanx〔Ring finger〕
7	末節骨〔母指（第一指）〕	Distal phalanx〔Thumb〕
8	尺骨神経の深枝が通る溝	
9	有鈎骨	Hamate
10	第五中手骨頭	Head of 5th metatarsal bone
11	第一中手骨頭	Head of 1st metatarsal bone
12	中節骨頭〔中指（第三指）〕	Head of middle phalanx〔Middle finger〕
13	基節骨頭〔薬指（第四指）〕	Head of proximal phalanx〔Ring finger〕
14	有鈎骨鈎	Hook of hamate
15	月状骨	Lunate
16	有鈎骨（の掌側面）	Hamate
17	豆状骨	Pisiform
18	基節骨〔示指（第二指）〕	Proximal phalanx〔Index finger〕
19	基節骨〔小指（第五指）〕	Proximal phalanx〔Little finger〕
20	基節骨〔母指（第一指）〕	Proximal phalanx〔Thumb〕
21	舟状骨	Scaphoid
22	第二中手骨体	Shaft of 2nd metacarpal bone：Body of 2nd metacarpal bone
23	第五中手骨体	Shaft of 5th metacarpal bone：Body of 5th metacarpal bone
24	第一中手骨体	Shaft of 1st metacarpal bone：Body of 1st metacarpal bone
25	中節骨体〔中指（第三指）〕	Shaft of Middle phalanx：Body of middle phalanx〔Middle finger〕
26	基節骨〔薬指（第四指）〕	Shaft of proximal phalanx：Body of proximal phalanx〔Ring finger〕
27	有頭骨との関節面	
28	月状骨との関節面	
29	三角骨との関節面	
30	大菱形骨	Trapezium
31	小菱形骨	Trapezoid
32	三角骨	Triquetrum
33	舟状骨結節〔舟状骨〕	Tubercle〔Scaphoid〕
34	大菱形骨結節	Tubercle of trapezium
35	峡部*〔舟状骨〕	Waist*〔Scaphoid〕

手の骨（右）

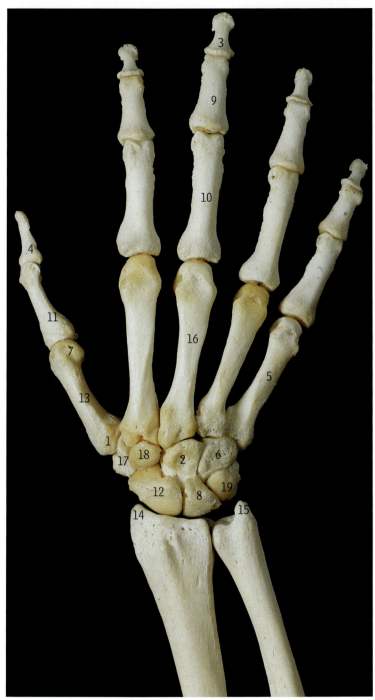

背側方から．

1 第一中手骨底
　Base of 1st metatarsal bone
2 有頭骨
　Capitate
3 末節骨〔中指（第三指）〕
　Distal phalanx〔Middle finger〕
4 末節骨〔母指（第一指）〕
　Distal phalanx〔Thumb〕
5 第五中手骨
　5th metacarpal bone
6 有鈎骨
　Hamate
7 第一中手骨頭
　Head of 1st metatarsal bone
8 月状骨
　Lunate
9 中節骨〔中指（第三指）〕
　Middle phalanx〔Middle finger〕
10 基節骨〔中指（第三指）〕
　Proximal phalanx〔Middle finger〕
11 基節骨〔母指（第一指）〕
　Proximal phalanx〔Thumb〕
12 舟状骨
　Scaphoid
13 第一中手骨体
　Shaft of 1st metacarpal bone：Body of 1st metacarpal bone
14 （橈骨の）茎状突起
　Radial styloid process
15 （尺骨の）茎状突起
　Ulnar styloid process
16 第三中手骨
　3rd metacarpal bone
17 大菱形骨
　Trapezium
18 小菱形骨
　Trapezoid
19 三角骨
　Triquetrum

- 手関節（橈骨手根関節とよばれる）は，橈骨の下端と関節円板（橈骨と尺骨の下端が離れないように保つ）を近位関節面とし，舟状骨，月状骨および三角骨を遠位関節面とする関節である．
- 手根中央関節は，近位手根骨列と遠位手根骨列との間の関節である（173，177頁の解説を参照）．
- 母指の手根中手関節は，大菱形骨と第一中手骨底の間の関節である．

ボクサー骨折

Colles 骨折

指関節脱臼

Smith 骨折

手の骨（右）［筋と靱帯の付着部］

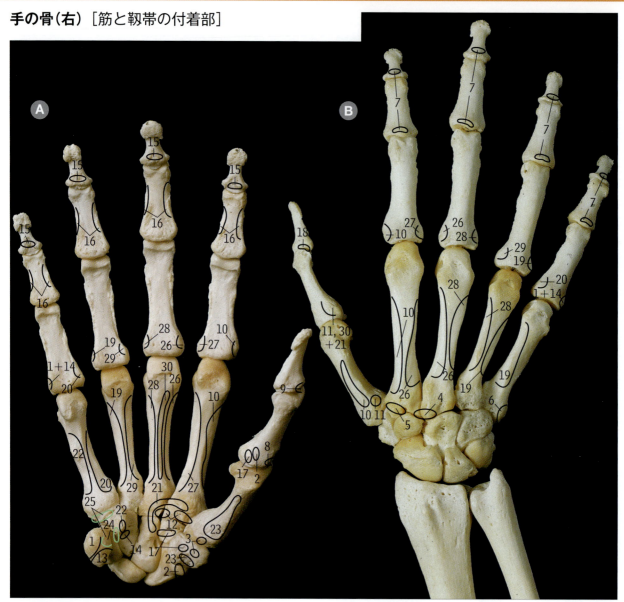

A：掌側方から．B：背側方から．（淡緑線：靱帯の付着部．）

1	小指外転筋 Abductor digiti minimi	12	橈側手根屈筋 Flexor carpi radialis	23	母指対立筋 Opponens pollicis
2	短母指外転筋 Abductor pollicis brevis	13	尺側手根屈筋 Flexor carpi ulnaris	24	豆鉤靱帯 Pisohamate ligament
3	長母指外転筋 Abductor pollicis longus	14	短小指屈筋 Flexor digiti minimi brevis	25	豆中手靱帯 Pisometacarpal ligament
4	短橈側手根伸筋 Extensor carpi radialis brevis	15	深指屈筋 Flexor digitorum profundus	26	第二背側骨間筋 2nd dorsal interosseous
5	長橈側手根伸筋 Extensor carpi radialis longus	16	浅指屈筋 Flexor digitorum superficialis	27	第二掌側骨間筋 訳注 2nd palmar interosseous
6	尺側手根伸筋 Extensor carpi ulnaris	17	短母指屈筋 Flexor pollicis brevis	28	第三背側骨間筋 3rd dorsal interosseous
7	指背腱膜* Extensor aponeurosis *	18	長母指屈筋 Flexor pollicis longus	29	第三掌側骨間筋 訳注 3rd palmar interosseous
8	短母指伸筋 Extensor pollicis brevis	19	第四背側骨間筋 4th dorsal interosseous	30	横頭〔母指内転筋〕 Transverse head〔Adductor pollicis〕
9	長母指伸筋 Extensor pollicis longus	20	第四掌側骨間筋 訳注 4th palmar interosseous		
10	第一背側骨間筋 1st dorsal interosseous	21	斜頭〔母指内転筋〕 Oblique head〔Adductor pollicis〕		
11	第一掌側骨間筋 訳注 1st palmar interosseous	22	小指対立筋 Opponens digiti minimi		

［訳注］11は痕跡的な筋であり，母指内転筋または短母指屈筋の一部とみなし，27，29，20をそれぞれ第一・第二・第三掌側骨間筋とすることもある．

- 中手指節関節は，中手骨頭と基節骨底の間の関節である．
- 指節間関節は，基節骨頭と中節骨底の間の，ならびに中節骨頭と末節骨底の間の関節である．母指の場合には，基節骨頭と末節骨底の間の関節である．
- 豆状骨は，尺側手根屈筋の腱の内部に生じた種子骨であり，豆鉤靱帯（24）および豆中手靱帯（25）によって固定されている．
- 背側骨間筋は，隣り合う2つの中手骨の側面から起始する（26が示すように，第二および第三中手骨の側面から起始している）．掌側骨間筋は，停止腱が着く指と同じ指の中手骨から起始する（27が示すように，第二中手骨から起こる）．176頁Bと比較してみよう．掌側から見た場合には掌側骨間筋に加えて背側骨間筋も見えること，しかし背側から見た場合には（176頁Aのように）背側骨間筋しか見えないことに注意せよ．

指の先天奇形

有鉤骨鉤骨折

Ⓐ〜Ⓙ 上肢骨（右）［二次骨化中心］

A：肩甲骨．上外側部．**B**：鎖骨．胸骨端．**C・D**：上腕骨．上端と下端．**E・F**：橈骨．上端と下端．**G・H**：尺骨．上端と下端．**I**：第一中手骨と母指の指節骨．**J**：第二中手骨と示指の指節骨．（図中の数字は年齢を表す．骨化開始→骨癒合．P：思春期．）

はじめの数字は二次骨化中心で骨化が始まるおおよその年齢を示す．2番目の数字（矢印の先）は，骨化中心が残りの骨と最終的に癒合する時期を示す．骨化の平均年齢しか記していない（下肢についても同様である（322, 323頁））．個体差はかなりあるが，最後に癒合が起こる成長端の位置は一定である．骨化の時期は，女性では男性より1年ないしそれ以上早いことが多い．

- Aに示されている肩峰，烏口突起および烏口突起下の各骨化中心以外に，肩甲骨には通常，下角，内側縁，関節窩縁の下部に骨化中心がある（すべて，思春期→20歳．143頁を参照）．
- 鎖骨は，全身で最初に骨化を始める骨である（発生第5週）．鎖骨は膜内骨化をするが，両端は軟骨内骨化をする時期がある．二次骨化中心は，胸骨端（B）に現れ，およそ25歳で鎖骨体と癒合する．
- 上腕骨の上端（C）では，上腕骨頭（1歳），大結節（3歳），小結節（5歳）の各骨化中心が，6歳で結合してできる．
- 上腕骨の下端（D）では，上腕骨小頭，上腕骨滑車および外側上顆の骨化中心が互いに癒合し，その後に上腕骨体と結合する．
- すべての指節骨（J）と第一中手骨（I）では，その近位端に二次骨化中心があり，第二〜第五中手骨（J）では遠位端にある．
- 手根骨は，出生時にはすべて軟骨性であり，二次骨化中心をもつものはない．最も大きな有頭骨が，最初に骨化を始める（生後2ヵ月）．続いておよそ1ヵ月以内に有鈎骨，3歳で三角骨，4歳で月状骨，5歳で舟状骨，大菱形骨，小菱形骨が骨化し，最後に9歳ないしそれ以後に豆状骨が骨化する．これらの時期にはしばしば変異が認められる．

肩と胸部（右）［体表解剖］

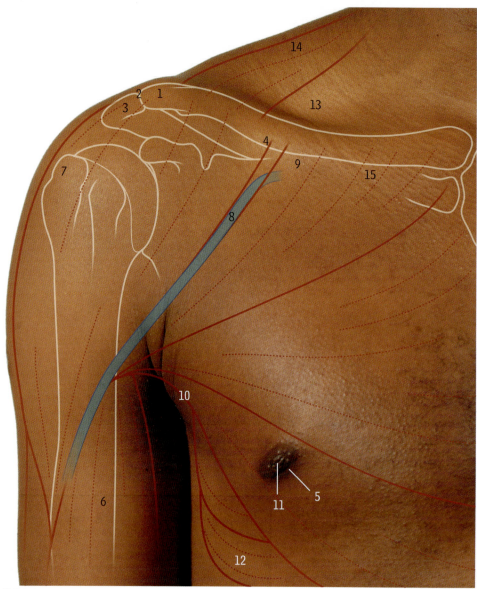

1	肩峰端〔鎖骨〕 Acromial end〔Clavicle〕
2	肩鎖関節 Acromioclavicular joint
3	肩峰 Acromion
4	三角筋（の前縁） Deltoid
5	乳輪 Areola
6	上腕二頭筋 Biceps brachii
7	三角筋（上腕骨の大結節を覆う） Deltoid
8	三角筋胸筋溝＊と橈側皮静脈 Deltopectoral groove＊ and Cephalic vein
9	鎖骨下窩 Infraclavicular fossa
10	大胸筋（の下縁） Pectoralis major
11	乳頭 Nipple
12	前鋸筋 Serratus anterior
13	大鎖骨上窩 Greater supraclavicular fossa
14	僧帽筋 Trapezius
15	大胸筋（の上縁） Pectoralis major

- 男性の乳頭(11)は，通常第四肋間に位置する．
- 大胸筋の下縁(10)は，前腋窩ヒダをつくる．
- 肩の最外側の骨の指標が大結節(7)であることに注意せよ．

前方から．

鎖骨は，全長にわたって皮下にある．肩鎖関節(2)を営む鎖骨の肩峰端(1)は，肩甲骨の肩峰(3)よりやや高い位置にある．肩の最外側では，三角筋が上腕骨を覆っている．肩峰は，外側へはそれほど延び出していない．ここに示す肩の特徴を次頁の剖出標本と比較せよ．

肩関節の脱臼

胸鎖関節脱臼

肩と胸部（右）

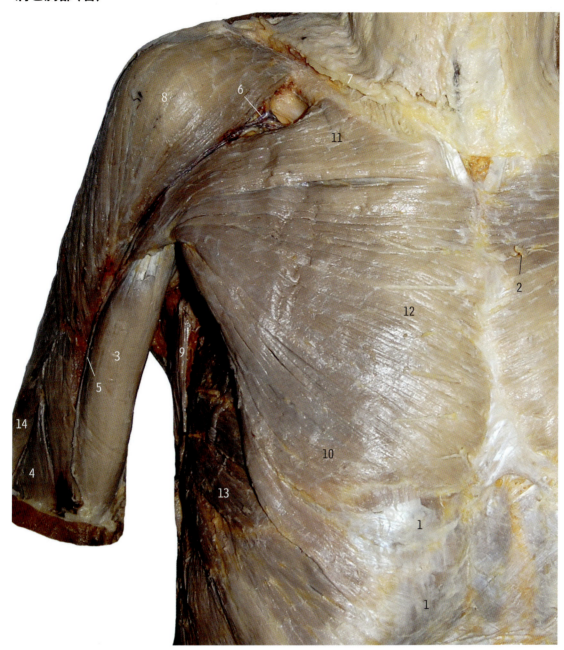

前方から．

皮膚と筋膜を除去し，肩と胸壁の前部の筋を示している．

1　前葉〔腹直筋鞘〕 　　Anterior layer (Rectus sheath)	6　橈側皮静脈（三角筋胸筋溝*を走る） 　　Cephalic vein	10　腹部〔大胸筋〕 　　Abdominal part (Pectoralis major)
2　肋間神経・血管の前貫通枝	7　鎖骨 　　Clavicle	11　鎖骨部〔大胸筋〕 　　Clavicular head (Pectoralis major)
3　長頭〔上腕二頭筋〕 　　Long head (Biceps brachii)	8　三角筋 　　Deltoid	12　胸骨部〔大胸筋〕 　　Sternal head (Pectoralis major)
4　腕橈骨筋 　　Brachioradialis	9　広背筋 　　Latissimus dorsi	13　前鋸筋 　　Serratus anterior
5　橈側皮静脈 　　Cephalic vein		14　外側頭〔上腕三頭筋〕 　　Lateral head (Triceps brachii)

骨髄内注射

肩と頸部の皮神経（右）

皮膚と筋膜を除去し，鎖骨(9)を乗り越える鎖骨上神経(6)の枝，また三角筋(13)と大胸筋(11)の間の三角筋胸筋溝*を走る橈側皮静脈(7)を示している．

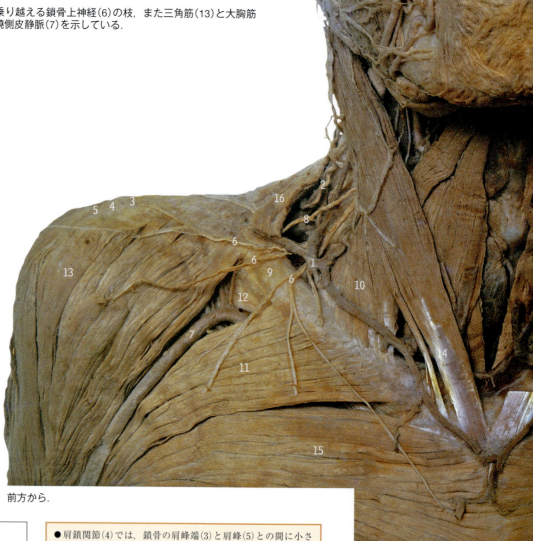

前方から．

1	浅層の静脈	
2	副神経 [XI]	Accessory nerve [XI]
3	肩峰端〔鎖骨〕	Acromial end〔Clavicle〕
4	肩鎖関節	Acromioclavicular joint
5	肩峰	Acromion
6	鎖骨上神経	Supraclavicular nerves
7	橈側皮静脈	Cephalic vein
8	僧帽筋への枝*〔頸神経〕	Branch to trapezius *〔Cervical nerves〕
9	鎖骨	Clavicle
10	鎖骨頭*〔胸鎖乳突筋〕	Clavicular head *〔Sternocleidomastoid〕
11	鎖骨部〔大胸筋〕	Clavicular head〔Pectoralis major〕
12	鎖骨胸筋筋膜	Clavipectoral fascia
13	三角筋	Deltoid
14	胸骨頭*〔胸鎖乳突筋〕	Sternal head *〔Sternocleidomastoid〕
15	胸肋部〔大胸筋〕	Sternocostal head〔Pectoralis major〕
16	僧帽筋	Trapezius

- 肩鎖関節(4)では，鎖骨の肩峰端(3)と肩峰(5)との間に小さな"段差"がみられる．132頁の体表解剖の図中の2と比較せよ．このような"段差"がみられることは正常であり，関節が脱臼し，肩峰が鎖骨の外側端の下に転位すると，この"段差"は非常に大きくなる．
- 橈側皮静脈(7)は，三角筋(13)と大胸筋(11)の間の三角筋胸筋溝*を走り，鎖骨胸筋筋膜(12)を貫き腋窩静脈に注ぐ．

肩(右)［深層］

前方から．

三角筋(10)と大胸筋(20)の大部分を除去し，下層の小胸筋(21)ならびに周囲の血管と神経を示している．鎖骨(7)と小胸筋(21)の上（内側）縁の間に張る鎖骨胸筋筋膜も除去し，腋窩静脈(3)が橈側皮静脈(6)を流入してから第一肋骨(11)をまたぐ鎖骨下静脈(27)を示している．

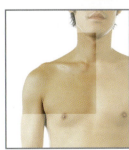

1	前上腕回旋動脈と筋皮神経 Anterior circumflex humeral artery and Musculocutaneous nerve
2	腋窩リンパ節（腫大している） Axillary lymph nodes
3	腋窩静脈 Axillary vein
4	内側胸筋神経の枝 Branches of Medial pectoral nerve
5	外側胸筋神経の枝 Branches of Lateral pectoral nerve
6	橈側皮静脈 Cephalic vein
7	鎖骨 Clavicle
8	烏口腕筋 Coracobrachialis
9	烏口突起と肩峰枝〔胸肩峰動脈〕 Coracoid process and Acromial branch〔Thoraco-acromial artery〕
10	三角筋 Deltoid
11	第一肋骨 1st rib : Rib I
12	下腹〔肩甲舌骨筋〕（上方にずらしている） Inferior belly〔Omohyoid〕
13	肋間上腕神経 Intercostobrachial nerves
14	内頸静脈 Internal jugular vein
15	外側胸動脈 Lateral thoracic artery
16	長胸神経（前鋸筋を支配） Long thoracic nerve
17	正中神経 Median nerve
18	胸骨甲状筋への枝 Nerve to Sternothyroid
19	胸筋枝〔胸肩峰動脈〕 Pectoral branches〔Thoraco-acromial artery〕
20	大胸筋 Pectoralis major
21	小胸筋 Pectoralis minor
22	横隔神経（前斜角筋の前を通る） Phrenic nerve
23	中斜角筋 Middle scalene
24	短頭〔上腕二頭筋〕 Short head〔Biceps brachii〕
25	胸骨舌骨筋 Sternohyoid
26	胸骨甲状筋 Sternothyroid
27	鎖骨下静脈 Subclavian vein
28	鎖骨下筋 Subclavius
29	肩甲下筋 Subscapularis
30	肩甲上神経 Suprascapular nerve
31	長頭〔上腕二頭筋〕(の腱) Long head〔Biceps brachii〕
32	僧帽筋 Trapezius
33	神経幹〔腕神経叢〕 Trunks〔Brachial plexus〕

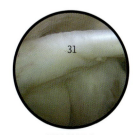

右肩を後方から見た関節鏡写真である．棘上筋の腱と上腕二頭筋の長頭は，正常の状態である．関節唇の前縁が，少し摩耗している．

関節鏡写真

Déjèrine-Klumpke 麻痺
（下位型腕神経叢麻痺）

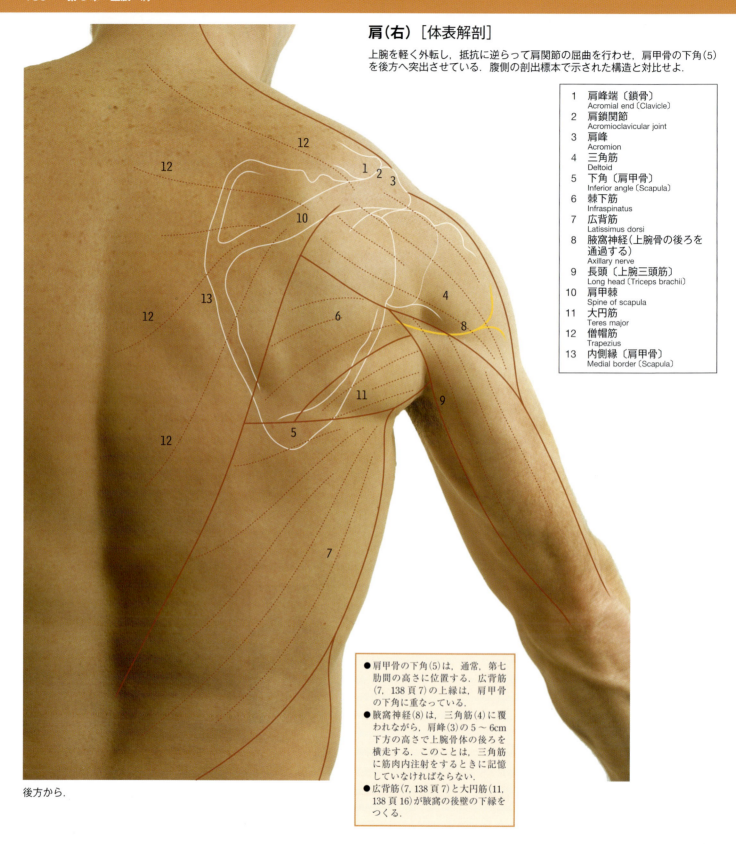

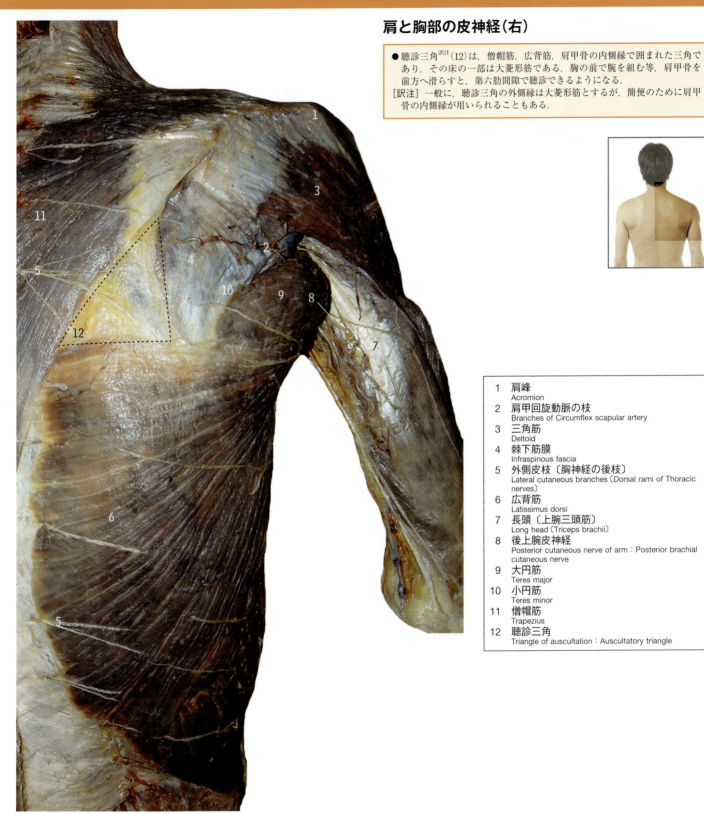

肩と胸部の皮神経（右）

- 聴診三角[訳注](12)は，僧帽筋，広背筋，肩甲骨の内側縁で囲まれた三角であり，その床の一部は大菱形筋である．胸の前で腕を組む等，肩甲骨を前方へ滑らすと，第六肋間隙で聴診できるようになる．
  [訳注] 一般に，聴診三角の外側縁は大菱形筋とするが，簡便のために肩甲骨の内側縁が用いられることもある．

1	肩峰	Acromion
2	肩甲回旋動脈の枝	Branches of Circumflex scapular artery
3	三角筋	Deltoid
4	棘下筋膜	Infraspinous fascia
5	外側皮枝〔胸神経の後枝〕	Lateral cutaneous branches〔Dorsal rami of Thoracic nerves〕
6	広背筋	Latissimus dorsi
7	長頭〔上腕三頭筋〕	Long head〔Triceps brachii〕
8	後上腕皮神経	Posterior cutaneous nerve of arm：Posterior brachial cutaneous nerve
9	大円筋	Teres major
10	小円筋	Teres minor
11	僧帽筋	Trapezius
12	聴診三角	Triangle of auscultation：Auscultatory triangle

後方から．

三角筋への筋肉内注射

肩（右）［肩甲部, 浅層］

1	肩峰	Acromion
2	肩甲回旋動脈の枝	Branches of Circumflex scapular artery
3	肩甲背動脈〔頸横動脈〕	Dorsal scapular artery〔Transverse cervical artery〕
4	三角筋	Deltoid
5	脊柱起立筋	Erector spinae
6	棘下筋	Infraspinatus
7	広背筋	Latissimus dorsi
8	肩甲挙筋	Levator scapulae
9	内側縁〔肩甲骨〕	Medial border〔Scapula〕
10	大菱形筋	Rhomboid major
11	小菱形筋	Rhomboid minor
12	脊髄根〔副神経［XI］〕	Spinal root〔Accessory nerve［XI］〕
13	肩甲棘	Spine of scapula
14	頭板状筋	Splenius capitis
15	棘上筋	Supraspinatus
16	大円筋	Teres major
17	小円筋	Teres minor
18	胸腰筋膜（胸部）	Thoracolumbar fascia
19	僧帽筋（切断して翻転してある）	Trapezius

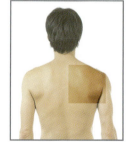

後方から. 僧帽筋を翻転してある.

肩関節への注射

A 肩(右)〔肩甲部, 中層〕

B 肩と上腕(右)

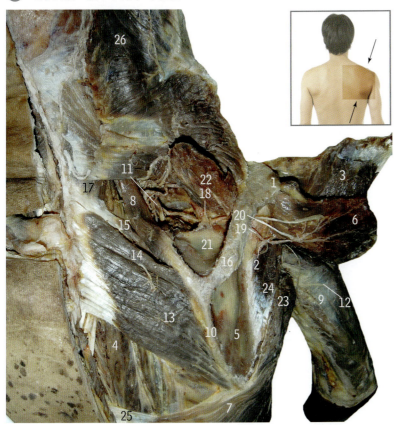

A：上後方から． B：右側方から．

1	肩峰 Acromion	14	小菱形筋 Rhomboid minor
2	肩甲回旋動脈の枝 Branches of Circumflex scapular artery	15	上後鋸筋 Serratus posterior superior
3	三角筋(切断して翻転してある) Deltoid	16	肩甲棘 Spine of scapula
4	脊柱起立筋 Erector spinae	17	頭板状筋 Splenius capitis
5	棘下窩 Infraspinous fossa	18	上肩甲横靱帯 Superior transverse scapular ligament
6	棘下筋(切断して翻転してある) Infraspinatus	19	肩甲上動脈 Suprascapular artery
7	広背筋 Latissimus dorsi	20	肩甲上神経 Suprascapular nerve
8	肩甲挙筋 Levator scapulae	21	棘上窩 Supraspinous fossa
9	長頭〔上腕三頭筋〕 Long head (Triceps brachii)	22	棘上筋(切断して翻転してある) Supraspinatus
10	内側縁〔肩甲骨〕 Medial border (Scapula)	23	大円筋 Teres major
11	肩甲舌骨筋 Omohyoid	24	小円筋 Teres minor
12	後上腕皮神経 Posterior cutaneous nerve of arm: Posterior brachial cutaneous nerve	25	胸腰筋膜(胸部) Thoracolumbar fascia
13	大菱形筋 Rhomboid major	26	僧帽筋(切断して翻転してある) Trapezius

三角筋(7)は，肩先を覆い，上腕の中程の高さまで下がり，上腕骨体の外側面に停止する．上腕二頭筋(3)は，大胸筋(8)の後方で上腕の前面にある．上腕三頭筋(11, 12)は，上腕の後面にある．

1	肩峰 Acromion	9	橈骨神経 Radial nerve
2	肘筋 Anconeus	10	後前腕皮神経〔橈骨神経〕 Posterior cutaneous nerve of forearm: Posterior antebrachial cutaneous nerve (Radial nerve)
3	上腕二頭筋 Biceps brachii	11	外側頭〔上腕三頭筋〕 Lateral head (Triceps brachii)
4	上腕筋 Brachialis	12	長頭〔上腕三頭筋〕 Long head (Triceps brachii)
5	腕橈骨筋 Brachioradialis	13	上腕三頭筋(の腱) Triceps brachii
6	橈側皮静脈 Cephalic vein		
7	三角筋 Deltoid		
8	大胸筋 Pectoralis major		

肩関節の後方脱臼

肩（右）［肩甲部，深層］

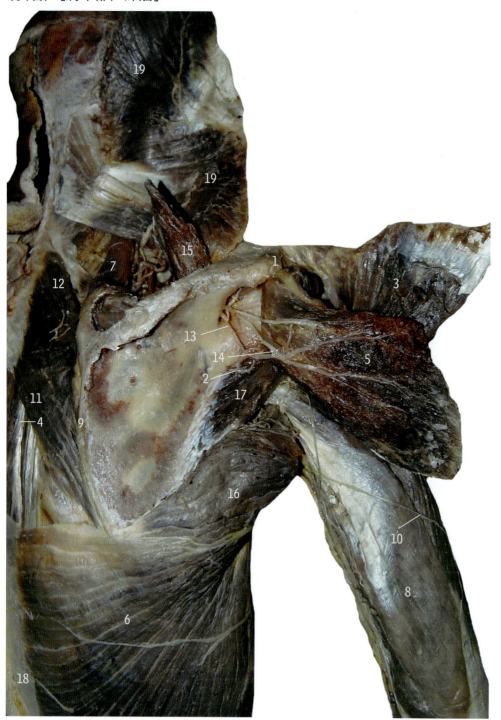

1 肩峰 Acromion	8 長頭〔上腕三頭筋〕 Long head（Triceps brachii）	14 肩甲上神経 Suprascapular nerve
2 肩甲回旋動脈の枝 Branches of Circumflex scapular artery	9 内側縁〔肩甲骨〕 Medial border（Scapula）	15 棘上筋（切断して翻転してある） Supraspinatus
3 三角筋（切断して翻転してある） Deltoid	10 後上腕皮神経 Posterior cutaneous nerve of arm：Posterior brachial cutaneous nerve	16 大円筋 Teres major
4 脊柱起立筋 Erector spinae	11 大菱形筋 Rhomboid major	17 小円筋 Teres minor
5 棘下筋（切断して翻転してある） Infraspinatus	12 小菱形筋 Rhomboid minor	18 胸腰筋膜（胸部） Thoracolumbar fascia
6 広背筋 Latissimus dorsi	13 肩甲上動脈 Suprascapular artery	19 僧帽筋（切断して翻転してある） Trapezius
7 肩甲挙筋 Levator scapulae		

肩（右）[深層]

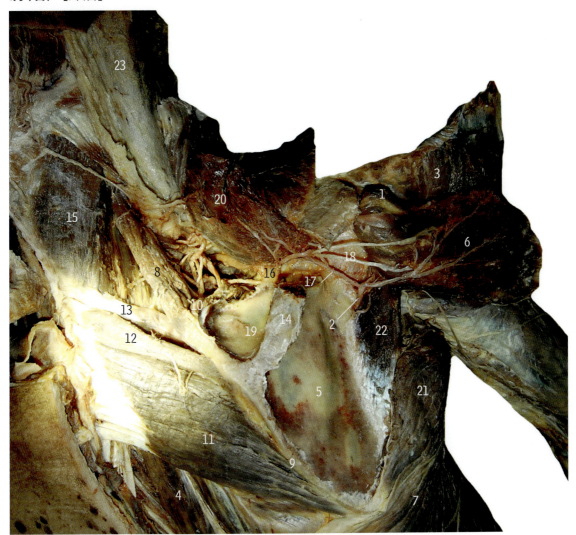

上後方から.

1	肩峰 Acromion	13	上後鋸筋 Serratus posterior superior
2	肩甲回旋動脈の枝（肩甲上動脈と吻合する） Branches of Circumflex scapular artery	14	肩甲棘 Spine of scapula
3	三角筋（切断して翻転してある） Deltoid	15	頭板状筋 Splenius capitis
4	脊柱起立筋 Erector spinae	16	上肩甲横靱帯 Superior transverse scapular ligament
5	棘下窩 Infraspinous fossa	17	肩甲上動脈 Suprascapular artery
6	棘下筋（切断して翻転してある） Infraspinatus	18	肩甲上神経 Suprascapular nerve
7	広背筋 Latissimus dorsi	19	棘上窩 Supraspinous fossa
8	肩甲挙筋 Levator scapulae	20	棘上筋（切断して翻転してある） Supraspinatus
9	内側縁〔肩甲骨〕 Medial border〔Scapula〕	21	大円筋 Teres major
10	肩甲舌骨筋 Omohyoid	22	小円筋 Teres minor
11	大菱形筋 Rhomboid major	23	僧帽筋（切断して翻転してある） Trapezius
12	小菱形筋 Rhomboid minor		

肩甲骨周囲の
動脈の吻合

A B 肩関節（右）

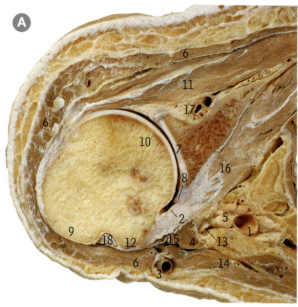

横断面．

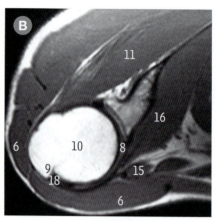

MR 横断画像

下方から見たこの横断標本では，上腕骨頭（10）と肩甲骨の関節窩（7）が，関節をつくる様子を示している．上腕二頭筋の長頭腱（18）が，上腕骨の大結節（9）と小結節（12）の間の結節間溝を通っている．肩甲下筋（16）の腱が肩関節のすぐ前を通り，棘下筋（11）が肩関節のすぐ後ろを通る．A の横断標本と B の MR 横断画像とを比較せよ．

1	腋窩動脈 Axillary artery	10	上腕骨頭 Head of humerus
2	関節包 Articular capsule	11	棘下筋 Infraspinatus
3	橈側皮静脈 Cephalic vein	12	小結節 Lesser tubercle
4	烏口腕筋 Coracobrachialis	13	筋皮神経 Musculocutaneous nerve
5	神経束〔腕神経叢〕 Cords〔Brachial plexus〕	14	大胸筋 Pectoralis major
6	三角筋 Deltoid	15	短頭〔上腕二頭筋〕 Short head〔Biceps brachii〕
7	関節窩 Glenoid cavity	16	肩甲下筋 Subscapularis
8	関節唇 Glenoid labrum	17	肩甲上神経・動／静脈 Suprascapular nerve and artery/vein
9	大結節 Greater tubercle	18	長頭〔上腕二頭筋〕 Long head〔Biceps brachii〕

C 肩関節（右）

前方から．

関節包（2）の関節腔と肩峰下包（5）のそれぞれに，緑色の樹脂を注入した．

1	肩鎖関節 Acromioclavicular joint
2	関節包〔肩関節〕 Articular capsule〔Glenohumeral joint : Shoulder joint〕
3	円錐靱帯 Conoid ligament
4	烏口肩峰靱帯 Coraco-acromial ligament
5	肩峰下包 Subacromial bursa
6	肩甲下筋の腱下包 Subtendinous bursa of subscapularis
7	上肩甲横靱帯 Superior transverse scapular ligament
8	長頭〔上腕二頭筋〕（の腱） Long head〔Biceps brachii〕
9	菱形靱帯 Trapezoid ligament

D 肩

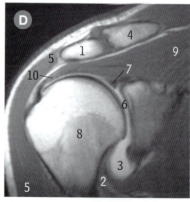

MR 冠状断画像

1	肩峰 Acromion
2	腋窩神経と上腕回旋動／静脈 Axillary nerve and Circumflex humeral artery/vein
3	肩関節（の腋窩陥凹） Glenohumeral joint : Shoulder joint
4	鎖骨 Clavicle
5	三角筋 Deltoid
6	関節窩 Glenoid cavity
7	関節唇 Glenoid labrum
8	上腕骨 Humerus
9	棘上筋 Supraspinatus
10	棘上筋（の腱） Supraspinatus

E F 肩

E

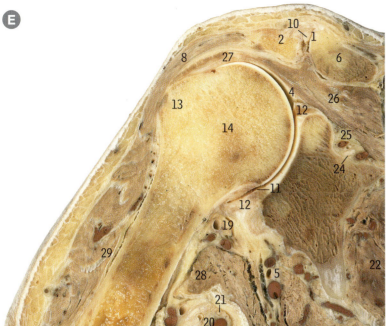

冠状断面.

関節鏡写真

関節鏡を肩関節の後方から挿入したときに最初に見える像である．上腕骨頭が左に，肩甲下筋の腱が中央に，関節腔と関節唇が右に見える．肩関節は，牽引されていることと関節鏡施行時に用いた液体により，わずかに広がっていることがわかる．

G 肩関節（右）

関節包の後部全体を取り除いてあるので，関節包(4)の前部の内面を補強する関節上腕靱帯(15, 17, 23)とともに見えている．

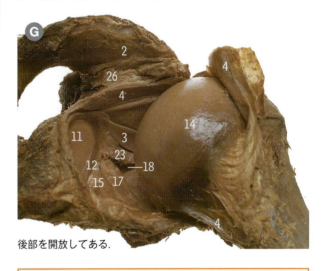

後部を開放してある．

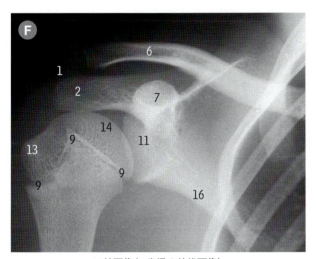

X線画像（9歳児の前後画像）

- 関節腔は，上関節上腕靱帯(23)と中関節上腕靱帯(17)の間の開口部(18)を通じて肩甲下部の腱下包と連絡している．
- 上腕二頭筋の長頭(3)の腱は，関節唇(12)に連続している．

1	肩鎖関節 Acromioclavicular joint	9	骨端線 Epiphysial line	17	中関節上腕靱帯 Middle glenohumeral ligament	24	肩甲上神経 Suprascapular nerve
2	肩峰 Acromion	10	関節円板〔肩鎖関節〕 Articular disc〔Acromioclavicular joint〕	18	肩甲下筋の腱下包への開口部	25	肩甲上動／静脈 Suprascapular artery/vein
3	長頭〔上腕二頭筋〕 Long head〔Biceps brachii〕	11	関節窩 Glenoid cavity	19	後上腕回旋動／静脈 Posterior circumflex humeral artery/vein	26	棘上筋 Supraspinatus
4	関節包 Articular capsule	12	関節唇 Glenoid labrum	20	上腕深動／静脈 Profunda brachii artery/vein	27	棘上筋（の腱） Supraspinatus
5	肩甲回旋動／静脈 Circumflex scapular artery/vein	13	大結節 Greater tubercle	21	橈骨神経 Radial nerve	28	大円筋 Teres major
6	鎖骨 Clavicle	14	上腕骨頭 Head of humerus	22	肩甲下筋 Subscapularis	29	外側頭〔上腕三頭筋〕 Lateral head〔Triceps brachii〕
7	烏口突起 Coracoid process	15	下関節上腕靱帯 Inferior glenohumeral ligament	23	上関節上腕靱帯 Superior glenohumeral ligament		
8	三角筋 Deltoid	16	外側縁〔肩甲骨〕 Lateral border〔Scapula〕				

上腕二頭筋腱炎と
上腕二頭筋断裂

石灰性腱炎

有痛弧／腱板断裂

A 腋窩(右) [胸壁の前部]

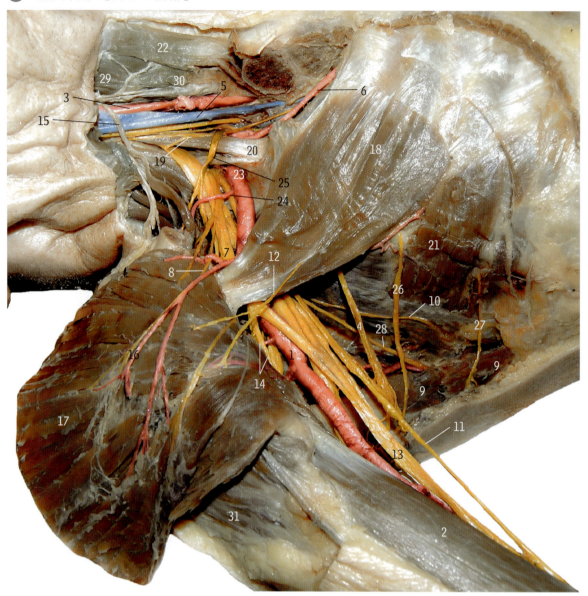

1 腋窩動脈 Axillary artery	11 内側前腕皮神経 Medial cutaneous nerve of forearm； Medial antebrachial cutaneous nerve	21 前鋸筋 Serratus anterior
2 上腕二頭筋 Biceps brachii	12 内側胸筋神経 Medial pectoral nerve	22 胸骨舌骨筋 Sternohyoid
3 総頸動脈 Common carotid artery	13 正中神経 Median nerve	23 鎖骨下動脈 Subclavian artery
4 肋間上腕神経 Intercostobrachial nerves	14 筋皮神経 Musculocutaneous nerve	24 肩甲上動脈 Suprascapular artery
5 内頸静脈 Internal jugular vein	15 肩甲舌骨筋(の中間腱) Omohyoid	25 肩甲上神経 Suprascapular nerve
6 内胸動脈 Internal thoracic artery	16 胸筋枝〔胸肩峰動脈〕 Pectoral branches〔Thoraco-acromial artery〕	26 第三胸神経 3rd thoracic nerve (T3)
7 外側神経束〔腕神経叢〕 Lateral cord〔Brachial plexus〕	17 大胸筋(翻転してある) Pectoralis major	27 第四胸神経 4th thoracic nerve (T4)
8 外側胸筋神経 Lateral pectoral nerve	18 小胸筋 Pectoralis minor	28 胸背神経 Thoracodorsal nerve
9 広背筋 Latissimus dorsi	19 横隔神経 Phrenic nerve	29 甲状舌骨筋 Thyrohyoid
10 長胸神経 Long thoracic nerve	20 前斜角筋 Anterior scalene	30 甲状腺 Thyroid gland
		31 上腕三頭筋 Triceps brachii

鎖骨下・
腋窩静脈血栓症

頸肋

B 腋窩と腕神経叢（右）

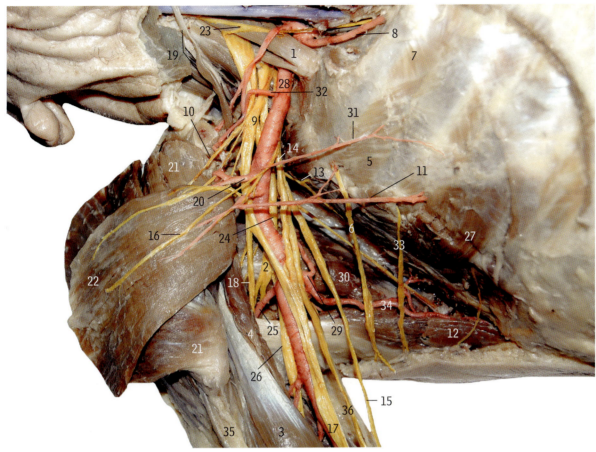

前方から．

1 前斜角筋 Anterior scalene	13 長胸神経 Long thoracic nerve	25 後上腕回旋動脈 Posterior circumflex humeral artery
2 腋窩神経 Axillary nerve	14 内側神経束〔腕神経叢〕 Medial cord〔Brachial plexus〕	26 橈骨神経 Radial nerve
3 上腕二頭筋 Biceps brachii	15 内側前腕皮神経 Medial cutaneous nerve of forearm : Medial antebrachial cutaneous nerve	27 前鋸筋 Serratus anterior
4 烏口腕筋 Coracobrachialis	16 内側胸筋神経 Medial pectoral nerve	28 鎖骨下動脈 Subclavian artery
5 外肋間筋 External intercostal muscle	17 正中神経 Median nerve	29 肩甲下動脈 Subscapular artery
6 肋間上腕神経 Intercostobrachial nerves	18 筋皮神経 Musculocutaneous nerve	30 肩甲下筋 Subscapularis
7 内肋間筋 Internal intercostal muscle	19 肩甲舌骨筋 Omohyoid	31 最上胸動脈 Superior thoracic artery
8 内胸動脈 Internal thoracic artery	20 胸筋枝〔胸肩峰動脈〕 Pectoral branches〔Thoraco-acromial artery〕	32 肩甲上動脈 Suprascapular artery
9 外側神経束〔腕神経叢〕 Lateral cord〔Brachial plexus〕	21 大胸筋（翻転してある） Pectoralis major	33 第三胸神経 3rd thoracic nerve (T3)
10 外側胸筋神経 Lateral pectoral nerve	22 小胸筋（翻転してある） Pectoralis minor	34 胸背動脈 Thoracodorsal artery
11 外側胸動脈 Lateral thoracic artery	23 横隔神経 Phrenic nerve	35 上腕三頭筋 Triceps brachii
12 広背筋 Latissimus dorsi	24 後神経束〔腕神経叢〕 Posterior cord〔Brachial plexus〕	36 尺骨神経 Ulnar nerve

Erb-Duchenne 麻痺
（上位型腕神経叢麻痺）

翼状肩甲骨

腕神経叢（右）

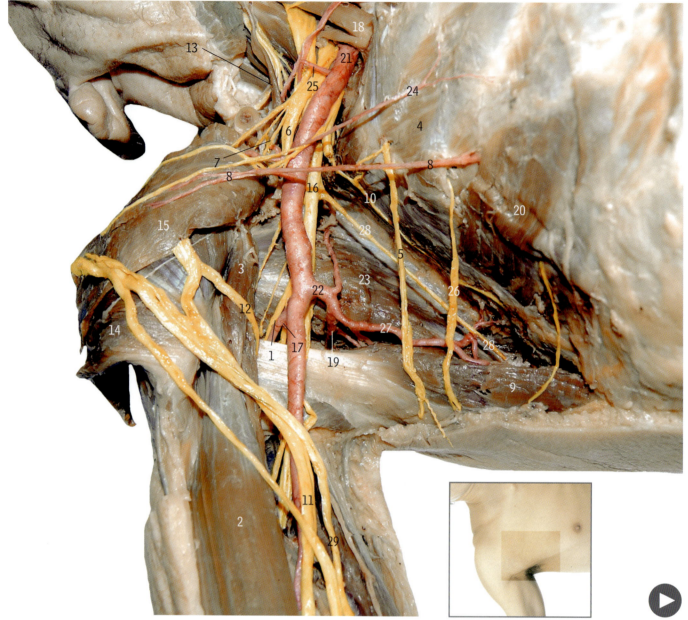

腕神経叢を除去し，腋窩動脈の枝が見えるように翻転してある．

1	腋窩神経	Axillary nerve
2	上腕二頭筋	Biceps brachii
3	烏口腕筋	Coracobrachialis
4	外肋間筋	External intercostal muscle
5	肋間上腕神経	Intercostobrachial nerves
6	外側神経束〔腕神経叢〕	Lateral cord〔Brachial plexus〕
7	外側胸筋神経	Lateral pectoral nerve
8	外側胸動脈	Lateral thoracic artery
9	広背筋	Latissimus dorsi
10	長胸神経	Long thoracic nerve
11	正中神経	Median nerve
12	筋皮神経	Musculocutaneous nerve
13	下腹〔肩甲舌骨筋〕	Inferior belly〔Omohyoid〕
14	大胸筋（翻転してある）	Pectoralis major
15	小胸筋（翻転してある）	Pectoralis minor
16	後神経束〔腕神経叢〕	Posterior cord〔Brachial plexus〕
17	後上腕回旋動脈	Posterior circumflex humeral artery
18	前斜角筋	Anterior scalene
19	肩甲回旋動脈	Circumflex scapular artery
20	前鋸筋	Serratus anterior
21	鎖骨下動脈	Subclavian artery
22	肩甲下動脈	Subscapular artery
23	肩甲下筋	Subscapularis
24	最上胸動脈	Superior thoracic artery
25	肩甲上動脈	Suprascapular artery
26	第三胸神経	3rd thoracic nerve (T3)
27	胸背動脈	Thoracodorsal artery
28	胸背神経	Thoracodorsal nerve
29	尺骨神経	Ulnar nerve

腋窩動脈の動脈瘤

血管の異常

腕神経叢と腋窩（右）

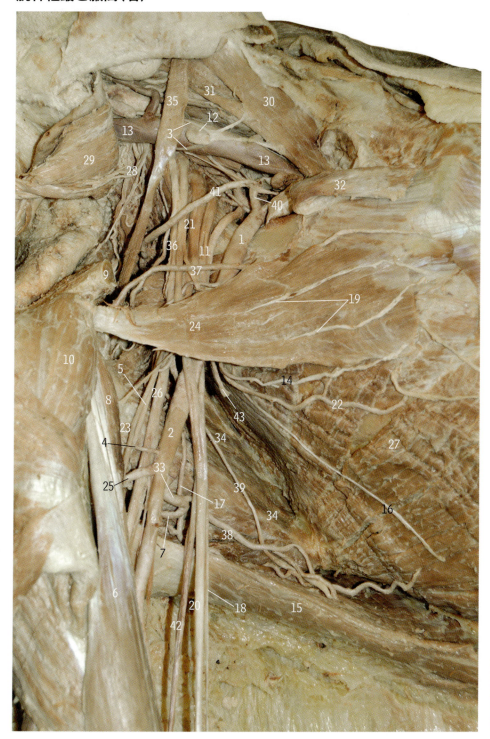

1	腋窩動脈（の第一部）	Axillary artery
2	腋窩動脈（の第三部）	Axillary artery
3	頸神経ワナ	Ansa cervicalis
4	前上腕回旋動脈	Anterior circumflex humeral artery
5	腋窩神経	Axillary nerve
6	短頭〔上腕二頭筋〕	Short head〔Biceps brachii〕
7	肩甲回旋動脈	Circumflex scapular artery
8	烏口腕筋	Coracobrachialis
9	鎖骨（切断縁）	Clavicle
10	三角筋	Deltoid
11	下神経幹〔腕神経叢〕	Inferior trunk：Lower trunk〔Brachial plexus〕
12	浅リンパ節〔外側頸リンパ節〕	Superficial nodes〔Lateral cervical nodes〕
13	内頸静脈	Internal jugular vein
14	外側胸動脈	Lateral thoracic artery
15	広背筋	Latissimus dorsi
16	長胸神経	Long thoracic nerve
17	下肩甲下神経*	Lower subscapular nerves*
18	内側前腕皮神経	Medial cutaneous nerve of forearm：Medial antebrachial cutaneous nerve
19	内側胸筋神経	Medial pectoral nerve
20	正中神経（内側に翻転してある）	Median nerve
21	中神経幹〔腕神経叢〕	Middle trunk〔Brachial plexus〕
22	外側胸動脈（前鋸筋への枝）	Lateral thoracic artery
23	筋皮神経	Musculocutaneous nerve
24	小胸筋	Pectoralis minor
25	後上腕回旋動脈	Posterior circumflex humeral artery
26	橈骨神経	Radial nerve
27	前鋸筋	Serratus anterior
28	脊髄根〔副神経［XI］〕	Spinal root〔Accessory nerve［XI］〕
29	胸鎖乳突筋（翻転してある）	Sternocleidomastoid
30	胸骨舌骨筋	Sternohyoid
31	胸骨甲状筋	Sternothyroid
32	鎖骨下筋（翻転してある）	Subclavius
33	肩甲下動脈	Subscapular artery
34	肩甲下筋	Subscapularis
35	上腹〔肩甲舌骨筋〕	Superior belly〔Omohyoid〕
36	上神経幹〔腕神経叢〕	Superior trunk：Upper trunk〔Brachial plexus〕
37	肩甲上動脈（変異）	Suprascapular artery
38	胸背動脈	Thoracodorsal artery
39	胸背神経	Thoracodorsal nerve
40	甲状頸動脈	Thyrocervical trunk
41	頸横動脈	Transverse cervical artery
42	尺骨神経	Ulnar nerve
43	上肩甲下神経*	Upper subscapular nerve*

腕神経叢と腋窩動脈・静脈(右)

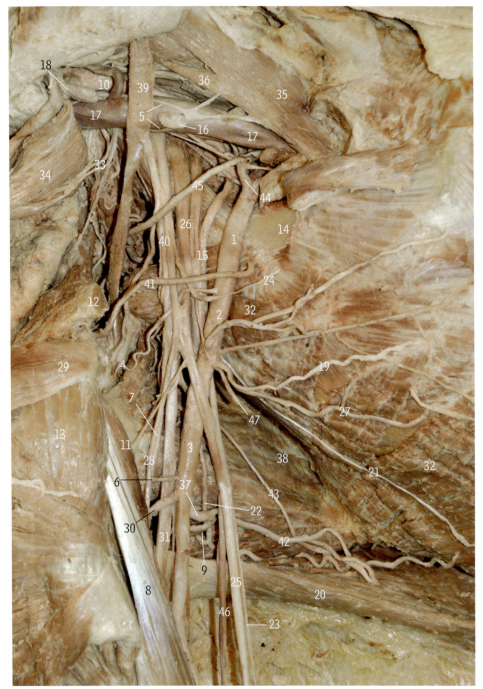

小胸筋を翻転してある.

1	腋窩動脈(の第一部)	Axillary artery
2	腋窩動脈(の第二部)	Axillary artery
3	腋窩動脈(の第三部)	Axillary artery
4	肩峰枝〔胸肩峰動脈〕	Acromial branch〔Thoraco-acromial artery〕
5	頸神経ワナ	Ansa cervicalis
6	前上腕回旋動脈	Anterior circumflex humeral artery
7	腋窩神経	Axillary nerve
8	短頭〔上腕二頭筋〕	Short head〔Biceps brachii〕
9	肩甲回旋動脈	Circumflex scapular artery
10	総頸動脈	Common carotid artery
11	烏口腕筋	Coracobrachialis
12	鎖骨(切断縁)	Clavicle
13	三角筋	Deltoid
14	第一肋骨	1st rib : Rib I
15	下神経幹〔腕神経叢〕	Inferior trunk : Lower trunk〔Brachial plexus〕
16	浅リンパ節〔外側頸リンパ節〕	Superficial nodes〔Lateral cervical nodes〕
17	内頸静脈	Internal jugular vein
18	頸静脈二腹筋リンパ節	Jugulodigastric nodes
19	外側胸動脈	Lateral thoracic artery
20	広背筋	Latissimus dorsi
21	長胸神経	Long thoracic nerve
22	下肩甲下神経*	Lower subscapular nerves*
23	内側前腕皮神経	Medial cutaneous nerve of forearm : Medial antebrachial cutaneous nerve
24	内側胸筋神経	Medial pectoral nerve
25	正中神経(内側に引き寄せてある)	Median nerve
26	中神経幹〔腕神経叢〕	Middle trunk〔Brachial plexus〕
27	外側胸動脈(前鋸筋への枝)	Lateral thoracic artery
28	筋皮神経	Musculocutaneous nerve
29	小胸筋(翻転してある)	Pectoralis minor
30	後上腕回旋動脈	Posterior circumflex humeral artery
31	橈骨神経	Radial nerve
32	前鋸筋	Serratus anterior
33	脊髄根〔副神経[XI]〕	Spinal root〔Accessory nerve [XI]〕
34	胸鎖乳突筋(翻転してある)	Sternocleidomastoid
35	胸骨舌骨筋	Sternohyoid
36	胸骨甲状筋	Sternothyroid
37	肩甲下動脈	Subscapular artery
38	肩甲下筋	Subscapularis
39	上腹〔肩甲舌骨筋〕	Superior belly〔Omohyoid〕
40	上神経幹〔腕神経叢〕	Superior trunk : Upper trunk〔Brachial plexus〕
41	肩甲上動脈(変異)	Suprascapular artery
42	胸背動脈	Thoracodorsal artery
43	胸背神経	Thoracodorsal nerve
44	甲状頸動脈	Thyrocervical trunk
45	頸横動脈	Transverse cervical artery
46	尺骨神経	Ulnar nerve
47	上肩甲下神経*	Upper subscapular nerves*

腕神経叢とその枝（左）

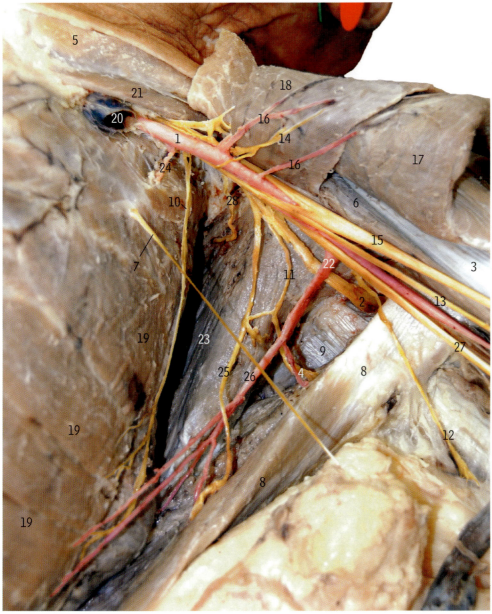

前下方から．

1 腋窩動脈 Axillary artery	11 下肩甲下神経* Lower subscapular nerves*	19 前鋸筋 Serratus anterior
2 腋窩神経（四角隙*を通る） Axillary nerve	12 内側上腕皮神経 Medial cutaneous nerve of arm； Medial brachial cutaneous nerve	20 鎖骨下静脈（切断してある） Subclavian vein
3 上腕二頭筋 Biceps brachii	13 内側前腕皮神経 Medial cutaneous nerve of forearm；Medial antebrachial cutaneous nerve	21 鎖骨下筋 Subclavius
4 肩甲回旋動脈 Circumflex scapular artery		22 肩甲下動脈 Subscapular artery
5 鎖骨 Clavicle	14 内側胸筋神経 Medial pectoral nerve	23 肩甲下筋 Subscapularis
6 烏口腕筋 Coracobrachialis	15 正中神経 Median nerve	24 最上胸動脈 Superior thoracic artery
7 肋間上腕神経 Intercostobrachial nerves	16 胸筋枝〔腋窩動脈〕 Pectoral branches〔Axillary artery〕	25 胸背神経 Thoracodorsal nerve
8 広背筋 Latissimus dorsi	17 大胸筋（翻転してある） Pectoralis major	26 胸背動脈 Thoracodorsal artery
9 長頭〔上腕三頭筋〕 Long head〔Triceps brachii〕	18 小胸筋（翻転してある） Pectoralis minor	27 尺骨神経 Ulnar nerve
10 長胸神経 Long thoracic nerve		28 上肩甲下神経* Upper subscapular nerves*

腕神経叢ブロック

腕神経叢とその枝（右）

血管をすべて除去し，腕神経叢を構成する神経束とそれらの枝が明瞭に見えるようにしてある．"大文字のM"のパターンが，筋皮神経(18)，正中神経の外側根(8)，正中神経(17)，正中神経内側根(16)ならびに尺骨神経(26)から形成されていることに留意せよ．本例では，広背筋(9)の停止腱が異常に幅広く，上腕三頭筋の長頭(10)の腱と癒合している．

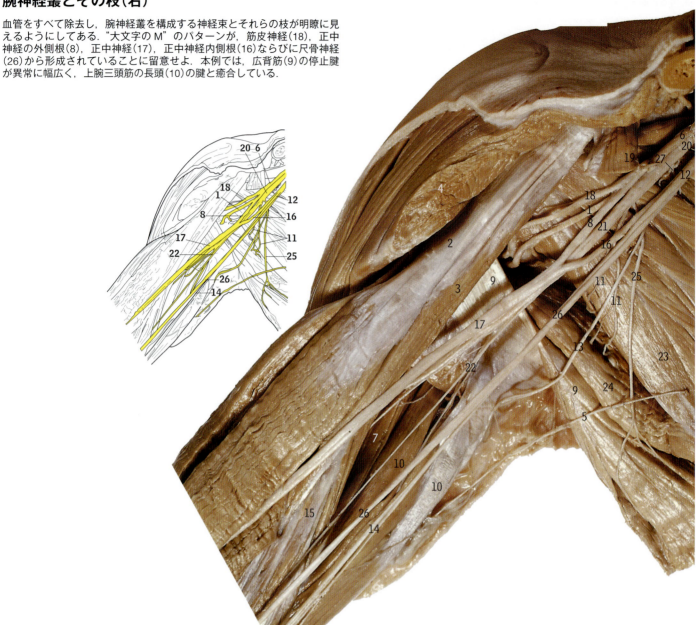

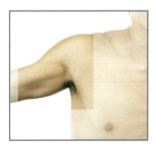

肩関節の後方脱臼

1	腋窩神経 Axillary nerve	10	長頭〔上腕三頭筋〕 Long head (Triceps brachii)
2	上腕二頭筋 Biceps brachii	11	下肩甲下神経* Lower subscapular nerves *
3	烏口腕筋 Coracobrachialis	12	内側神経束 Medial cord
4	三角筋（切断面） Deltoid	13	内側上腕皮神経 Medial cutaneous nerve of arm：Medial brachial cutaneous nerve
5	肋間上腕神経 Intercostobrachial nerves	14	内側前腕皮神経 Medial cutaneous nerve of forearm：Medial antebrachial cutaneous nerve
6	外側神経束 Lateral cord	15	内側頭〔上腕三頭筋〕 Medial head (Triceps brachii)
7	外側頭〔上腕三頭筋〕 Lateral head (Triceps brachii)	16	正中神経内側根 Medial root of median nerve
8	正中神経外側根 Lateral root of median nerve	17	正中神経 Median nerve
9	広背筋 Latissimus dorsi	18	筋皮神経 Musculocutaneous nerve
19	小胸筋と外側胸筋神経 Pectoralis minor and Lateral pectoral nerve		
20	後神経束 Posterior cord		
21	橈骨神経 Radial nerve		
22	橈骨神経の枝（上腕三頭筋の支配枝） Branches of Radial nerve		
23	肩甲下筋 Subscapularis		
24	大円筋 Teres major		
25	胸背神経 Thoracodorsal nerve		
26	尺骨神経 Ulnar nerve		
27	上肩甲下神経* Upper subscapular nerves *		

上腕(右) [A 血管と神経]

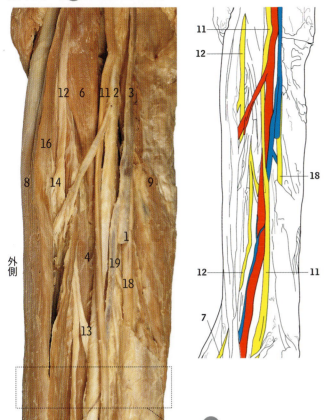

上腕二頭筋(8, 16)を外側へ翻転し, 烏口腕筋(6)を貫いた筋皮神経(12)が上腕二頭筋と上腕筋に筋枝(14, 13)を与え, 上腕二頭筋の腱(17)の外側で外側前腕皮神経(7)に続いている.
正中神経(11)は, 上腕動脈(2)の前を, 徐々に外側から内側へと乗り越えている. 尺骨神経(18)は, 内側上腕筋間中隔(10)の後ろを走る. 尺側皮静脈(1)の終末部は, 上腕動脈の伴行静脈(19)と合して上腕静脈(3)を形成している.

1	尺側皮静脈(切断端) Basilic vein	10	内側上腕筋間中隔 Medial intermuscular septum of arm
2	上腕動脈 Brachial artery	11	正中神経 Median nerve
3	上腕静脈 Brachial veins	12	筋皮神経 Musculocutaneous nerve
4	上腕筋 Brachialis	13	上腕筋への枝
5	腕橈骨筋 Brachioradialis	14	短頭〔上腕二頭筋〕への枝
6	烏口腕筋 Coracobrachialis	15	円回内筋 Pronator teres
7	外側前腕皮神経 Lateral cutaneous nerve of forearm； Lateral antebrachial cutaneous nerve	16	短頭〔上腕二頭筋〕 Short head〔Biceps brachii〕
8	長頭〔上腕二頭筋〕 Long head〔Biceps brachii〕	17	上腕二頭筋(の腱) Biceps brachii
9	長頭〔上腕三頭筋〕 Long head〔Triceps brachii〕	18	尺骨神経 Ulnar nerve
		19	上腕動脈の伴行静脈* Vena comitans of Brachial artery *

- 筋皮神経(12)は, 烏口腕筋(6), 上腕二頭筋(8, 16)および上腕筋(4)に支配枝を与えた後, 上腕二頭筋の筋線維が腱になるところ(17)で筋膜を貫き, 外側前腕皮神経(7)となる.
- 正中神経は, 上腕では筋枝を出さない.
- 尺骨神経(18)は, 内側上腕筋間中隔(10)を貫き, 上腕の前区画(屈筋区画)から出るが, 上腕では筋枝を出さない.

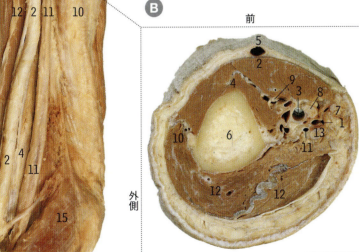

1	尺側皮静脈 Basilic vein
2	上腕二頭筋 Biceps brachii
3	上腕動脈 Brachial artery
4	上腕筋 Brachialis
5	橈側皮静脈 Cephalic vein
6	上腕骨 Humerus
7	内側前腕皮神経 Medial cutaneous nerve of forearm；Medial antebrachial cutaneous nerve
8	正中神経 Median nerve
9	筋皮神経 Musculocutaneous nerve
10	橈骨神経と上腕深動／静脈 Radial nerve and Profunda brachii artery/vein
11	上尺側側副動脈 Superior ulnar collateral artery
12	上腕三頭筋 Triceps brachii
13	尺骨神経 Ulnar nerve

A：前方から. B：横断面. 下方から.

上腕の中央の高さで横断し, 肘から肩の方を見ている. 筋皮神経(9)は, 上腕筋(4)と上腕二頭筋(2)の間に位置する. また正中神経(8)は, 上腕動脈(3)の内側に位置する. 動脈に接して数本の伴行静脈が見える(番号は付けられていない). 尺骨神経(13)は, 上尺側側副動脈(11)を伴い, 正中神経(8)と尺側皮静脈(1)の後ろに位置する. 橈骨神経と上腕深動静脈(10)は, 上腕骨(6)の外側で上腕の後区画(伸筋区画)の内部を走行する.

Volkmann 拘縮

A B 上腕（右）

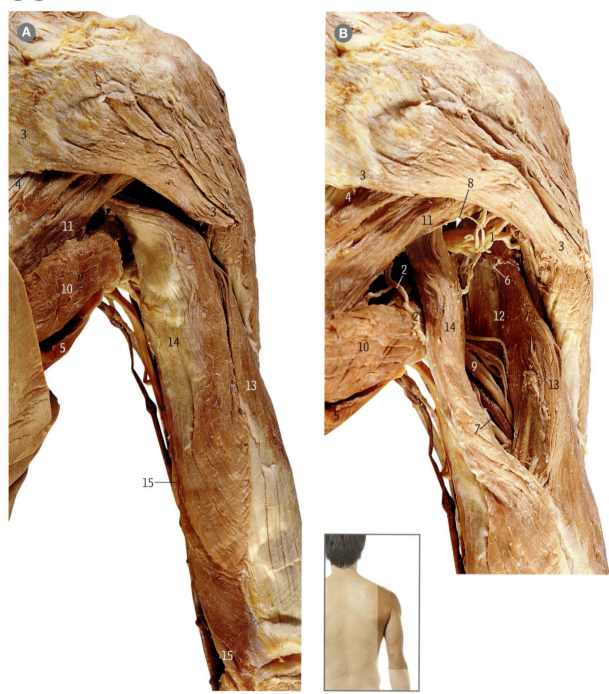

A：後方から．皮膚と皮下脂肪を除去してある． B：後方から．筋の間を広げ，神経血管束を示している．

1	腋窩神経 Axillary nerve	6	後上腕回旋動脈 Posterior circumflex humeral artery	11	小円筋 Teres minor
2	肩甲回旋動脈 Circumflex scapular artery	7	上腕深動脈 Profunda brachii artery	12	三角間隔* Triangular interval *
3	三角筋 Deltoid	8	四角隙* Quadrangular space *	13	外側頭〔上腕三頭筋〕 Lateral head〔Triceps brachii〕
4	棘下筋 Infraspinatus	9	橈骨神経（橈骨神経溝を走る部分） Radial nerve	14	長頭〔上腕三頭筋〕 Long head〔Triceps brachii〕
5	広背筋 Latissimus dorsi	10	大円筋 Teres major	15	尺骨神経 Ulnar nerve

橈骨神経麻痺

C 肘（左）［体表解剖］

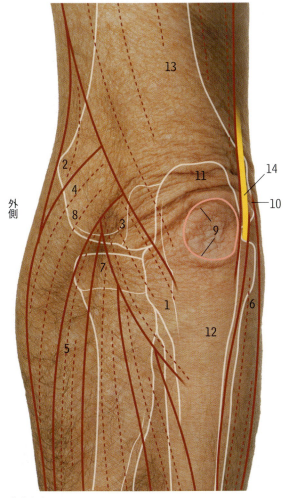

後方から．

肘を十分に伸ばすと，前腕の外側に，伸筋群(5, 4)がふくらみをつくる．その隣のくぼみに，肘関節の腕橈関節をつくる橈骨頭(7)と上腕骨小頭(3)を触知することができる．上腕骨の外側上顆(8)と内側上顆(10)が，両側で触れる．尺骨の突出した肘頭(11)の後面では皮膚にしわがよっている．本例では，肘頭皮下包(9)という滑液包の輪郭がわかる．肘部で最も重要なのは尺骨神経(14)であり，内側上顆(10)の後ろで上腕骨と接しているのが触知できる．尺骨の後縁(12)は，全長にわたって皮下にある．

1 肘筋 Anconeus	8 外側上顆〔上腕骨〕 Lateral epicondyle〔Humerus〕
2 腕橈骨筋 Brachioradialis	9 肘頭皮下包（の辺縁） Subcutaneous olecranon bursa
3 上腕骨小頭 Capitulum of humerus	10 内側上顆〔上腕骨〕 Medial epicondyle〔Humerus〕
4 長橈側手根伸筋 Extensor carpi radialis longus	11 肘頭〔尺骨〕 Olecranon〔Ulna〕
5 前腕伸筋群 Extensor muscles	12 後縁〔尺骨〕 Posterior border〔Ulna〕
6 尺側手根屈筋 Flexor carpi ulnaris	13 上腕三頭筋 Triceps brachii
7 橈骨頭 Head of radius	14 尺骨神経 Ulnar nerve

D 肘（左）

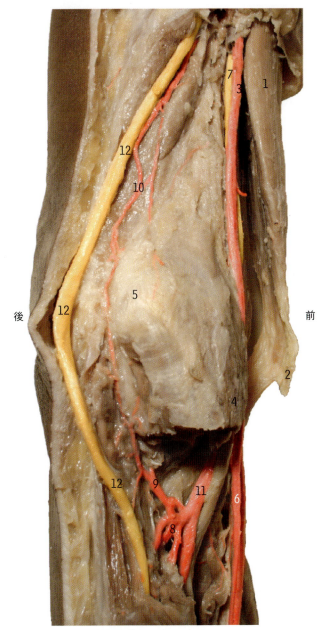

内側方から．尺骨神経を後方に引いてある．

注：高位で分かれた正中動脈が遺残している．

1 上腕二頭筋 Biceps brachii	7 正中神経 Median nerve
2 上腕二頭筋腱膜 Bicipital aponeurosis	8 前腕屈筋群への動脈の枝
3 上腕動脈 Brachial artery	9 後枝〔尺側反回動脈〕 Posterior branch〔Ulnar recurrent artery〕
4 前腕屈筋群の共同起始部	10 上尺側側副動脈 Superior ulnar collateral artery
5 内側上顆〔上腕骨〕 Medial epicondyle〔Humerus〕	11 尺骨動脈 Ulnar artery
6 正中動脈 Median artery	12 尺骨神経 Ulnar nerve

肘頭滑液包炎

上腕三頭筋腱反射

尺骨神経麻痺

A B 肘と上橈尺関節（左）　　C D 肘と上橈尺関節（右）

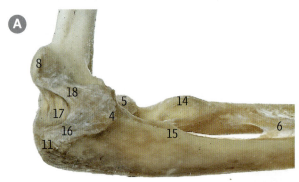

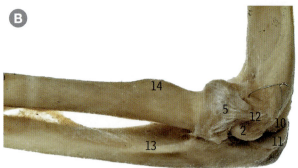
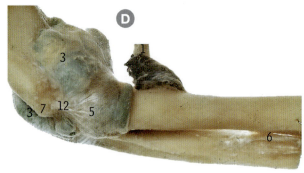

A：内側方から．B：外側方から．　　C：内側方から．D：外側方から．

A, Bでは，肘を直角に屈曲させてある．C, Dでは，肘をわずかに屈曲させ，関節包（3）に包まれた関節腔と上腕二頭筋の腱の下にある二頭筋橈骨包（1）に緑色の樹脂を注入してある．

1. 上腕二頭筋（の腱）と二頭筋橈骨包　Biceps brachii and Bicipitoradial bursa
2. 上腕骨小頭　Capitulum of humerus
3. 関節包（拡張させてある）　Articular capsule
4. 鈎状突起〔尺骨〕　Coronoid process (Ulna)
5. 橈骨頭（橈骨輪状靱帯に覆われている）　Head of radius
6. 前腕骨間膜　Interosseous membrane of forearm
7. 外側上顆　Lateral epicondyle
8. 内側上顆　Medial epicondyle
9. 斜索　Oblique cord
10. 肘頭窩　Olecranon fossa
11. 肘頭〔尺骨〕　Olecranon (Ulna)
12. 外側側副靱帯　Radial collateral ligament
13. 回外筋稜〔尺骨〕　Supinator crest (Ulna)
14. 橈骨粗面　Radial tuberosity
15. 尺骨粗面　Tuberosity of ulna
16. 斜束*：横走靱帯*〔内側側副靱帯〕　Oblique band*: Transverse ligament* (Ulnar collateral ligament)
17. 後束*：後斜走靱帯*〔内側側副靱帯〕　Posterior band*: Posterioroblique ligament* (Ulnar collateral ligament)
18. 上束*：前斜走靱帯*〔内側側副靱帯〕　Upper band*: Anterior oblique ligament* (Ulnar collateral ligament)

E F 肘

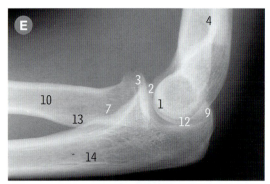

X線画像（側面画像）

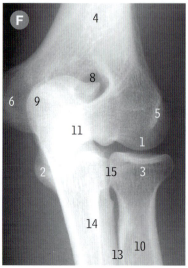

X線画像（前後画像）

橈骨頭亜脱臼（肘内障）

1. 上腕骨小頭　Capitulum of humerus
2. 鈎状突起〔尺骨〕　Coronoid process (Ulna)
3. 橈骨頭　Head of radius
4. 上腕骨　Humerus
5. 外側上顆〔上腕骨〕　Lateral epicondyle (Humerus)
6. 内側上顆〔上腕骨〕　Medial epicondyle (Humerus)
7. 橈骨頸　Neck of radius
8. 肘頭窩〔上腕骨〕　Olecranon fossa (Humerus)
9. 肘頭〔尺骨〕　Olecranon (Ulna)
10. 橈骨　Radius
11. 上腕骨滑車　Trochlea of humerus
12. 滑車切痕〔尺骨〕　Trochlear notch (Ulna)
13. 橈骨粗面　Radial tuberosity
14. 尺骨　Ulna
15. 上橈尺関節　Proximal radio-ulnar joint

骨間膜(左)

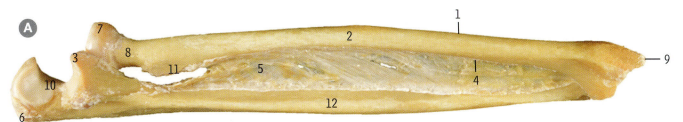

回内したものを前内側方から見たところ.

1	前縁〔橈骨〕 Anterior border〔Radius〕	7	橈骨頭 Head of radius
2	前面〔橈骨〕 Anterior surface〔Radius〕	8	橈骨頸 Neck of radius
3	鈎状突起〔尺骨〕 Coronoid process〔Ulna〕	9	(橈骨の)茎状突起 Radial styloid process
4	骨間縁 Interosseous border	10	滑車切痕 Trochlear notch
5	前腕骨間膜 Interosseous membrane of forearm	11	橈骨粗面 Radial tuberosity
6	肘頭〔尺骨〕 Olecranon〔Ulna〕	12	尺骨 Ulna

Aを少し回外したものを内側方から見たところ.

1	鈎状突起〔尺骨〕 Coronoid process〔Ulna〕	8	橈骨頭 Neck of radius
2	下橈尺関節 Distal radio-ulnar joint	9	肘頭〔尺骨〕 Olecranon〔Ulna〕
3	背側結節：Lister 結節* Dorsal tubercle：Lister's tubercle *	10	(橈骨の)茎状突起 Radial styloid process
4	〔総〕指伸筋および示指伸筋が通る溝	11	(尺骨の)茎状突起 Ulnar styloid process
5	橈骨頭 Head of radius	12	滑車切痕〔尺骨〕 Trochlear notch〔Ulna〕
6	骨間縁 Interosseous border	13	橈骨粗面 Radial tuberosity
7	前腕骨間膜 Interosseous membrane of forearm	14	尺骨粗面 Tuberosity of ulna

A 肘関節（左）

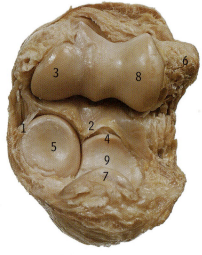

肘関節を後方から開き、強制的に屈曲させている。上腕骨の下端にある上腕骨小頭(3)と上腕骨滑車(8)が下方から、橈骨と尺骨の上端部(5, 9)が上方から見えている。

1	橈骨輪状靱帯	Anular ligament of radius
2	関節包（の前部）	Articular capsule
3	上腕骨小頭	Capitulum of humerus
4	鈎状突起〔尺骨〕	Coronoid process〔Ulna〕
5	橈骨頭	Head of radius
6	内側上顆〔上腕骨〕	Medial epicondyle〔Humerus〕
7	肘頭〔尺骨〕	Olecranon〔Ulna〕
8	上腕骨滑車	Trochlea of humerus
9	滑車切痕〔尺骨〕	Trochlear notch〔Ulna〕

関節包の後方を開いてある。

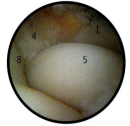

肘関節の関節鏡写真である。上方から見たもので、腕橈関節が確認できる。橈骨頭のすぐ遠位にあるのは橈骨輪状靱帯の近位縁である。橈骨頭が、尺骨の鈎状突起と関節をつくっているのが見える。

肘関節の関節鏡写真

B C 肘（左）

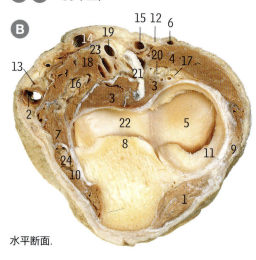

水平断面。

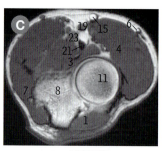

MR 横断画像

上腕動脈が、橈骨動脈(19)と尺骨動脈(23)に分岐する位置のすぐ下方で横断し、下方から肩方向を見ている。横断面は、上腕骨滑車(22)と上腕骨小頭(5)のすぐ下方ならびに尺骨の鈎状突起(8)を通過している。橈骨神経(20)と後骨間神経(17)は、腕橈骨筋(4)と上腕筋(3)の間を通る。正中神経(16)は、円回内筋(18)の上腕頭の下を通り、尺骨神経(24)は尺側手根屈筋(10)の下を通過している。
［訳注］MR 画像の断面は、断面標本よりやや下方である。

1	肘筋 Anconeus		13	内側前腕皮神経 Medial cutaneous nerve of forearm：Medial antebrachial cutaneous nerve
2	尺側皮静脈 Basilic vein		14	尺側正中皮静脈 Basilic vein of forearm
3	上腕筋 Brachialis		15	橈側正中皮静脈 Cephalic vein of forearm
4	腕橈骨筋 Brachioradialis		16	正中神経 Median nerve
5	上腕骨小頭 Capitulum of humerus		17	後骨間神経 Posterior interosseous nerve
6	橈側皮静脈 Cephalic vein		18	円回内筋 Pronator teres
7	前腕屈筋群の共同起始部		19	橈骨動脈 Radial artery
8	鈎状突起〔尺骨〕 Coronoid process〔Ulna〕		20	橈骨神経 Radial nerve
9	長橈側手根伸筋と短橈側手根伸筋 Extensor carpi radialis longus and Extensor carpi radialis brevis		21	上腕二頭筋（の腱） Biceps brachii
			22	上腕骨滑車 Trochlea of humerus
10	尺側手根屈筋 Flexor carpi ulnaris		23	尺骨動脈 Ulnar artery
11	橈骨頭（の辺縁） Head of Radius		24	尺骨神経 Ulnar nerve
12	外側前腕皮神経 Lateral cutaneous nerve of forearm：Lateral antebrachial cutaneous nerve			

D 肘

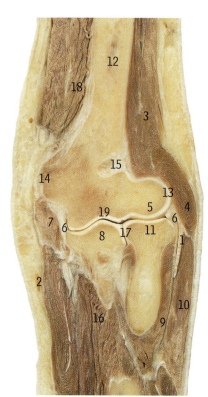

冠状断面。

肘関節の関節鏡

1	橈骨輪状靱帯	Anular ligament of radius
2	尺側皮静脈	Basilic vein
3	上腕筋	Brachialis
4	腕橈骨筋	Brachioradialis
5	上腕骨小頭	Capitulum of humerus
6	関節包	Articular capsule
7	前腕屈筋群の共同起始部	
8	鈎状突起〔尺骨〕	Coronoid process〔Ulna〕
9	短橈側手根伸筋	Extensor carpi radialis brevis
10	長橈側手根伸筋	Extensor carpi radialis longus
11	橈骨頭	Head of radius
12	上腕骨	Humerus
13	外側上顆	Lateral epicondyle
14	内側上顆	Medial epicondyle
15	肘頭窩	Olecranon fossa
16	円回内筋	Pronator teres
17	上橈尺関節	Proximal radio-ulnar joint
18	内側頭〔上腕三頭筋〕	Medial head〔Triceps brachii〕
19	上腕骨滑車	Trochlea of humerus

肘窩（左）［A 体表解剖，B 皮静脈］

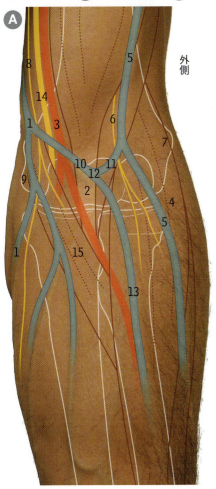

上肢の静脈造影画像

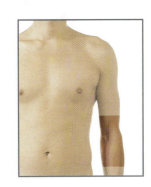

	A	
1	尺側皮静脈 Basilic vein	
2	上腕二頭筋（の腱） Biceps brachii	
3	上腕動脈 Brachial artery	
4	腕橈骨筋 Brachioradialis	
5	橈側皮静脈 Cephalic vein	
6	外側前腕皮神経 Lateral cutaneous nerve of forearm：Lateral antebrachial cutaneous nerve	
7	外側上顆 Lateral epicondyle	
8	内側前腕皮神経 Medial cutaneous nerve of forearm：Medial antebrachial cutaneous nerve	
9	内側上顆 Medial epicondyle	
10	尺側正中皮静脈 Basilic vein of forearm	
11	橈側正中皮静脈 Cephalic vein of forearm	
12	肘正中皮静脈 Median cubital vein	
13	前腕正中皮静脈 Median antebrachial vein	
14	正中神経 Median nerve	
15	円回内筋 Pronator teres	

	B	
1	副尺側皮静脈* Accessory basilic vein *	
2	尺側皮静脈 Basilic vein	
3	上腕二頭筋（の腱） Biceps brachii	
4	上腕動脈 Brachial artery	
5	腕橈骨筋 Brachioradialis	
6	橈側皮静脈 Cephalic vein	
7	外側前腕皮神経 Lateral cutaneous nerve of forearm：Lateral antebrachial cutaneous nerve	
8	内側上腕皮神経 Medial cutaneous nerve of arm：Medial brachial cutaneous nerve	
9	内側前腕皮神経 Medial cutaneous nerve of forearm：Medial antebrachial cutaneous nerve	
10	内側上顆 Medial epicondyle	
11	肘正中皮静脈 Median cubital vein	
12	前腕正中皮静脈 Median antebrachial vein	
13	正中神経 Median nerve	
14	円回内筋 Pronator teres	

- 肘の前面の皮静脈である橈側皮静脈（A5，B6），尺側皮静脈（A1，B2）ならびにそれらを相互に連絡する静脈は，静脈内注射や静脈血採血に最も一般的に利用される．肘の皮静脈のパターンは，Aに見られるようなM型あるいはBに見られるH型が標準であるが，変異が多く見られるため，すべての静脈に用語を当てはめることは不可能であり，またその必要もない．
- 肘窩を通るものは外側から順に，上腕二頭筋の腱（A2，B3），上腕動脈（A3，B4），正中神経（A14，B13）である．

腕の脈拍の聴診法

上腕二頭筋腱反射

ゴルフ肘（上腕骨内側上顆炎）

テニス肘（上腕骨外側上顆炎）

肘と前腕上部（左）［C 深層，D 深層の神経と動脈］

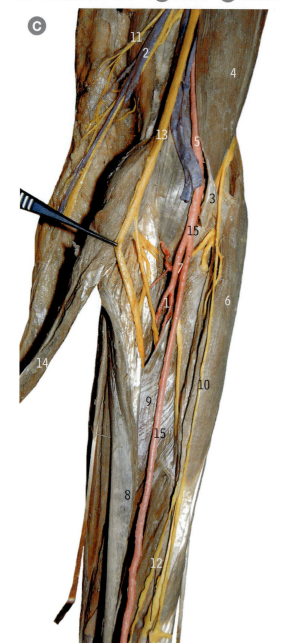

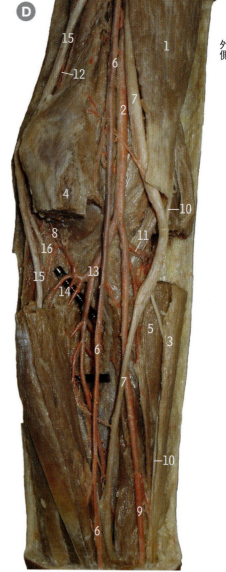

注：高位で分かれた正中動脈が遺残している．

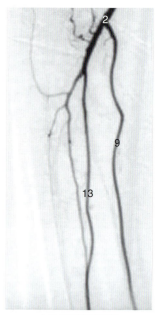
上腕動脈造影画像

1	前骨間動脈 Anterior interosseous artery	9	深指屈筋 Flexor digitorum profundus
2	尺側皮静脈 Basilic vein	10	外側前腕皮神経 Lateral cutaneous nerve of forearm； Lateral antebrachial cutaneous nerve
3	上腕二頭筋腱膜（翻転してある） Bicipital aponeurosis	11	内側上腕皮神経 Medial cutaneous nerve of arm；Medial brachial cutaneous nerve
4	上腕二頭筋 Biceps brachii	12	正中神経 Median nerve
5	上腕動脈 Brachial artery	13	正中神経（内側に牽引している） Median nerve
6	腕橈骨筋 Brachioradialis	14	円回内筋（翻転してある） Pronator teres
7	総骨間動脈 Common interosseous artery	15	尺骨動脈 Ulnar artery
8	尺側手根屈筋 Flexor carpi ulnaris		

1	上腕二頭筋 Biceps brachii	9	橈骨動脈 Radial artery
2	上腕動脈 Brachial artery	10	浅枝〔橈骨神経〕 Superficial branch（Radial nerve）
3	腕橈骨筋 Brachioradialis	11	橈側反回動脈 Radial recurrent artery
4	前腕屈筋群の共同起始部	12	上尺側側副動脈 Superior ulnar collateral artery
5	長橈側手根伸筋 Extensor carpi radialis longus	13	尺骨動脈 Ulnar artery
6	正中動脈 Median artery	14	尺骨動脈（前腕屈筋への枝） Ulnar artery
7	正中神経（外側に牽引してある） Median nerve	15	尺骨神経 Ulnar nerve
8	後枝〔尺側反回動脈〕 Posterior branch（Ulnar recurrent artery）	16	尺側手根屈筋への枝〔尺骨神経〕 Branch to flexor carpi ulnaris（Ulnar nerve）

前骨間神経の絞扼

肘における動脈穿刺

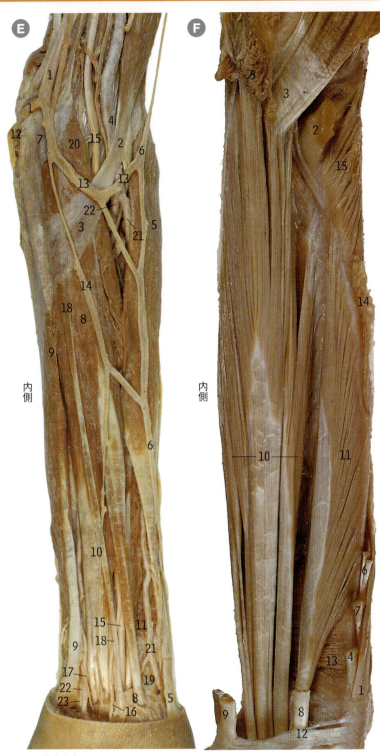

E 前腕（左）［浅層］

皮膚と筋膜を除去し，太い皮静脈（1，6，13）は残してある．外側では，橈骨動脈（21）の大部分は腕橈骨筋（5）に覆われている．手根では，橈側手根屈筋（8）の外側に橈骨動脈（21）が，内側に正中神経（15）が位置する．正中神経の内側縁は，長掌筋（18）の腱でわずかに覆われている（13％において，長掌筋は欠損する）．

1	尺側皮静脈 Basilic vein	13	肘正中皮静脈 Median cubital vein
2	上腕二頭筋（の腱） Biceps brachii	14	前腕正中皮静脈 Median antebrachial vein
3	上腕二頭筋腱膜 Bicipital aponeurosis	15	正中神経 Median nerve
4	上腕動脈 Brachial artery	16	掌枝〔正中神経〕 Palmar branch〔Median nerve〕
5	腕橈骨筋 Brachioradialis	17	掌枝〔尺骨神経〕 Palmar branch〔Ulnar nerve〕
6	橈側皮静脈 Cephalic vein	18	長掌筋 Palmaris longus
7	前腕屈筋群の共同起始部	19	方形回内筋 Pronator quadratus
8	橈側手根屈筋 Flexor carpi radialis	20	円回内筋 Pronator teres
9	尺側手根屈筋 Flexor carpi ulnaris	21	橈骨動脈 Radial artery
10	浅指屈筋 Flexor digitorum superficialis	22	尺骨動脈 Ulnar artery
11	長母指屈筋 Flexor pollicis longus	23	尺骨神経 Ulnar nerve
12	内側上顆 Medial epicondyle		

F 前腕（左）［深層］

すべての血管と神経を浅層の筋とともに除去し，前腕の深層筋群である深指屈筋（10），長母指屈筋（11）ならびに方形回内筋（13）を明らかにしている．

1	長母指外転筋 Abductor pollicis longus
2	上腕二頭筋 Biceps brachii
3	上腕筋 Brachialis
4	腕橈骨筋 Brachioradialis
5	前腕屈筋群の共同起始部
6	短橈側手根伸筋 Extensor carpi radialis brevis
7	長橈側手根伸筋 Extensor carpi radialis longus
8	橈側手根屈筋 Flexor carpi radialis
9	尺側手根屈筋 Flexor carpi ulnaris
10	深指屈筋 Flexor digitorum profundus
11	長母指屈筋 Flexor pollicis longus
12	屈筋支帯 Flexor retinaculum
13	方形回内筋 Pronator quadratus
14	円回内筋 Pronator teres
15	回外筋 Supinator

E・F：前方から．

上肢の静脈切開

上肢の静脈穿刺

A 肘窩と前腕（右）［動脈］

動脈に色素を注入し，大半の浅層筋を除去してある．上腕動脈(4)が橈骨動脈(18)と尺骨動脈(20)に分岐しているのが見える．橈骨動脈から起こった橈側反回動脈(19)は，回外筋の前を上行し，長橈側手根伸筋(10)と短橈側手根伸筋(9)に枝を与えている．尺骨動脈は，尺側反回動脈の前枝(2)と後枝(15)を分枝する．尺骨動脈の枝である総骨間動脈(8)から前骨間動脈(1)が分かれ，長母指屈筋(13)と深指屈筋(12)の間を通って骨間膜の前面を下行している．

1	前骨間動脈（骨間膜の前面を通る） Anterior interosseous artery	7	前腕屈筋群の共同起始部	14	内側上顆〔上腕骨〕 Medial epicondyle〔Humerus〕
2	前枝〔尺側反回動脈〕 Anterior branch〔Ulnar recurrent artery〕	8	総骨間動脈 Common interosseous artery	15	後枝〔尺側反回動脈〕 Posterior branch〔Ulnar recurrent artery〕
3	上腕二頭筋（の腱） Biceps brachii	9	短橈側手根伸筋 Extensor carpi radialis brevis	16	方形回内筋 Pronator quadratus
4	上腕動脈 Brachial artery	10	長橈側手根伸筋 Extensor carpi radialis longus	17	円回内筋 Pronator teres
5	上腕筋 Brachialis	11	尺側手根屈筋 Flexor carpi ulnaris	18	橈骨動脈 Radial artery
6	腕橈骨筋 Brachioradialis	12	深指屈筋 Flexor digitorum profundus	19	橈側反回動脈（回外筋よりも浅層を通る） Radial recurrent artery
		13	長母指屈筋 Flexor pollicis longus	20	尺骨動脈 Ulnar artery

B 肘窩と前腕（右）［動脈と神経］

円回内筋の上腕頭(9)と橈側手根屈筋の大部分（前腕屈筋群の共同起始部，7）ならびに長掌筋を除去してある．正中神経(12)が，円回内筋の尺骨頭(18)より浅層を走り，浅指屈筋の橈骨頭(14)の上縁でこの筋の深層に入っている．

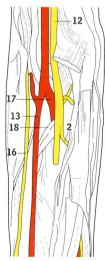

1	筋枝〔正中神経〕 Muscular branches〔Median nerve〕
2	前骨間神経 Anterior interosseous nerve
3	上腕二頭筋 Biceps brachii
4	上腕動脈 Brachial artery
5	上腕筋 Brachialis
6	腕橈骨筋（外側に牽引してある） Brachioradialis
7	前腕屈筋群の共同起始部
8	尺側手根屈筋（内側に転位） Flexor carpi ulnaris
9	上腕頭〔円回内筋〕 Humeral head〔Pronator teres〕
10	上腕尺骨頭〔浅指屈筋〕 Humero-ulnar head〔Flexor digitorum superficialis〕
11	外側前腕皮神経 Lateral cutaneous nerve of forearm：Lateral antebrachial cutaneous nerve
12	正中神経 Median nerve
13	橈骨動脈 Radial artery
14	橈骨頭〔浅指屈筋〕 Radial head〔Flexor digitorum superficialis〕
15	橈側反回動脈 Radial recurrent artery
16	浅枝〔橈骨神経〕（長橈側手根伸筋よりも浅層を通る） Superficial branch〔Radial nerve〕
17	尺骨動脈 Ulnar artery
18	尺骨頭〔円回内筋〕 Ulnar head〔Pronator teres〕
19	尺骨神経と尺骨動脈 Ulnar nerve and Ulnar artery

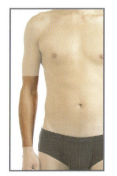

前骨間神経の絞扼

Volkmann 拘縮

A 肘（左）

前腕を中間位とし，外側から見ているので，橈骨(7)が尺骨の前方に位置している．回外筋(8)以外のすべての筋を除去してあるため，回外筋が上腕骨と尺骨から起始しているのが見える（下の解説参照）．

1	橈骨輪状靱帯	Anular ligament of radius
2	上腕骨小頭	Capitulum of humerus
3	前腕骨間膜	Interosseous membrane of forearm
4	外側上顆	Lateral epicondyle
5	後骨間神経	Posterior interosseous nerve
6	外側側副靱帯	Radial collateral ligament
7	橈骨	Radius
8	回外筋	Supinator
9	回外筋稜〔尺骨〕	Supinator crest (Ulna)

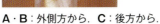

A・B：外側方から．C：後方から．

B 前腕（左）［深層の筋］

1	長母指外転筋 Abductor pollicis longus		6	短母指伸筋 Extensor pollicis brevis
2	上腕二頭筋 Biceps brachii		7	長母指伸筋 Extensor pollicis longus
3	短橈側手根伸筋 Extensor carpi radialis brevis		8	伸筋支帯 Extensor retinaculum
4	長橈側手根伸筋（分束が見られる） Extensor carpi radialis longus		9	長母指屈筋 Flexor pollicis longus
5	示指伸筋 Extensor indicis		10	円回内筋 Pronator teres
			11	回外筋 Supinator

C 前腕（左）［後骨間神経］

1	長母指外転筋 Abductor pollicis longus		7	示指伸筋 Extensor indicis
2	後骨間動脈の枝 Branch of Posterior interosseous artery		8	短母指伸筋 Extensor pollicis brevis
3	短橈側手根伸筋 Extensor carpi radialis brevis		9	長母指伸筋 Extensor pollicis longus
4	長橈側手根伸筋 Extensor carpi radialis longus		10	伸筋支帯 Extensor retinaculum
5	尺側手根伸筋 Extensor carpi ulnaris		11	後骨間神経 Posterior interosseous nerve
6	［総］指伸筋 Extensor digitorum		12	回外筋 Supinator

- 前腕骨間膜(A3)の線維は，橈骨(A7)から下内側へ斜走し，尺骨に達する．それを通じて手および橈骨の力が尺骨に伝えられる．
- 回外筋(A8)は，上腕骨の外側上顆(A4)，肘関節の外側側副靱帯(A6)，上橈尺関節の橈骨輪状靱帯(A1)，尺骨の回外筋稜(A9，125頁D10)ならびにこの稜の前の骨の領域から起始しており，腱膜が筋を覆っている．これらの起始部からの線維は，円回内筋と靱帯の付着部の上方で，橈骨上端の周囲を覆い，外側面の前後に広がるように停止する．また，前方は橈骨粗面にまで達する．

後骨間神経の絞扼

前腕と手（左）［D 浅層の筋, E 深層の筋］

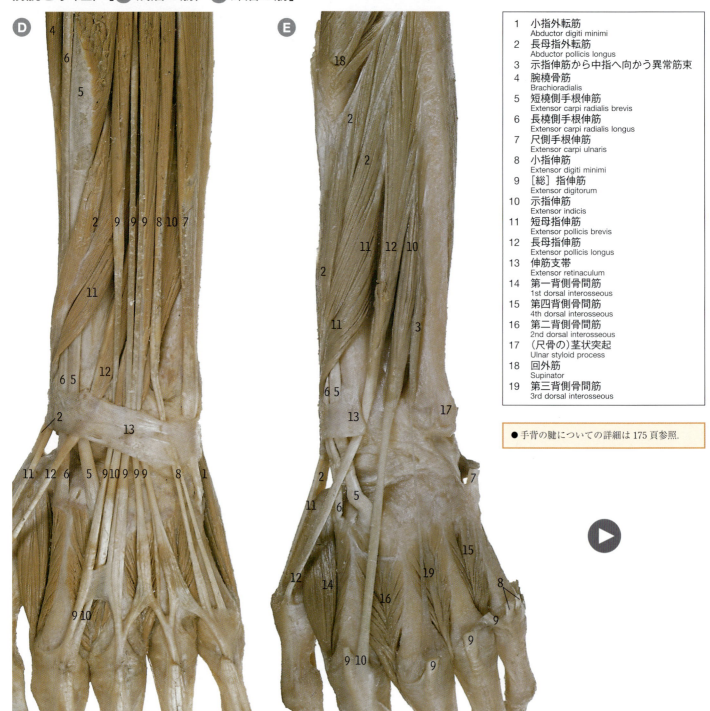

1	小指外転筋 Abductor digiti minimi
2	長母指外転筋 Abductor pollicis longus
3	示指伸筋から中指へ向かう異常筋束
4	腕橈骨筋 Brachioradialis
5	短橈側手根伸筋 Extensor carpi radialis brevis
6	長橈側手根伸筋 Extensor carpi radialis longus
7	尺側手根伸筋 Extensor carpi ulnaris
8	小指伸筋 Extensor digiti minimi
9	［総］指伸筋 Extensor digitorum
10	示指伸筋 Extensor indicis
11	短母指伸筋 Extensor pollicis brevis
12	長母指伸筋 Extensor pollicis longus
13	伸筋支帯 Extensor retinaculum
14	第一背側骨間筋 1st dorsal interosseous
15	第四背側骨間筋 4th dorsal interosseous
16	第二背側骨間筋 2nd dorsal interosseous
17	（尺骨の）茎状突起 Ulnar styloid process
18	回外筋 Supinator
19	第三背側骨間筋 3rd dorsal interosseous

● 手背の腱についての詳細は 175 頁参照.

D・E：後方から.

de Quervain 病

下垂手

A 手掌（左）

#	日本語	Latin/English
1	小指外転筋	Abductor digiti minimi
2	短母指外転筋	Abductor pollicis brevis
3	母指内転筋	Adductor pollicis
4	遠位手掌皮線*	Distal palmar crease*
5	遠位手首皮線*	Distal wrist crease*
6	橈側手根屈筋	Flexor carpi radialis
7	尺側手根屈筋	Flexor carpi ulnaris
8	短小指屈筋	Flexor digiti minimi brevis
9	短母指屈筋	Flexor pollicis brevis
10	中手骨頭	Head of metacarpal bone
11	有鈎骨鈎	Hook of hamate
12	深掌動脈弓の位置	
13	浅掌動脈弓の位置	
14	縦走手掌皮線*	Longitudinal crease*
15	正中神経	Median nerve
16	中手首皮線*	Middle wrist crease*
17	短掌筋	Palmaris brevis
18	長掌筋	Palmaris longus
19	豆状骨	Pisiform
20	近位手掌皮線*	Proximal palmer crease*
21	近位手首皮線*	Proximal wrist crease*
22	橈骨動脈	Radial artery
23	母指球	Thenar eminence
24	尺骨動脈と尺骨神経	Ulnar artery and Ulnar nerve

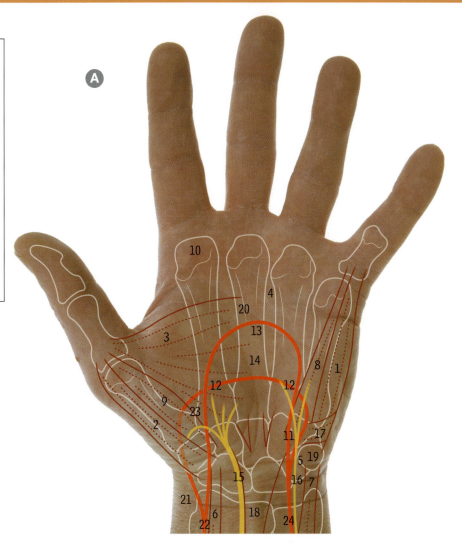

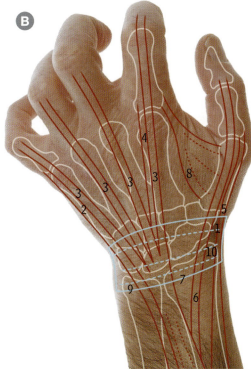

B 手背（左）

指（2，3，4）の伸筋の腱を浮き上がらせるために，中手指節関節を伸展し，指節間関節をやや屈曲させてある．母指は，手根中手関節で伸ばし，中手指節関節と指節間関節で少し屈曲させてある．指の基部の近位に描かれた曲線は，中手骨頭の先端と中手指節関節の位置を表している．解剖学的嗅ぎタバコ入れ（1）は，外側の長母指外転筋と短母指伸筋（5）の腱と，内側の長母指伸筋（6）の腱の間のくぼみのことである．

1	解剖学的嗅ぎタバコ入れ*	Anatomical snuffbox*
2	小指伸筋	Extensor digiti minimi
3	［総］指伸筋	Extensor digitorum
4	示指伸筋	Extensor indicis
5	長母指外転筋と短母指伸筋	Abductor pollicis longus and Extensor pollicis brevis
6	長母指伸筋	Extensor pollicis longus
7	伸筋支帯	Extensor retinaculum
8	第一背側骨間筋	1st dorsal interosseous
9	尺骨頭	Head of ulna
10	（橈骨の）茎状突起	Radial styloid process

指の運動

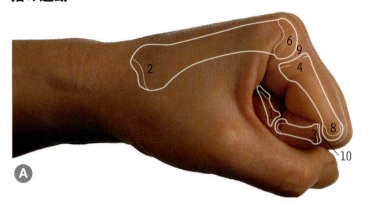

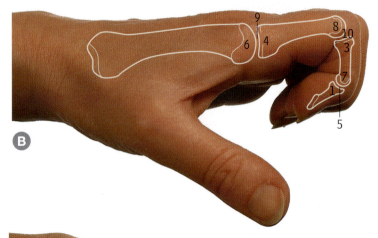

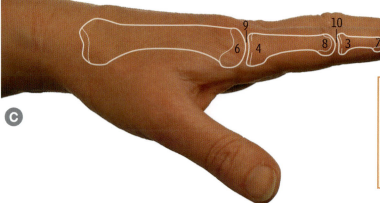

A：中手指節関節と指節間関節の屈曲．B：中手指節関節の伸展と指節間関節の屈曲．C：中手指節関節と指節間関節の伸展．

●中手指節関節の運動にかかわる筋
- 屈曲：深指屈筋，浅指屈筋，虫様筋，骨間筋，短小指屈筋(小指の屈曲)，長母指屈筋，短母指屈筋，第一掌側骨間筋(母指の屈曲)．
- 伸展：[総] 指伸筋，示指伸筋(示指の伸展)，小指伸筋(小指の伸展)，長母指伸筋，短母指伸筋(母指の伸展)．
- 内転：掌側骨間筋，浅・深指屈筋(屈曲したとき補助する)．
- 外転：背側骨間筋，長い指の伸筋，小指外転筋(小指の外転)．

●指節間関節の運動にかかわる筋
- 屈曲：浅指屈筋，深指屈筋(近位指節間関節)，深指屈筋(遠位指節間関節)，長母指屈筋(母指の指節間関節)．
- 伸展：[総] 指伸筋，示指伸筋，小指伸筋(中手指節関節を屈曲している場合)，骨間筋，虫様筋(中手指節関節を伸展している場合)，長母指伸筋(母指の場合)．

●橈骨手根関節の運動にかかわる筋
- 屈曲：橈側手根屈筋，尺側手根屈筋，長掌筋，浅指屈筋，深指屈筋，長母指屈筋，長母指外転筋(補助筋として働く)．
- 伸展：長・短橈側手根伸筋，尺側手根伸筋，指伸筋，示指伸筋，小指伸筋，長母指伸筋(補助筋として働く)．
- 外転：橈側手根屈筋，橈側手根伸筋，長・短橈側手根伸筋，長母指外転筋，短母指伸筋．
- 内転：尺側手根屈筋，尺側手根伸筋．

1	末節骨底 Base of distal phalanx	6	中手骨頭 Head of metacarpal bone
2	中手骨底 Base of metacarpal bone	7	中節骨頭 Head of middle phalanx
3	中節骨底 Base of middle phalanx	8	基節骨頭 Head of proximal phalanx
4	基節骨底 Base of proximal phalanx	9	中手指節関節 Metacarpophalangeal joint
5	遠位指節間関節 Distal interphalangeal joint	10	近位指節間関節 Proximal interphalangeal joint

すべての指の関節を屈曲して握りこぶしをつくると(A)，中手骨頭(6)が突出する．中手指節関節(B9)を伸展させるには，長い指の伸筋群の腱の働きが必要である．しかし指節間関節(C10, C5)の伸展には，指背腱膜を引き寄せる骨間筋と虫様筋の働きも必要となる(176頁B)．中手指節関節が屈曲したままの場合にのみ，長い指の伸筋群が，指節間関節を伸展することができる．

母指の運動

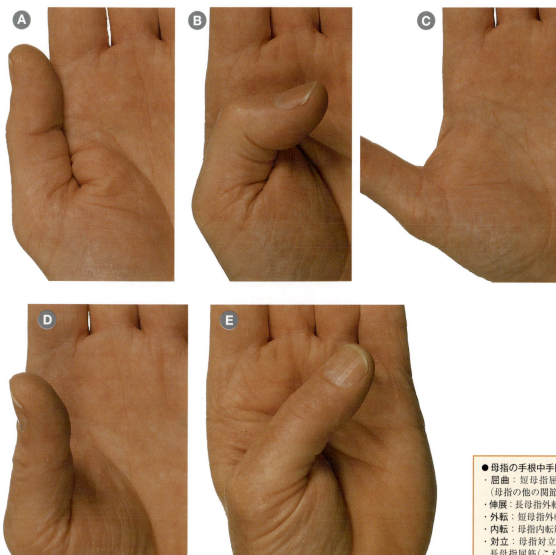

A：解剖学的正位．B：屈曲．C：伸展．D：外転．E：対立．

● 母指の手根中手関節の運動にかかわる筋
- 屈曲：短母指屈筋，母指対立筋，長母指屈筋（母指の他の関節が屈曲位のときに作用する）．
- 伸展：長母指外転筋，長母指伸筋，短母指伸筋．
- 外転：短母指外転筋，長母指外転筋．
- 内転：母指内転筋．
- 対立：母指対立筋，短母指屈筋，母指内転筋，長母指屈筋（これらは前2者に対して補助的に作用する）．

解剖学的正位（A）をとると，母指の爪の向きは，他の指の爪の向きに対し直角になる．それは第一中手骨が，他の指の中手骨に対して直角になるからである（129〜130頁）．これは，どちらかというと故意につくり出された肢位であり，平常時には，母指は手掌面に対して約60°の角度となる（すなわち，わずかに外転位となる）．
屈曲（B）とは，母指の指節骨を，手掌に対して直角に保ったまま手掌と交叉するように母指を曲げることである．
伸展（C）とは，屈曲の逆の運動で，手掌から母指を遠ざけるようにすることである．
外転（D）とは，母指を手掌面から前方へ浮かすことである．この運動を継続すると，必然的に対立（E）になる．
対立とは，第一中手骨の回旋を伴いながら指全体をねじることであり，母指の腹は手掌に向かい，小指の基部に達する（日常生活において，屈曲した他の指に触れたり重ねたりする動作に当たる）．
対立は，手根中手関節の外転に屈曲と内旋が組み合わさった運動であり，母指の他の関節の屈曲は必ずしも伴わない．

下垂手

166　第3章　上肢：手

手掌（左）　[A 手掌腱膜]

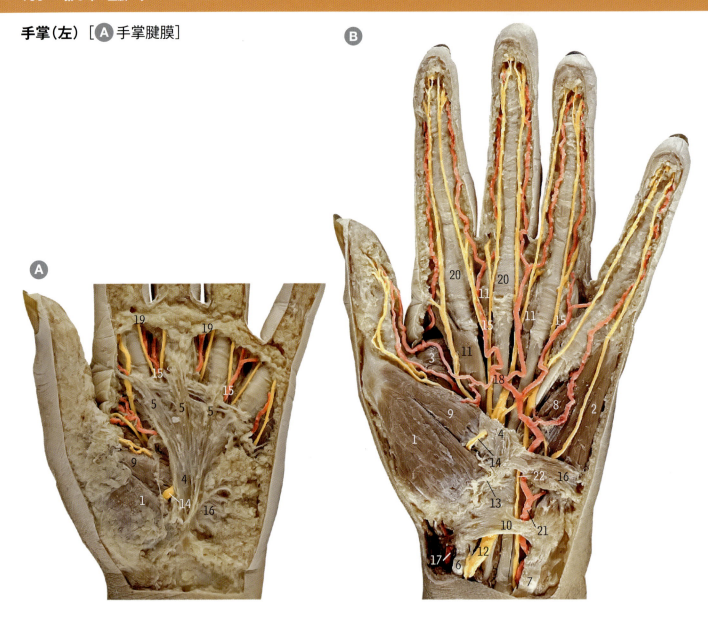

A　手掌の皮膚を除去し，手掌腱膜を明らかにしている．

B　手掌腱膜を除去して手掌の深層を剖出し，屈筋支帯，正中神経と尺骨神経の掌側枝，浅掌動脈弓を明らかにしている母指球筋と小指球筋の高まりが見える．

1　短母指外転筋 Abductor pollicis brevis	9　短母指屈筋 Flexor pollicis brevis	16　短掌筋 Palmaris brevis
2　小指外転筋 Abductor digiti minimi	10　屈筋支帯 Flexor retinaculum	17　橈骨動脈 Radial artery
3　母指内転筋 Adductor pollicis	11　虫様筋 Lumbrical	18　浅掌動脈弓 Superficial palmar arch
4　手掌腱膜（中央部）Palmar aponeurosis	12　正中神経 Median nerve	19　浅横中手靱帯 Superficial transverse metacarpal ligament
5　手掌腱膜（指に延び出しているところ）Palmar aponeurosis	13　掌枝〔正中神経〕Palmar branch (Median nerve)	20　屈筋群（の腱）の腱鞘 Tendon sheath of Flexor tendons
6　橈側手根屈筋 Flexor carpi radialis	14　反回枝＊〔正中神経〕Recurrent branch＊(Median nerve)	21　尺骨動脈 Ulnar artery
7　尺側手根屈筋 Flexor carpi ulnaris	15　総掌側指神経と総掌側指動脈 Common palmar digital nerve and Common palmar digital artery	22　尺骨神経 Ulnar nerve
8　短小指屈筋 Flexor digiti minimi brevis		

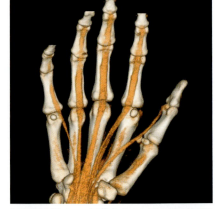

深指屈筋腱のCT画像からの三次元構築画像

動静脈瘻

Dupuytren拘縮

第3章 上肢：手　167

A　手掌（右）［滑液鞘］

手根と指の滑液鞘を，青色の薄布によって強調してある．中指では線維鞘を除去し，滑液鞘（22）を全長にわたって露出させている（他の指では，3のように腱鞘の線維層を残してある）．示指と薬指の滑液鞘は，腱鞘より少し近位へ延び出している．小指の滑液鞘は，屈筋支帯の下にある指屈筋の総腱鞘（24）へと続いている．橈側滑液鞘（20）も，屈筋支帯（9）の下へと続いている．

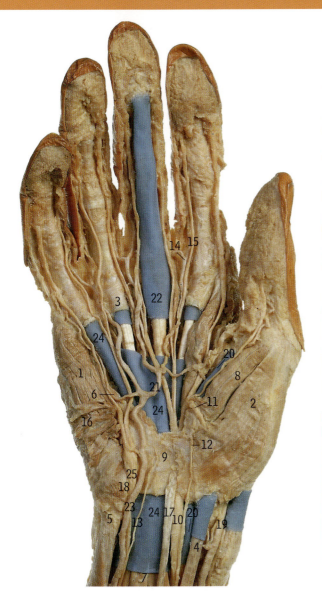

1. 小指外転筋　Abductor digiti minimi
2. 短母指外転筋　Abductor pollicis brevis
3. 指の線維鞘　Fibrous sheaths of digits of hand
4. 橈側手根屈筋　Flexor carpi radialis
5. 尺側手根屈筋　Flexor carpi ulnaris
6. 短小指屈筋　Flexor digiti minimi brevis
7. 浅指屈筋　Flexor digitorum superficialis
8. 短母指屈筋　Flexor pollicis brevis
9. 屈筋支帯　Flexor retinaculum
10. 正中神経　Median nerve
11. 反回枝＊〔正中神経〕　Recurrent branch＊〔Median nerve〕
12. 掌枝〔正中神経〕　Palmar branch〔Median nerve〕
13. 掌枝〔尺骨神経〕　Palmar branch〔Ulnar nerve〕
14. 固有掌側指動脈　Proper palmar digital artery
15. 固有掌側指神経　Proper palmar digital nerve
16. 短掌筋　Palmaris brevis
17. 長掌筋　Palmaris longus
18. 豆状骨　Pisiform
19. 橈骨動脈　Radial artery
20. 橈側滑液鞘＊と長母指屈筋　Radial bursa＊ and Flexor pollicis longus
21. 浅掌動脈弓　Superficial palmar arch
22. 指の滑液鞘　Synovial sheaths of digits of hand
23. 尺骨動脈　Ulnar artery
24. 指屈筋の総腱鞘　Common flexor sheath
25. 尺骨神経　Ulnar nerve

- 手根管（屈筋支帯の下にある）には，浅指屈筋および深指屈筋の8本の腱を包む滑液鞘（22），橈側滑液鞘（20），橈側手根屈筋（4）の滑液鞘（固有の腱鞘に包まれ，他の腱とは別に屈筋支帯を貫く）が認められる．橈側手根屈筋ならびに長母指屈筋の滑液鞘は，腱の停止部まで延びている．
- 指屈筋の総腱鞘（24）は，小指の滑液鞘には連続しているが，薬指，中指，示指の滑液鞘には連続していない．これらの3本の指は固有の滑液鞘をもち，それらの近位端は，線維鞘をわずかに越えて延び出している．
- 正中神経の反回枝（11）は，通常，短母指外転筋，短母指屈筋，母指対立筋を支配する．短母指屈筋（8）は，人体のすべての筋のうち，神経支配の変異が見られる頻度が最も高い筋である．この筋は，約1/3の例で正中神経に支配され，約1/3の例では尺骨神経に支配され，残りの約1/3の例では正中神経と尺骨神経の二重支配を受けている．

B　示指（右）［長い腱とヒモ，それらの位置関係］

1. 第一虫様筋　1st lumbrical
2. 深指屈筋　Flexor digitorum profundus
3. 浅指屈筋　Flexor digitorum superficialis
4. 長いヒモ〔浅指屈筋（の腱）〕　Vinculum longum〔Flexor digitorum superficialis〕
5. 背側中手動脈への枝
6. 固有掌側指神経　Proper palmar digital nerves
7. 母指主動脈　Princeps pollicis artery
8. 示指橈側動脈　Radialis indicis artery
9. 短いヒモ〔深指屈筋腱〕　Vinculum breve〔Tendon of Flexor digitorum profundus〕
10. 浅掌動脈弓　Superficial palmar arch
11. 母指：第一指　Thumb

指神経ブロック

槌指

手根と手掌（左）［A 掌側面］

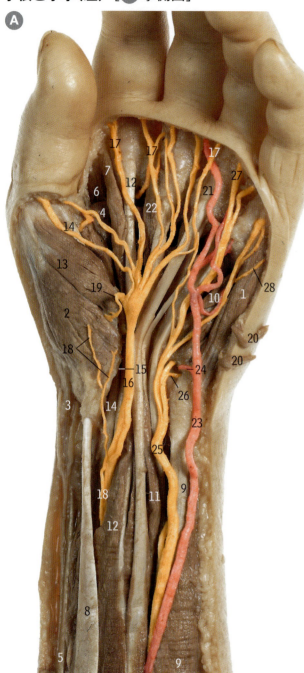

手指の腱鞘(21)の一部を切除して，鞘内に含まれる浅指屈筋(12)と深指屈筋(11)の腱を露出させている．手掌を見ると，虫様筋(7, 22)が深指屈筋腱から起始することがわかる．剖出標本(A)とMR画像(B)を比較せよ．

● 虫様筋は，骨には付着しない．虫様筋は，深指屈筋(11)の腱に起始する．第一虫様筋(7)は示指の腱から，第二虫様筋(22)は中指の腱から起始する．一方，第三虫様筋は隣接する中指の腱と薬指の腱から，同様に第四虫様筋は薬指の腱から起始している．各筋束は，それぞれ指背腱膜の橈側縁に停止している（176頁）．

1	小指外転筋 Abductor digiti minimi	15	屈筋支帯（切断縁） Flexor retinaculum
2	短母指外転筋 Abductor pollicis brevis	16	正中神経 Median nerve
3	長母指外転筋 Abductor pollicis longus	17	総掌側指神経〔正中神経〕 Common palmar digital nerves〔Median nerve〕
4	母指内転筋 Adductor pollicis	18	掌枝〔正中神経〕 Palmar branch〔Median nerve〕
5	腕橈骨筋 Brachioradialis	19	反回枝*〔正中神経〕 Recurrent branch*〔Median nerve〕
6	第一背側骨間筋 1st dorsal interosseous	20	短掌筋 Palmaris brevis
7	第一虫様筋 1st lumbrical	21	指の腱鞘（残存部） Tendon sheaths of digits of hand
8	橈側手根屈筋 Flexor carpi radialis	22	第二虫様筋 2nd lumbrical
9	尺側手根屈筋 Flexor carpi ulnaris	23	尺骨動脈 Ulnar artery
10	短小指屈筋 Flexor digiti minimi brevis	24	深掌枝〔尺骨動脈〕 Deep palmar branch〔Ulnar artery〕
11	深指屈筋 Flexor digitorum profundus	25	尺骨神経 Ulnar nerve
12	浅指屈筋 Flexor digitorum superficialis	26	深枝〔尺骨神経〕 Deep branch〔Ulnar nerve〕
13	短母指屈筋 Flexor pollicis brevis	27	総掌側指神経〔尺骨神経〕 Common palmar digital nerve〔Ulnar nerve〕
14	長母指屈筋 Flexor pollicis longus	28	筋枝〔尺骨神経〕 Muscular branch〔Ulnar nerve〕

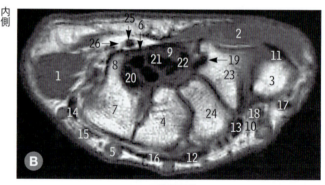

MR 横断画像

1	小指外転筋 Abductor digiti minimi	9	正中神経 Median nerve	18	長母指伸筋（の腱） Extensor pollicis longus
2	短母指外転筋 Abductor pollicis brevis	10	橈骨動脈 Radial artery	19	橈側手根屈筋（の腱） Flexor carpi radialis
3	第一中手骨底 Base of 1st metatarsal bone	11	長母指外転筋（の腱） Abductor pollicis longus	20	深指屈筋（の腱） Flexor digitorum profundus
4	有頭骨 Capitate	12	短橈側手根伸筋（の腱） Extensor carpi radialis brevis	21	浅指屈筋（の腱） Flexor digitorum superficialis
5	手背静脈網 Dorsal venous network of hand	13	長橈側手根伸筋（の腱） Extensor carpi radialis longus	22	長母指屈筋（の腱） Flexor pollicis longus
6	屈筋支帯 Flexor retinaculum	14	尺側手根伸筋（の腱） Extensor carpi ulnaris	23	大菱形骨 Trapezium
7	有鈎骨 Hamate	15	小指伸筋（の腱） Extensor digiti minimi	24	小菱形骨 Trapezoid
8	有鈎骨鈎 Hook of hamate	16	［総］指伸筋（の腱） Extensor digitorum	25	尺骨動脈 Ulnar artery
		17	短母指伸筋（の腱） Extensor pollicis brevis	26	尺骨神経 Ulnar nerve

手根管症候群

正中神経麻痺

浅掌動脈弓 [A 不完全な浅掌動脈弓（左），B 完全な浅掌動脈弓（右）]

- 2/3の例において，浅掌動脈弓の形成が（A29のように）不完全な場合が見られる．残りの1/3では，橈骨動脈の浅掌枝（B30）との間に完全な動脈弓が形成される．
- 手掌では浅掌動脈弓（29）とその枝（総掌側指動脈，1）が総掌側指神経（22，7）より浅層にある．しかし，手指では固有掌側指神経（3）が同名の動脈（固有掌側指動脈，2）より浅層（前）に位置する．

1 総掌側指動脈 Common palmar digital artery
2 固有掌側指動脈 Proper palmar digital artery
3 固有掌側指神経 Proper palmar digital nerves
4 小指外転筋 Abductor digiti minimi
5 短母指外転筋 Abductor pollicis brevis
6 長母指外転筋 Abductor pollicis longus
7 総掌側指神経〔尺骨神経〕 Common palmar digital nerve〔Ulnar nerve〕
8 示指橈側動脈（28）と母指主動脈（26）の共通幹
9 深掌枝〔尺骨動脈〕 Deep palmar branch〔Ulnar artery〕
10 深枝〔尺骨神経〕 Deep branch〔Ulnar nerve〕
11 深掌動脈弓 Deep palmar arch
12 第一虫様筋 1st lumbrical
13 橈側手根屈筋 Flexor carpi radialis
14 尺側手根屈筋と豆状骨 Flexor carpi ulnaris and Pisiform
15 深指屈筋 Flexor digitorum profundus
16 浅指屈筋 Flexor digitorum superficialis
17 短母指屈筋 Flexor pollicis brevis
18 長母指屈筋 Flexor pollicis longus
19 屈筋支帯 Flexor retinaculum
20 第四虫様筋 4th lumbrical
21 正中神経 Median nerve
22 正中神経（総掌側指神経に分かれる）Median nerve
23 反回枝*〔正中神経〕Recurrent branch*〔Median nerve〕
24 小指対立筋 Opponens digiti minimi
25 短掌筋 Palmaris brevis
26 母指主動脈 Princeps pollicis artery
27 橈骨動脈 Radial artery
28 示指橈側動脈 Radialis indicis artery
29 浅掌動脈弓 Superficial palmar arch
30 浅掌枝〔橈骨動脈〕 Superficial palmar branch〔Radial artery〕
31 尺骨動脈 Ulnar artery
32 尺骨神経 Ulnar nerve

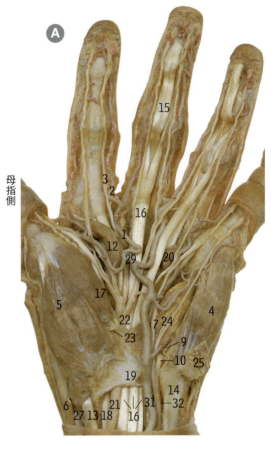

A

母指側

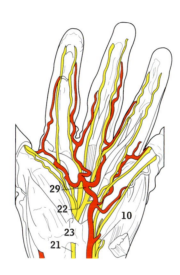

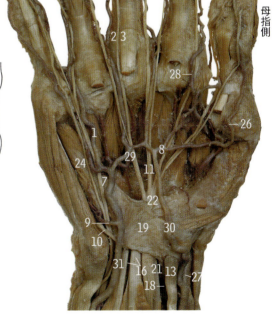

母指側

B

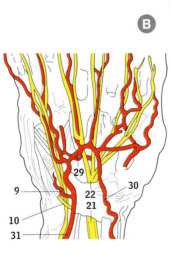

手根における動脈穿刺

Guyon管症候群

A B 手掌（右）［A 深掌動脈弓，B 手掌の動脈］

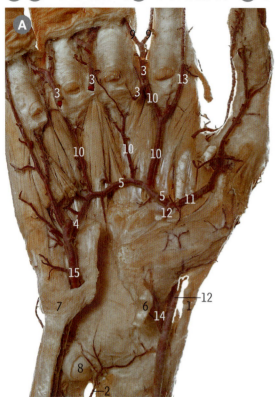

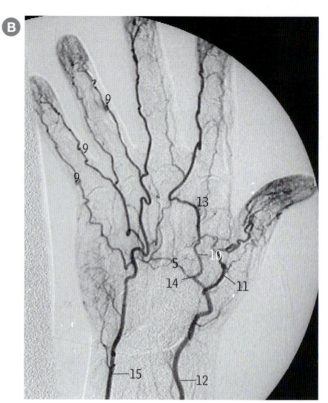

手掌の動脈の血管造影画像

大半の筋と腱を除去し，動脈色素を注入し拡張させている．深掌動脈弓（5）から出た掌側中手動脈（10）と浅掌動脈弓から起こった総掌側指動脈（3）が合している．剖出標本（A）と血管造影画像（B）を比較せよ．

1	長母指外転筋 Abductor pollicis longus	9	固有掌側指動脈 Proper palmar digital arteries
2	前骨間動脈の枝（掌側手根枝への枝） Branch of Anterior interosseous artery	10	掌側中手動脈 Palmar metacarpal arteries
3	総掌側指動脈（浅掌動脈弓から出る） Common palmar digital arteries	11	母指主動脈 Princeps pollicis artery
4	深掌枝〔尺骨動脈〕 Deep palmar branch〔Ulnar artery〕	12	橈骨動脈 Radial artery
5	深掌動脈弓 Deep palmar arch	13	示指橈側動脈（通常とは起始が異なる） Radialis indicis artery
6	橈側手根屈筋 Flexor carpi radialis	14	浅掌枝〔橈骨動脈〕 Superficial palmar branch〔Radial artery〕
7	尺側手根屈筋と豆状骨 Flexor carpi ulnaris and Pisiform	15	尺骨動脈 Ulnar artery
8	尺骨頭 Head of ulna		

ばね指

第3章 上肢：手 171

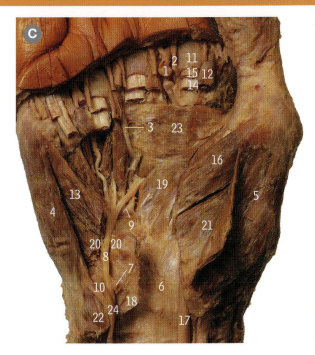

C 手掌(右) [尺骨神経の深枝]

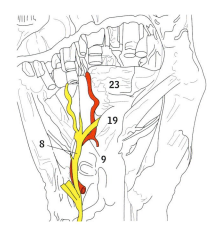

浅指屈筋(15)および深指屈筋(14)ならびに虫様筋(12)の近位部を，中手骨頭の近くで切断してある．また，小指球筋の一部を除去し，手掌を走る尺骨神経(8)と尺骨動脈(7)を示している．手掌を走る尺骨神経と尺骨動脈は，外側へ曲がり，母指内転筋の横頭(23)と斜頭(19)の間を通過する．

1	総掌側指動脈 Common palmar digital artery	13	短小指屈筋 Flexor digiti minimi brevis
2	固有掌側指神経 Proper palmar digital nerves	14	深指屈筋 Flexor digitorum profundus
3	掌側中手動脈 Palmar metacarpal artery	15	浅指屈筋 Flexor digitorum superficialis
4	小指外転筋 Abductor digiti minimi	16	短母指屈筋 Flexor pollicis brevis
5	短母指外転筋 Abductor pollicis brevis	17	長母指屈筋 Flexor pollicis longus
6	手根管 Carpal tunnel	18	屈筋支帯(切断縁) Flexor retinaculum
7	深掌枝〔尺骨動脈〕 Deep palmar branch〔Ulnar artery〕	19	斜頭〔母指内転筋〕 Oblique head〔Adductor pollicis〕
8	深枝〔尺骨神経〕 Deep branch〔Ulnar nerve〕	20	小指対立筋 Opponens digiti minimi
9	深掌動脈弓 Deep palmar arch	21	母指対立筋 Opponens pollicis
10	掌側指神経*〔尺骨神経〕 Digital branches*〔Ulnar nerve〕	22	豆状骨 Pisiform
11	指の線維鞘 Fibrous sheaths of digits of hand	23	横頭〔母指内転筋〕 Transverse head〔Adductor pollicis〕
12	第一虫様筋 1st lumbrical	24	尺骨神経 Ulnar nerve

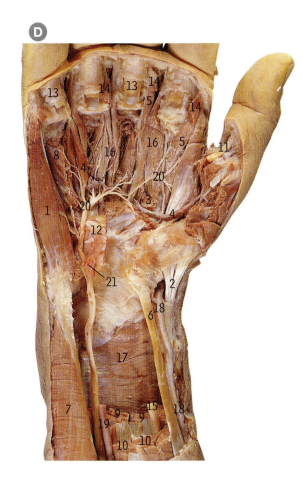

D 手掌(右) [深層]

母指内転筋(3)と屈筋群の腱の深部には，近位に方形回内筋(17)が，遠位には広い範囲に分布した尺骨神経の深枝(20)と深掌動脈弓(4)が見られる．

1	小指外転筋 Abductor digiti minimi	12	屈筋支帯(切断してある) Flexor retinaculum
2	長母指外転筋 Abductor pollicis longus	13	屈筋群(の腱)の腱鞘 Tendon sheath of Flexor tendons
3	母指内転筋(切断してある) Adductor pollicis	14	虫様筋(切断してある) Lumbrical
4	深掌動脈弓 Deep palmar arch	15	正中神経(切断してある) Median nerve
5	背側骨間筋 Dorsal interossei	16	掌側骨間筋 Palmar interossei
6	橈側手根屈筋 Flexor carpi radialis	17	方形回内筋 Pronator quadratus
7	尺側手根屈筋 Flexor carpi ulnaris	18	橈骨動脈 Radial artery
8	短小指屈筋(切断してある) Flexor digiti minimi brevis	19	尺骨動脈(切断してある) Ulnar artery
9	深指屈筋(切断してある) Flexor digitorum profundus	20	深枝〔尺骨神経〕(手の筋への枝) Deep branch〔Ulnar nerve〕
10	浅指屈筋(切断してある) Flexor digitorum superficialis	21	浅枝〔尺骨神経〕(手根で切断してある) Superficial branch〔Ulnar nerve〕
11	長母指屈筋 Flexor pollicis longus		

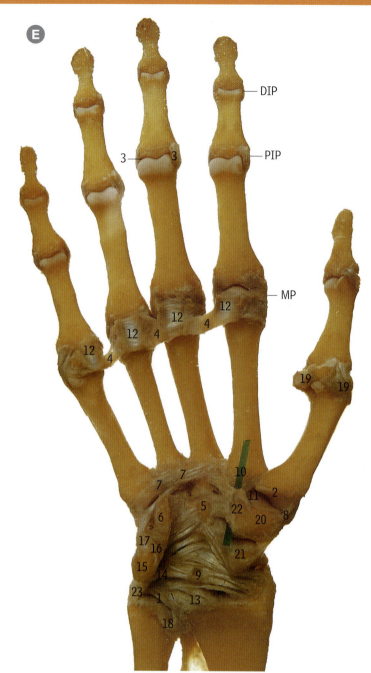

E 手掌（右）［靱帯と関節］

母指の手根中手関節（第一中手骨底と大菱形骨の間につくられる）の関節包を除去し，母指に特有の運動である対立をつくる鞍状の関節面を示している．この関節の掌側靱帯(11)と外側靱帯(8)は，保存されている．下橈尺関節の関節包も除去し，関節円板(1)を示しているが，円板の遠位にある下橈尺関節の尺側部は開放していない．

1	関節円板〔下橈尺関節〕 Articular disc〔Distal radio-ulnar joint〕
2	第一中手骨底 Base of 1st metatarsal bone
3	側副靱帯〔指節間関節〕 Collateral ligament〔Interphalangeal joint of hand〕
4	深横中手靱帯 Deep transverse metacarpal ligament
5	有頭骨頭* Head of capitate*
6	有鈎骨鈎 Hook of hamate
7	骨間中手靱帯 Interosseous metacarpal ligament
8	外側靱帯*〔母指の手根中手関節〕 Lateral ligament*〔Carpometacarpal joint of thumb〕
9	月状骨 Lunate
10	橈側手根屈筋腱の通る大菱形骨の溝（マーカーを挿入して示す）
11	掌側靱帯*〔母指の手根中手関節〕 Palmar ligament*〔Carpometacarpal joint of thumb〕
12	掌側靱帯〔中手指節関節〕（屈筋腱の通る溝を伴う） Palmar ligament〔Metacarpophalangeal joint〕
13	掌側橈骨手根靱帯 Palmar radiocarpal ligament
14	掌側尺骨手根靱帯 Palmar ulnocarpal ligament
15	豆状骨 Pisiform
16	豆鈎靱帯 Pisohamate ligament
17	豆中手靱帯 Pisometacarpal ligament
18	囊状陥凹〔下橈尺関節の関節包〕 Sacciform recess〔Capsule of distal radio-ulnar joint〕
19	短母指屈筋腱の種子骨（尺側の種子骨に母指内転筋が着く）
20	大菱形骨 Trapezium
21	舟状骨結節〔舟状骨〕 Tubercle〔Scaphoid〕
22	大菱形骨結節 Tubercle of trapezium
23	内側手根側副靱帯 Ulnar collateral ligament of wrist joint

DIPJ (Distal interphalangeal joint*)：遠位指節間関節*
PIPJ (Proximal interphalangeal joint*)：近位指節間関節*
MCPJ (Metacarpophalangeal joint)：中手指節関節

- 中手指節関節と指節間関節の側副靱帯(E3, F2)は，関節の近位側の骨頭の側面後部より斜めに走り，遠位側の骨底の側面前部に付着する．
- 母指の対立とは，第一中手骨の屈曲と外転を内旋と組み合わせた運動である(165頁)．第一中手骨底と大菱形骨の間の関節は，鞍関節である．この関節の関節包と補強靱帯の骨への付着の形態は，短母指屈筋と母指対立筋が収縮する時に，中手骨の回旋運動を可能とする．
- 関節円板(E1)は，橈骨と尺骨の下端を固定しており，下橈尺関節を橈骨手根関節から分離している．そのため2つの関節腔は連絡していない（肘関節と上橈尺関節の場合のように関節腔が連絡しているわけではない．154頁）．

橈側方から.

F 示指（右）［中手指節関節（MP）］

関節包の一部を除去して，側副靱帯(2)の輪郭を明確にしてある．

1	基節骨底 Base of proximal phalanx
2	側副靱帯 Collateral ligament
3	線維鞘〔腱鞘〕 Fibrous sheath〔Tendon sheath〕
4	第二中手骨頭 Head of 2nd metatarsal bone

ゲームキーパー母指
（母指中手指節関節
尺側側副靱帯損傷）

第3章 上肢：手　173

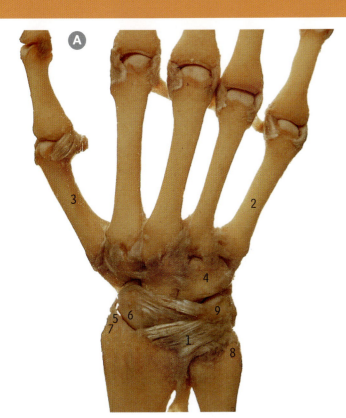

A 手背（右）［靱帯と関節］

橈骨手根関節包の橈側部を含めた大半の関節包を除去し，舟状骨(6)と橈骨の下端部(7)の関節の形態を示してある．

1	背側橈骨手根靱帯 Dorsal radiocarpal ligament
2	第五中手骨 5th metacarpal bone
3	第一中手骨 1st metacarpal bone
4	有鉤骨 Hamate
5	外側手根側副靱帯 Radial collateral ligament of wrist joint
6	舟状骨 Scaphoid
7	（橈骨の）茎状突起 Radial styloid process
8	（尺骨の）茎状突起 Ulnar styloid process
9	三角骨 Triquetrum

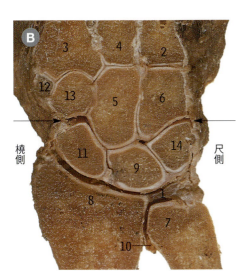

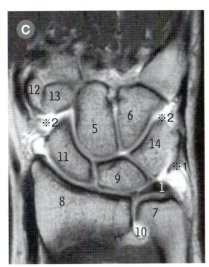

MR関節造影画像

B C 手根（右）［冠状断］

1	関節円板（三角線維軟骨複合体※） Articular disc (Triangular fibrocartilage complex*, TFCC)
2	第四中手骨底 Base of 4th metatarsal bone
3	第二中手骨底 Base of 2nd metatarsal bone
4	第三中手骨底 Base of 3rd metatarsal bone
5	有頭骨 Capitate
6	有鉤骨 Hamate
7	尺骨頭 Head of ulna
8	橈骨（下端部） Radius
9	月状骨 Lunate
10	嚢状陥凹〔下橈尺関節〕 Sacciform recess〔Distal radio-ulnar joint〕
11	舟状骨 Scaphoid
12	大菱形骨 Trapezium
13	小菱形骨 Trapezoid
14	三角骨 Triquetrum

手根の断面を背側から見ている．切断面が手根を通る位置は，手掌よりも手背に近い．したがって，第一および第五中手骨は，この切断面では含まれない．手根骨の近位列と遠位列の間の矢印は，手根中央関節面の並びを示す．この断面(B)とMR画像(C)を比較せよ．

※1：三角線維軟骨複合体(TFCC)への正常な血管進入．
※2：手根中央関節に見られる強いコントラストは，橈骨手根関節と手根中央関節の間に異常な交通があることを示している．

月状骨脱臼

舟状骨無腐性壊死

A 手背（左）

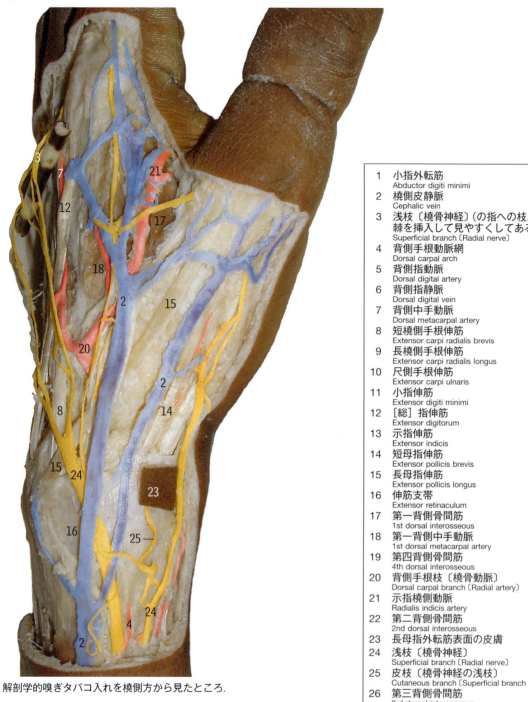

解剖学的嗅ぎタバコ入れを橈側方から見たところ．

1	小指外転筋	Abductor digiti minimi
2	橈側皮静脈	Cephalic vein
3	浅枝〔橈骨神経〕（の指への枝．下にヤマアラシの棘を挿入して見やすくしてある） Superficial branch〔Radial nerve〕	
4	背側手根動脈網	Dorsal carpal arch
5	背側指動脈	Dorsal digital artery
6	背側指静脈	Dorsal digital vein
7	背側中手動脈	Dorsal metacarpal artery
8	短橈側手根伸筋	Extensor carpi radialis brevis
9	長橈側手根伸筋	Extensor carpi radialis longus
10	尺側手根伸筋	Extensor carpi ulnaris
11	小指伸筋	Extensor digiti minimi
12	［総］指伸筋	Extensor digitorum
13	示指伸筋	Extensor indicis
14	短母指伸筋	Extensor pollicis brevis
15	長母指伸筋	Extensor pollicis longus
16	伸筋支帯	Extensor retinaculum
17	第一背側骨間筋	1st dorsal interosseous
18	第一背側中手動脈	1st dorsal metacarpal artery
19	第四背側骨間筋	4th dorsal interosseous
20	背側手根枝〔橈骨動脈〕	Dorsal carpal branch〔Radial artery〕
21	示指橈側動脈	Radialis indicis artery
22	第二背側骨間筋	2nd dorsal interosseous
23	長母指外転筋表面の皮膚	
24	浅枝〔橈骨神経〕	Superficial branch〔Radial nerve〕
25	皮枝〔橈骨神経の浅枝〕	Cutaneous branch〔Superficial branch of Radial nerve〕
26	第三背側骨間筋	3rd dorsal interosseous
27	手背枝〔尺骨神経〕	Dorsal branch〔Ulnar nerve〕

槌指

第3章 上肢：手　175

B 手背（左）

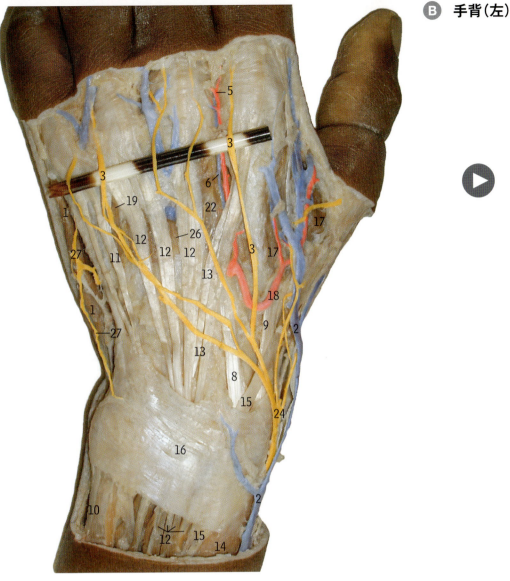

用語は前頁参照.

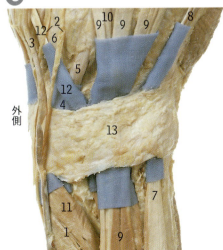

C 手根の背側と手背（右）［滑液鞘］

筋膜と尺骨神経の皮枝を除去し，伸筋支帯(13)と橈骨神経(2)は残してある．滑液鞘を青色の薄布で強調してある．伸筋支帯の6つの区画に含まれる腱を橈側から尺側の順に挙げる：長母指外転筋(1)と短母指伸筋(11)⇒長橈側手根伸筋(6)と短橈側手根伸筋(5)⇒長母指伸筋(12)⇒総指伸筋(9)と示指伸筋(10)⇒小指伸筋(8)⇒尺側手根伸筋(7).

1	長母指外転筋 Abductor pollicis longus	7	尺側手根伸筋 Extensor carpi ulnaris
2	浅枝〔橈骨神経〕 Superficial branch〔Radial nerve〕	8	小指伸筋 Extensor digiti minimi
3	橈側皮静脈 Cephalic vein	9	［総］指伸筋 Extensor digitorum
4	短橈側手根伸筋(5)および長橈側手根伸筋(6)の腱鞘	10	示指伸筋 Extensor indicis
5	短橈側手根伸筋 Extensor carpi radialis brevis	11	短母指伸筋 Extensor pollicis brevis
6	長橈側手根伸筋 Extensor carpi radialis longus	12	長母指伸筋 Extensor pollicis longus
		13	伸筋支帯 Extensor retinaculum

爪の異常

手根のガングリオン

A 手背（右）[動脈]

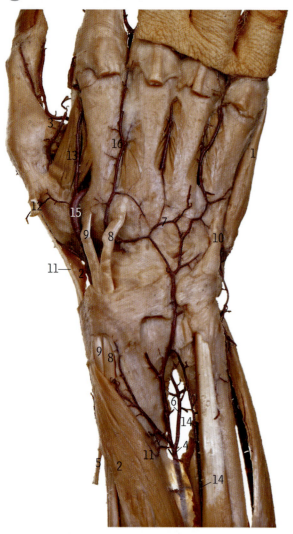

B 薬指（左）[指背腱膜]

指を背側に伸展してある．

1	［総］指伸筋（の腱） Extensor digitorum	8	翼状腱* Wing tendon *
2	深横中手靱帯 Deep transverse metacarpal ligament	9	虫様筋 Lumbrical
3	指背腱膜* Extensor aponeurosis *	10	骨間筋の腱からの斜線維束
4	背側骨間筋 Dorsal interossei	11	掌側骨間筋 Palmar interossei
5	背側骨間筋（指節骨付着部） Dorsal interossei	12	支靱帯 Retinacular ligament *
6	［総］指伸筋（の腱） Extensor digitorum	13	［総］指伸筋（の腱）（終末部） Extensor digitorum
7	側索* Lateral band *	14	指背腱膜腱帽* Extensor hood *
		15	指三角靱帯* Triangular ligament *

動脈に色素を注入してある．指に行く長い腱を，背側手根動脈網(7)と背側中手動脈(13, 16)が見えるように除去してある．手根の上方では，方形回内筋を除去し，前骨間動脈(4)から手掌に向かう枝(6)を示してある．前骨間動脈の本幹は，背側面に移って走り，後骨間動脈(14)と合流している．

1	小指外転筋 Abductor digiti minimi	9	長橈側手根伸筋 Extensor carpi radialis longus
2	長母指外転筋 Abductor pollicis longus	10	尺側手根伸筋 Extensor carpi ulnaris
3	母指内転筋と母指主動脈の枝 Adductor pollicis and Branch of Princeps pollicis artery	11	短母指伸筋 Extensor pollicis brevis
4	前骨間動脈 Anterior interosseous artery	12	長母指伸筋 Extensor pollicis longus
5	腕橈骨筋 Brachioradialis	13	第一背側骨間筋と第一背側中手動脈 1st dorsal interosseous and 1st dorsal metacarpal artery
6	前骨間動脈の枝（掌側手根枝への枝） Branch of Anterior interosseous artery	14	後骨間動脈 Posterior interosseous artery
7	背側手根動脈網 Dorsal carpal arch	15	橈骨動脈 Radial artery
8	短橈側手根伸筋 Extensor carpi radialis brevis	16	第二背側骨間筋と第二背側中手動脈 2nd dorsal interosseous and 2nd dorsal metacarpal artery

● 母指では，3つの腱がそれぞれ異なる高さに向かっている．第一中手骨底に長母指外転筋(2)が，基節骨底に短母指伸筋(11)が，また末節骨底に長母指伸筋(12)が停止する．

橈骨手根関節と手根中央関節（右）　[A 手根中央関節，B 橈骨手根関節]

右手の後面母指縁

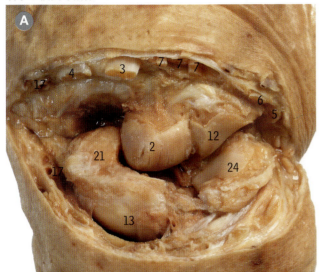
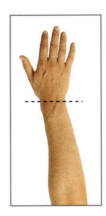

関節を開放し，屈曲させてある．

右手の前面母指縁

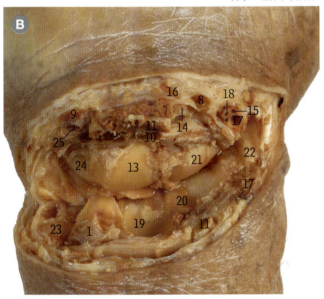
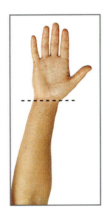

関節を開放し，伸展させてある．

1	関節円板	Articular disc
2	有頭骨	Capitate
3	短橈側手根伸筋	Extensor carpi radialis brevis
4	長橈側手根伸筋	Extensor carpi radialis longus
5	尺側手根伸筋	Extensor carpi ulnaris
6	小指伸筋	Extensor digiti minimi
7	［総］指伸筋	Extensor digitorum
8	橈側手根屈筋（の腱）	Flexor carpi radialis
9	尺側手根屈筋（の腱）	Flexor carpi ulnaris
10	深指屈筋（の腱）	Flexor digitorum profundus
11	浅指屈筋（の腱）	Flexor digitorum superficialis
12	有鈎骨	Hamate
13	月状骨	Lunate
14	正中神経	Median nerve
15	浅掌静脈弓から出る静脈	
16	長掌筋（の腱）	Palmaris longus
17	橈骨動脈	Radial artery
18	橈骨動脈（浅掌動脈弓へ続く）	Radial artery
19	月状骨（の橈側面）	Lunate
20	舟状骨（の橈側面）	Scaphoid
21	舟状骨	Scaphoid
22	（橈骨の）茎状突起	Radial styloid process
23	（尺骨の）茎状突起	Ulnar styloid process
24	三角骨	Triquetrum
25	尺骨動脈	Ulnar artery

関節面を構成する骨を観察するために，2つの関節とも開放し，正常の運動範囲をはるかに超えて曲げてある．Aでは，手根中央関節を過度な屈曲位にしてある．Bでは，橈骨手根関節を過度な伸展位にしてある．また，遠位の手根中央関節の関節面はAで見られ，近位の橈骨手根関節の舟状骨（21），月状骨（13），三角骨（24）の関節面はBで見られる．

手根と手

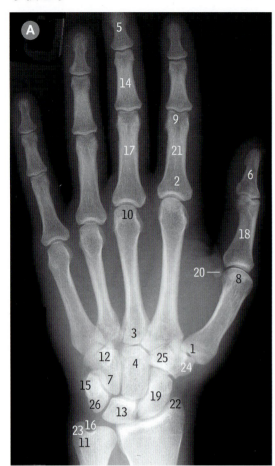
X線画像（後前画像）

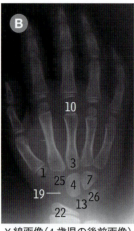
X線画像（4歳児の後前画像）

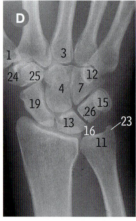
X線画像（後前画像）

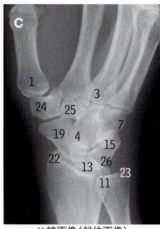
X線画像（斜位画像）

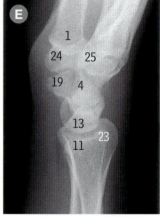
X線画像（側面画像）

Bの中手骨と指節骨の骨端を，131頁のIとJの骨標本と比較せよ．

● 橈骨の遠位の骨端は，X線画像では2歳で見え始め，尺骨は6歳で見えるようになる．最初に見えるようになる手根骨は有頭骨で，1歳で出現する．

1	第一中手骨底 Base of 1st metatarsal bone	14	中節骨〔中指（第三指）〕 Middle phalanx〔Middle finger〕
2	指節骨底 Base of phalanx	15	豆状骨 Pisiform
3	第三中手骨底 Base of 3rd metatarsal bone	16	関節円板（三角線維軟骨複合体*） Articular disc (Triangular fibrocartilage complex*, TFCC)
4	有頭骨 Capitate	17	基節骨〔中指（第三指）〕 Proximal phalanx〔Middle finger〕
5	末節骨〔中指（第三指）〕 Distal phalanx〔Middle finger〕	18	基節骨〔母指（第一指）〕 Proximal phalanx〔Thumb〕
6	末節骨〔母指（第一指）〕 Distal phalanx〔Thumb〕	19	舟状骨 Scaphoid
7	有鈎骨 Hamate	20	短母指屈筋と母指内転筋の腱に含まれた種子骨
8	第一中手骨頭 Head of 1st metatarsal bone	21	指節骨体 Body of phalanx
9	指節骨頭 Head of phalanx	22	（橈骨の）茎状突起 Radial styloid process
10	第三中手骨頭 Head of 3rd metatarsal bone	23	（尺骨の）茎状突起 Ulnar styloid process
11	尺骨頭 Head of ulna	24	大菱形骨 Trapezium
12	有鈎骨鈎 Hook of hamate	25	小菱形骨 Trapezoid
13	月状骨 Lunate	26	三角骨 Triquetrum

胸部

胸部 [**A** 体表解剖, **B** 骨格, **C** 軸骨格]

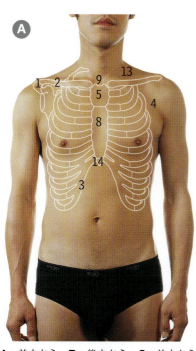 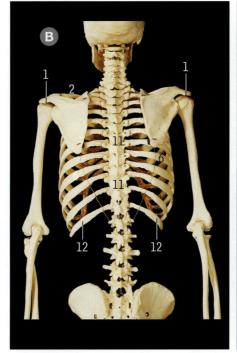 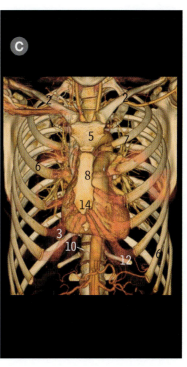

A：前方から. **B**：後方から. **C**：前方から（脊柱と胸郭）.

1	肩峰 Acromion	8	胸骨体 Body of sternum
2	鎖骨 Clavicle	9	頸切痕 Jugular notch：Suprasternal notch
3	肋骨弓 Costal margin：Costal arch	10	胸椎（椎体） Thoracic vertebra
4	三角筋胸筋溝* Deltopectoral groove*	11	胸椎（棘突起） Thoracic vertebra
5	胸骨柄 Manubrium of sternum	12	第十二肋骨 12th rib：Rib XII
6	肋骨 Rib	13	僧帽筋 Trapezius
7	第二肋骨 2nd rib：Rib II	14	剣状突起 Xiphoid process

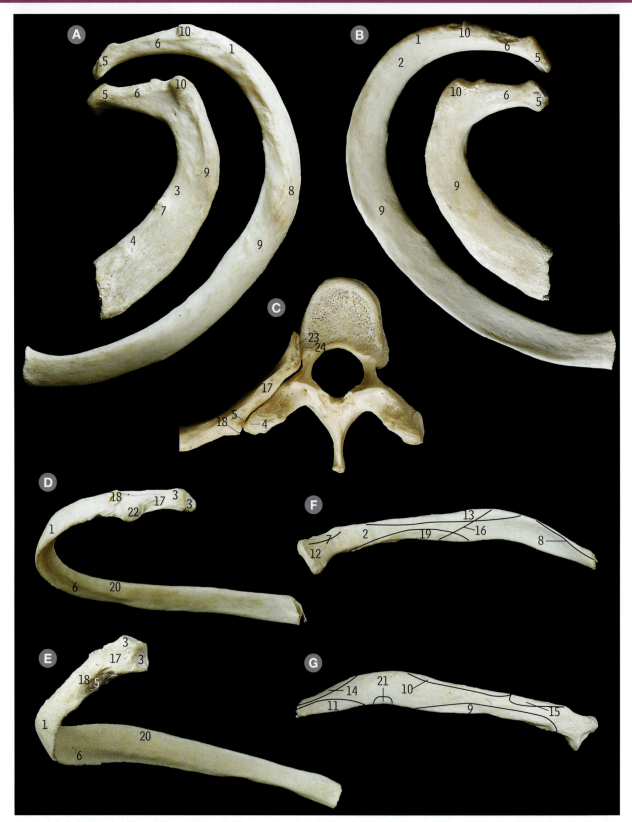

A：上方から（写真の左が第一肋骨，右が第二肋骨）．B：下方から（写真の左が第二肋骨，右が第一肋骨）．C：上方から．D・E・G：後方から．F：前方から．

Ⓐ Ⓑ 第一肋骨と第二肋骨（左）

1	肋骨角 Angle of rib	3	鎖骨下動脈溝（第一胸神経も通る） Groove for subclavian artery	5	肋骨頭 Head of rib	8	前鋸筋粗面 Tuberosity for serratus anterior
2	肋骨溝 Costal groove	4	鎖骨下静脈溝 Groove for subclavian vein	6	肋骨頸 Neck of rib	9	肋骨体 Body of rib：Shaft of rib
				7	前斜角筋結節 Scalene tubercle	10	肋骨結節 Tubercle of rib

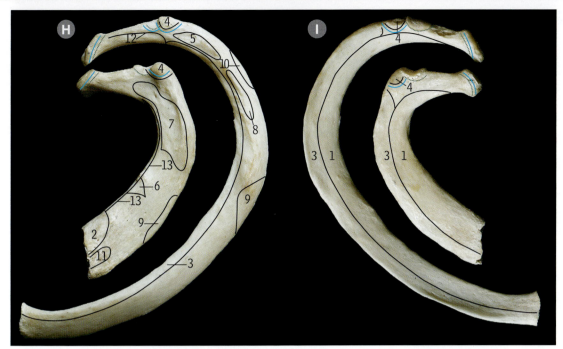

H：上方から（写真の左が第一肋骨，右が第二肋骨）．I：下方から（写真の左が第二肋骨，右が第一肋骨）．（青線：骨端線．緑点線：肋椎関節包の付着部．）

C 肋骨（左）と椎骨の位置関係 [C 典型的な肋骨と胸椎との組み合わせ]
D～G 肋骨（左） [D 第五肋骨（典型的な上位の肋骨），E 第七肋骨（典型的な下位の肋骨），F G 第十二肋骨と筋と靱帯の付着部]

1	肋骨角 Angle of rib	7	肋横突靱帯 Costotransverse ligament	13	内肋間筋 Internal intercostal muscle	19	腰方形筋 Quadratus lumborum
2	胸膜に覆われた領域	8	横隔膜 Diaphragm	14	広背筋 Latissimus dorsi	20	肋骨体 Body of rib：Shaft of rib
3	肋骨頭関節面 Articular facet of head of rib	9	脊柱起立筋 Erector spinae	15	肋骨挙筋 Levatores costarum	21	下後鋸筋 Serratus posterior inferior
4	横突肋骨窩 Transverse costal facet	10	外肋間筋 External intercostal muscle	16	胸膜の反転する線	22	肋骨結節 Tubercle of rib
5	肋骨結節（関節部） Tubercle of rib	11	外腹斜筋 External oblique	17	肋骨頸 Neck of rib	23	（上の）肋骨頭関節面 Articular facet of head of rib
6	肋骨溝 Costal groove	12	肋骨頭 Head of rib	18	肋骨結節（非関節部） Tubercle of rib	24	上肋骨窩〔椎体〕 Superior costal facet〔Vertebral body〕

- 典型的でない肋骨とは，第一・第二・第十・第十一・第十二肋骨のことである．
- 第一肋骨は，肋骨頭（A5，B5）の関節面が一つであり，肋骨結節（A10，B10）が目立って発達しており，肋骨角と肋骨溝を欠いている．肋骨体は，上面と下面を有する．
- 第二肋骨は，2つの関節面をもつ肋骨頭（A5，B5），肋骨結節（A10，B10）の近くにある肋骨角（A1，B1），後部で広い肋骨溝（B2），上外方を向く外面，下内方を向く内面がある．
- 第十二肋骨は，1つの関節面をもつ肋骨頭（F12）があるが，肋骨結節，肋骨角，肋骨溝は見られない．肋骨体は，先端が次第に細くなる（他のすべての肋骨の先端は少し太くなる）．

H I 第一肋骨と第二肋骨（左） [筋と靱帯の付着部]

1	胸膜に覆われた領域	7	中斜角筋 Middle scalene
2	肋鎖靱帯 Costoclavicular ligament	8	後斜角筋 Posterior scalene
3	肋間筋と肋間膜 Intercostal muscles and Intercostal membranes	9	前鋸筋 Serratus anterior
4	外側肋横突靱帯 Lateral costotransverse ligament	10	上後鋸筋 Serratus posterior superior
5	肋骨挙筋 Levatores costarum	11	鎖骨下筋 Subclavius
6	前斜角筋 Anterior scalene	12	上肋横突靱帯 Superior costotransverse ligament
		13	胸膜上膜 Suprapleural membrane

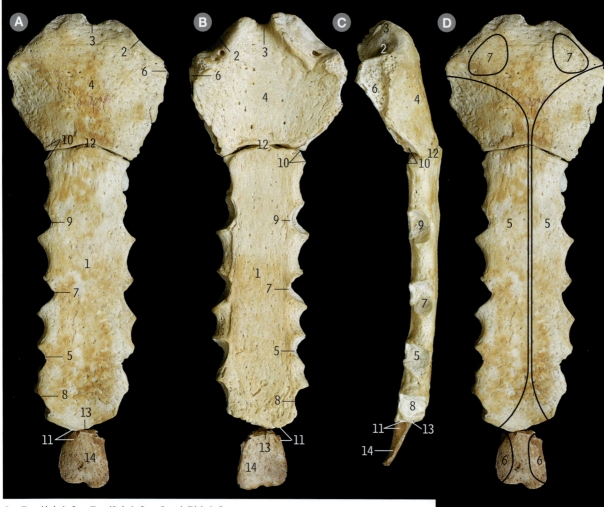

A・D：前方から．B：後方から．C：右側方から．

Ⓐ～Ⓒ 胸骨

1. 胸骨体
   Body of sternum
2. 鎖骨切痕
   Clavicular notch
3. 頸切痕
   Jugular notch：Suprasternal notch
4. 胸骨柄
   Manubrium of sternum
5. 第五肋骨切痕
   5th costal notch
6. 第一肋骨切痕
   1st costal notch
7. 第四肋骨切痕
   4th costal notch
8. 第六肋骨切痕
   6th costal notch
9. 第三肋骨切痕
   3rd costal notch
10. 第二肋骨切痕
    2nd costal notch
11. 第七肋骨切痕
    7th costal notch
12. 胸骨角と胸骨柄結合
    Sternal angle and Manubriosternal joint
13. 胸骨剣結合
    Xiphisternal joint
14. 剣状突起
    Xiphoid process

- 胸骨は胸骨柄(4)，胸骨体(1)および剣状突起(14)からなる．
- 胸骨体(1)は，4つの胸骨分節(sternebrae)が癒合して形成される．3ヵ所の癒合したところには，横稜(わずかな高まり)が認められることがある．
- 胸骨柄(4)と胸骨体(1)は，骨性である．剣状突起(14)は，軟骨性で，骨化の程度はさまざまであり，大きさや形にかなり変異がみられる．
- 胸骨柄結合(12)および胸骨剣結合(13)は，ともに線維軟骨結合である．表面は硝子軟骨で覆われ，線維軟骨性の円板により結合している．

胸骨正中切開術

胸骨の変異

第4章 胸部：胸郭

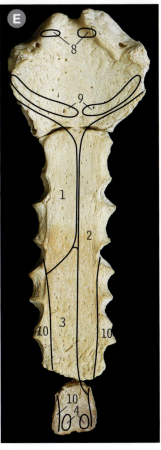

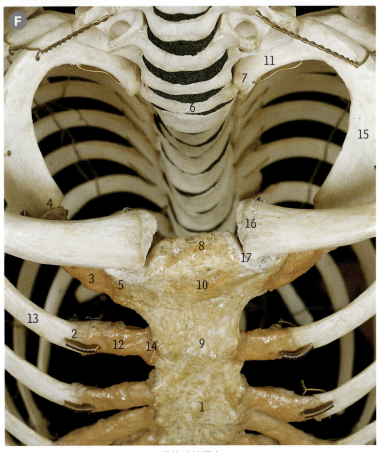

E：後方から．F：上前方から．

骨格連結標本

D E 胸骨［筋と靱帯の付着部］

1. 左の胸膜に覆われた領域
2. 右の胸膜に覆われた領域
3. 心膜と接する領域
4. 横隔膜 Diaphragm
5. 大胸筋 Pectoralis major
6. 腹直筋 Rectus abdominis
7. 胸鎖乳突筋 Sternocleidomastoid
8. 胸骨舌骨筋 Sternohyoid
9. 胸骨甲状筋 Sternothyroid
10. 胸横筋 Transversus thoracis

F 胸郭上口

1. 胸骨体 Body of sternum
2. 肋骨肋軟骨連結 Costochondral joint
3. 第一肋軟骨 1st costal cartilage
4. 第一肋骨の軟骨結合 Synchondrosis of 1st rib
5. 第一胸肋関節 1st sternocostal joint
6. 第一胸椎 1st thoracic vertebra (T I)
7. 第一肋骨頭 Head of 1st rib
8. 頸切痕 Jugular notch：Suprasternal notch
9. 胸骨柄結合（Louis 角*） Manubriosternal joint（Angle of Louis*）
10. 胸骨柄 Manubrium of sternum
11. 第一肋骨頸 Neck of 1st rib
12. 第二肋軟骨 2nd costal cartilage
13. 第二肋骨 2nd rib：Rib II
14. 第二胸肋関節 2nd sternocostal joint
15. 第一肋骨体 Body of 1st rib：Shaft of 1st rib
16. 胸骨端〔鎖骨〕 Sternal end〔Clavicle〕
17. 胸鎖関節 Sternoclavicular joint

● 左右の胸膜は，第二〜第四肋軟骨の高さで互いに接している（E1，E2）．

● 胸郭上口（胸郭入口または胸郭出口）は，およそ腎臓の輪郭とほぼ同じ大きさ，同じ形で，第一胸椎（6），左右の第一肋骨と第一肋軟骨（3）および胸骨柄の上縁（頸切痕，8）で囲まれている．胸郭入口または胸郭出口は，水平ではなく，前下方に傾斜している．
● 第二肋軟骨（12）は，胸骨柄結合（9）の高さで胸骨柄（10）および胸骨体（1）と連結している．胸骨柄結合は，重要な体表の目印である．胸骨柄と胸骨体の間は少し角度をなしているので，結合線は稜線として触知可能であり，外側へたどると第二肋軟骨と第二肋骨を同定できる．他の肋骨は，第二肋骨から下方へ数えていけば同定できる．

肋軟骨の病変

動揺胸郭

心臓，胸膜および肺（左）［体表解剖］

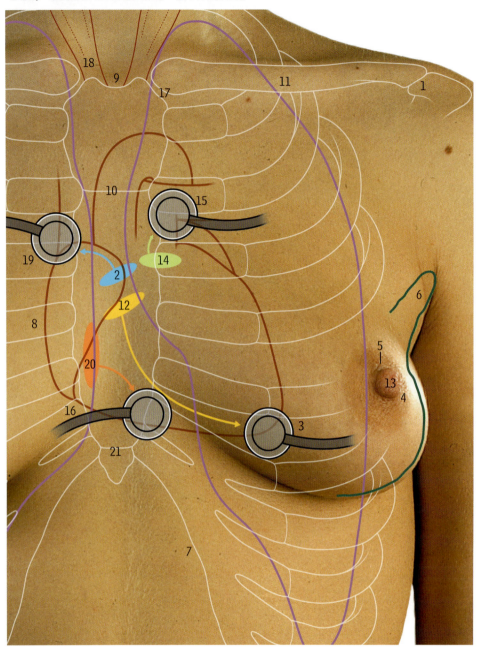

心臓の4つの弁の位置を色付きの楕円で示し，それぞれの弁の音が最もよく聴取できる位置を，聴診器で示してある．

- 胸骨柄結合(10)は，体表から触知でき，この高さで胸骨と結合する第二肋軟骨(15)を同定する目印となる(183頁 F9, F14, F12 参照)．
- 胸膜と肺は，頸部（鎖骨の内側1/3の2.5cm上方）にまで達している．
- 鎖骨中線では，胸膜の下縁は，第八肋骨に，中腋窩線では第十肋骨に達しており，脊柱起立筋の外側縁では第十二肋骨と交叉する．肺の下縁は，胸膜の反転部より肋骨2つ分ほど高い．
- 胸骨の後ろでは，左右の胸膜は第二～第四肋軟骨の高さの正中線で互いに接している．それより下方では，左右の胸膜は心臓が左寄りの位置をとるため，隔てられている．

女性．（茶線：心臓．紫線：胸膜．緑線：乳房の腋窩突起．）

1	肩鎖関節 Acromioclavicular joint	7	肋骨弓〔第八肋軟骨〕 Costal arch (8th costal cartilage)	13	乳頭 Nipple	19	第三肋軟骨 3rd costal cartilage
2	大動脈弁 Aortic valve	8	第四肋軟骨 4th costal cartilage	14	肺動脈弁 Pulmonary valve	20	右房室弁：三尖弁 Right atrioventricular valve：Tricuspid valve
3	心尖 Apex of heart	9	頸切痕 Jugular notch：Suprasternal notch	15	第二肋軟骨 2nd costal cartilage	21	胸骨剣結合 Xiphisternal joint
4	乳輪 Areola	10	胸骨柄結合 Manubriosternal joint	16	第六肋軟骨 6th costal cartilage		
5	乳輪腺 Areolar glands	11	鎖骨（の中点） Clavicle	17	胸鎖関節 Sternoclavicular joint		
6	腋窩突起：外側突起 Axillary process：Axillary tail	12	左房室弁：僧帽弁 Left atrioventricular valve：Mitral valve	18	胸鎖乳突筋 Sternocleidomastoid		

心音の聴診

A～C 女性の乳房 ［乳腺． A 乳房， B 乳輪，乳頭，乳房組織］

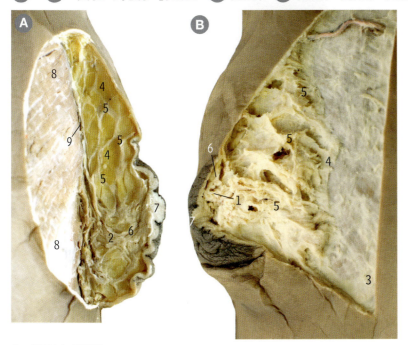

A：傍正中矢状断面．

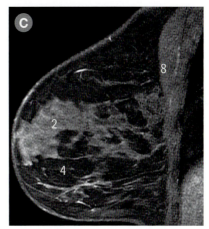

乳房の MR 矢状断画像

1	乳管洞	Lactiferous sinus
2	凝集した乳腺組織	
3	胸筋筋膜	Pectoral fascia
4	乳房脂肪体*	Mammary fat pad*
5	乳房堤靱帯	Suspensory ligaments of breast：Suspensory retinaculum of breast
6	乳管	Lactiferous duct
7	乳頭	Nipple
8	大胸筋	Pectoralis major
9	乳腺後隙*	Retromammary space*

D 乳房 ［リンパ経路］

乳房には表面の皮膚を含めてリンパ管が吻合し，広範なネットワークをつくっている．したがって，乳房のある部分のリンパは他のどこへでも移動できる．リンパの大半は，太いリンパ管を通って腋窩リンパ節へ注ぐが，内側部のリンパは，胸骨の近くで胸壁を貫いて内胸動／静脈に隣接する胸骨傍リンパ節へ入る．これらの2つのリンパ節は，乳癌が最初にかつ最も高頻度に転移するリンパ節群である．（病期が進行したときには）他のリンパ節に転移することもある．具体的には鎖骨下リンパ節，鎖骨上リンパ節（深頸リンパ節），縦隔のリンパ節および腹部のリンパ節（横隔膜と腹直筋鞘を経由する）等である．対側の乳腺に転移することもある．

胸骨傍リンパ節 Parasternal nodes
鎖骨上リンパ節：Virchow リンパ節* Supraclavicular nodes：Virchow node*
上［腋窩］リンパ節 Apical nodes
三角筋胸筋リンパ節 Infraclavicular nodes
中心［腋窩］リンパ節 Central nodes
胸筋間リンパ節 Interpectoral nodes
外側［腋窩］リンパ節 Lateral nodes
後［腋窩］リンパ節 Posterior nodes
前［腋窩］リンパ節 Anterior nodes

乳房の異常

乳房（乳腺）の診察

乳癌

乳房切除術

橙皮状皮膚と乳頭陥凹

A 胸部（右）

上腕を十分に外転し内旋させると，肩甲骨の内側縁(5)は，垂直線に対し約60°の角度になる．この線は，肺の斜裂の投影線（破線）の方向とほぼ一致する．赤線は，僧帽筋，三角筋，広背筋の筋線維の走向を示している．

1	三角筋 Deltoid	6	肩甲棘 Spine of scapula
2	第五肋間隙 5th intercostal space	7	棘突起〔第三胸椎〕 Spinous process〔T III〕
3	下角〔肩甲骨〕 Inferior angle〔Scapula〕	8	大円筋 Teres major
4	広背筋 Latissimus dorsi	9	僧帽筋 Trapezius
5	内側縁〔肩甲骨〕 Medial border〔Scapula〕		

● 右肺の斜裂の投影線は，第三胸椎の棘突起(7)の高さから胸骨の外側縁と第六肋軟骨の交点へ向かって走る（Bを参照）．上腕を十分に外転し内旋させると，肩甲骨の内側縁(5)が，斜裂の走っている方向を示すよい指標となる．

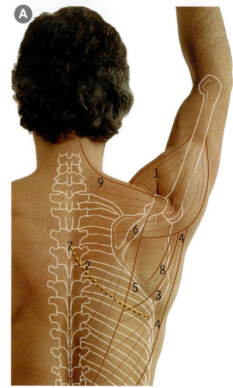

後方から．上腕を外転し，内旋している．

B 胸部（右）［体表の指標］

紫線は胸膜の広がりを，また橙の実線は肺の下端を示す．胸部の下部に見られる2色の実線の高さの差は，肋骨横隔洞という胸膜による陥凹の存在を示している．吸気の時，肺はこの腔に広がる．肺の水平裂と斜裂は，橙の破線で示されている．

1	肋骨弓 Costal margin：Costal arch	4	腋窩（の床） Axilla
2	鋸状の前鋸筋の起始	5	広背筋 Latissimus dorsi
3	外腹斜筋 External oblique	6	大胸筋 Pectoralis major

● Aにおいて黒い破線で示された斜裂は，Bでは前方で第六肋軟骨に達している．第四肋軟骨から後ろへ走り斜裂と出合う水平線が，右肺の水平裂に相当する．このようにしてつくられた三角形の輪郭が中葉であり，その上方に上葉が，下後方に下葉が位置を占める．中葉は，右の乳腺で覆われている．
● 左肺は，上葉と下葉の2葉しかもたないため，水平裂がない．左肺の斜裂の体表における指標は，右肺のものと同様である．
● ※は，中腋窩線において，肺と胸膜の下端が，それぞれ第八肋骨と第十肋骨と交わる位置を示す．

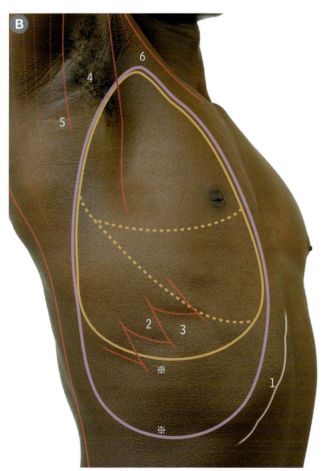

右側方から．上腕を外転し，内旋している．

胸郭前部の筋 ［肋間筋］

前方から．

1	外肋間筋 External intercostal muscle	6	第二肋骨 2nd rib：Rib II
2	外肋間膜 External intercostal membrane	7	第六肋軟骨 6th costal cartilage
3	内肋間筋 Internal intercostal muscle	8	胸骨角：Louis 角* Sternal angle：Angle of Louis*
4	小胸筋 Pectoralis minor	9	剣状突起 Xiphoid process
5	第二肋軟骨 2nd costal cartilage		

- 外肋間筋(1)の筋線維は，下内側に向かって走り，肋骨肋軟骨連結（5 と 6 の間）の近くで外肋間膜となる（本例では外肋間膜を取り除いてある）．外肋間膜は，薄いシート状の結合組織であり，下層の内肋間筋(3)が透けて見える．
- 内肋間筋(3)の筋線維は，下外側に向かって走る．この筋は，前方では外肋間膜に覆われ，後方では内肋間膜に続く．筋線維の走向が異なるので，内外の肋間筋は識別される（下内側に走るのが外肋間筋(1)，下外側に走るのが内肋間筋(3)である）．
- 第七肋軟骨は，胸骨と結合する最下位の肋軟骨であり，第八〜第十軟骨とともに肋骨弓を形成している．

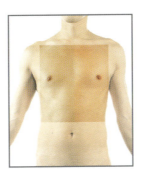

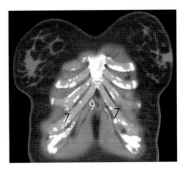

動揺胸郭

胸郭の筋 ［肋間筋（右）］

1 第八肋骨
　8th rib：Rib VIII
2 外肋間筋
　External intercostal muscle
3 第五肋間神経
　5th intercostal nerve
4 第五肋間動脈
　5th posterior intercostal artery
5 第五肋間静脈
　5th posterior intercostal vein
6 第五肋骨
　5th rib：Rib V
7 第四肋骨
　4th rib：Rib IV
8 最内肋間筋
　Innermost intercostal muscle
9 内肋間筋
　Internal intercostal muscle
10 胸膜
　Pleura
11 第七肋骨
　7th rib：Rib VII
12 第六肋間神経
　6th intercostal nerve
13 第六肋骨
　6th rib：Rib VI

● **内肋間筋**は，後方では内肋間膜に続く．内肋間膜は，外肋間筋(2)の内側端部で覆われている．

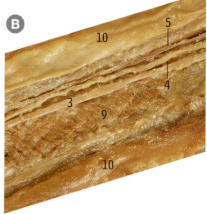

A：外面．B：内面．

Aでは，それぞれの肋間隙を，異なる深さで剖出し，上から順に，外肋間筋(2)，内肋間筋(9)，最内肋間筋(8)ならびに胸膜(10)を示してある．肋間動静脈と肋間神経の主幹は，内肋間筋と最内肋間筋の間を通る．第六肋間隙では，肋間神経(12)が，第六肋骨(13)のすぐ下方で最内肋間筋(8)の外面に接している．しかし，肋間動静脈は，肋骨溝に覆われている．Bのように，胸郭の内面から解剖した時には，肋間動静脈(4, 5)と肋間神経(3)は，第五肋間隙で，内肋間筋(9)の内面に接して走る．

肋間神経ブロック

A 胸郭の筋［胸郭の内景］

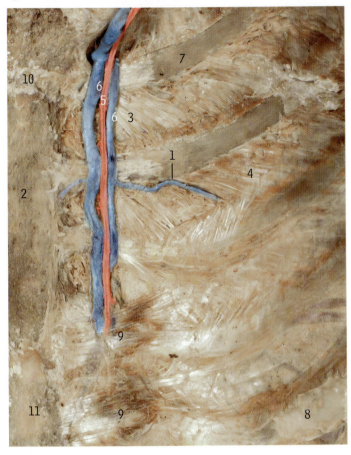

胸膜を除去して胸壁内面を見たところ．

胸骨の右半分と，隣接する前胸壁の後面が見える．胸横筋（9．以前は胸肋筋 sternocostalis とよばれていた）の筋束の前を通る内胸動脈（5）が見えている．

B 胸郭の筋［下位の肋間筋（左）］

胸郭左半の下部を，胸膜，血管，神経を除去し，右前方から見たところ．

胸郭の筋の最内層に位置する最内肋間筋（4）が見える．

1	前肋間静脈 Anterior intercostal vein	7	第二肋骨 2nd rib：Rib II
2	胸骨体 Body of sternum	8	第六肋骨 6th rib：Rib VI
3	内肋間膜 Internal intercostal membrane	9	胸横筋（の筋束） Transversus thoracis
4	内肋間筋 Internal intercostal muscle	10	胸骨角：Louis 角* Sternal angle：Angle of Louis*
5	内胸動脈 Internal thoracic artery	11	剣状突起 Xiphoid process
6	内胸静脈 Internal thoracic veins		

1	胸大動脈〔下行大動脈〕 Thoracic aorta〔Descending aorta〕
2	第八肋間の神経血管束
3	第八肋骨 8th rib：Rib VIII
4	最内肋間筋 Innermost intercostal muscle
5	第十二肋骨 12th rib：Rib XII

肋軟骨の病変

頸基部と胸部内臓

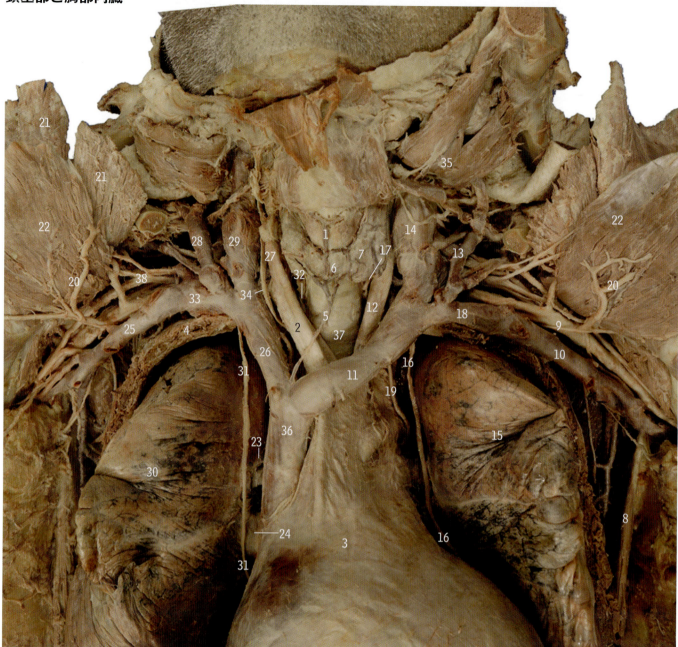

1	輪状軟骨弓 Arch of cricoid cartilage	14	（左の）内頸静脈 Internal jugular vein	27	（右の）総頸動脈 Common carotid artery
2	腕頭動脈 Brachiocephalic trunk	15	左肺 Left lung	28	（右の）外頸静脈 External jugular vein
3	線維性心膜 Fibrous pericardium	16	（左の）横隔神経 Phrenic nerve	29	（右の）内頸静脈 Internal jugular vein
4	第一肋骨（切断縁） 1st rib：Rib I	17	（左の）反回神経 Recurrent laryngeal nerve	30	右肺 Right lung
5	下甲状腺静脈 Inferior thyroid vein	18	（左の）鎖骨下静脈 Subclavian vein	31	（右の）横隔神経 Phrenic nerve
6	甲状腺峡部 Isthmus of thyroid gland	19	（左の）迷走神経［X］ Vagus nerve [X]	32	（右の）反回神経 Recurrent laryngeal nerve
7	左葉〔甲状腺〕 Left lobe〔Thyroid gland〕	20	胸筋枝〔胸肩峰動脈〕 Pectoral branches〔Thoraco-acromial artery〕	33	（右の）鎖骨下静脈 Subclavian vein
8	広背筋 Latissimus dorsi	21	大胸筋 Pectoralis major	34	（右の）迷走神経［X］ Vagus nerve [X]
9	（左の）腋窩動脈 Axillary artery	22	小胸筋 Pectoralis minor	35	舌骨下筋（翻転してある） Infrahyoid muscles
10	（左の）腋窩静脈 Axillary vein	23	右肺動脈 Right pulmonary artery	36	上大静脈 Superior vena cava
11	左腕頭静脈 Left brachiocephalic vein	24	肺静脈 Pulmonary vein	37	気管 Trachea
12	（左の）総頸動脈 Common carotid artery	25	（右の）腋窩静脈 Axillary vein	38	上神経幹〔腕神経叢〕 Superior trunk：Upper trunk〔Brachial plexus〕
13	（左の）外頸静脈 External jugular vein	26	右腕頭静脈 Right brachiocephalic vein		

胸部内臓

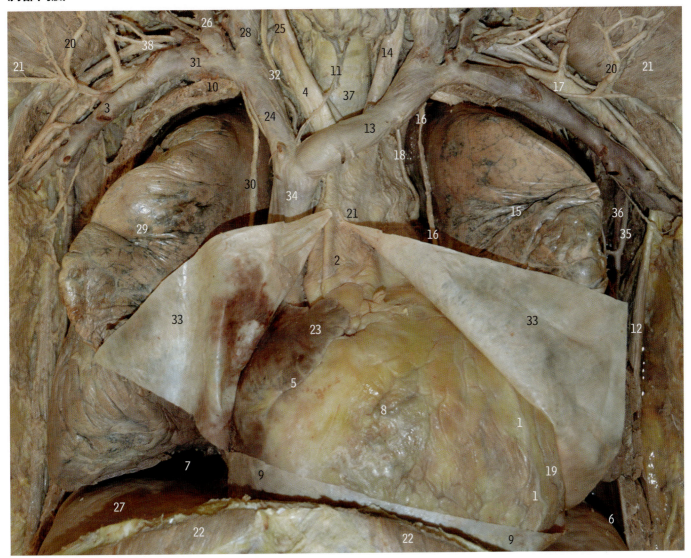

心臓は原位置のままである．

1	前室間枝：前下行枝	Anterior interventricular branch
2	上行大動脈	Ascending aorta
3	腋窩静脈	Axillary vein
4	腕頭動脈	Brachiocephalic trunk
5	冠状溝：房室溝*	Coronary sulcus；Atrioventricular sulcus *
6	肋骨横隔洞	Costodiaphragmatic recess
7	肋骨縦隔洞	Costomediastinal recess
8	臓側板：心外膜	Visceral layer：Epicardium
9	線維性心膜	Fibrous pericardium
10	第一肋骨（切断縁）	1st rib：Rib I
11	下甲状腺静脈	Inferior thyroid vein
12	広背筋	Latissimus dorsi
13	左腕頭静脈	Left brachiocephalic vein
14	（左の）総頸動脈	Common carotid artery
15	左肺	Left lung
16	（左の）横隔神経	Phrenic nerve
17	（左の）腋窩動脈	Axillary artery
18	（左の）迷走神経 [X]	Vagus nerve [X]
19	左心室	Left ventricle
20	胸筋枝〔胸肩峰動脈〕	Pectoral branches〔Thoraco-acromial artery〕
21	小胸筋（翻転してある）	Pectoralis minor
22	腹直筋	Rectus abdominis
23	右心耳	Right auricle
24	右腕頭静脈	Right brachiocephalic vein
25	（右の）総頸動脈	Common carotid artery
26	（右の）外頸静脈	External jugular vein
27	（右半の）横隔膜	Diaphragm
28	（右の）内頸静脈	Internal jugular vein
29	右肺	Right lung
30	（右の）横隔神経	Phrenic nerve
31	（右の）鎖骨下静脈	Subclavian vein
32	（右の）反回神経	Recurrent laryngeal nerve
33	壁側板〔漿膜性心膜〕	Parietal layer〔Serous pericardium〕
34	上大静脈	Superior vena cava
35	胸背動脈	Thoracodorsal artery
36	胸背静脈	Thoracodorsal vein
37	気管	Trachea
38	上神経幹〔腕神経叢〕	Superior trunk：Upper trunk〔Brachial plexus〕

胸部内臓

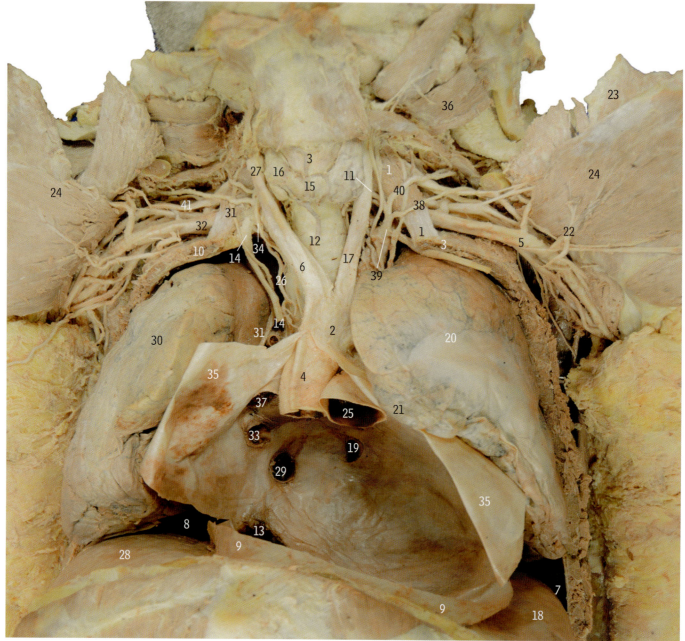

心臓は除去してある.

1	前斜角筋と前斜角筋（の腱） Anterior scalene and Anterior scalene	12	下甲状腺静脈 Inferior thyroid vein	22	胸筋枝〔胸肩峰動脈〕 Pectoral branches〔Thoraco-acromial artery〕	32	（右の）鎖骨下動脈 Subclavian artery
2	大動脈弓 Arch of aorta：Aortic arch	13	下大静脈 Inferior vena cava	23	大胸筋 Pectoralis major	33	右上肺静脈 Right superior pulmonary vein
3	輪状軟骨弓 Arch of cricoid cartilage	14	内胸動脈 Internal thoracic artery	24	小胸筋（翻転してある） Pectoralis minor	34	（右の）迷走神経［X］ Vagus nerve［X］
4	上行大動脈 Ascending aorta	15	甲状腺峡部 Isthmus of thyroid gland	25	肺動脈［幹］ Pulmonary trunk	35	壁側板〔漿膜性心膜〕 Parietal layer（Serous pericardium）
5	腋窩動脈（の第二部） Axillary artery	16	右葉〔甲状腺〕 Right lobe〔Thyroid gland〕	26	（右の）気管支動脈 Bronchial branch	36	舌骨下筋（翻転してある） Infrahyoid muscles
6	腕頭動脈 Brachiocephalic trunk	17	（左の）総頸動脈 Common carotid artery	27	（右の）総頸動脈 Common carotid artery	37	上大静脈 Superior vena cava
7	肋骨横隔洞 Costodiaphragmatic recess	18	（左半の）横隔膜 Diaphragm	28	（右半の）横隔膜 Diaphragm	38	肩甲上動脈 Suprascapular artery
8	肋骨縦隔洞 Costomediastinal recess	19	左下肺静脈 Left inferior pulmonary vein	29	右下肺静脈 Right inferior pulmonary vein	39	甲状頸動脈 Thyrocervical trunk
9	線維性心膜 Fibrous pericardium	20	左肺 Left lung	30	右肺 Right lung	40	頸横動脈 Transverse cervical artery
10	第一肋骨（切断縁） 1st rib：Rib I	21	［左肺の］小舌 Lingula of left lung	31	（右の）横隔神経 Phrenic nerve	41	上神経幹〔腕神経叢〕 Superior trunk：Upper trunk〔Brachial plexus〕
11	下甲状腺動脈 Inferior thyroid artery						

A 胸部の内容物

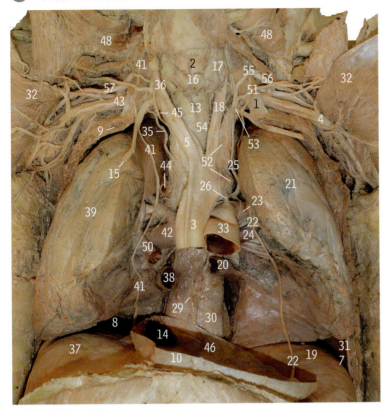

心臓は除去してある．

1	前斜角筋	Anterior scalene
2	輪状軟骨弓	Arch of cricoid cartilage
3	上行大動脈	Ascending aorta
4	腋窩動脈(の第二部)	Axillary artery
5	腕頭動脈	Brachiocephalic trunk
6	気管竜骨：気管カリナ(気管内部に突出している)	Carina of trachea
7	肋骨横隔洞	Costodiaphragmatic recess
8	肋骨縦隔洞	Costomediastinal recess
9	第一肋骨(切断縁)	1st rib：Rib I
10	線維性心膜	Fibrous pericardium
11	左下葉気管支	Left inferior lobar bronchus
12	右下葉気管支	Right inferior lobar bronchus
13	下甲状腺静脈	Inferior thyroid veins
14	下大静脈	Inferior vena cava
15	内胸動脈(外側に引いてある)	Internal thoracic artery
16	甲状腺峡部	Isthmus of thyroid gland
17	左葉〔甲状腺〕	Left lobe〔Thyroid gland〕
18	(左の)総頸動脈	Common carotid artery
19	(左半の)横隔膜	Diaphragm
20	左下肺静脈	Left inferior pulmonary vein
21	左肺	Left lung
22	(左の)横隔神経	Phrenic nerve
23	左肺動脈	Left pulmonary artery
24	左上肺静脈	Left superior pulmonary vein
25	(左の)迷走神経［X］	Vagus nerve [X]
26	動脈管索	Ligamentum arteriosum
27	白線	Linea alba
28	右中葉気管支	Middle lobar bronchus
29	食道神経叢	Esophageal plexus
30	食道	Esophagus
31	壁側胸膜	Parietal pleura
32	小胸筋(翻転してある)	Pectoralis minor
33	肺動脈［幹］	Pulmonary trunk
34	腹直筋	Rectus abdominis
35	(右の)気管支動脈(内胸動脈に起始)	Bronchial branch
36	(右の)総頸動脈	Common carotid artery
37	(右半の)横隔膜	Diaphragm
38	右下肺静脈	Right inferior pulmonary vein
39	右肺	Right lung
40	右主気管支	Right main bronchus
41	(右の)横隔神経	Phrenic nerve
42	右肺動脈	Right pulmonary artery
43	(右の)鎖骨下動脈	Subclavian artery
44	右肺動脈の上を通る気管支	
45	(右の)迷走神経［X］	Vagus nerve [X]
46	壁側板〔漿膜性心膜〕	Parietal layer〔Serous pericardium〕
47	胸骨	Sternum
48	舌骨下筋(翻転してある)	Infrahyoid muscles
49	右上葉気管支	Right superior lobar bronchus
50	右上肺静脈	Superior right pulmonary vein
51	肩甲上動脈	Suprascapular artery
52	胸心臓神経	Thoracic cardiac branches
53	甲状頸動脈	Thyrocervical trunk
54	気管	Trachea
55	頸横動脈	Transverse cervical artery
56	上神経幹〔腕神経叢〕	Superior trunk：Upper trunk〔Brachial plexus〕
57	上神経幹〔腕神経叢〕	Superior trunk：Upper trunk〔Brachial plexus〕

B 胸腔と横隔膜

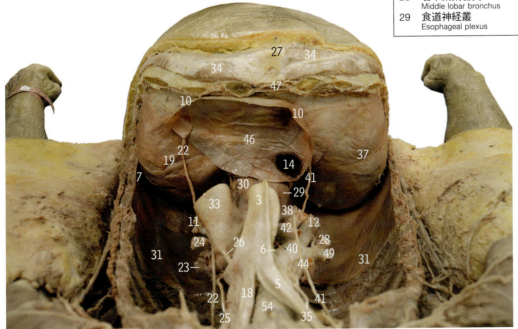

上方から心膜が付いた横隔膜を見たところ．肺は除去してある．

上縦隔と後縦隔，心臓神経叢

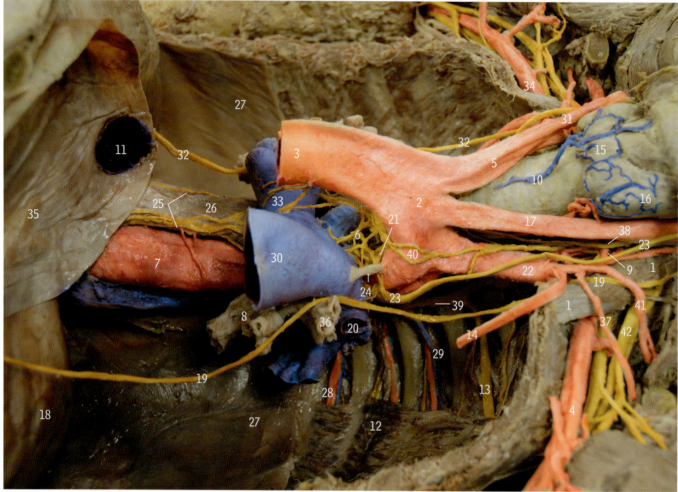

左側方から．

1	前斜角筋とその腱 Anterior scalene	15	甲状腺峡部 Isthmus of thyroid gland	29	肋間静脈 Posterior intercostal vein
2	大動脈弓 Arch of aorta；Aortic arch	16	左葉〔甲状腺〕 Left lobe〔Thyroid gland〕	30	肺動脈［幹］ Pulmonary trunk
3	上行大動脈 Ascending aorta	17	（左の）総頸動脈 Common carotid artery	31	（右の）総頸動脈 Common carotid artery
4	腋窩動脈 Axillary artery	18	（左半の）横隔膜 Diaphragm	32	（右の）横隔神経 Phrenic nerve
5	腕頭動脈 Brachiocephalic trunk	19	（左の）横隔神経 Phrenic nerve	33	右肺動脈 Right pulmonary artery
6	浅心臓神経叢＊ Superficial cardiac plexus＊	20	左肺動脈 Left pulmonary artery	34	（右の）鎖骨下動脈 Subclavian artery
7	胸大動脈〔下行大動脈〕 Thoracic aorta〔Descending aorta〕	21	（左の）反回神経 Recurrent laryngeal nerve	35	壁側板〔漿膜性心膜〕 Parietal layer〔Serous pericardium〕
8	左下葉気管支 Left inferior lobar bronchus	22	（左の）鎖骨下動脈 Subclavian artery	36	上葉気管支 Superior lobar bronchus
9	下甲状腺動脈 Inferior thyroid artery	23	（左の）迷走神経［X］ Vagus nerve［X］	37	肩甲上動脈 Suprascapular artery
10	下甲状腺静脈 Inferior thyroid vein	24	動脈管索 Ligamentum arteriosum	38	交感神経幹（頸部の） Sympathetic trunk
11	下大静脈 Inferior vena cava	25	食道神経叢 Esophageal plexus	39	交感神経幹（胸部の） Sympathetic trunk
12	最内肋間筋 Innermost intercostal muscle	26	食道 Esophagus	40	胸心臓神経〔交感神経幹〕 Thoracic cardiac branches〔Sympathetic trunk〕
13	肋間神経 Intercostal nerve	27	壁側胸膜 Parietal pleura	41	頸横動脈 Transverse cervical artery
14	内胸動脈 Internal thoracic artery	28	肋間動脈 Posterior intercostal artery	42	上神経幹〔腕神経叢〕 Superior trunk；Upper trunk〔Brachial plexus〕

上縦隔と後縦隔

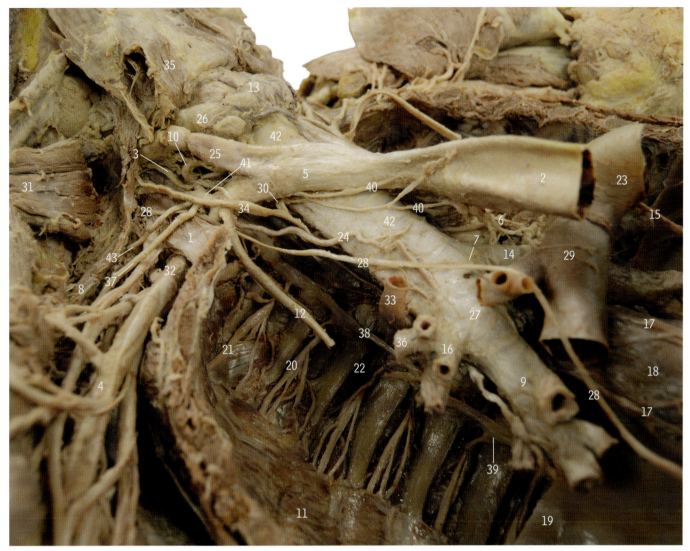

右側方から.

1	前斜角筋	Anterior scalene
2	上行大動脈	Ascending aorta
3	上行頸動脈	Ascending cervical artery
4	腋窩動脈	Axillary artery
5	腕頭動脈	Brachiocephalic trunk
6	心臓神経叢	Cardiac plexus
7	気管竜骨：気管カリナ（気管内部に突出している）	Carina of trachea
8	下腹〔肩甲舌骨筋〕	Inferior belly〔Omohyoid〕
9	右下葉気管支	Right inferior lobar bronchus
10	下甲状腺動脈	Inferior thyroid artery
11	最内肋間筋	Innermost intercostal muscle
12	内胸動脈	Internal thoracic artery
13	甲状腺峡部	Isthmus of thyroid gland
14	左主気管支	Left main bronchus
15	（左の）横隔神経	Phrenic nerve
16	右中葉気管支	Middle lobar bronchus
17	食道神経叢	Esophageal plexus
18	食道	Esophagus
19	壁側胸膜	Parietal pleura
20	肋間動脈	Posterior intercostal artery
21	肋間神経	Intercostal nerve
22	肋間静脈	Posterior intercostal vein
23	肺動脈［幹］	Pulmonary trunk
24	（右の）気管支動脈	Bronchial branch
25	（右の）総頸動脈	Common carotid artery
26	右葉〔甲状腺〕	Right lobe〔Thyroid gland〕
27	右主気管支	Right main bronchus
28	（右の）横隔神経	Phrenic nerve
29	右肺動脈	Right pulmonary artery
30	（右の）反回神経	Recurrent laryngeal nerve
31	（右の）胸鎖乳突筋（翻転してある）	Sternocleidomastoid
32	（右の）鎖骨下動脈	Subclavian artery
33	右肺動脈の上を通る気管支	
34	（右の）迷走神経［X］	Vagus nerve [X]
35	舌骨下筋（翻転してある）	Infrahyoid muscles
36	右上葉気管支	Right superior lobar bronchus
37	肩甲上動脈	Suprascapular artery
38	交感神経幹	Sympathetic trunk
39	交感神経幹神経節	Ganglion of sympathetic trunk
40	胸心臓神経	Thoracic cardiac branches
41	甲状頸動脈	Thyrocervical trunk
42	気管	Trachea
43	頸横動脈	Transverse cervical artery

心臓と心膜

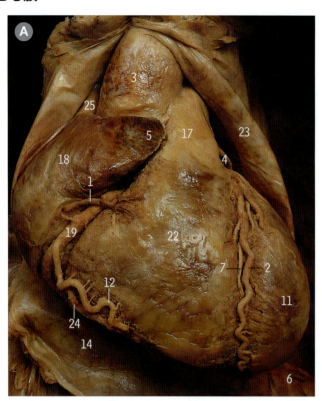
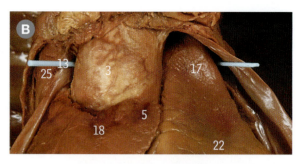
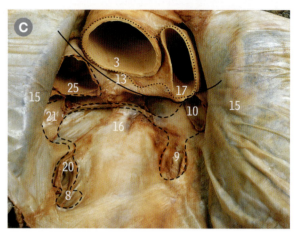

A：前方から．B：心膜横洞にマーカーを挿入してある．C：心臓を除去して心膜斜洞を示してある．

1	前心臓静脈 Anterior cardiac vein	14	心膜（横隔膜の腱中心と癒合している） Pericardium
2	前室間枝：前下行枝〔左冠状動脈〕 Anterior interventricular branch〔Left coronary artery〕	15	心膜（外側へ翻転し肺の表面に広げた） Pericardium
3	上行大動脈 Ascending aorta	16	心膜腔の後壁と心膜斜洞 Posterior wall of pericardial cavity and Oblique pericardial sinus
4	左心耳 Left auricle	17	肺動脈［幹］ Pulmonary trunk
5	右心耳 Right auricle	18	右心房 Right atrium
6	横隔膜 Diaphragm	19	右冠状動脈 Right coronary artery
7	大心臓静脈 Great cardiac vein	20	右下肺静脈 Right inferior pulmonary vein
8	下大静脈 Inferior vena cava	21	右上肺静脈 Right superior pulmonary vein
9	左下肺静脈 Left inferior pulmonary vein	22	右心室 Right ventricle
10	左上肺静脈 Left superior pulmonary vein	23	漿膜性心膜（外側へ翻転してある） Serous pericardium
11	左心室 Left ventricle	24	小心臓静脈 Small cardiac vein
12	右縁枝：鋭［角］縁枝〔右冠状動脈〕 Right marginal branch〔Right coronary artery〕	25	上大静脈 Superior vena cava
13	心膜横洞（マーカーを挿入して示す） Transverse pericardial sinus		

Aでは，心膜(23)を切開して後方へ翻転し，心臓の前面を露出してある．肺動脈幹(17)は，上行大動脈(3)の左前方で，右心室(22)を出る．上行大動脈は，右心房(18)の右心耳(5)に覆われている．上大静脈(25)は，大動脈の右側に位置し，そのほとんどを心膜に覆われている．左冠状動脈の前室間枝(2)と大心臓静脈(7)は，左心室(11)と右心室(22)の間の室間溝を走る．右冠状動脈(19)は，右心室(22)と右心房(18)の間の溝を走る．

Bでは，心臓の上部のみを示している（Aとは異なる標本）．大動脈(3)と肺動脈幹(17)の後方の空間である心膜横洞にマーカーを挿入してある．

Cでは，心膜腔から心臓を除去し，大血管の開口部を示している．点線は，大動脈(3)と肺動脈幹(17)を袖のようにとりまく漿膜性心膜の付着部を示している．破線は，やはり袖のようにとりまく漿膜性心膜であるが，もっと複雑である．すなわち，6本の大血管（4本の肺静脈9，10，20，21と上大静脈25，下大静脈8）のすべてを包んでいる．2つの袖の間の狭い間隙が心膜横洞であり，Bでマーカーが挿入された経路が，Cでは実線で示されている．左右の肺静脈に挟まれた心膜の部分(16)は，漿膜性心膜が心臓の後面に向かって折れ返る上方のところで，心膜斜洞を形成する．

- 心臓の右縁は，右心房(A18)でつくられている．
- 心臓の左縁は，主として左心室(A11)でつくられており，上端部は右心室(A22)の最上部（動脈円錐）と左心耳(A4)の先端部でつくられている．
- 心臓の下縁は，右心室(A22)と左心室の一部である心尖でつくられている．

心タンポナーデ　　心嚢液貯留

A B 心臓 [血管注入標本]

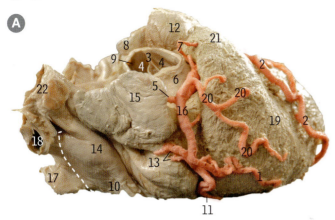

右前側方から．(破線は，右心房と左心房のおおよその境界を示している．)

1	右縁枝：鋭[角]縁枝 Right marginal branch	13	右心房枝*〔右冠状動脈〕 Right atrial branches*〔Right coronary artery〕
2	前室間枝：前下行枝[訳注] Anterior interventricular branch	14	右心房 Right atrium
3	大動脈弁 Aortic valve	15	右心耳 Right auricle
4	大動脈洞：Valsalva 洞* Aortic sinus : Sinus of Valsalva *	16	右冠状動脈 Right coronary artery
5	洞房結節枝 Sinu-atrial nodal branch	17	右下肺静脈 Right inferior pulmonary vein
6	上行大動脈 Ascending aorta	18	右上肺静脈 Right superior pulmonary vein
7	円錐枝〔右冠状動脈〕 Conus branch〔Right coronary artery〕	19	右心室 Right ventricle
8	左心耳 Left auricle	20	右心室枝*〔右冠状動脈〕 Right ventricular branches *〔Right coronary artery〕
9	左冠状動脈口* Opening for left coronary artery *	21	動脈円錐 Conus arteriosus : Infundibulum
10	下大静脈口 Opening of inferior vena cava	22	上大静脈 Superior vena cava
11	後室間枝：後下行枝〔右冠状動脈〕 Posterior interventricular branch〔Right coronary artery〕		
12	肺動脈［幹］ Pulmonary trunk		

［訳注］冠状動脈とその分枝の名称については，さまざまな命名法があるが，本書では解剖学用語に従っている．

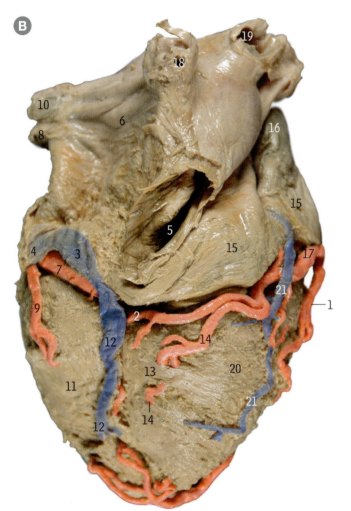

後方から．

1	右縁枝：鋭角縁枝：鋭縁枝 Right marginal branch	12	中心臓静脈 Middle cardiac vein
2	房室結節枝〔右冠状動脈〕 Atrioventricular nodal branch〔Right coronary artery〕	13	心筋架橋* Myocardial bridge *
3	冠状静脈洞 Coronary sinus	14	後室間枝：後下行枝〔右冠状動脈〕 Posterior interventricular branch〔Right coronary artery〕
4	大心臓静脈 Great cardiac vein	15	右心房 Right atrium
5	下大静脈 Inferior vena cava	16	右心耳 Right auricle
6	左心房 Left atrium	17	右冠状動脈 Right coronary artery
7	回旋枝〔左冠状動脈〕 Circumflex branch〔Left coronary artery〕	18	右下肺静脈 Right inferior pulmonary vein
8	左下肺静脈 Left inferior pulmonary vein	19	右上肺静脈 Right superior pulmonary vein
9	左縁枝：鈍[角]縁枝 Left marginal artery	20	右心室(の下面) Right ventricle
10	左上肺静脈 Left superior pulmonary vein	21	小心臓静脈 Small cardiac vein
11	左心室(の下面) Left ventricle		

● 室間枝は，臨床ではしばしば下行枝（前室間枝：前下行枝，後室間枝：後下行枝）とよばれる．

心臓 [血管注入標本]

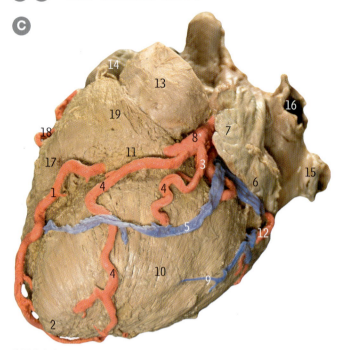

左側方から.

#	名称
1	前室間枝：前下行枝 / Anterior interventricular branch
2	心尖 / Apex of heart
3	回旋枝〔左冠状動脈〕 / Circumflex branch (Left coronary artery)
4	外側枝：対角枝 / Lateral branch
5	大心臓静脈 / Great cardiac vein
6	左心房 / Left atrium
7	左心耳 / Left auricle
8	左冠状動脈 / Left coronary artery
9	左辺縁静脈 / Left marginal vein
10	左心室 / Left ventricle
11	心筋架橋* / Myocardial bridge *
12	左縁枝：鈍［角］縁枝 / Left marginal artery
13	肺動脈［幹］ / Pulmonary trunk
14	右心耳 / Right auricle
15	右下肺静脈 / Right inferior pulmonary vein
16	右上肺静脈 / Right superior pulmonary vein
17	右心室 / Right ventricle
18	右心室枝*〔右冠状動脈〕 / Right ventricular branches * (Right coronary artery)
19	動脈円錐 / Conus arteriosus : Infundibulum

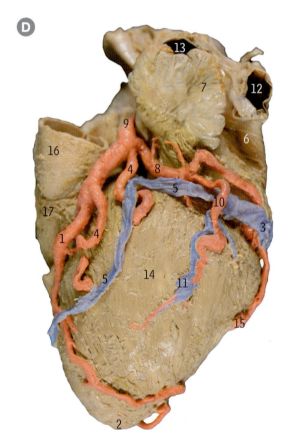

左後方から.

#	名称
1	前室間枝：前下行枝 / Anterior interventricular branch
2	心尖 / Apex of heart
3	冠状静脈洞 / Coronary sinus
4	外側枝：対角枝 / Lateral branch
5	大心臓静脈 / Great cardiac vein
6	左心房 / Left atrium
7	左心耳（翻転してある） / Left auricle
8	回旋枝〔左冠状動脈〕 / Circumflex branch (Left coronary artery)
9	左冠状動脈 / Left coronary artery
10	縁枝*〔左冠状動脈〕 / Marginal branch * (Left coronary artery)
11	左辺縁静脈 / Left marginal vein
12	左下肺静脈 / Left inferior pulmonary vein
13	左上肺静脈 / Left superior pulmonary vein
14	左心室 / Left ventricle
15	左縁枝：鈍［角］縁枝 / Left marginal artery
16	肺動脈［幹］ / Pulmonary trunk
17	動脈円錐 / Conus arteriosus : Infundibulum

A 右心房

右心房の前壁を，右心房の左縁近くで切開して右方へ翻転し，内面を縦走する分界稜(2)と水平に走る櫛状筋(7)を示している．心房中隔に卵円窩(3)があり，冠状静脈口(6)は下大静脈口(4)の左にある．

1	右心耳 Right auricle	8	房室結節の位置
2	分界稜 Crista terminalis	9	静脈間隆起：Lower 結節* Intervenous tubercle：Tubercle of Lower*
3	卵円窩 Fossa ovalis	10	上大静脈 Superior vena cava
4	下大静脈口 Opening of inferior vena cava	11	右房室弁：三尖弁 Right atrioventricular valve：Tricuspid valve
5	卵円窩縁 Limbus fossae ovali：Border of oval fossa	12	冠状静脈弁：Thebesian 弁* Valve of coronary sinus：Thebesian valve*
6	冠状静脈口 Opening of coronary sinus	13	下大静脈弁：Eustachian 弁* Valve of inferior vena cava：Eustachian valve*
7	櫛状筋 Musculi pectinati：Pectinate muscles		

- 卵円窩(3)は，心房中隔の一部を形成する．胎生期の心房の一次中隔の一部である．
- 卵円窩縁(5)は，卵円窩(3)の辺縁をつくる．胎生期の心房の二次中隔の下縁に相当する．出生時に一次中隔と二次中隔が癒合するが，その前に両中隔の間に存在する間隙が卵円孔である．
- 洞房結節(SA node, 図には示されていない)は，右心房の前壁に含まれている．その位置は，分界稜の上端で上大静脈口のすぐ下方である．
- 房室結節(AV node, 8)は，冠状静脈口(6)のすぐ左上方の心房中隔に含まれている．

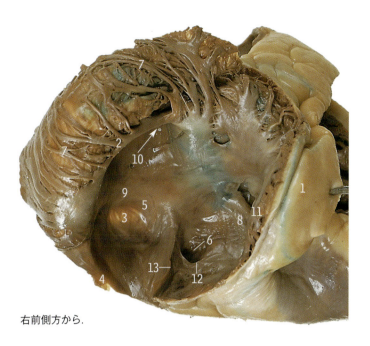

右前側方から．

B 右心室

1	前尖〔三尖弁〕 Anterior cusp〔Tricuspid valve〕
2	前乳頭筋 Anterior papillary muscle
3	上行大動脈 Ascending aorta
4	右心耳 Right auricle
5	腱索 Chordae tendineae：Tendinous cords
6	下大静脈 Inferior vena cava
7	動脈円錐 Conus arteriosus：Infundibulum
8	後乳頭筋 Posterior papillary muscle
9	肺動脈［幹］ Pulmonary trunk
10	右心房 Right atrium
11	中隔縁柱：調節帯* Septomarginal trabeculum：Moderator band
12	中隔乳頭筋（動脈円錐から起こっている） Septal papillary muscle
13	上大静脈 Superior vena cava

- 中隔縁柱(11)は，心室中隔から房室束の右脚を前乳頭筋(2)に導いており，調節帯(moderator band)ともよばれる．
- 腱索(5)は，三尖弁の弁尖を乳頭筋に接続している．

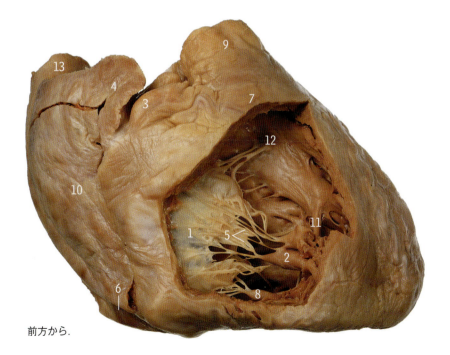

前方から．

人工心臓ペースメーカー

人工心臓ペースメーカー

左心室肥大

A 左心室

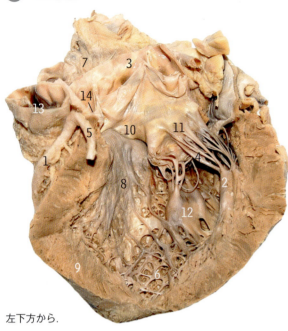

左下方から.

左心室の左壁，前壁，後壁の大部分を除去し，開いたものを下から見ている．僧帽弁(11)の弁尖の下面を見上げており，それらは腱索(4)によって，前後の乳頭筋(2，12)と接続している．僧帽弁の後尖は，この標本では，大部分が前尖(B1)の陰になっている．

1	前室間枝：前下行枝 Anterior interventricular branch	8	左脚（の枝） Left bundle
2	前乳頭筋 Anterior papillary muscle	9	左心室（心室壁の切断面） Left ventricle
3	上行大動脈 Ascending aorta	10	膜性部（心室中隔） Membranous part (Interventricular septum)
4	腱索 Chordae tendineae：Tendinous cords	11	左房室弁：僧帽弁 Left atrioventricular valve：Mitral valve
5	回旋枝〔左冠状動脈〕 Circumflex branch〔Left coronary artery〕	12	後乳頭筋 Posterior papillary muscle
6	粗な肉柱	13	肺動脈弁 Pulmonary valve
7	左心房 Left atrium	14	右冠状動脈口* Opening for right coronary artery*

B 心臓

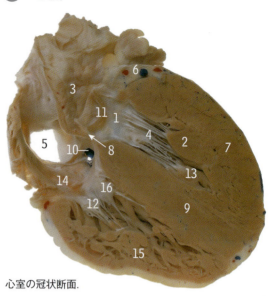

心室の冠状断面.

心臓を冠状断し，後部を前方から見ている．この断面は，僧帽弁の前尖(1)と大動脈弁の後半月弁(11)のすぐ前を通っている．

1	前尖〔僧帽弁〕 Anterior cusp〔Mitral valve〕	9	筋性部〔心室中隔〕 Muscular part (Interventricular septum)
2	前乳頭筋 Anterior papillary muscle	10	冠状静脈口 Opening of coronary sinus
3	上行大動脈 Ascending aorta	11	後半月弁〔大動脈弁〕 Posterior semilunar cusp：Noncoronary cusp (Aortic valve)
4	腱索 Chordae tendineae：Tendinous cords	12	後尖〔三尖弁〕 Posterior cusp (Tricuspid valve)
5	下大静脈 Inferior vena cava	13	後乳頭筋 Posterior papillary muscle
6	左冠状動脈の枝と大心臓静脈 Left coronary artery branches and Great cardiac vein	14	右心房 Right atrium
7	左心室（心室壁の切断面） Left ventricle	15	右心室（心室壁の切断面） Right ventricle
8	膜性部〔心室中隔〕 Membranous part (Interventricular septum)	16	中隔尖〔三尖弁〕 Septal cusp (Tricuspid valve)

C 心臓

僧帽弁の異常

心房を除去し，線維性の心臓骨格を示している．

1	前尖〔三尖弁〕 Anterior cusp (Tricuspid valve)	15	後室間枝：後下行枝〔右冠状動脈〕 Posterior interventricular branch〔Right coronary artery〕
2	前尖〔僧帽弁〕 Anterior cusp (Mitral valve)	16	後尖〔三尖弁〕 Posterior cusp (Tricuspid valve)
3	右半月弁〔大動脈弁〕 Right semilunar cusp：Right coronary cusp (Aortic valve)	17	後尖〔僧帽弁〕 Posterior cusp (Mitral valve)
4	上行大動脈 Ascending aorta	18	肺動脈〔幹〕 Pulmonary trunk
5	房室結節枝 Atrioventricular nodal branch	19	右冠状動脈 Right coronary artery
6	回旋枝〔左冠状動脈〕 Circumflex branch〔Left coronary artery〕	20	右線維輪〔右房室口〕 Right fibrous ring (Right atrioventricular orifice)
7	円錐枝〔右冠状動脈〕 Conus branch (Right coronary artery)	21	右線維三角 Right fibrous trigone
8	左冠状動脈 Left coronary artery	22	後半月弁〔大動脈弁〕 Posterior semilunar cusp：Noncoronary cusp (Aortic valve)
9	左線維輪〔左房室口〕 Left fibrous ring (Left atrioventricular orifice)	23	右心室 Right ventricle
10	左線維三角 Left fibrous trigone	24	右心室枝*〔右冠状動脈〕 Right ventricular branches*〔Right coronary artery〕
11	左半月弁〔大動脈弁〕 Left semilunar cusp：Left coronary cusp (Aortic valve)	25	洞房結節枝 Sinu-atrial nodal branch
12	左心室 Left ventricle	26	中隔尖〔三尖弁〕 Septal cusp (Tricuspid valve)
13	左縁枝：鈍〔角〕縁枝 Left marginal artery	27	右心室枝*〔右冠状動脈〕 Right ventricular branches*〔Right coronary artery〕
14	右冠状動脈口* Opening for right coronary artery*		

第4章 胸部：心臓　201

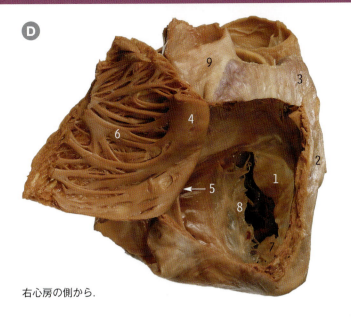

D 三尖弁（右房室弁）

右心房の前壁(2)をコの字形に切開して外側（そとがわ）に翻転すると、房室口が心房側から見える．房室口は、前尖(1)，後尖(7)，中隔尖(8)の3つの弁尖で塞がれている．

1	前尖〔三尖弁〕 Anterior cusp〔Tricuspid valve〕	6	櫛状筋 Musculi pectinati：Pectinate muscles
2	右心房（前壁の切断面） Right atrium	7	後尖〔三尖弁〕 Posterior cusp〔Tricuspid valve〕
3	右心耳 Right auricle	8	中隔尖〔三尖弁〕 Septal cusp〔Tricuspid valve〕
4	分界稜 Crista terminalis	9	上大静脈 Superior vena cava
5	心房中隔 Interatrial septum		

●三尖弁の弁尖の中で，後尖(7)が最も小さい．

右心房の側から．

E 肺動脈弁，大動脈弁および僧帽弁（左房室弁）

肺動脈幹(12)と上行大動脈(3)を，肺動脈弁の半月弁(2, 7, 15)と大動脈弁の半月弁(6, 10, 14)のすぐ上方で切断してある．左心房(5)の上部も除去し，僧帽弁の前尖(1)と後尖(11)の上面を示してある．

1	前尖〔僧帽弁〕 Anterior cusp〔Mitral valve〕	9	左冠状動脈口* Opening for left coronary artery*
2	前半月弁〔肺動脈弁〕 Anterior semilunar cusp〔Pulmonary valve〕	10	後半月弁〔大動脈弁〕 Posterior semilunar cusp：Noncoronary cusp〔Aortic valve〕
3	上行大動脈 Ascending aorta	11	後尖〔僧帽弁〕 Posterior cusp〔Mitral valve〕
4	右心耳 Right auricle	12	肺動脈〔幹〕 Pulmonary trunk
5	左心房 Left atrium	13	右心房 Right atrium
6	左半月弁〔大動脈弁〕 Left semilunar cusp：Left coronary cusp〔Aortic valve〕	14	右半月弁〔大動脈弁〕 Right semilunar cusp：Right coronary cusp〔Aortic valve〕
7	左半月弁〔肺動脈弁〕 Left semilunar cusp〔Pulmonary valve〕	15	右半月弁〔肺動脈弁〕 Right semilunar cusp〔Pulmonary valve〕
8	右冠状動脈口*（マーカーを挿入して示す） Opening for right coronary artery*	16	上大静脈 Superior vena cava

上方から．

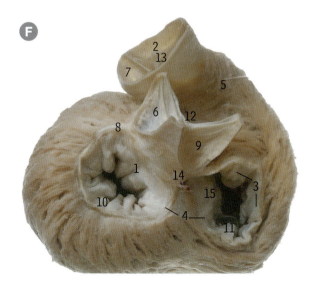

F 心臓［線維性心臓骨格］

左右の心房を除去し，心臓を右後方から見ている．左右の房室口を取り囲み，弁尖の基部の付着部となる線維輪(4)が観察できる．肺動脈の半月弁(2, 7, 13)が，右心室の動脈円錐(5)の上端部に見える．大動脈弁の半月弁(6, 9, 12)は，大動脈の基部で剖出してある．

1	前尖〔僧帽弁〕 Anterior cusp〔Mitral valve〕	8	左線維三角 Left fibrous trigone
2	前半月弁〔肺動脈弁〕 Anterior semilunar cusp〔Pulmonary valve〕	9	後半月弁〔大動脈弁〕 Posterior semilunar cusp：Noncoronary cusp〔Aortic valve〕
3	前尖〔三尖弁〕 Anterior cusp〔Tricuspid valve〕	10	後尖〔僧帽弁〕 Posterior cusp〔Mitral valve〕
4	左線維輪と右線維輪 Left fibrous ring and Right fibrous ring	11	後尖〔三尖弁〕 Posterior cusp〔Tricuspid valve〕
5	動脈円錐〔右心室〕 Conus arteriosus：Infundibulum〔Right ventricle〕	12	右半月弁〔大動脈弁〕 Right semilunar cusp：Right coronary cusp〔Aortic valve〕
6	左半月弁〔大動脈弁〕 Left semilunar cusp：Left coronary cusp〔Aortic valve〕	13	右半月弁〔肺動脈弁〕 Right semilunar cusp〔Pulmonary valve〕
7	左半月弁〔肺動脈弁〕 Left semilunar cusp〔Pulmonary valve〕	14	右線維三角 Right fibrous trigone
		15	中隔尖〔三尖弁〕 Septal cusp〔Tricuspid valve〕

Ⓐ～Ⓓ 冠状動脈

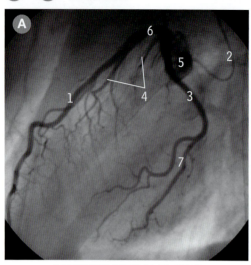

左冠状動脈造影画像（左側面投影）

1	前室間枝：前下行枝 Anterior interventricular branch
2	上行大動脈に挿入されたカテーテル
3	回旋枝 Circumflex branch
4	外側枝：対角枝 Lateral branch
5	（左の）大動脈洞：Valsalva 洞＊ Aortic sinus：Sinus of Valsalva＊
6	左冠状動脈（の主幹） Left coronary artery
7	左縁枝：鈍［角］縁枝 Left marginal artery

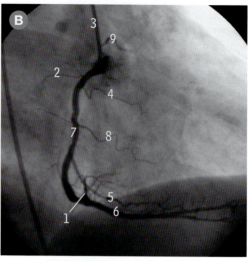

右冠状動脈造影画像（左前斜位投影）

1	房室結節枝 Atrioventricular nodal branch
2	心房枝 Atrial branches
3	大動脈基部に挿入されたカテーテル
4	円錐枝〔右冠状動脈〕 Conus branch〔Right coronary artery〕
5	右縁枝：鋭［角］縁枝〔右冠状動脈〕 Right marginal branch〔Right coronary artery〕
6	後室間枝：後下行枝 Posterior interventricular branch
7	右冠状動脈 Right coronary artery
8	右心室枝＊ Right ventricular branch＊
9	洞房結節枝 Sinu-atrial nodal branch

鋳型標本

前方から．

1	前室間枝：前下行枝〔左冠状動脈〕 Anterior interventricular branch〔Left coronary artery〕
2	上行大動脈 Ascending aorta
3	房室結節枝 Atrioventricular nodal branch
4	回旋枝 Circumflex branch
5	円錐枝 Conus branch
6	外側枝：対角枝 Lateral branch
7	左冠状動脈（の主幹） Left coronary artery
8	右縁枝：鋭［角］縁枝〔右冠状動脈〕 Right marginal branch〔Right coronary artery〕
9	後室間枝：後下行枝〔右冠状動脈〕 Posterior interventricular branch〔Right coronary artery〕
10	右冠状動脈 Right coronary artery
11	洞房結節枝 Sinu-atrial nodal branch

●臨床では，室間枝をしばしば下行枝とよぶ（前室間枝：前下行枝，後室間枝：後下行枝）．

狭心症

冠状動脈造影

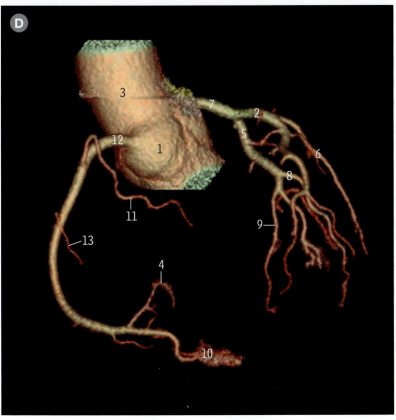

1	（右の）大動脈洞：Valsalva 洞*	Aortic sinus：Sinus of Valsalva*
2	前室間枝：前下行枝〔左冠状動脈〕	Anterior interventricular branch〔Left coronary artery〕
3	上行大動脈	Ascending aorta
4	房室結節枝	Atrioventricular nodal branch
5	回旋枝〔左冠状動脈〕	Circumflex branch〔Left coronary artery〕
6	外側枝：対角枝	Lateral branch
7	左冠状動脈（の主幹）	Left coronary artery
8	左縁枝：鈍［角］縁枝	Left marginal artery
9	縁枝*〔左冠状動脈〕	Marginal branch*〔Left coronary artery〕
10	後室間枝：後下行枝〔右冠状動脈〕	Posterior interventricular branch〔Right coronary artery〕
11	円錐枝〔右冠状動脈〕	Conus branch〔Right coronary artery〕
12	右冠状動脈	Right coronary artery
13	右心室枝*〔右冠状動脈〕	Right ventricular branch*〔Right coronary artery〕

CT 画像からの三次元構築画像

E 心臓と大血管

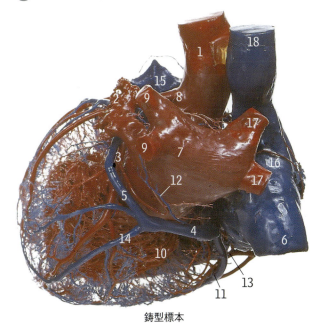

鋳型標本

下後方から．

この鋳型標本では，冠状溝を走る冠状静脈洞(4)とそれに流入する種々の静脈が見える（解説を参照）．

1	上行大動脈 Ascending aorta		10	左心室 Left ventricle
2	左心耳 Left auricle		11	中心臓静脈 Middle cardiac vein
3	回旋枝〔左冠状動脈〕 Circumflex branch〔Left coronary artery〕		12	左心房斜静脈 Oblique vein of left atrium
4	冠状静脈洞 Coronary sinus		13	後室間枝：後下行枝〔右冠状動脈〕 Posterior interventricular branch〔Right coronary artery〕
5	大心臓静脈 Great cardiac vein		14	左心室後静脈 Posterior vein of left ventricle
6	下大静脈 Inferior vena cava		15	肺動脈［幹］ Pulmonary trunk
7	左心房 Left atrium		16	右心房 Right atrium
8	左冠状動脈 Left coronary artery		17	右肺静脈 Right pulmonary veins
9	左肺静脈 Left pulmonary veins		18	上大静脈 Superior vena cava

- 心底とは，大部分が左心房(7)からなる心臓の後面をいう．上大静脈や大動脈，肺動脈幹と連絡する部分のことではないことに注意されたい．大血管との連絡部には特別な名称は付けられていない．
- 左心房斜静脈(12)は非常に細いが，大心臓静脈(5)が冠状静脈洞(4)に移行する位置を示す目印となる．しかし E では，左心房斜静脈の流入部が通常とは異なり，かなり右方に寄っている．そのため，左心室後静脈(14)は冠状静脈洞に注がず，大心臓静脈(5)に流入している．
- 冠状静脈洞(4)は心臓の静脈血の大部分を受け入れ，左心房と左心室の間にある冠状溝の後部を走り，右心房に開口する．
- 冠状静脈洞は，通常，大心臓静脈(5)，中心臓静脈(11)，小心臓静脈，左心室後静脈(14)ならびに左心房斜静脈(12)を受け入れる．

冠状動脈の異常

右胸心

A 肺根と縦隔胸膜（右）

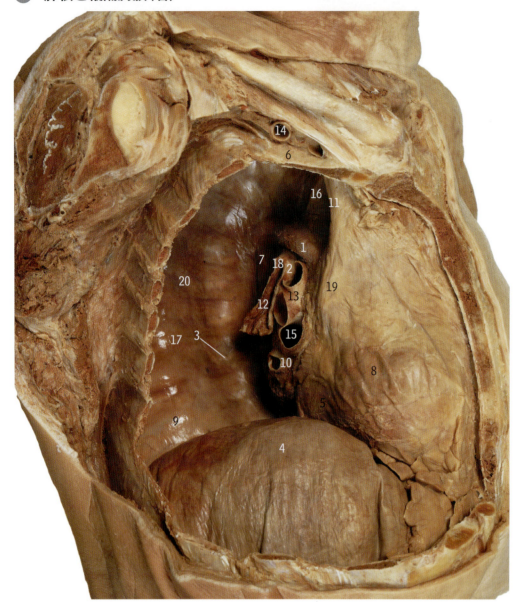

肺は除去したが，壁側胸膜は剥がさずに残し，縦隔の右側を見ている．

1. 奇静脈 Azygos vein
2. 上葉動脈〔右肺動脈〕 Superior lobar artery〔Right pulmonary artery〕
3. 大内臓神経への枝〔交感神経幹〕 Branches to Greater splanchnic nerve〔Sympathetic trunk〕
4. 横隔膜 Diaphragm
5. 下大静脈 Inferior vena cava
6. 第一肋骨体 Body of 1st rib：Shaft of 1st rib
7. 食道 Esophagus
8. 心膜（右心房を覆う） Pericardium
9. 肋骨胸膜 Costal pleura
10. 右下肺静脈 Right inferior pulmonary vein
11. （右の）横隔神経 Phrenic nerve
12. 右主気管支 Right main bronchus
13. 右肺動脈 Right pulmonary artery
14. （右の）鎖骨下動脈 Subclavian artery
15. 右上肺静脈 Right superior pulmonary vein
16. （右の）迷走神経［X］ Vagus nerve［X］
17. （右の）第六肋間動／静脈（壁側胸膜下を走る） 6th posterior intercostal artery/vein
18. 右上葉気管支 Right superior lobar bronchus
19. 上大静脈 Superior vena cava
20. 交感神経幹と交感神経節 Sympathetic trunk and Sympathetic ganglion

B～D 肺根と縦隔（右）

BはAに似ているが異なる標本である．胸膜の大部分を除去し，胸膜に覆われていた構造物を明らかにしている．奇静脈(1)は，肺根を構成する構造の上をアーチ状に越えて上大静脈(24)に入る．肺根の最も高い位置を通るものは，右上葉動脈(2)と右上葉気管支(23)である．右上肺静脈(18)は右肺動脈の前を通り，右下肺静脈(12)は肺根で最も低い位置を通る．奇静脈弓より上方では，気管(28)とこれに接する右の迷走神経(19)は，食道(8)の前に位置する．第一肋骨の一部を切除し，その肋骨頸(7)の前を通る，交感神経幹(27)，最上肋間静脈(25)，第六肋間動脈(20)ならびに第一胸神経の前枝を示している．右の反回神経は，鎖骨下動脈(16)の下を鉤状に曲がる．右の横隔神経(13)は，上大静脈(24)と右心房表面の心膜(9)の側面を下行し，下大静脈の脇で横隔膜(4)に進入する．交感神経幹から出た枝(3)が肋間動静脈(20，21)の浅層を通って下行し，大内臓神経をつくる．食道(8)の下部は，肺根と心臓の後ろにあり，その右側を奇静脈(1)が走る．

外科手術後の気腫

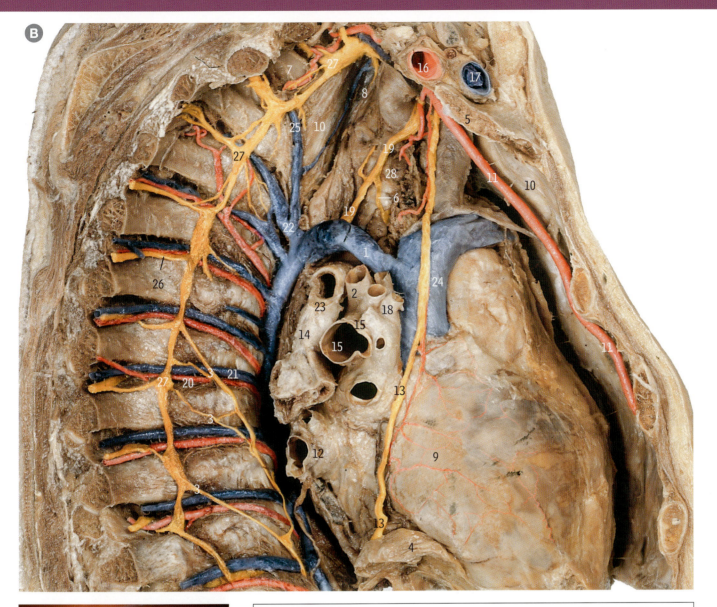

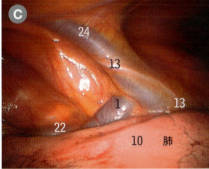

胸腔鏡写真

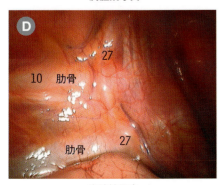

胸腔鏡写真

1	奇静脈弓 Arch of azygos vein	9	心膜（右心房を覆う） Pericardium	19	（右の）迷走神経［X］ Vagus nerve [X]
2	上葉動脈〔右肺動脈〕 Superior lobar artery (Right pulmonary artery)	10	胸膜 Pleura	20	（右の）第六肋間動脈 6th posterior intercostal artery
3	大内臓神経への枝〔交感神経幹〕 Branches to Greater splanchnic nerve (Sympathetic trunk)	11	（右の）内胸動脈 Internal thoracic artery	21	（右の）第六肋間静脈 6th posterior intercostal vein
4	横隔膜 Diaphragm	12	右下肺静脈 Right inferior pulmonary vein	22	右上肋間静脈 Right superior intercostal vein
5	第一肋骨（切断してある） 1st rib : Rib I	13	（右の）横隔神経 Phrenic nerve	23	右上葉気管支 Right superior lobar bronchus
6	下頸心臓枝〔迷走神経［X］〕 Inferior cervical cardiac branches (Vagus nerve [X])	14	右主気管支 Right main bronchus	24	上大静脈 Superior vena cava
7	第一肋骨頸 Neck of 1st rib	15	右肺動脈 Right pulmonary artery	25	最上肋間静脈 Supreme intercostal vein
		16	（右の）鎖骨下動脈 Subclavian artery	26	交通枝〔交感神経〕 Rami communicantes (Sympathetic part)
8	食道 Esophagus	17	（右の）鎖骨下静脈（血栓がある） Subclavian vein	27	交感神経幹と交感神経節 Sympathetic trunk and Sympathetic ganglion
		18	右上肺静脈 Right superior pulmonary vein	28	気管 Trachea

胸水

胸腔鏡検査

経胸腔的交感神経切除術

Ⓐ～Ⓒ 肺根と縦隔胸膜（左）

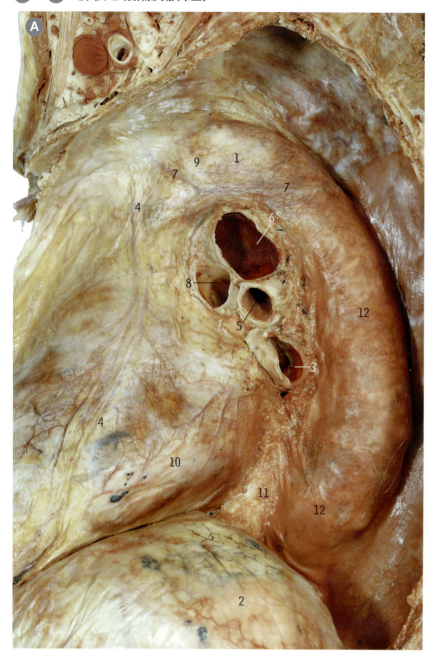

1	大動脈弓 Arch of aorta：Aortic arch
2	横隔膜 Diaphragm
3	左下肺静脈 Left inferior pulmonary vein
4	（左の）横隔神経と心膜横隔動／静脈 Phrenic nerve and Pericardiacophrenic artery/veins
5	左主気管支 Left main bronchus
6	左肺動脈 Left pulmonary artery
7	左上肋間静脈 Left superior intercostal vein
8	左上肺静脈 Left superior pulmonary vein
9	（左の）迷走神経［X］ Vagus nerve［X］
10	縦隔胸膜と心膜（左心室を覆っている） Mediastinal pleura and Pericardium
11	食道 Esophagus
12	胸大動脈〔下行大動脈〕 Thoracic aorta〔Descending aorta〕

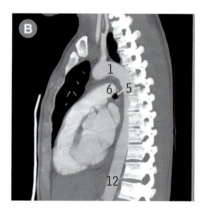

肺は除去したが，壁側胸膜を剥がさずに残し，縦隔の左側を見ている．胸膜下の構造を，次頁の胸膜を剥離した標本（本例とは別の標本）と比較せよ．

● 横隔膜より上方の左側では，食道の下部は，下方を横隔膜（2），前を心臓，後ろを下行大動脈（12）で囲まれた三角を通過する．

気胸

胸部大動脈瘤

第4章 胸部：縦隔　207

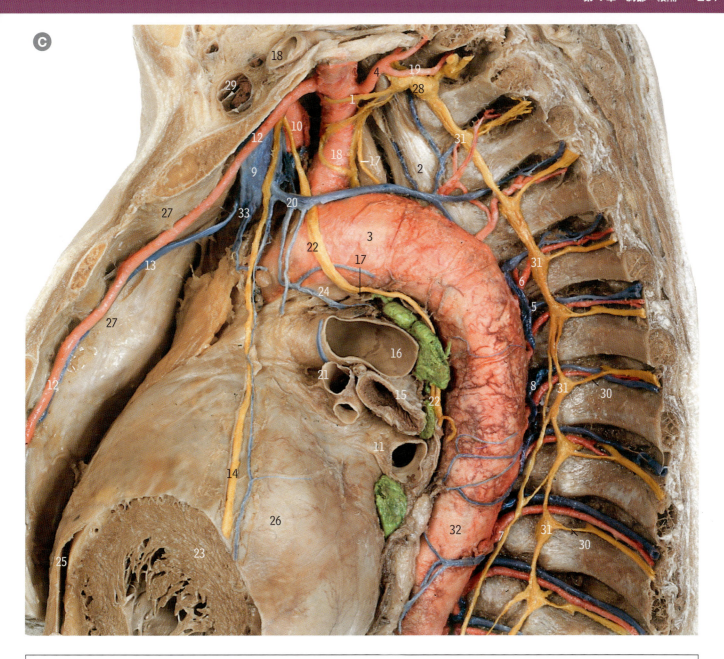

1	鎖骨下ワナ Ansa subclavia	10	（左の）総頸動脈 Common carotid artery	18	（左の）鎖骨下動脈 Subclavian artery	26	心膜（左心室を覆う） Pericardium
2	頸長筋 Longus colli	11	左下肺静脈 Left inferior pulmonary vein	19	（左の）最上肋間動脈 Supreme intercostal artery	27	胸膜（切断縁） Pleura
3	大動脈弓 Arch of aorta：Aortic arch	12	（左の）内胸動脈 Internal thoracic artery	20	左上肋間静脈 Left superior intercostal vein	28	頸胸神経節：星状神経節 Cervicothoracic ganglion：Stellate ganglion
4	肋頸動脈 Costocervical trunk	13	（左の）内胸静脈 Internal thoracic vein	21	左上肺静脈 Left superior pulmonary vein	29	鎖骨下静脈 Subclavian vein
5	（左の）第五肋間静脈 5th posterior intercostal vein	14	（左の）横隔神経と心膜横隔動／静脈 Phrenic nerve and Pericardiacophrenic artery/veins	22	（左の）迷走神経［X］ Vagus nerve [X]	30	交通枝（交感神経） Rami communicantes（Sympathetic part）
6	（左の）第四肋間動脈 4th posterior intercostal artery	15	左主気管支 Left main bronchus	23	左心室（心臓壁が肥厚している） Left ventricle	31	交感神経幹と交感神経節 Sympathetic trunk and Sympathetic ganglion
7	大内臓神経 Greater splanchnic nerve	16	左肺動脈 Left pulmonary artery	24	動脈管索 Ligamentum arteriosum	32	胸大動脈 Thoracic aorta
8	半奇静脈 Hemi-azygos vein	17	（左の）反回神経 Recurrent laryngeal nerve	25	心膜腔 Pericardial cavity	33	胸腺静脈（366頁参照） Thymic veins
9	左腕頭静脈 Left brachiocephalic vein						

大動脈縮窄症

鎖骨下動脈病変に対する
ステント留置術

A B 縦隔

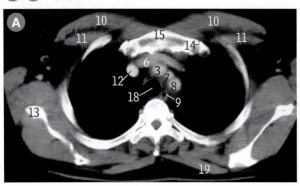

A CT 横断造影画像 T2 の高さ．

B CT 横断造影画像 T4 の高さ．

1	大動脈弓	Arch of aorta：Aortic arch
2	奇静脈	Azygos vein
3	腕頭動脈	Brachiocephalic trunk
4	下行大動脈	Descending aorta
5	半奇静脈	Hemi-azygos vein
6	左腕頭静脈	Left brachiocephalic vein
7	（左の）総頸動脈	Common carotid artery
8	（左の）鎖骨下動脈	Subclavian artery
9	食道	Esophagus
10	大胸筋	Pectoralis major
11	小胸筋	Pectoralis minor
12	右腕頭静脈	Right brachiocephalic vein
13	肩甲骨	Scapula
14	胸鎖関節	Sternoclavicular joint
15	胸骨	Sternum
16	上大静脈	Superior vena cava
17	気管	Trachea
18	僧帽筋	Trapezius

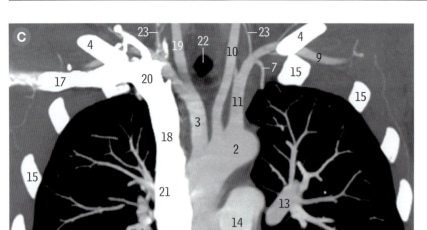

64 列 CT 冠状断造影画像（静脈相）

C 縦隔と肺

1	心尖	Apex of heart
2	大動脈弓	Arch of aorta：Aortic arch
3	腕頭動脈	Brachiocephalic trunk
4	鎖骨	Clavicle
5	（右の）横隔膜による円蓋	
6	下大静脈	Inferior vena cava
7	内胸動脈	Internal thoracic artery
8	心室中隔	Interventricular septum
9	（左の）腋窩動脈	Axillary artery
10	（左の）総頸動脈	Common carotid artery
11	（左の）鎖骨下動脈	Subclavian artery
12	右肺動脈	Right pulmonary artery
13	上葉動脈〔左肺動脈〕	Superior lobar artery〔Left pulmonary artery〕
14	肺動脈［幹］	Pulmonary trunk
15	肋骨	Rib
16	右心房	Right atrium
17	（右の）腋窩静脈	Axillary vein
18	右腕頭静脈	Right brachiocephalic vein
19	（右の）総頸動脈	Common carotid artery
20	（右の）鎖骨下静脈	Subclavian vein
21	上大静脈	Superior vena cava
22	気管	Trachea
23	椎骨動脈	Vertebral artery
24	左心室	Left ventricle

横隔神経麻痺

気管の下部と気管支

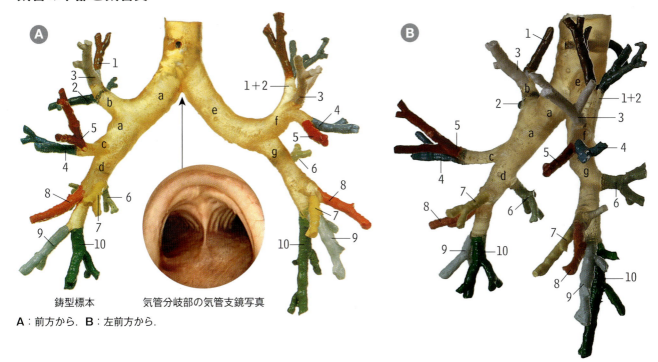

A：前方から．B：左前方から．

主気管支と葉気管支にはアルファベットの文字を付け，区域気管支には公式に付けられた番号で示している．側方から見た B では，気管支の重なりを避けるため標本をやや回旋させている．そのため，右気管支が左気管支よりも前方に位置している．

鋳型標本

右肺 Right lung	左肺 Left lung
葉気管支 Lobar bronchi	
a 主気管支 Main bronchus	e 主気管支 Main bronchus
b 上葉気管支 Superior lobar bronchus	f 上葉気管支 Superior lobar bronchus
c 中葉気管支 Middle lobe bronchus	g 下葉気管支 Inferior lobar bronchus
d 下葉気管支 Inferior lobar bronchus	
区域気管支 Segmental bronchi	
上葉 Superior lobe	上葉 Superior lobe
1 肺尖枝（B1） Apical segmental bronchus（B I）	1+2 肺尖後枝（B1＋2） Apicoposterior segmental bronchus（B I + II）
2 後上葉枝（B2） Posterior segmental bronchus（B II）	3 前上葉枝（B3） Anterior segmental bronchus（B III）
3 前上葉枝（B3） Anterior segmental bronchus（B III）	4 上舌枝（B4） Superior lingular bronchus（B IV）
中葉 Middle lobe	5 下舌枝（B5） Inferior lingular bronchus（B V）
4 外側中葉枝（B4） Lateral segmental bronchus（B IV）	下葉 Inferior lobe
5 内側中葉枝（B5） Medial segmental bronchus（B V）	6 上－下葉枝（B6） Superior segmental bronchus（B VI）
下葉 Inferior lobe	7 内側肺底枝（B7） Medial basal segmental bronchus（B VII）
6 上－下葉枝（B6） Superior segmental bronchus（B VI）	8 前肺底枝（B8） Anterior basal segmental bronchus（B VIII）
7 内側肺底枝（B7） Medial basal segmental bronchus（B VII）	9 外側肺底枝（B9） Lateral basal segmental bronchus（B IX）
8 前肺底枝（B8） Anterior basal segmental bronchus（B VIII）	10 後肺底枝（B10） Posterior basal segmental bronchus（B X）
9 外側肺底枝（B9） Lateral basal segmental bronchus（B IX）	
10 後肺底枝（B10） Posterior basal segmental bronchus（B X）	

- 気管は左右の主気管支に分岐する（a, e）．
- 右主気管支（a）は，左主気管支（e）より短く，太く，垂直に近い．
- 左主気管支（e）は，右主気管支（a）より長く，細く，水平に近い．したがって，異物は左主気管支より右主気管支に入りやすい．
- 右主気管支（a）は，まず上葉気管支（b）を分岐し，次いで右肺門に入り，中葉気管支（c）と下葉気管支（d）に分岐する．
- 左主気管支（e）は，肺門に入ってから上葉気管支（f）と下葉気管支（g）に分岐する．
- 葉気管支の分枝は区域気管支とよばれ，それぞれ肺実質の気管支肺区域すなわち肺区域に分布している．区域気管支と肺区域は同じ名称でよばれ，左右の肺のそれぞれ 10 区域に，公式名と公式番号が付けられている（210 頁）．
- 左右の肺の葉気管支は，基本的には同じであるが，次の点が異なっている．①左肺上葉の肺尖枝と後上葉枝は共通幹をつくり，肺尖後枝とよばれ，1＋2 と番号が付けられている．②左肺には中葉がない．③左肺の上葉の上舌枝（4）と下舌枝（5）が，右肺の中葉の外側中葉枝と内側中葉枝に対応しており，同じ番号が付けられている．④左肺の内側肺底枝（7）は，通常，前肺底枝（8）と共通幹をつくる．
- 両肺の上－下葉枝（6）は，B に示してあるように気管支の後面から出る最初でかつ最上方の区域気管支である．したがって，仰臥位をとると，分泌物がこの気管支に流れ込みやすい．

気管支樹

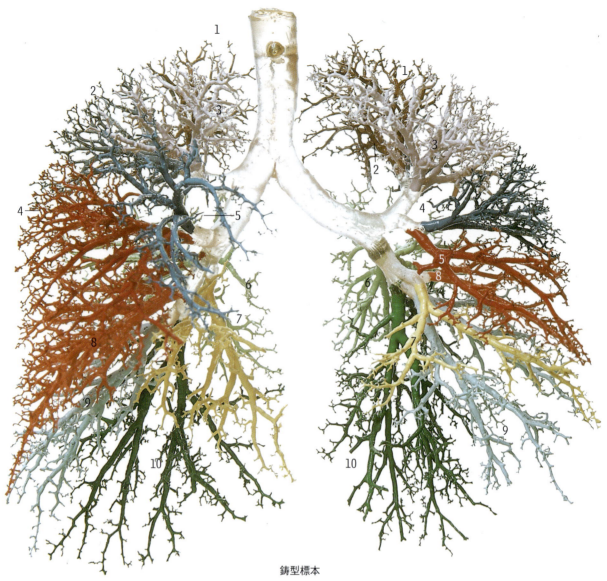

鋳型標本

肺区域ごとに気管支を色分けして示し，番号を付した．

右肺 Right lung	
上葉 Superior lobe	下葉 Inferior lobe
1　肺尖区（S1） 　　Apical segment (S I)	6　上-下葉区（S6） 　　Superior segment (S VI)
2　後上葉区（S2） 　　Posterior segment (S II)	7　内側肺底区（S7） 　　Medial basal segment (S VII)
3　前上葉区（S3） 　　Anterior segment (S III)	8　前肺底区（S8） 　　Anterior basal segment (S VIII)
中葉 Middle lobe	9　外側肺底区（S9） 　　Lateral basal segment (S IX)
4　外側中葉区（S4） 　　Lateral segment (S IV)	10　後肺底区（S10） 　　Posterior basal segment (S X)
5　内側中葉区（S5） 　　Medial segment (S V)	

左肺 Left lung	
上葉 Superior lobe	下葉 Inferior lobe
1＋2　肺尖後区（S1＋2） 　　　 Apicoposterior segment (S I + II)	6　上-下葉区（S6） 　　Superior segment (S VI)
3　前上葉区（S3） 　　Anterior segment (S III)	7　内側肺底区（S7） 　　Medial basal segment (S VII)
4　上舌区（S4） 　　Superior lingular segment (S IV)	8　前肺底区（S8） 　　Anterior basal segment (S VIII)
5　下舌区（S5） 　　Inferior lingular segment (S V)	9　外側肺底区（S9） 　　Lateral basal segment (S IX)
	10　後肺底区（S10） 　　 Posterior basal segment (S X)

気管支鏡検査

膿胸

右肺の肺区域

上葉 Superior lobe	下葉 Inferior lobe
1　肺尖区（S1） Apical segment（S I）	6　上-下葉区（S6） Superior segment（S VI）
2　後上葉区（S2） Posterior segment（S II）	7　内側肺底区（S7） Medial basal segment（S VII）
3　前上葉区（S3） Anterior segment（S III）	8　前肺底区（S8） Anterior basal segment（S VIII）
中葉 Middle lobe	9　外側肺底区（S9） Lateral basal segment（S IX）
4　外側中葉区（S4） Lateral segment（S IV）	10　後肺底区（S10） Posterior basal segment（S X）
5　内側中葉区（S5） Medial segment（S V）	

● 上枝下-下葉枝および上枝下-下葉区は50％以上の肺に見られ，この標本では白色で示してある．
● 後肺底区（10）は，異なる2つの色（黄土色と黄緑色）で示されている．

A：前方から．B：後方から．

左肺の肺区域

上葉 Superior lobe	下葉 Inferior lobe
1＋2　肺尖後区（S1＋2） Apicoposterior segment（S I＋II）	6　上-下葉区（S6） Superior segment（S VI）
3　前上葉区（S3） Anterior segment（S III）	7　内側肺底区（S7） Medial basal segment（S VII）
4　上舌区（S4） Superior lingular segment（S IV）	8　前肺底区（S8） Anterior basal segment（S VIII）
5　下舌区（S5） Inferior lingular segment（S V）	9　外側肺底区（S9） Lateral basal segment（S IX）
	10　後肺底区（S10） Posterior basal segment（S X）

● 肺尖後区（1＋2）は，肺尖枝と後上葉枝の共通幹である肺尖後枝から色素を注入したので，1，2ともに緑色で示されている（209頁参照）．

C：前方から．D：後方から．

A 右肺の肺区域

外側方から．

- Aにおいて，内側肺底区(7)はこの方向からは見えない．
- 後肺底区(10)は，異なる2つの色（黄土色と黄緑色）で示されている．

B 右肺の気管支

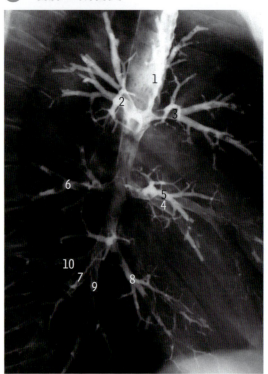

気管支造影画像

上葉 Superior lobe
1 肺尖区(S1)
　Apical segment (S I)
2 後上葉区(S2)
　Posterior segment (S II)
3 前上葉区(S3)
　Anterior segment (S III)

中葉 Middle lobe
4 外側中葉区(S4)
　Lateral segment (S IV)
5 内側中葉区(S5)
　Medial segment (S V)

下葉 Inferior lobe
6 上-下葉区(S6)
　Superior segment (S VI)
7 内側肺底区(S7)
　Medial basal segment (S VII)
8 前肺底区(S8)
　Anterior basal segment (S VIII)
9 外側肺底区(S9)
　Lateral basal segment (S IX)
10 後肺底区(S10)
　Posterior basal segment (S X)

C 肺と気道

1 気管竜骨：気管カリナ
　Carina of trachea
2 左肺
　Left lung
3 左下葉気管支
　Left inferior lobar bronchus
4 左主気管支
　Left main bronchus
5 左上葉気管支
　Left superior lobar bronchus
6 右肺
　Right lung
7 右主気管支
　Right main bronchus
8 右上葉気管支
　Right superior lobar bronchus

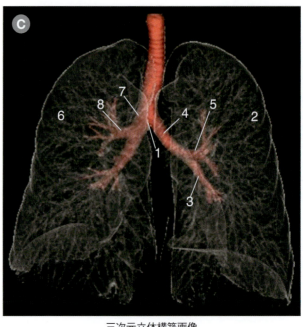

三次元立体構築画像

膿胸

D 左肺の肺区域

外側方から．

上葉 Superior lobe		下葉 Inferior lobe	
1＋2	肺尖後区（S1＋2） Apicoposterior segment（S I＋II）	6	上-下葉区（S6） Superior segment（S VI）
3	前上葉区（S3） Anterior segment（S III）	7	内側肺底区（S7） Medial basal segment（S VII）
4	上舌区（S4） Superior lingular segment（S IV）	8	前肺底区（S8） Anterior basal segment（S VIII）
5	下舌区（S5） Inferior lingular segment（S V）	9	外側肺底区（S9） Lateral basal segment（S IX）
		10	後肺底区（S10） Posterior basal segment（S X）

● 肺尖後区（1＋2）は，肺尖枝と後上葉枝の共同幹である肺尖後枝から色素を注入したので，1，2ともに緑色で示されている（211頁D）．

E 左肺の気管支

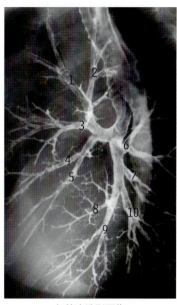

気管支造影画像

F 左肺の上葉

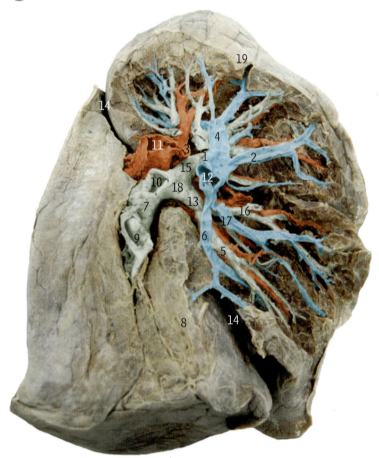

肺区域を明らかにしている．

1 前上葉枝（B3）
　Anterior segmental bronchus（B III）
2 前上葉静脈
　Anterior vein
3 肺尖後枝（B1＋2）
　Apicoposterior segmental bronchus（B I＋II）
4 肺尖後静脈
　Apicoposterior vein
5 下舌枝（B5）〔上葉気管支〕
　Inferior lingular bronchus（B V）〔Superior lobar bronchus〕
6 下舌枝〔肺舌静脈〕
　Inferior part〔Lingular vein〕
7 左下葉気管支
　Left inferior lobar bronchus
8 下葉
　Inferior lobe
9 左下肺静脈
　Left inferior pulmonary vein
10 左主気管支
　Left main bronchus
11 左肺動脈
　Left pulmonary artery
12 左上肺静脈
　Left superior pulmonary vein
13 舌枝＊〔上葉気管支〕
　Lingular bronchus＊〔Superior lobar bronchus〕
14 斜裂
　Oblique fissure
15 前上葉枝と肺尖後枝の共同幹
16 上舌枝（B4）〔上葉気管支〕
　Superior lingular bronchus（B IV）〔Superior lobar bronchus〕
17 上舌枝〔肺舌静脈〕
　Superior part〔Lingular vein〕
18 左上葉気管支
　Left superior lobar bronchus
19 上葉
　Superior lobe

血胸

A 気管支樹と肺動静脈

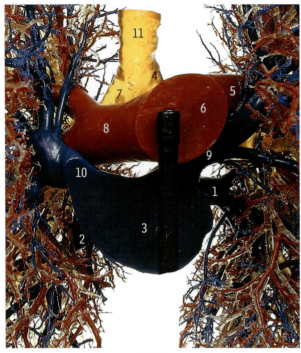

鋳型標本
前方から．

肺動脈幹(6)は，左右の肺動脈(5, 8)に分岐する．これらの血管には赤色の樹脂を注入してある．左心房(3)に注ぐ4本の肺静脈(9, 1, 2, 10)には青色の樹脂を充填してある．生体の肺静脈は酸素分圧の高い血液で満たされているので，通常この標本とは逆に赤色で示されることに注意せよ．同様に，酸素分圧の低い血液を含む肺動脈は，青色で示されるべきである．

1	左下肺静脈 Left inferior pulmonary vein	7	右主気管支 Right main bronchus
2	右下肺静脈 Right inferior pulmonary vein	8	右肺動脈 Right pulmonary artery
3	左心房 Left atrium	9	左上肺静脈 Superior left pulmonary vein
4	左主気管支 Left main bronchus	10	右上肺静脈 Superior right pulmonary vein
5	左肺動脈 Left pulmonary artery	11	気管 Trachea
6	肺動脈［幹］ Pulmonary trunk		

B 肺根と気管支動脈

右側を上方から見たところ．

第三胸椎(17)の高さで胸郭を横断してある．この高さは大動脈弓(1)のすぐ上方であるので，大動脈弓の3つの大きな枝(3, 6, 8)は切断されている．また，肺門周囲の肺組織は上方から除去してある．食道(10)と気管(19)を前方へ引き出し，気管支動脈(11)の1つを示している．

1	大動脈弓 Arch of aorta：Aortic arch	11	（右の）気管支動脈 Bronchial branch
2	奇静脈 Azygos vein	12	右主気管支 Right main bronchus
3	腕頭動脈 Brachiocephalic trunk	13	右肺動脈 Right pulmonary artery
4	下葉動脈 Inferior lobar arteries	14	（右の）迷走神経［X］ Vagus nerve [X]
5	右下葉気管支 Right inferior lobar bronchus	15	右上葉気管支 Right superior lobar bronchus
6	（左の）総頸動脈 Common carotid artery	16	上大静脈 Superior vena cava
7	（左の）反回神経（切断端） Recurrent laryngeal nerve	17	第三胸椎 3rd thoracic vertebra (T III)
8	（左の）鎖骨下動脈 Subclavian artery	18	胸管 Thoracic duct
9	右中葉気管支 Middle lobar bronchus	19	気管 Trachea
10	食道 Esophagus	20	下肺静脈に入る静脈

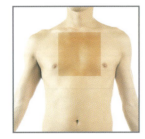

食道癌

肺塞栓症

第4章　胸部：肺　215

C 肺動脈と気管支

鋳型標本

前方から．

D 肺動脈

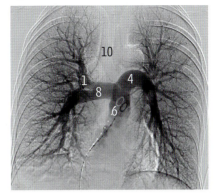

肺動脈造影画像

肺動脈幹(6)の下部を切り離し，上部の断端を見ている．肺動脈幹の左・右肺動脈(4，8)への分岐部は，左主気管支(3)の起始部の前に位置する．生体において肺動脈は酸素分圧の低い血液を含むため，通常，青色で示されるが，本例では赤色の樹脂を充填してある．鋳型標本の血管と動脈造影画像(D)を比較せよ．

1	上葉動脈 Superior lobar artery	6	肺動脈［幹］ Pulmonary trunk
2	［右・左］下葉気管支 Right/Left inferior lobar bronchus	7	右主気管支 Right main bronchus
3	左主気管支 Left main bronchus	8	右肺動脈 Right pulmonary artery
4	左肺動脈 Left pulmonary artery	9	［右・左］上葉気管支 Right/Left superior lobar bronchus
5	右中葉気管支 Middle lobar bronchus	10	気管 Trachea

E 気管支と気管支動脈

大動脈の一部(1，10)から赤色の樹脂を注入し，気管支動脈に満たしてある．通常，気管支動脈は気管支とその分枝の後ろを走るが，本例では前を走行している．

1	大動脈弓 Arch of aorta：Aortic arch	7	（左上の）気管支動脈（の起始部） Bronchial branch
2	［右・左］下葉気管支 Right/Left inferior lobar bronchus	8	右主気管支 Right main bronchus
3	左主気管支 Left main bronchus	9	［右・左］上葉気管支 Right/Left superior lobar bronchus
4	右中葉気管支 Middle lobar bronchus	10	胸大動脈 Thoracic aorta
5	（左下の）気管支動脈（の起始部） Bronchial branch	11	気管 Trachea
6	（右の）気管支動脈（の起始部） Bronchial branch		

鋳型標本

前方から．

A 左肺

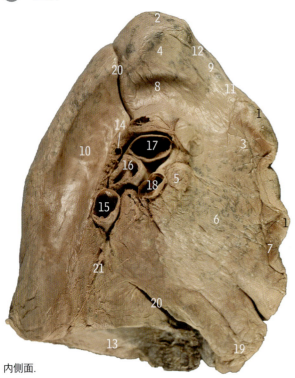

内側面．

B 右肺

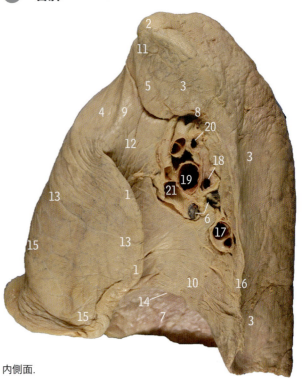

内側面．

	左肺
1	前縁 Anterior border
2	心尖 Apex of heart
3	前縦隔の胸腺と脂肪組織の領域
4	気管と食道の領域
5	気管支肺リンパ節：肺門リンパ節* Bronchopulmonary nodes：Hilar lymph nodes*
6	心圧痕 Cardiac impression
7	［左肺の］心切痕 Cardiac notch of left lung
8	大動脈弓が通る溝
9	腕頭静脈による溝
10	下行大動脈が通る溝
11	第一肋骨が通る溝
12	鎖骨下動脈が通る溝
13	下縁，横隔面 Inferior border, Diaphragmatic surface
14	気管支動脈 Bronchial branch
15	左下肺静脈 Left inferior pulmonary vein
16	左主気管支 Left main bronchus
17	左肺動脈 Left pulmonary artery
18	左上肺静脈 Left superior pulmonary vein
19	［左肺の］小舌 Lingula of left lung
20	斜裂 Oblique fissure
21	肺間膜 Pulmonary ligament

	右肺
1	前縁（内側へ引いてある） Anterior border
2	肺尖 Apex of lung
3	食道が通る溝
4	前縦隔の胸腺と脂肪組織の領域
5	気管が通る領域
6	気管支肺リンパ節：肺門リンパ節* Bronchopulmonary nodes：Hilar lymph nodes*
7	横隔面 Diaphragmatic surface
8	奇静脈が通る溝
9	腕頭静脈が通る溝
10	下大静脈が通る溝
11	鎖骨下動脈が通る溝
12	上大静脈が通る溝
13	水平裂 Horizontal fissure
14	下縁 Inferior border
15	斜裂 Oblique fissure
16	肺間膜 Pulmonary ligament
17	右下肺静脈 Right inferior pulmonary vein
18	右中葉気管支 Middle lobar bronchus
19	右肺動脈 Right pulmonary artery
20	右上葉気管支 Right superior lobar bronchus
21	右上肺静脈 Right superior pulmonary vein

肺癌

中皮腫

肺結核

頸胸移行部［体表解剖］

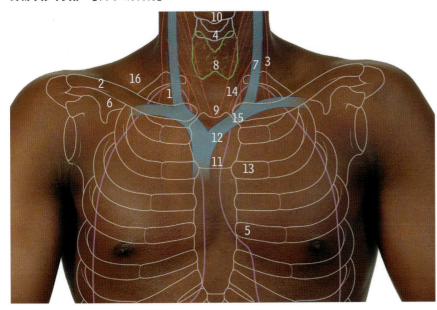

1	胸膜頂と肺尖 Dome of pleura：Pleural cupula and Apex of lung
2	鎖骨 Clavicle
3	鎖骨頭＊〔胸鎖乳突筋〕 Clavicular head＊〔Sternocleidomastoid〕
4	輪状軟骨 Cricoid cartilage
5	第四肋軟骨 4th costal cartilage
6	鎖骨下窩 Infraclavicular fossa
7	内頸静脈 Internal jugular vein
8	甲状腺峡部（気管の表面） Isthmus of thyroid gland
9	頸切痕 Jugular notch：Suprasternal notch
10	喉頭隆起〔甲状軟骨〕 Laryngeal prominence〔Thyroid cartilage〕
11	胸骨柄結合 Manubriosternal joint
12	胸骨柄（中央部） Manubrium of sternum
13	第二肋軟骨 2nd costal cartilage
14	胸骨頭＊〔胸鎖乳突筋〕 Sternal head＊〔Sternocleidomastoid〕
15	胸鎖関節 Sternoclavicular joint
16	大鎖骨上窩 Greater supraclavicular fossa

頸胸移行部の静脈

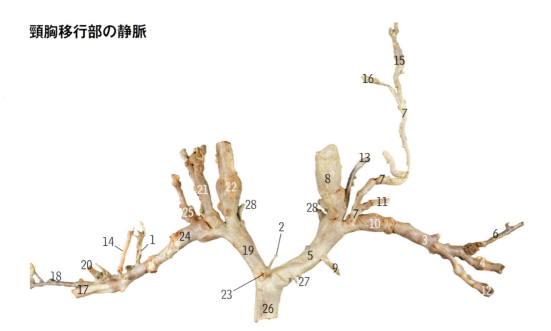

1	胸肩峰静脈（肩峰から流入する静脈） Thoraco-acromial vein	10	（左の）鎖骨下静脈 Subclavian vein	19	右腕頭静脈 Right brachiocephalic vein
2	下甲状腺静脈 Inferior thyroid vein	11	（左の）肩甲上静脈 Suprascapular vein	20	（右の）橈側皮静脈 Cephalic vein
3	（左の）腋窩静脈 Axillary vein	12	（左の）胸背静脈 Thoracodorsal vein	21	（右の）外頸静脈 External jugular vein
4	（左の）尺側皮静脈 Basilic vein	13	頸横静脈（内頸静脈に流入する） Transverse cervical vein	22	（右の）内頸静脈 Internal jugular vein
5	左腕頭静脈 Left brachiocephalic vein	14	胸肩峰静脈（胸筋から流入する静脈） Thoraco-acromial vein	23	（右の）内胸静脈 Internal thoracic vein
6	（左の）橈側皮静脈 Cephalic vein	15	後耳介静脈 Posterior auricular vein	24	（右の）鎖骨下静脈 Subclavian vein
7	（左の）外頸静脈 External jugular vein	16	下顎後静脈 Retromandibular vein	25	（右の）肩甲上静脈 Suprascapular vein
8	（左の）内頸静脈 Internal jugular vein	17	（右の）尺側皮静脈 Basilic vein	26	上大静脈 Superior vena cava
9	（左の）内胸静脈 Internal thoracic vein	18	（右の）上腕静脈 Brachial vein	27	胸腺静脈 Thymic veins
				28	椎骨静脈 Vertebral vein

上大静脈の閉塞

大きな静脈の変異

胸郭上口と上縦隔

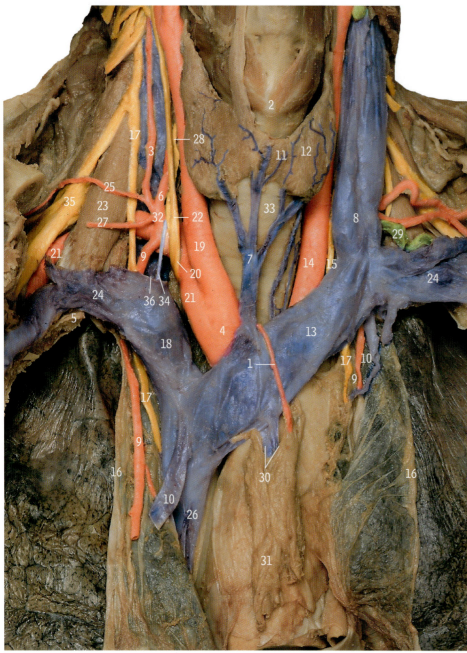

前方から．

前胸壁と左右の鎖骨の内側端を除去し，壁側胸膜(16)の一部を両肺の内側部の表面に残したままにしてある．右の内頸静脈も除去し，甲状頸動脈(32)と内胸動脈(9)の起始部がわかるようにしている．下甲状腺静脈(7)は，気管(33)の前面を下行し，左腕頭静脈(13)に流入する．胸腺(31)は，縦隔の脂肪から剖出して示してある．胸腺静脈(30)が左腕頭静脈に流入している．また本例では，胸腺動脈(1)が腕頭動脈(4)から起こるという変異例が見られる．

1	胸腺動脈*	Thymic artery*
2	輪状軟骨弓	Arch of cricoid cartilage
3	上行頸動脈	Ascending cervical artery
4	腕頭動脈	Brachiocephalic trunk
5	第一肋骨（切断縁）	1st rib：Rib I
6	下甲状腺動脈	Inferior thyroid artery
7	下甲状腺静脈	Inferior thyroid vein
8	内頸静脈	Internal jugular vein
9	内胸動脈	Internal thoracic artery
10	内胸静脈	Internal thoracic vein
11	甲状腺峡部	Isthmus of thyroid gland
12	左葉〔甲状腺〕	Left lobe〔Thyroid gland〕
13	左腕頭静脈	Left brachiocephalic vein
14	（左の）総頸動脈	Common carotid artery
15	（左の）迷走神経［X］	Vagus nerve［X］
16	壁側胸膜（肺を覆っている．切断縁）	Parietal pleura
17	横隔神経	Phrenic nerve
18	右腕頭静脈	Right brachiocephalic vein
19	（右の）総頸動脈	Common carotid artery
20	（右の）反回神経	Recurrent laryngeal nerve
21	（右の）鎖骨下動脈	Subclavian artery
22	（右の）迷走神経［X］	Vagus nerve［X］
23	前斜角筋	Anterior scalene
24	鎖骨下静脈	Subclavian vein
25	浅枝：浅頸動脈〔頸横動脈〕	Superficial cervical artery〔Transverse cervical artery〕
26	上大静脈	Superior vena cava
27	肩甲上動脈	Suprascapular artery
28	交感神経幹	Sympathetic trunk
29	胸管	Thoracic duct
30	胸腺静脈	Thymic veins
31	胸腺	Thymus
32	甲状頸動脈	Thyrocervical trunk
33	気管	Trachea
34	右腕頭静脈に頸部から流入する静脈（変異）	
35	上神経幹〔腕神経叢〕	Superior trunk：Upper trunk〔Brachial plexus〕
36	椎骨静脈	Vertebral vein

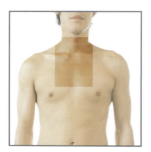

Pancoast 腫瘍

胸郭出口症候群

胸郭上口と上縦隔［腋窩と頸の根部］

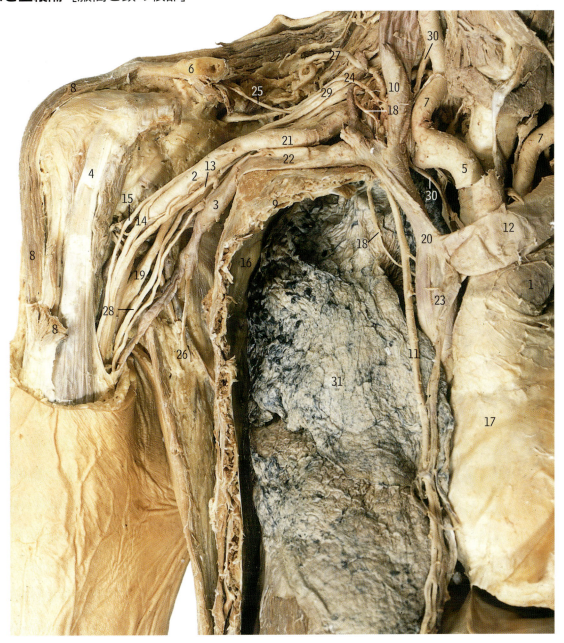

1	大動脈弓 Arch of aorta：Aortic arch	8	三角筋 Deltoid	16	壁側胸膜（胸壁内面を覆う） Parietal pleura	24	肩甲上動脈 Suprascapular artery
2	腋窩動脈 Axillary artery	9	第一肋骨 1st rib：Rib I	17	線維性心膜 Fibrous pericardium	25	肩甲上神経 Suprascapular nerve
3	腋窩静脈 Axillary vein	10	内頸静脈 Internal jugular vein	18	横隔神経 Phrenic nerve	26	胸背静脈 Thoracodorsal vein
4	短頭〔上腕二頭筋〕 Short head（Biceps brachii）	11	内胸動脈 Internal thoracic artery	19	橈骨神経 Radial nerve	27	頸横動脈 Transverse cervical artery
5	腕頭動脈 Brachiocephalic trunk	12	左腕頭静脈 Left brachiocephalic vein	20	右腕頭静脈 Right brachiocephalic vein	28	尺骨神経 Ulnar nerve
6	鎖骨（切断の後に除去してある） Clavicle	13	内側神経束〔腕神経叢〕 Medial cord（Brachial plexus）	21	鎖骨下動脈 Subclavian artery	29	上神経幹〔腕神経叢〕 Superior trunk：Upper trunk（Brachial plexus）
7	総頸動脈 Common carotid artery	14	正中神経 Median nerve	22	鎖骨下静脈 Subclavian vein	30	迷走神経［X］ Vagus nerve［X］
		15	筋皮神経 Musculocutaneous nerve	23	上大静脈 Superior vena cava	31	臓側胸膜：肺胸膜（肺を覆う） Visceral pleura：Pulmonary pleura

気管支拡張症　　サルコイドーシス

胸郭上口［上位肋骨（右）］

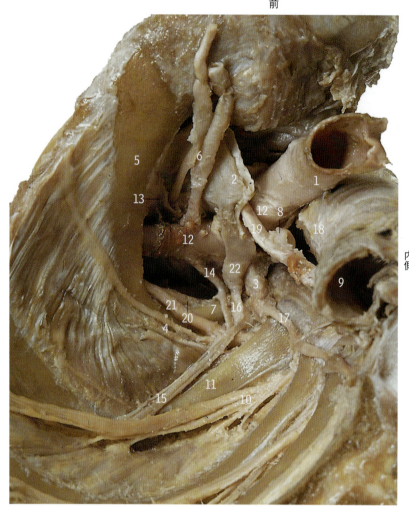

下方から.

1	腕頭動脈 Brachiocephalic trunk
2	腕頭静脈 Brachiocephalic vein
3	頸胸神経節：星状神経節 Cervicothoracic ganglion：Stellate ganglion
4	第一肋間神経 1st intercostal nerve
5	第一肋骨 1st rib：Rib I
6	内胸動／静脈 Internal thoracic artery/vein
7	第一肋骨頸 Neck of 1st rib
8	反回神経 Recurrent laryngeal nerve
9	右主気管支 Right main bronchus
10	第二肋間神経 2nd intercostal nerve
11	第二肋骨 2nd rib：Rib II
12	鎖骨下動脈 Subclavian artery
13	鎖骨下静脈 Subclavian vein
14	最上肋間動脈 Supreme intercostal artery
15	右上肋間静脈 Right superior intercostal vein
16	最上肋間静脈（通常より太い） Supreme intercostal vein
17	交感神経幹 Sympathetic trunk
18	気管 Trachea
19	迷走神経［X］ Vagus nerve［X］
20	前枝〔第八頸神経〕 Ventral ramus〔C8〕
21	第一胸神経 1st intercostal nerve
22	椎骨静脈 Vertebral vein

● 第一肋骨頸(7)は，内側から外側にかけて，交感神経幹(17)，最上肋間静脈(16)，最上肋間動脈(14)ならびに第一胸神経の前枝（肋間神経，21）と交叉する．

右側の胸郭上口を下から見たところである．胸膜頂を除去してある．第一肋骨(5)の下面の大部分が見えており，鎖骨下動脈(12)は，内胸動脈(6)を分枝した後に第一肋骨を越える．内胸動脈は，図の上端（前胸壁）に向かって走り，肋頸動脈の枝である最上肋間動脈(14)が第一肋骨頸(7)の前を越えて下行する．頸部から下行してきた椎骨静脈(22)は，腕頭静脈（切断端を2で示す）に流入する手前の後面に番号を付してある．椎骨静脈には，通常より太い最上肋間静脈(16)が流入している．また椎骨静脈の内側には交感神経幹(17)と頸胸神経節（星状神経節，3）が見える．第一肋骨頸(7)の上を第八頸神経の前枝(20)が走り，その下を第一胸神経の前枝（肋間神経，21）が通っている．

鎖骨下静脈カテーテル法

胸郭出口症候群

後縦隔

1. 奇静脈弓 Arch of azygos vein
2. 奇静脈 Azygos vein
3. 灰白交通枝と白交通枝 Gray ramus communicans and White ramus communicans
4. 大内臓神経 Greater splanchnic nerve
5. 肋間動脈 Posterior intercostal artery
6. 肋間神経 Intercostal nerve
7. 肋間静脈 Posterior intercostal vein
8. 食道神経叢 Esophageal plexus
9. 食道 Esophagus
10. 横隔神経 Phrenic nerve
11. 交感神経幹 Sympathetic trunk
12. 交感神経節 Sympathetic ganglion
13. 胸管 Thoracic duct

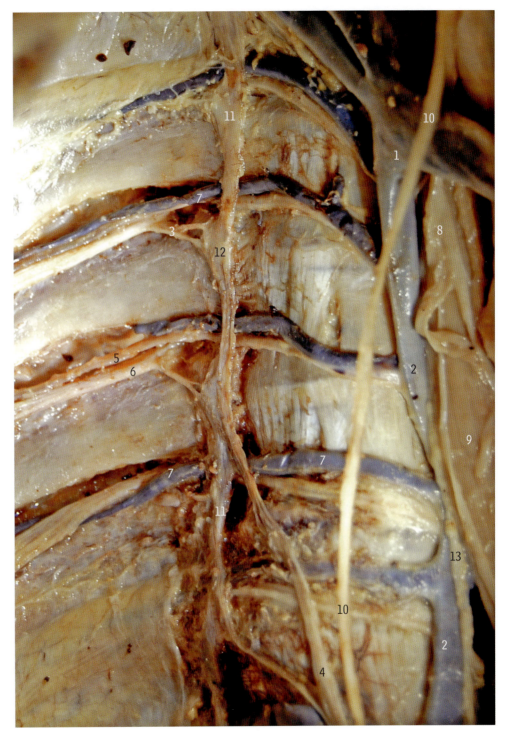

右側方から.

奇静脈葉

A 食道［下位胸部］

心臓を，心膜腔から除去してある．肺動脈幹は，左右の肺動脈(6, 11)に分岐する箇所で切断してある．心膜(9)の後方の一部を除去し，食道(8)を明らかにしている．左主気管支(5)より下方に食道が見えており，右肺動脈(11)の起始部が食道と交叉して横走している．

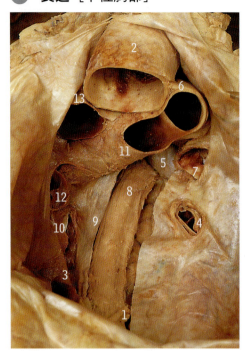
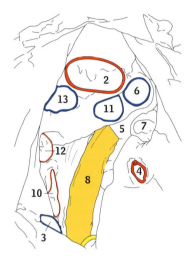

1	前迷走神経幹	Anterior vagal trunk
2	上行大動脈	Ascending aorta
3	下大静脈	Inferior vena cava
4	左下肺静脈	Left inferior pulmonary vein
5	左主気管支	Left main bronchus
6	左肺動脈	Left pulmonary artery
7	左上肺静脈	Left superior pulmonary vein
8	食道	Esophagus
9	心膜（切断縁）	Pericardium
10	右下肺静脈	Right inferior pulmonary vein
11	右肺動脈	Right pulmonary artery
12	右上肺静脈	Right superior pulmonary vein
13	上大静脈	Superior vena cava

前方から．

B 肋間隙

右側の数個の肋間隙の内側端部を剖出し，前方やや右側方から見ている．胸膜は除去してあり，外側に肋下筋(7)があり，肋間隙を神経と血管(2, 3, 4)が横走する．椎体(1)の側面を交感神経幹と交感神経節(8)，大内臓神経(6)が縦走している．

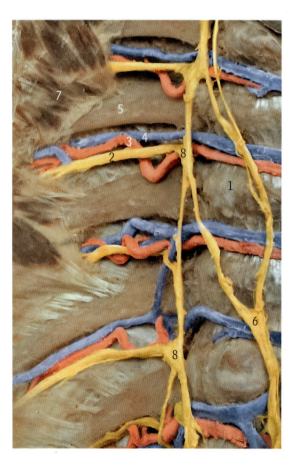
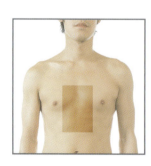

1	椎体〔第九胸椎〕Vertebral body〔T IX〕		5	第八肋骨 8th rib：Rib VIII
2	第八肋間神経 8th intercostal nerve		6	大内臓神経 Greater splanchnic nerve
3	第八肋間動脈 8th posterior intercostal artery		7	肋下筋 Subcostales
4	第八肋間静脈 8th posterior intercostal vein		8	交感神経幹と交感神経節 Sympathetic trunk and Sympathetic ganglion

後内面．

胸腔ドレナージ

A 肋骨頭関節

右側の中位胸部の肋骨結節を越えたところで肋骨を短く切ってある．肋骨頭関節は，肋骨頭の2つの関節面，隣接する上下の椎体側面(9)の関節窩，ならびに介在する椎間円板(2)からなる小さな関節であり，関節包は放線状肋骨頭靱帯(4)で覆われている．

1	大内臓神経	Greater splanchnic nerve
2	椎間円板	Intervertebral disc
3	肋骨頸	Neck of rib
4	放線状肋骨頭靱帯	Radiate ligament of head of rib
5	交通枝	Rami communicantes
6	上肋横突靱帯	Superior costotransverse ligament
7	交感神経幹	Sympathetic trunk
8	肋間神経	Intercostal nerve
9	椎体	Vertebral body

B 肋横突関節

胸椎の右半側を後方から見ている．胸椎の横突起と肋骨頭の間につくられる肋横突関節は，外側肋横突靱帯(4)で覆われている．胸神経の後枝(2)は上肋横突靱帯(6)の内側を通過し，前枝(肋間神経, 8)はこの靱帯の前を走行する．

1	肋横突靱帯	Costotransverse ligament
2	後枝（胸神経）	Posterior ramus : Dorsal ramus（Thoracic nerve）
3	椎弓板	Lamina
4	外側肋横突靱帯	Lateral costotransverse ligament
5	棘突起	Spinous process
6	上肋横突靱帯	Superior costotransverse ligament
7	横突起	Transverse process
8	肋間神経	Intercostal nerve

A：右側方から．B：後方から．

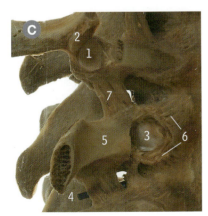

C 肋椎関節

上にある肋骨では，肋骨頸(5)を切り，肋横突関節の関節包を切開し，肋骨頭を上方に翻転して肋骨結節関節面(2)と横突肋骨窩(1)を明らかにしている．下にある肋骨では，放線状肋骨頭靱帯(6)を横切したのちに肋骨頭を除去し，肋骨頭関節の関節腔(3)を明らかにしている．

1	横突肋骨窩 Transverse costal facet		5	肋骨頸 Neck of rib	
2	肋骨結節関節面 Articular facet of tubercle of rib		6	放線状肋骨頭靱帯 Radiate ligament of head of rib	
3	関節腔（肋骨頭関節の） Articular cavity		7	上肋横突靱帯 Superior costotransverse ligament	
4	上肋横突靱帯の前部と後部の間に挿入したマーカー				

関節を外してある．右側方から．

胸壁の帯状疱疹

大動脈と周囲の血管

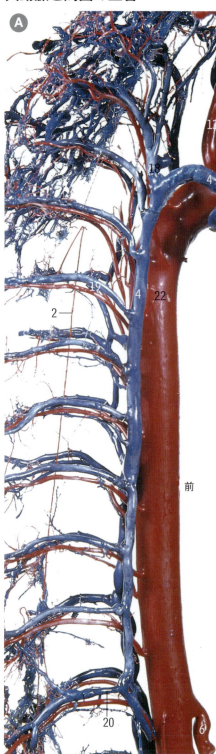

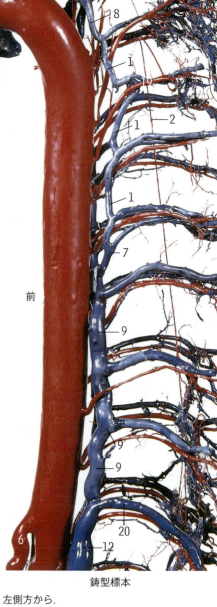

動脈系に赤色の樹脂を，静脈系に青色の樹脂を注入してある．Aは右側方から見たところで，奇静脈(4)は右の最上肋間静脈(18)，ならびにその他の肋間静脈(19)を受け入れ，上大静脈(21)に流入している．Bは左側方から見たところで，左の最上肋間静脈(14)が大動脈弓(3)の上部と交叉して左腕頭静脈(10)に流入している．半奇静脈(9)は副半奇静脈(1)と交通している．A，Bいずれにおいても，多くの肋間動脈が胸大動脈(22)から起始しているところが見られる．

1	副半奇静脈	Accessory hemi-azygos vein
2	前脊髄動脈	Anterior spinal artery
3	大動脈弓	Arch of aorta：Aortic arch
4	奇静脈	Azygos vein
5	腕頭動脈	Brachiocephalic trunk
6	腹腔動脈	Celiac trunk
7	1と9の交通枝	
8	14と1の交通枝	
9	半奇静脈	Hemi-azygos vein
10	左腕頭静脈	Left brachiocephalic vein
11	（左の）総頸動脈	Common carotid artery
12	（左の）上行腰静脈	Ascending lumbar vein
13	（左の）鎖骨下動脈	Subclavian artery
14	（左の）最上肋間静脈	Supreme intercostal vein
15	（左の）椎骨静脈	Vertebral vein
16	右腕頭静脈	Right brachiocephalic vein
17	（右の）鎖骨下静脈	Subclavian vein
18	（右の）最上肋間静脈	Right supreme intercostal vein
19	第六肋間動／静脈	6th posterior intercostal artery/vein
20	肋下動／静脈	Subcostal artery/vein
21	上大静脈	Superior vena cava
22	胸大動脈	Thoracic aorta

鋳型標本　右側方から．

鋳型標本　左側方から．

大動脈解離

大きな動脈の変異

横隔膜

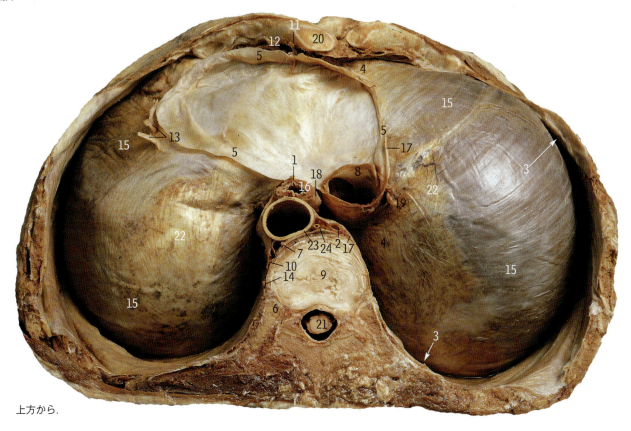

上方から.

胸部を第九・第十胸椎間の椎間円板の高さで横断してある.

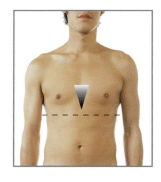

1	前迷走神経幹 Anterior vagal trunk	13	（左の）横隔神経 Phrenic nerve
2	奇静脈 Azygos vein	14	交感神経幹 Sympathetic trunk
3	肋骨横隔洞 Costodiaphragmatic recess	15	横隔膜（筋性部） Diaphragm
4	肋骨縦隔洞 Costomediastinal recess	16	食道 Esophagus
5	線維性心膜（切断縁） Fibrous pericardium	17	胸膜（切断縁） Pleura
6	第九肋骨頭 Head of 9th rib	18	（後）食道神経叢 Esophageal plexus
7	半奇静脈 Hemi-azygos vein	19	（右の）横隔神経 Phrenic nerve
8	下大静脈 Inferior vena cava	20	第七肋軟骨 7th costal cartilage
9	椎間円板 Intervertebral disc	21	脊髄 Spinal cord
10	大内臓神経 Greater splanchnic nerve	22	腱中心〔横隔膜〕 Central tendon〔Diaphragm〕
11	内胸動脈 Internal thoracic artery	23	胸大動脈 Thoracic aorta
12	筋横隔動脈 Musculophrenic artery	24	胸管 Thoracic duct

- 標準的な教科書の記載によると，大静脈孔は第八・第九胸椎間の椎間円板の高さにあり，食道裂孔は第十胸椎の高さにあり，大動脈裂孔は第十二胸椎の高さに位置する．しかし本例のように，食道(16)が正中にかなり近接し，下大静脈(8)が通る大静脈孔が通常よりも低くなっていることも，しばしば見られる．
- 大静脈孔は横隔膜の腱性部にあり，食道裂孔は筋性部を貫く．大動脈裂孔は横隔膜の内部ではなく後方に位置する．
- 横隔膜の腱中心は，三つ葉形であり，骨には付着していない．
- 右の横隔神経(19)は腱性部の大静脈孔を通過する．しかし，左の横隔神経(13)は心膜に覆われた部分のすぐ外側で，腱中心の前の筋性部を貫く．
- 横隔神経は，左右の脚を含む横隔膜を支配する唯一の運動神経である．横隔膜に分布する下位の胸神経（肋間神経と肋下神経）は純粋に感覚神経である．左右の横隔神経の一方が傷害されると，傷害された側の横隔膜が完全に麻痺する．

横隔膜ヘルニア　　胃食道逆流

Ⓐ～Ⓒ 食道 [Ⓐ 下咽頭と上部食道，Ⓑ 中部食道，Ⓒ 食道の下端]

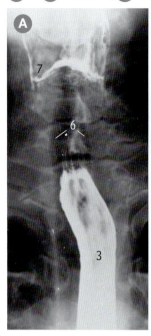 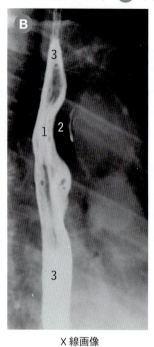 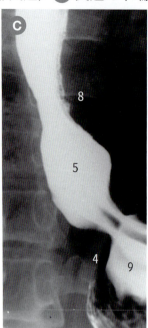

1	大動脈弓による圧痕
2	大動脈弓 Arch of aorta：Aortic arch
3	食道（バリウムで満たされている） Esophagus
4	横隔膜 Diaphragm
5	食道（胸部下部） Esophagus
6	気管（内腔の辺縁．空気を含むため透亮像として見える） Trachea
7	梨状陥凹（咽頭の喉頭部にある） Piriform fossa：Piriform recess
8	左心房の位置
9	胃 Stomach

X線画像

バリウムを嚥下させながら撮影している．

Aは前方から見たところであるが，少量のバリウム（造影剤）が咽頭壁に付着し，梨状陥凹(7)の輪郭がわかる．しかし，大部分のバリウムは咽頭を通過して食道(3)へ達する．Bは左斜方から見たところであり，食道が大動脈弓(2)によって圧排されているのがわかる．大動脈弓の壁には多少の石灰化が認められ，これが大動脈弓の識別に役立つ．Cでは，食道(5)の胸部下部がやや拡張しており，横隔膜(4)を通過して胃(9)に合する箇所にくびれが認められる．食道の胸部下部(222頁A8)の前に左心房(8)があり，肥大した時には食道を圧排する．

Ⓓ Ⓔ 食道 [Ⓓ 頸部食道，Ⓔ 胸部食道]

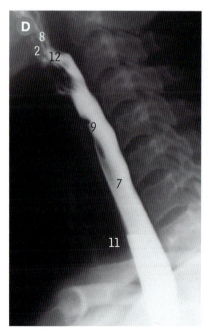 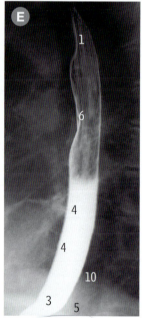

1	大動脈弓による圧痕
2	舌根 Root of tongue
3	食道胃接合部
4	左心房の位置
5	（左半の）横隔膜 Diaphragm
6	左気管支による圧痕
7	食道 Esophagus
8	［咽頭］口部 Oropharynx
9	輪状軟骨後方の静脈叢による圧痕
10	（右半の）横隔膜 Diaphragm
11	気管 Trachea
12	喉頭蓋谷 Epiglottic vallecula

X線画像

バリウムを嚥下させながら撮影している．

腹部と骨盤

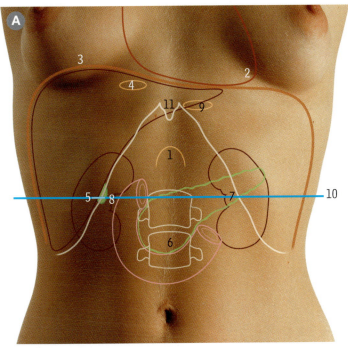

臍より上方．

A 前腹壁［体表解剖］

白色の線は肋骨弓を，青線は幽門（を通る）平面（10）を示している．C字状の十二指腸をピンク線，腎臓と肝臓を茶線，膵臓を黄緑線で示している．

1 大動脈裂孔〔横隔膜〕
  Aortic hiatus〔Diaphragm〕
2 心尖（左の第五肋間隙に位置する）
  Apex of heart
3 横隔膜による円蓋および肝臓の上縁
4 大静脈孔〔横隔膜〕
  Caval opening〔Diaphragm〕
5 胆嚢底（第九肋軟骨と腹直筋鞘外側縁との交点）
  Fundus of gallbladder
6 膵頭（第二腰椎の高さ）
  Head of pancreas
7 （左の）腎門
  Hilum of kidney
8 （右の）腎門
  Hilum of kidney
9 食道裂孔〔横隔膜〕
  Esophageal hiatus〔Diaphragm〕
10 幽門平面
  Transpyloric plane
11 剣状突起
  Xiphoid process

● 幽門平面（幽門を通る横断面，10）は，胸骨の頸切痕と恥骨結合の上縁の中点，すなわち胸骨剣結合のおおよそ1手幅ほど下方にある．これは第一腰椎の椎体の下部の高さに相当する．

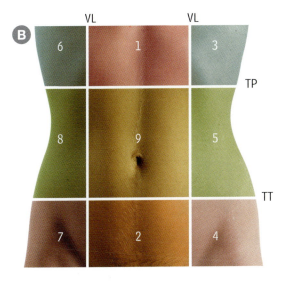

B 腹部の部位

腹部は2本の垂線と2本の水平線によって区分される．垂線（VL）は左右の鼠径中点を通る．上の水平線は幽門平面（TP，A10）に相当し，下の水平線は腸骨稜の腸骨結節間に引かれる線である（結節横断平面，TT）．

1 上胃部　Epigastric region
2 恥骨上部；下腹部　Suprapubic region；Hypogastrium
3 （左の）下肋部　Hypochondrium
4 （左の）鼠径部　Groin：Inguinal region
5 （左の）側腹部　Flank：Lateral region
6 （右の）下肋部　Hypochondrium
7 （右の）鼠径部　Groin：Inguinal region
8 （右の）側腹部　Flank：Lateral region
9 臍部　Umbilical region

腹壁の水痘・帯状疱疹ウイルス感染症

A 前腹壁

1 腹前皮枝〔第八肋間神経〕
  Anterior abdominal cutaneous branch〔8th intercostal nerve〕
2 腹前皮枝〔第十肋間神経〕
  Anterior abdominal cutaneous branch〔10th intercostal nerve〕
3 腱膜の前葉〔内腹斜筋〕
  Anterior layer of aponeurosis〔Internal oblique〕
4 腱膜〔外腹斜筋〕
  Aponeurosis〔External oblique〕
5 外腹斜筋
  External oblique
6 腸骨鼠径神経
  Ilio-inguinal nerve
7 腸脛靱帯
  Iliotibial tract
8 白線
  Linea alba
9 半月線
  Linea semilunaris
10 恥丘
  Mons pubis
11 腹部〔大胸筋〕
  Abdominal part〔Pectoralis major〕
12 腱膜の後葉〔内腹斜筋〕
  Posterior layer of aponeurosis〔Internal oblique〕
13 錐体筋
  Pyramidalis
14 腹直筋
  Rectus abdominis
15 前葉〔腹直筋鞘〕
  Anterior layer〔Rectus sheath〕
16 子宮円索
  Round ligament of uterus
17 前鋸筋
  Serratus anterior
18 浅鼠径リンパ節〔水平群〕
  Superficial inguinal nodes
19 浅鼠径リンパ節〔垂直群〕
  Superficial inguinal nodes
20 浅鼠径輪
  Superficial inguinal ring
21 浅鼠径静脈＊
  Superficial inguinal veins＊
22 腱画〔腹直筋〕
  Tendinous intersection〔Rectus abdominis〕
23 臍
  Umbilicus

● 内腹斜筋の腱膜（A3）は，腹直筋外側縁の半月線（A9）で2葉に分かれて，腹直筋鞘（A15）を形成する．腱膜の後葉（A12）は，腹直筋の後面で腹横筋（B19）の腱膜と癒合して腹直筋鞘の後葉（B13）をつくる．腱膜の前葉（A3）は，腹直筋の前面を通り外腹斜筋の腱膜（A4）と癒合して腹直筋鞘の前葉（A15）をつくる．
● 腹直筋鞘の前葉と後葉は，腹直筋の内側縁で合し，正中線に白線をつくる（A8，B11）．

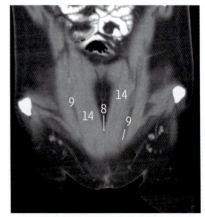

前腹壁のCT冠状断画像

腹直筋鞘の血腫

半月状線ヘルニア

B 腹直筋鞘

1	腹前皮枝〔第十肋間神経〕 Anterior abdominal cutaneous branch〔10th intercostal nerve〕
2	腱膜の前葉〔内腹斜筋〕 Anterior layer of aponeurosis〔Internal oblique〕
3	前葉〔腹直筋鞘〕 Anterior layer〔Rectus sheath〕
4	第八肋骨 8th rib：Rib VIII
5	腱膜〔外腹斜筋〕 Aponeurosis〔External oblique〕
6	外腹斜筋 External oblique
7	腸骨鼠径神経 Ilio-inguinal nerve
8	下腹壁動／静脈 Inferior epigastric artery/vein
9	腱膜〔内腹斜筋〕 Aponeurosis〔Internal oblique〕
10	内腹斜筋 Internal oblique
11	白線 Linea alba
12	恥丘 Mons pubis
13	後葉〔腹直筋鞘〕 Posterior layer〔Rectus sheath〕
14	腹直筋 Rectus abdominis
15	腹直筋（内側に翻転してある） Rectus abdominis
16	子宮円索 Round ligament of uterus
17	浅鼠径リンパ節 Superficial inguinal nodes
18	腱画 Tendinous intersection
19	腹横筋 Transversus abdominis
20	臍 Umbilicus

● 弓状線（232頁A1）より下方である腹直筋の下1/3には，腹直筋鞘の後葉はない．

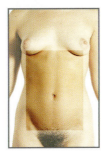

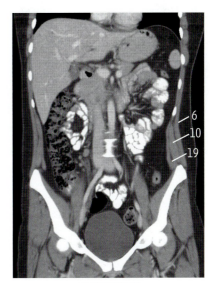

CT 冠状断画像

Cushing 病の皮膚線条

男性の鼠径部

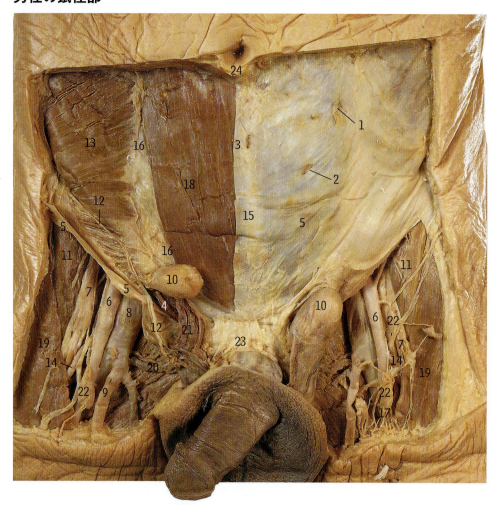

#	日本語	English
1	腹前皮枝〔第十一肋間神経〕	Anterior abdominal cutaneous branch〔11th intercostal nerve〕
2	腹前皮枝〔肋下神経〕	Anterior abdominal cutaneous branch〔Subcostal nerve〕
3	前葉〔腹直筋鞘〕（切断縁）	Anterior layer〔Rectus sheath〕
4	精管	Ductus deferens
5	腱膜〔外腹斜筋〕	Aponeurosis〔External oblique〕
6	大腿動脈	Femoral artery
7	大腿神経	Femoral nerve
8	大腿静脈	Femoral vein
9	大伏在静脈	Great saphenous vein：Long saphenous vein
10	ヘルニア嚢（間接鼠径ヘルニア）	
11	腸骨筋	Iliacus
12	腸骨鼠径神経	Ilio-inguinal nerve
13	内腹斜筋	Internal oblique
14	外側大腿回旋動脈	Lateral circumflex femoral artery
15	白線	Linea alba
16	半月線	Linea semilunaris
17	リンパ管	Lymphatic vessels
18	腹直筋	Rectus abdominis
19	縫工筋	Sartorius
20	外陰部静脈	External pudendal veins
21	精索	Spermatic cord
22	浅鼠径リンパ節	Superficial inguinal nodes
23	陰茎提靱帯	Suspensory ligament of penis
24	臍	Umbilicus

● この標本で示したヘルニア嚢(10)は，正常では見られない．

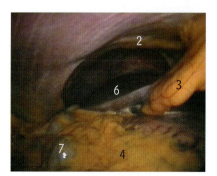

腹腔上部の腹腔鏡写真

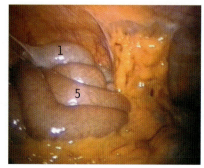

腹腔下部の腹腔鏡写真

#	日本語	English
1	盲腸	Cecum
2	横隔膜	Diaphragm
3	〔肝〕鎌状間膜	Falciform ligament
4	大網	Greater omentum
5	回腸	Ileum
6	（肝臓の）右葉	Right lobe of liver
7	横行結腸	Transverse colon

鼠径ヘルニアの修復術

腹壁の水痘・帯状疱疹ウイルス感染症

成人男性の前腹壁［体表解剖．腸骨窩（右）］

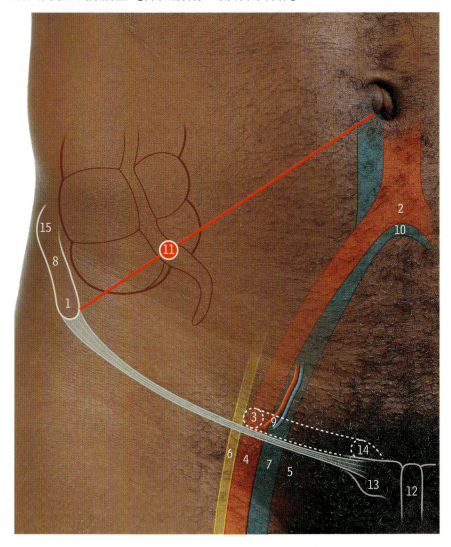

1	上前腸骨棘	Anterior superior iliac spine
2	大動脈分岐部（第四腰椎の高さ）	Aortic bifurcation
3	深鼠径輪	Deep inguinal ring
4	大腿動脈	Femoral artery
5	大腿管	Femoral canal
6	大腿神経	Femoral nerve
7	大腿静脈	Femoral vein
8	腸骨稜	Iliac crest
9	下腹壁動／静脈	Inferior epigastric artery/vein
10	下大静脈（下端，第五腰椎の高さ）	Inferior vena cava
11	McBurney 点*	McBurney's point*
12	恥骨結合	Pubic symphysis
13	恥骨結節	Pubic tubercle
14	浅鼠径輪	Superficial inguinal ring
15	腸骨結節	Tuberculum of iliac crest

● 大腿動脈（4．通常では拍動を触知できる）は，恥骨結合（12）と上前腸骨棘（1）の中点を通って大腿に入る．この点を鼠径中点とよぶこともある．

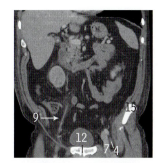

腹部の CT 冠状断画像

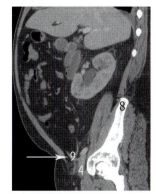

腹部の CT 矢状断画像
（矢印は下腹壁動脈を示す．）

虫垂の開口が左側にある盲腸と，ここから上方に続く上行結腸を，茶線で示してある．上前腸骨棘（1）と恥骨結節（13）の間に張る鼠径靱帯を薄青線で示してある．
大腿動脈（4）の内側を大腿静脈（7）が通り，外側を大腿神経（6）が走る．大腿管（5）は，大腿静脈の内側にある．深鼠径輪（3）と下腹壁動静脈（9）は，大腿動脈より上方にあり，浅鼠径輪（14）は恥骨結節（13）より上内側に位置する．McBurney点（11）は，前腹壁の体表点で，内部にある虫垂基部の位置を示している．この点は，右の上前腸骨棘から臍を結ぶ赤線上の 1/3 のところにある．

大腿ヘルニア

McBurney 点

A 成人の前腹壁［臍ヒダ］

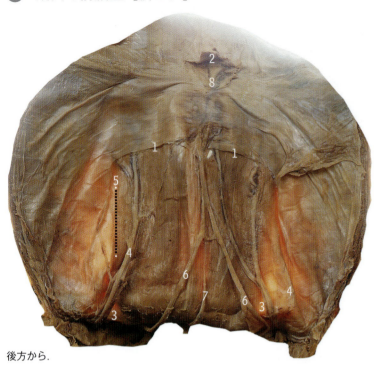

後方から．

前腹壁中央部の腹膜に覆われた後面には，その下層にある索状物によって浮き上がった腹膜ヒダが見える．臍より上方には，肝鎌状間膜(2)というヒダがある．臍より下方には，5つのヒダ，すなわち正中線に正中臍ヒダ(正中臍索(7)を含む)，左右に1対の内側臍ヒダ(内側臍索(6)を含む)と外側臍ヒダ(4)がある．

1	弓状線	Arcuate line
2	［肝］鎌状間膜	Falciform ligament
3	鼠径三角：Hesselbach 三角*	Inguinal triangle：Hesselbach's triangle*
4	外側臍ヒダ(下腹壁動／静脈を含む)	Lateral umbilical fold：Epigastric fold
5	半月線(黒点線)	Linea semilunaris
6	臍動脈索：内側臍索*	Cord of umbilical artery：Medial umbilical ligament*
7	正中臍索	Median umbilical ligament
8	臍	Umbilicus

● 鼠径三角(Hesselbach 三角)は，腹直筋と下腹壁動静脈の間にある，生まれつき腹圧に対する抵抗に弱い領域である．直接鼠径ヘルニアはこの領域に現れる．

B 胎児の前腹壁

後方から．

この胎児においては，腹膜と腹膜下組織を前腹壁から除去し，臍（番号は付けられていない）の後ろに収束している臍動脈(13)と臍静脈(7)が見えている．

1	深鼠径輪 Deep inguinal ring		8	腹直筋 Rectus abdominis
2	横隔膜 Diaphragm		9	後葉〔腹直筋鞘〕 Posterior layer (Rectus sheath)
3	外腹斜筋 External oblique		10	精巣（下降していない） Testis
4	［肝］鎌状間膜 Falciform ligament		11	腹横筋 Transversus abdominis
5	下腹壁動／静脈 Inferior epigastric artery/vein		12	尿膜管 Urachus
6	内腹斜筋 Internal oblique		13	臍動脈 Umbilical artery
7	臍静脈 Umbilical vein		14	膀胱 Urinary bladder

メデューサの頭

臍ヘルニア

出生後臍静脈カテーテル

臍ヘルニアと傍臍ヘルニア

A 成人男性の深鼠径輪

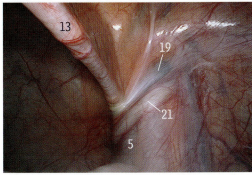

深鼠径輪（右）の腹腔鏡写真

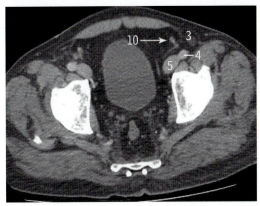

深鼠径輪（左）を通る CT 横断画像

B 前腹壁

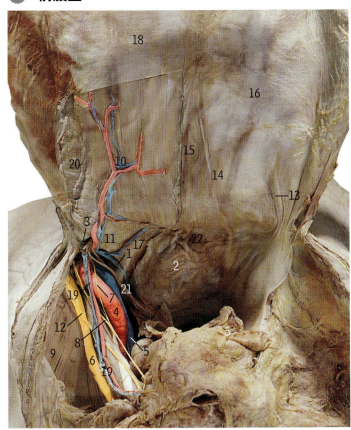

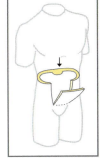

腹腔面.

腹部内臓を除去し，前腹壁を切り出して前下方へ翻転したため，腹壁の腹腔面が見える．左側では壁側腹膜を除去し，骨盤壁と腹壁の深部の構造を見せている．

1	副閉鎖動脈	Accessory obturator artery
2	膀胱	Urinary bladder
3	深鼠径輪	Deep inguinal ring
4	外腸骨動脈	External iliac artery
5	外腸骨静脈	External iliac vein
6	大腿神経	Femoral nerve
7	大腿枝〔陰部大腿神経〕	Femoral branch〔Genitofemoral nerve〕
8	陰部枝〔陰部大腿神経〕	Genital branch〔Genitofemoral nerve〕
9	腸骨筋	Iliacus
10	下腹壁動／静脈	Inferior epigastric artery/vein
11	鼠径三角：Hesselbach 三角*	Inguinal triangle：Hesselbach's triangle*
12	外側大腿皮神経	Lateral femoral cutaneous nerve
13	外側臍ヒダ（下腹壁動／静脈を包む）	Lateral umbilical fold：Epigastric fold
14	内側臍ヒダ（臍動脈索を包む）	Medial umbilical fold
15	正中臍ヒダ（尿膜管の遺残物を覆う）	Median umbilical fold
16	壁側腹膜	Parietal peritoneum
17	骨盤縁*	Pelvic brim*
18	後葉〔腹直筋鞘〕	Posterior layer (Rectus sheath)
19	精巣動／静脈	Testicular artery/vein
20	腹横筋	Transversus abdominis
21	精管	Ductus deferens
22	臓側腹膜（膀胱の上面）	Visceral peritoneum

鼠径ヘルニア

間接鼠径ヘルニア

右鼠径部（男性）［浅層］

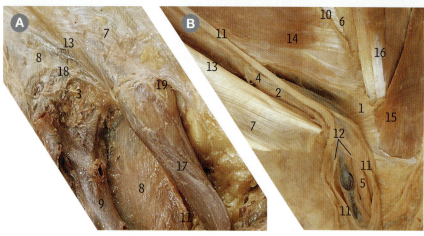

Aでは，精索(17)が浅鼠径輪(19)から現れており，外精筋膜に覆われている．Bでは，外腹斜筋の腱膜を翻転し，腹直筋鞘の前葉を除去してある．精索が深鼠径輪(4)から現れており，精巣挙筋膜(2)が一番浅層にある．精索を覆う3層の膜を切開し(12)，精管(5)が見えるようにしている．

B：外腹斜筋の腱膜は残し，精索は切開してある．

1	結合腱：鼠径鎌 Conjoint tendon：Inguinal falx	11	腸骨鼠径神経 Ilio-inguinal nerve
2	精巣挙筋膜と精巣挙筋（精索を覆う） Cremasteric fascia and Cremaster	12	精索の被膜の切開縁
3	篩状筋膜 Cribriform fascia	13	鼠径靱帯 Inguinal ligament
4	深鼠径輪 Deep inguinal ring	14	内腹斜筋 Internal oblique
5	精管 Ductus deferens	15	錐体筋 Pyramidalis
6	腹直筋鞘の切断縁	16	腹直筋 Rectus abdominis
7	腱膜〔外腹斜筋〕 Aponeurosis〔External oblique〕	17	精索 Spermatic cord
8	大腿筋膜 Fascia lata	18	伏在裂孔(の上縁) Saphenous opening
9	大伏在静脈 Great saphenous vein：Long saphenous vein	19	浅鼠径輪(の上縁) Superficial inguinal ring
10	腸骨下腹神経 Iliohypogastric nerve		

右鼠径部（女性）

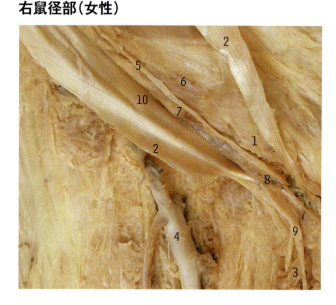

外腹斜筋の腱膜(2)を切開して翻転し，鼠径管の外側縁となる深鼠径輪(7)を明らかにしている．子宮円索(9)は，鼠径管の内側縁となる浅鼠径輪(8)から現れ，大陰唇(3)の脂肪の中に消える．腸骨鼠径神経(5)も鼠径管を通過して浅鼠径輪から出る．

1	結合腱：鼠径鎌 Conjoint tendon：Inguinal falx
2	腱膜〔外腹斜筋〕 Aponeurosis〔External oblique〕
3	大陰唇（の脂肪） Labium majus
4	大伏在静脈 Great saphenous vein：Long saphenous vein
5	腸骨鼠径神経 Ilio-inguinal nerve
6	内腹斜筋 Internal oblique
7	深鼠径輪（の位置） Deep inguinal ring
8	浅鼠径輪（の位置） Superficial inguinal ring
9	子宮円索 Round ligament of uterus
10	鼠径靱帯（の上面） Inguinal ligament

- 女性では，鼠径管は，子宮円索と腸骨鼠径神経が通過する．
- 鞘状突起は通常閉塞する．しかし，女性の鼠径管において残存していた場合はNuck管とよばれる．

A 右の深鼠径輪と鼠径三角

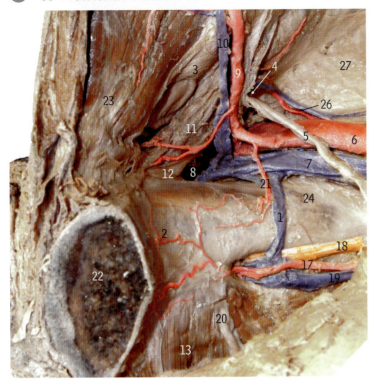

内面から．

骨盤の右半を左側方から見たところで，恥骨結合の上方に前腹壁の下部の後面が見えている．大腿管の開口である大腿輪(8)が，鼠径靱帯(11)の内側端の下方にある．下腹壁動静脈(9, 10)が，深鼠径輪(4)の内側に位置する．

- 鼠径三角(Hesselbach三角)は，外側は下腹壁動静脈，内側は腹直筋の外側縁，下方は鼠径靱帯によって囲まれる領域である．直接鼠径ヘルニアは下腹壁動静脈の内側で，この三角を前方に通り抜ける．
- 間接鼠径ヘルニアは下腹壁動静脈の外側で，深鼠径輪を通り抜ける．

1	閉鎖静脈(変異) Obturator vein	15	臍動脈索：内側臍索＊ Cord of umbilical artery：Medial umbilical ligament＊
2	恥骨体 Body of pubis	16	正中臍ヒダ Median umbilical fold
3	結合腱：鼠径鎌 Conjoint tendon：Inguinal falx	17	閉鎖動脈 Obturator artery
4	深鼠径輪 Deep inguinal ring	18	閉鎖神経 Obturator nerve
5	精管 Ductus deferens	19	閉鎖静脈 Obturator vein
6	外腸骨動脈 External iliac artery	20	内閉鎖筋を覆っている筋膜からの肛門挙筋の起始
7	外腸骨静脈 External iliac vein	21	恥骨枝〔下腹壁動脈〕 Pubic branch (Inferior epigastric artery)
8	大腿輪 Femoral ring	22	恥骨体(切断してある) Body of pubis
9	下腹壁動脈 Inferior epigastric artery	23	腹直筋 Rectus abdominis
10	下腹壁静脈 Inferior epigastric vein	24	恥骨上枝 Superior pubic ramus
11	鼠径靱帯 Inguinal ligament	25	膀胱(上面を腹膜が覆っている) Urinary bladder
12	裂孔靱帯 Lacunar ligament	26	精巣動／静脈 Testicular artery/vein
13	肛門挙筋 Levator ani	27	横筋筋膜(腹横筋を覆う) Transversalis fascia
14	内側臍ヒダ Medial umbilical fold		

B 男性の左の深鼠径輪

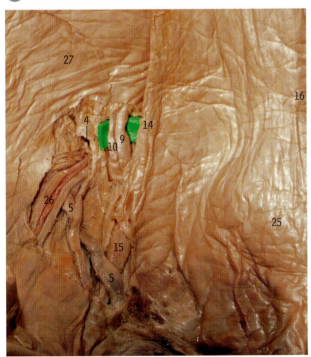

腹腔内から(腹腔鏡で観察するように見る)．

腹膜のヒダ

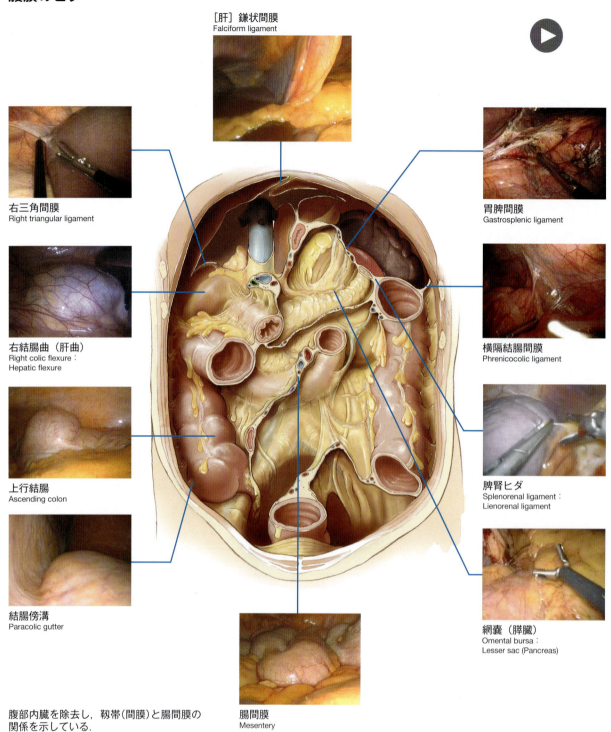

[肝]鎌状間膜
Falciform ligament

右三角間膜
Right triangular ligament

右結腸曲（肝曲）
Right colic flexure：
Hepatic flexure

上行結腸
Ascending colon

結腸傍溝
Paracolic gutter

胃脾間膜
Gastrosplenic ligament

横隔結腸間膜
Phrenicocolic ligament

脾腎ヒダ
Splenorenal ligament：
Lienorenal ligament

網嚢（膵臓）
Omental bursa：
Lesser sac (Pancreas)

腸間膜
Mesentery

腹部内臓を除去し，靱帯（間膜）と腸間膜の関係を示している．

横隔膜下膿瘍の排液

腹腔洗浄

腹膜炎

Ⓐ~Ⓒ 腹部の内臓

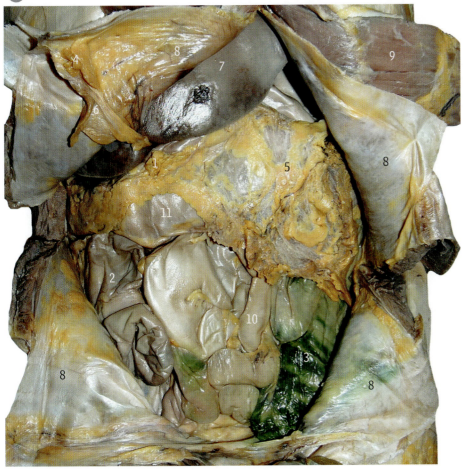

1	腹膜垂 Omental appendices：Fatty appendices of colon	
2	上行結腸 Ascending colon	
3	下行結腸 Descending colon	
4	［肝］鎌状間膜 Falciform ligament	
5	大網 Greater omentum	
6	肝円索 Round ligament of liver	
7	肝臓 Liver	
8	壁側腹膜（前腹壁の） Parietal peritoneum	
9	腹直筋（外側に牽引している） Rectus abdominis	
10	小腸 Small intestine	
11	横行結腸 Transverse colon	

前方から．腹壁を広げたところ．

● 腹膜，靱帯（間膜），ヒダの解説は236，243頁の模型図を参照．

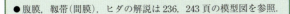

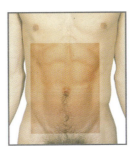

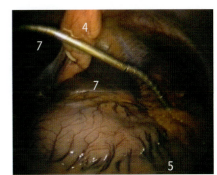

腹腔上部の腹腔鏡写真

肝生検

全内臓逆位

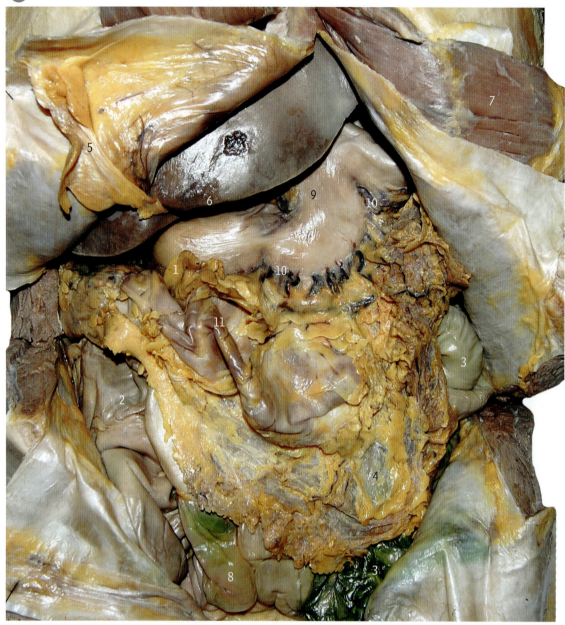

前方から．胃を下方に引き出したところ．

1	腹膜垂 Omental appendices：Fatty appendices of colon	7	腹直筋（外側に牽引している） Rectus abdominis
2	上行結腸 Ascending colon	8	小腸 Small intestine
3	下行結腸 Descending colon	9	胃 Stomach
4	大網 Greater omentum	10	大弯〔胃〕 Greater curvature〔Stomach〕
5	肝円索（肝鎌状間膜内部に含まれる） Round ligament of liver	11	横行結腸 Transverse colon
6	（肝臓の）左葉 Left lobe of liver		

胆嚢切除術

第5章 腹部と骨盤：上腹部　239

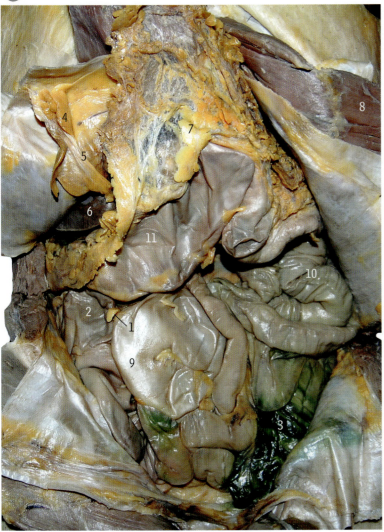

1	腹膜垂 Omental appendices：Fatty appendices of colon
2	上行結腸 Ascending colon
3	下行結腸 Descending colon
4	［肝］鎌状間膜 Falciform ligament
5	肝円索 Round ligament of liver
6	（肝臓の）右葉 Right lobe of liver
7	大網（の後面） Greater omentum
8	腹直筋（外側に牽引している） Rectus abdominis
9	回腸〔小腸〕 Ileum〔Small intestine〕
10	空腸〔小腸〕 Jejunum〔Small intestine〕
11	横行結腸 Transverse colon

前方から．大網を上方に翻転したところ．

● 腹膜垂(1)は，結腸の各部（上行，横行，下行，S状結腸）に見られる脂肪のつまった腹膜の小突起である．腹膜垂は，小腸と直腸にはなく，盲腸と虫垂では痕跡的であることから，腹部手術の際に結腸と他の腸管を区別する目安の1つになる．

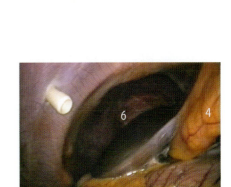

腹部内臓の腹腔鏡写真

大網ケーキ
（大網播種）

A B 小網と網嚢孔

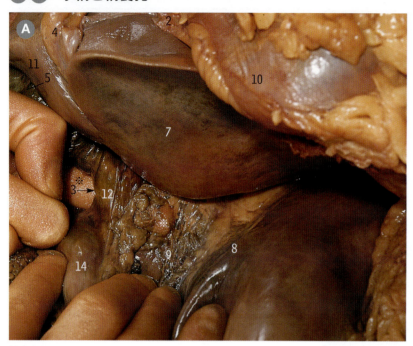

前方から．

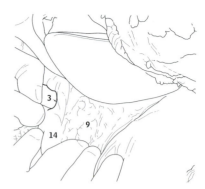

1	下行部〔十二指腸〕 Descending part（Duodenum）	8	小弯〔胃〕 Lesser curvature（Stomach）
2	横隔膜 Diaphragm	9	小網 Lesser omentum
3	網嚢孔：Winslow 孔* Omental foramen：Epiploic foramen：Foramen of Winslow*	10	心膜 Pericardium
4	〔肝〕鎌状間膜 Falciform ligament	11	方形葉〔肝臓〕 Quadrate lobe（Liver）
5	胆嚢 Gallbladder	12	小網（右の自由縁） Lesser omentum
6	下大静脈 Inferior vena cava	13	（肝臓の）右葉 Right lobe of liver
7	（肝臓の）左葉 Left lobe of liver	14	上部〔十二指腸〕 Superior part（Duodenum）
		15	（右の）上端〔腎臓〕 Superior pole：Superior extremity（Kidney）

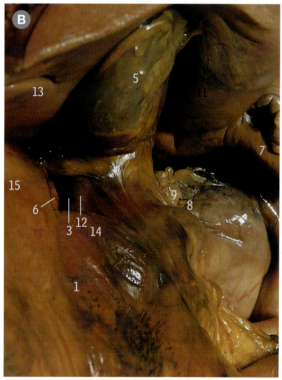

右前方から．

Aでは，小網の右の自由縁（12）の後ろにある網嚢孔（3）に示指※を挿入してある．透明な小網（9）を通して，網嚢内に挿入した指先※が見えている．小網は，肝臓（7）と胃の小弯（8）の間に張っている．Bはより右外側方から見たところであり，網嚢孔を右から眺めている．網嚢孔（3）は，前方にある小網の右の自由縁（12）と後方にある下大静脈（6）の間で，十二指腸上部（14）に見られる．

● 網嚢孔またはWinslow 孔（3）は，腹膜腔（大嚢*，greater sac*とよばれることがある）と網嚢（小嚢*，lesser sac*）の連絡孔である．網嚢は，胃（8）と小網（9，12）の後ろにある腹膜で内張りされた空間であり，膵臓の一部と左腎の一部の前方に位置する．

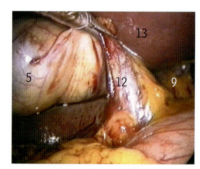

小網（自由縁）の腹腔鏡写真

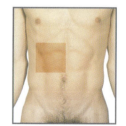

A 上腹部の内臓

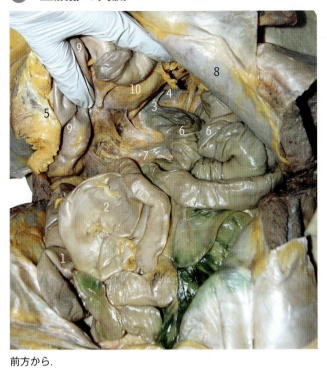

前方から．

胃，横行結腸(9)および大網(5)を上方へ牽引し，十二指腸空腸曲(3)の領域を示している．

1	上行結腸 Ascending colon	6	空腸 Jejunum
2	小腸（渦状になっている） Small intestine	7	腸間膜 Mesentery
3	十二指腸空腸曲 Duodenojejunal flexure	8	壁側腹膜（前腹壁を上方に翻転してある） Parietal peritoneum
4	上部〔十二指腸〕 Superior part〔Duodenum〕	9	横行結腸（上方に翻転してある） Transverse colon
5	大網 Greater omentum	10	横行結腸間膜 Transverse mesocolon

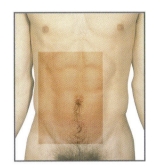

B 上腹部の網嚢

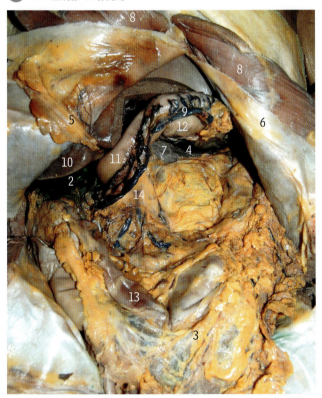

1	腹膜垂 Omental appendices：Fatty appendices of colon	8	腹直筋（翻転してある） Rectus abdominis
2	胆嚢 Gallbladder	9	［右・左］胃大網静脈 Right/Left gastro-omental veins：Right/Left gastro-epiploic veins
3	大網（下方に翻転してある） Greater omentum	10	（肝臓の）右葉 Right lobe of liver
4	網嚢 Omental bursa：Lesser sac	11	大弯〔胃〕 Greater curvature〔Stomach〕
5	肝円索（肝鎌状間膜内部に含まれる） Round ligament of liver	12	胃（の後面） Stomach
6	壁側腹膜（前腹壁の） Parietal peritoneum	13	横行結腸（下方に翻転してある） Transverse colon
7	腹膜（網嚢内で膵臓を覆う） Peritoneum	14	横行結腸間膜 Transverse mesocolon

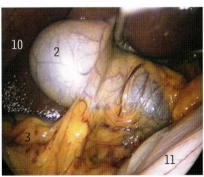

胆嚢の腹腔鏡写真

腹水

腹腔鏡

腸間膜と結腸

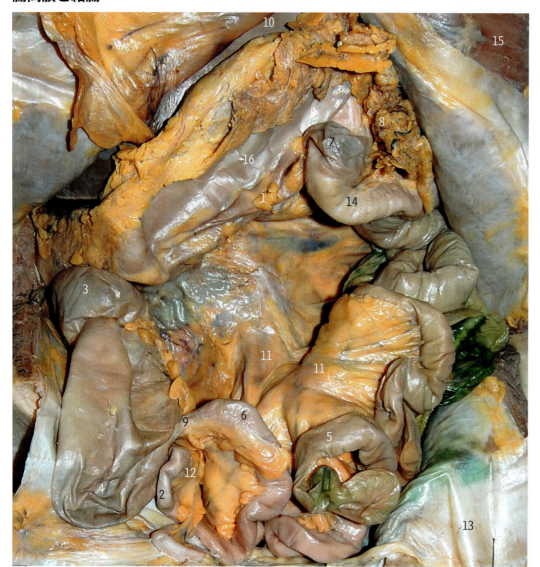

1	腹膜垂	Omental appendices：Fatty appendices of colon
2	虫垂	Appendix：Vermiform appendix
3	上行結腸	Ascending colon
4	盲腸	Cecum
5	小腸（渦状になっている）	Small intestine
6	回腸終末部	Terminal ileum
7	十二指腸と空腸の接合部	
8	大網	Greater omentum
9	回腸と盲腸の接合部	
10	肝臓	Liver
11	腸間膜（小腸）	Mesentery〔Small intestine〕
12	虫垂間膜	Meso-appendix
13	壁側腹膜（前腹壁の）	Parietal peritoneum
14	空腸（近位部）	Jejunum
15	腹直筋（翻転してある）	Rectus abdominis
16	横行結腸	Transverse colon

前方から．

憩室性疾患

腸捻転

第5章　腹部と骨盤：上腹部　243

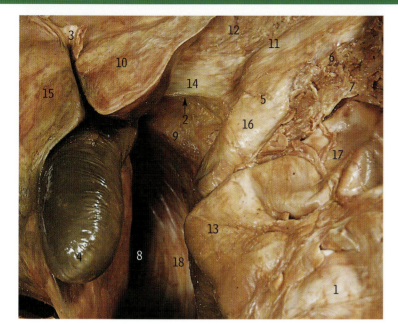

A 腹膜の肝腎陥凹

仰臥位にして，右から眺めている．肝臓(15)は上方(図の左方)へ牽引し，肝臓と右の腎臓の上端(18)間の隙間，すなわち腹膜陥凹の1つである肝腎陥凹(Morison窩，腹膜腔の右肝下腔)を露出した．

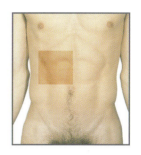

右下方から．

1 上行結腸 Ascending colon	7 大網 Greater omentum	13 右結腸曲：肝曲* Right colic flexure：Hepatic flexure
2 網嚢孔 Omental foramen：Epiploic foramen：Foramen of Winslow*	8 肝腎陥凹：Morison窩* Hepatorenal recess：Morrison's pouch*	14 小網(右の自由縁) Lesser omentum
3 〔肝〕鎌状間膜 Falciform ligament	9 下大静脈 Inferior vena cava	15 (肝臓の)右葉 Right lobe of liver
4 胆嚢 Gallbladder	10 (肝臓の)左葉 Left lobe of liver	16 上部〔十二指腸〕 Superior part〔Duodenum〕
5 胃と十二指腸の接合部	11 小弯〔胃〕 Lesser curvature〔Stomach〕	17 横行結腸 Transverse colon
6 大弯〔胃〕 Greater curvature〔Stomach〕	12 小網(膵臓の前方に位置する) Lesser omentum	18 上端〔(右の)腎臓〕 Superior pole：Superior extremity〔Kidney〕

腹膜の模型図（237〜242頁参照）

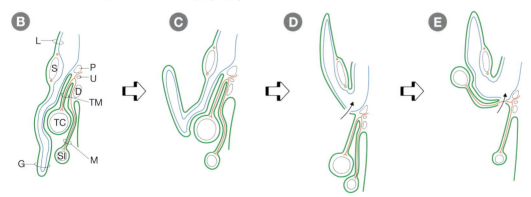

B：正常位．C：大網の下部を挙上した．D：大網を横行結腸間膜と横行結腸を分離して挙上し，網嚢を開いた．
E：大網と横行結腸間膜，横行結腸を挙上し，結腸間膜から網嚢を開いた．

腹部の中央部を通る矢状断面を左から見た模型図で，小網(L，胃(S)へ向かって下がる)，大網(G)，横行結腸(TC)に続く横行結腸間膜(TM)，ならびに小腸(SI)の腸間膜(M)が，どのように腹膜から形成されたかという過程を理論的に図示したものである．青色で示した漿膜は，腹膜のうち網嚢の内腔に面した漿膜である．上腸間膜動脈は膵頭(P)と鉤状突起(U)の間を通り抜け，十二指腸(D)をまたいで腸間膜(M)に入り，小腸(SI)に達する．この動脈から出た中結腸動脈は，横行結腸間膜(TM)内を走り，横行結腸(TC)に達する．大網(G)は4葉の腹膜でつくられているが，互いに癒合し，また2葉からなる横行結腸間膜(TM)と横行結腸の前面と癒合する．それらを解剖して分離しようとしても，大網と横行結腸間膜の間以外は分離できない．胃と横行結腸の間の6葉の腹膜をまとめて胃結腸間膜とよぶことがある．Bは237，238頁，Cは239頁，Dは241頁A，Eは241頁Bの各所見に相当する．DとEの矢印は，網嚢を開放するために切開した層を示している．

腹腔動脈

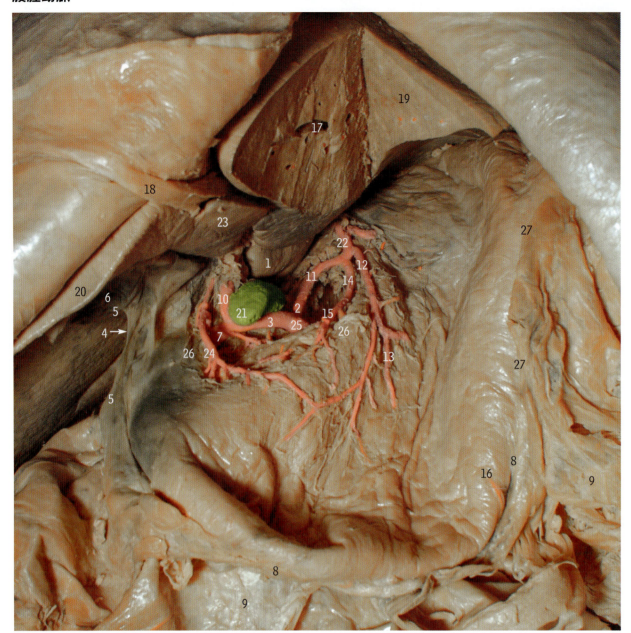

1	尾状葉〔肝臓〕	Caudate lobe〔Liver〕
2	腹腔動脈	Celiac trunk
3	総肝動脈	Common hepatic artery
4	網嚢孔（矢印）	Omental foramen；Epiploic foramen；Foramen of Winslow *
5	小網（自由縁）	Lesser omentum
6	胆嚢	Gallbladder
7	胃十二指腸動脈	Gastroduodenal artery
8	大弯〔胃〕	Greater curvature〔Stomach〕
9	大網	Greater omentum
10	固有肝動脈	Hepatic artery proper
11	左胃動脈	Left gastric artery
12	前枝*〔左胃動脈〕	Anterior branch *〔Left gastric artery〕
13	前枝*〔左胃動脈〕（胃体への枝）	Anterior branch *〔Left gastric artery〕
14	後枝*〔左胃動脈〕	Posterior branch *〔Left gastric artery〕
15	後枝*〔左胃動脈〕（小弯への枝）	Posterior branch *〔Left gastric artery〕
16	左胃大網動脈	Left gastro-omental artery；Left gastro-epiploic artery
17	左枝〔肝〕門脈	Left branch (Hepatic portal vein)
18	肝円索（肝鎌状間膜内部に含まれる）	Round ligament of liver
19	（肝臓の）左葉	Left lobe of liver
20	（肝臓の）右葉	Right lobe of liver
21	腹腔リンパ節（腫大している）	Celiac nodes
22	食道枝〔左胃動脈〕	Esophageal branch (Left gastric artery)
23	方形葉〔肝臓〕	Quadrate lobe〔Liver〕
24	幽門洞枝*〔右胃動脈〕	Antral branch *〔Right gastric artery〕
25	脾動脈	Splenic artery
26	小弯〔胃〕	Lesser curvature〔Stomach〕
27	臓側腹膜（切断縁）	Visceral peritoneum

腹部の血管の変異

胃癌

Ⓐ Ⓑ 上腸間膜動脈・静脈の根部

A：十二指腸と膵臓を原位置に留めてある．B：十二指腸を翻転して，後方における動脈と静脈の位置関係を明らかにしている．

1	大動脈	Aorta
2	十二指腸（翻転し，ピンで留めてある）	Duodenum
3	上行部〔十二指腸〕	Ascending part〔Duodenum〕
4	下行部〔十二指腸〕	Descending part〔Duodenum〕
5	水平部：横行部〔十二指腸〕	Horizontal part：Transverse part〔Duodenum〕
6	〔肝〕鎌状間膜	Falciform ligament
7	胆囊底	Fundus of gallbladder
8	下腸間膜動脈	Inferior mesenteric artery
9	下腸間膜静脈	Inferior mesenteric vein
10	下大静脈	Inferior vena cava
11	空腸（の起始部）	Jejunum
12	左精巣（卵巣）静脈	Left testicular（ovarian）vein
13	（左の）腎動脈	Renal artery
14	（左の）腎静脈	Renal vein
15	（肝臓の）左葉	Left lobe of liver
16	Riedel 葉*〔肝臓〕	Riedel's lobe*〔Liver〕
17	（肝臓の）右葉	Right lobe of liver
18	大動脈前リンパ節と大動脈傍リンパ節*（やや腫大している）	Pre-aortic nodes and Para-aortic nodes*
19	膵体	Body of pancreas
20	膵頭	Head of pancreas
21	膵尾	Tail of pancreas
22	鉤状突起〔膵臓〕	Uncinate process〔Pancreas〕
23	腎囊胞（良性）	
24	右精巣（卵巣）静脈	Right testicular（ovarian）vein
25	脾臓	Spleen
26	脾動脈	Splenic artery
27	脾静脈	Splenic vein
28	肋下神経	Subcostal nerve
29	上腸間膜動脈	Superior mesenteric artery
30	上腸間膜静脈	Superior mesenteric vein
31	尿管	Ureter

下大静脈閉塞症

膵臓の病変

膵炎

A B 腹腔動脈

胃を半切し，胃の背側にある肝臓，胆道系，膵臓，十二指腸，上腸間膜静脈を剖出してある．

A

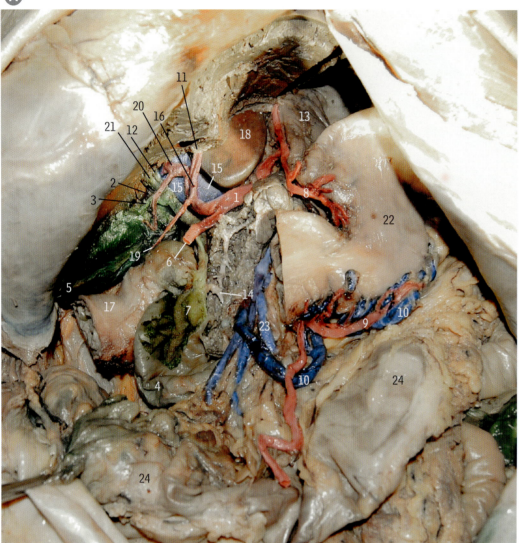

1 総肝動脈 Common hepatic artery	9 左胃大網動脈 Left gastro-omental artery：Left gastro-epiploic artery	17 幽門 Pylorus
2 胆嚢動脈 Cystic artery	10 左胃大網静脈 Left gastro-omental vein：Left gastro-epiploic vein	18 尾状葉〔肝臓〕 Caudate lobe〔Liver〕
3 胆嚢管 Cystic duct	11 左枝〔固有肝動脈〕 Left branch〔Hepatic artery proper〕	19 右胃動脈 Right gastric artery
4 十二指腸 Duodenum	12 左肝管 Left hepatic duct	20 右枝〔固有肝動脈〕 Right branch〔Hepatic artery proper〕
5 胆嚢 Gallbladder	13 食道 Esophagus	21 右肝管 Right hepatic duct
6 胃十二指腸動脈 Gastroduodenal artery	14 膵管 Pancreatic duct	22 胃 Stomach
7 胆膵管膨大部 Hepatopancreatic ampulla：Biliaropancreatic ampulla	15 〔肝〕門脈 Hepatic portal vein	23 上腸間膜静脈 Superior mesenteric vein
8 左胃動脈 Left gastric artery	16 固有肝動脈 Hepatic artery proper	24 横行結腸 Transverse colon

幽門狭窄症（成人）

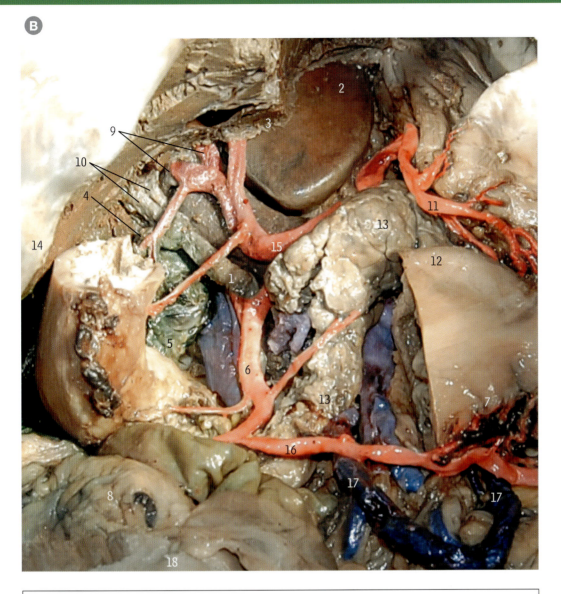

1	総胆管 Bile duct	10	左肝管と右肝管 Left hepatic duct and Right hepatic duct
2	尾状葉〔肝臓〕 Caudate lobe〔Liver〕	11	左胃動脈 Left gastric artery
3	肝臓（切断縁） Liver	12	小弯〔胃〕 Lesser curvature〔Stomach〕
4	胆嚢管 Cystic duct	13	膵臓 Pancreas
5	胆嚢底 Fundus of gallbladder	14	壁側腹膜（前腹壁を外側に翻転してある） Parietal peritoneum
6	胃十二指腸動脈 Gastroduodenal artery	15	固有肝動脈 Hepatic artery proper
7	大弯〔胃〕 Greater curvature〔Stomach〕	16	右胃大網動脈 Right gastro-omental artery：Right gastro-epiploic artery
8	大網 Greater omentum	17	右胃大網静脈 Right gastro-omental vein：Right gastro-epiploic vein
9	左枝と右枝〔固有肝動脈〕 Left branch and Right branch〔Hepatic artery proper〕	18	横行結腸 Transverse colon

上腸間膜動脈・静脈

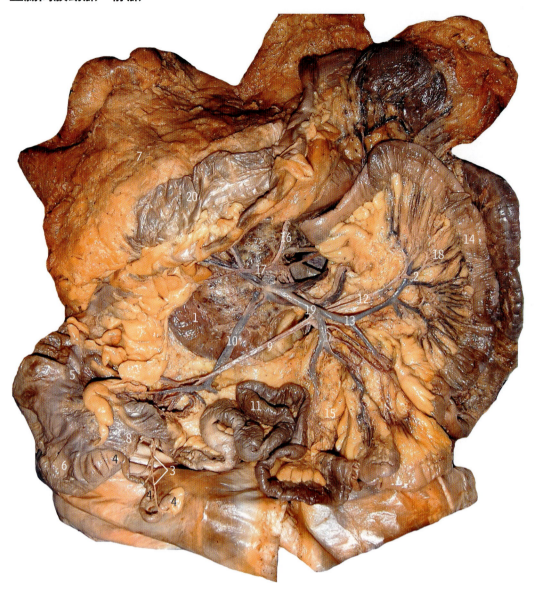

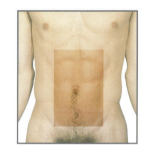

1	横行部〔十二指腸〕 Transverse part〔Duodenum〕	8	回腸と盲腸の接合部	15	腸間膜（回腸の） Mesentery
2	吻合血管弓	9	回結腸動脈 Ileocolic artery	16	中結腸動脈 Middle colic artery
3	虫垂動脈 Appendicular artery	10	回結腸静脈 Ileocolic vein	17	右結腸動脈 Right colic artery
4	虫垂 Appendix：Vermiform appendix	11	回腸 Ileum	18	直動脈* Straight arteries *
5	上行結腸 Ascending colon	12	空腸動脈 Jejunal artery	19	上腸間膜静脈 Superior mesenteric vein
6	盲腸 Cecum	13	空腸静脈 Jejunal vein	20	横行結腸 Transverse colon
7	大網 Greater omentum	14	空腸 Jejunum		

Meckel 憩室

下腸間膜動脈・静脈

前方から．

1 腹大動脈 Abdominal aorta	8 結腸辺縁動脈：結腸辺縁弓 Marginal artery：Marginal arcade	15 脾臓 Spleen
2 下行結腸 Descending colon	9 腹横筋 Transversus abdominis	16 上下腹神経叢 Superior hypogastric plexus
3 大網 Greater omentum	10 腎動脈 Renal artery	17 上直腸動脈 Superior rectal artery
4 空腸と回腸 Jejunum and Ileum	11 腎静脈 Renal vein	18 上直腸静脈 Superior rectal vein
5 下腸間膜動脈 Inferior mesenteric artery	12 （右の）総腸骨動脈 Common iliac artery	19 横行結腸 Transverse colon
6 左結腸動脈 Left colic artery	13 （左の）腎臓 Kidney	
7 （左の）総腸骨動脈 Common iliac artery	14 S状結腸動脈 Sigmoid arteries	

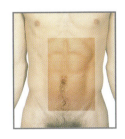

腸の虚血

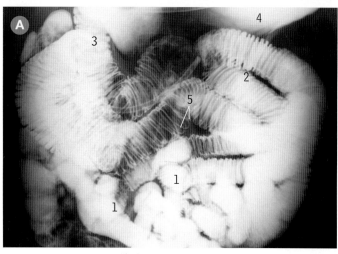

X線バリウム注腸造影画像

近位空腸のチューブから造影している．

A 小腸

1	回腸（渦状になっている） Ileum	
2	空腸（渦状になっている） Jejunum	
3	下行部〔十二指腸〕 Descending part〔Duodenum〕	
4	胃 Stomach	
5	輪状ヒダ Circular folds：Valvulae conniventes *	

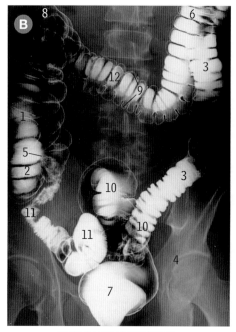

X線バリウム注腸造影画像

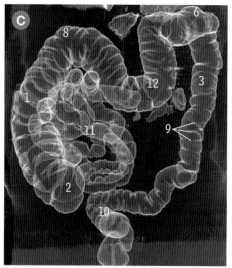

CT画像から三次元構築した
バーチャル大腸内視鏡画像

B C 大腸

バリウム注腸による二重造影法（バリウムと空気）のX線画像である．結腸膨起（9）が結腸各部に認められる．回腸口（5）を通り抜けたバリウムが回腸の終末部（11）の一部を満たし始めているので，膨起形成が見られる大腸とそれよりも細い回腸終末部との見分けがつく．

1	上行結腸 Ascending colon		7	直腸 Rectum
2	盲腸 Cecum		8	右結腸曲：肝曲* Right colic flexure：Hepatic flexure
3	下行結腸 Descending colon		9	結腸膨起 Haustra of colon
4	股関節 Hip joint		10	S状結腸 Sigmoid colon
5	回腸口 Ileal orifice：Orifice of ileal papilla		11	回腸終末部 Terminal ileum
6	左結腸曲：脾曲* Left colic flexure：Splenic flexure		12	横行結腸 Transverse colon

結腸ステント

人工肛門造設術

Crohn病

直腸S状結腸異物

胃［動脈・静脈と迷走神経］

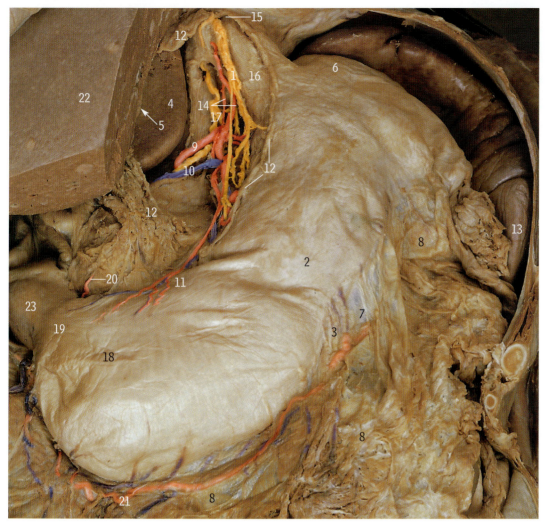
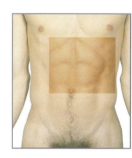

前方から．

前胸腹壁と肝左葉，さらに小網（12）の一部を除去し，胃（6，2，18，19）を原位置に保ったまま示してある．

1 （左の）前迷走神経幹 Anterior vagal trunk	9 左胃動脈 Left gastric artery	17 （右の）後迷走神経幹 Posterior vagal trunk
2 胃体 Body of stomach	10 左胃静脈 Left gastric vein	18 幽門洞 Pyloric antrum
3 左胃大網動／静脈（の枝） Left gastro-omental artery/vein：Left gastro-epiploic artery/vein	11 小弯〔胃〕 Lesser curvature〔Stomach〕	19 幽門管 Pyloric canal
4 尾状葉〔肝臓〕 Caudate lobe〔Liver〕	12 小網（切断縁） Lesser omentum	20 右胃動脈 Right gastric artery
5 静脈管索裂 Fissure for ligamentum venosum	13 下極*〔脾臓〕 Inferior pole *〔Spleen〕	21 右胃大網動／静脈（の枝） Right gastro-omental artery/vein：Right gastro-epiploic artery/vein
6 胃底 Fundus of stomach	14 食道枝〔左胃動脈〕 Esophageal branch〔Left gastric artery〕	22 （肝臓の）右葉 Right lobe of liver
7 大弯〔胃〕 Greater curvature〔Stomach〕	15 食道裂孔〔横隔膜〕 Esophageal hiatus〔Diaphragm〕	23 上部〔十二指腸〕 Superior part〔Duodenum〕
8 大網 Greater omentum	16 食道 Esophagus	

幼児の胃食道逆流症

食道静脈瘤

幼児の幽門狭窄症

迷走神経切離術

上腹部 [A 胃, B 後壁（腹腔神経節とその位置関係）]

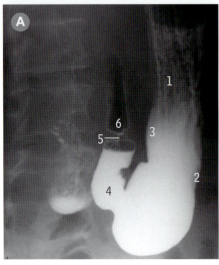

バリウム経口摂取後.

1	胃体	Body of stomach
2	大弯〔胃〕	Greater curvature〔Stomach〕
3	小弯〔胃〕	Lesser curvature〔Stomach〕
4	幽門洞	Pyloric antrum
5	幽門管	Pyloric canal
6	［十二指腸］球部	Bulb of duodenum

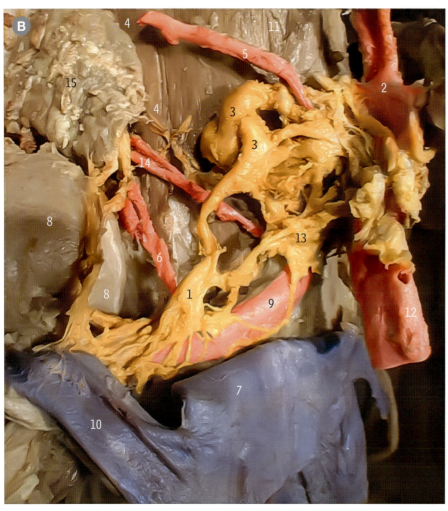

腹大動脈は除去してある.

上方 / 下方 / 外側 / 内側

1	大動脈腎動脈神経節	Aorticorenal ganglia
2	腹腔動脈（前方に翻転してある）	Celiac trunk
3	腹腔神経節	Celiac ganglia
4	横隔膜	Diaphragm
5	下横隔動脈	Inferior phrenic artery
6	下副腎動脈	Inferior suprarenal artery
7	下大静脈（下方に翻転してある）	Inferior vena cava
8	（右の）上端〔腎臓〕	Superior pole：Superior extremity〔Kidney〕
9	（右の）腎動脈	Renal artery
10	（左の）腎静脈（翻転してある）	Renal vein
11	右脚〔横隔膜〕	Right crus〔Diaphragm〕
12	上腸間膜動脈	Superior mesenteric artery
13	上腸間膜動脈神経節	Superior mesenteric ganglion
14	上副腎動脈	Superior suprarenal arteries
15	副腎	Suprarenal gland：Adrenal gland

腹腔神経叢ブロック

胃のペースメーカー

食道裂孔ヘルニア

A 膵臓，十二指腸，上腸間膜動脈・静脈

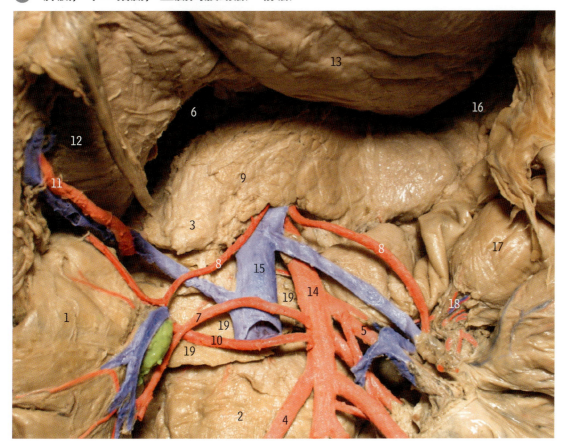

胃は大網とともに"胃床 stomach bed"が見えるように上方に引き上げてある．
[訳注] 胃床とは，胃体と網嚢を介して接する構造を指す言葉であり，横隔膜，左副腎，左腎の上部，膵体・尾の前面，右結腸曲，横行結腸等が含まれる．

1	上行結腸 Ascending colon	5	空腸動脈〔上腸間膜動脈〕 Jejunal arteries〔Superior mesenteric artery〕	10	右結腸動脈 Right colic artery	15	上腸間膜静脈 Superior mesenteric vein
2	水平部：横行部〔十二指腸〕 Horizontal part：Transverse part〔Duodenum〕	6	網嚢 Omental bursa：Lesser sac	11	右胃大網動／静脈 Right gastro-omental artery/vein：Right gastro-epiploic artery/vein	16	膵尾 Tail of pancreas
3	膵頭 Head of pancreas	7	中結腸動脈 Middle colic artery	12	幽門洞（前方へ翻転してある） Pyloric antrum	17	横行結腸 Transverse colon
4	回結腸動脈 Ileocolic artery	8	中結腸動脈の変異	13	胃体 Body of stomach	18	横行結腸への動脈と静脈
		9	膵頸 Neck of pancreas	14	上腸間膜動脈 Superior mesenteric artery	19	鉤状突起〔膵臓〕 Uncinate process〔Pancreas〕

B 十二指腸乳頭

十二指腸の下行部（第二部）の前壁を除去してある．

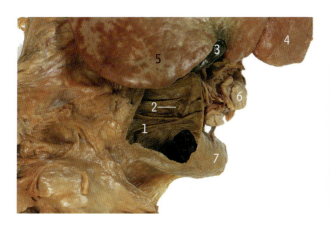

1	粘膜の輪状ヒダ
2	大十二指腸乳頭 Major duodenal papilla
3	胆嚢 Gallbladder
4	（肝臓の）左葉 Left lobe of liver
5	（肝臓の）右葉 Right lobe of liver
6	膵臓 Pancreas
7	水平部：横行部〔十二指腸〕 Horizontal part：Transverse part〔Duodenum〕

膵炎

肝臓

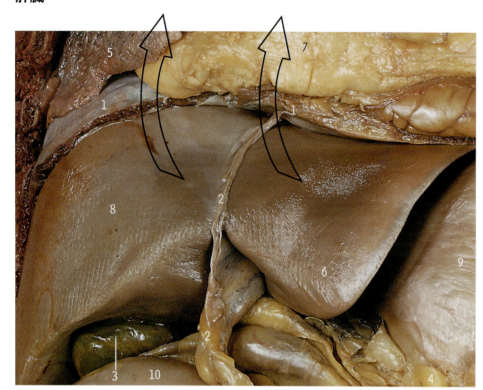

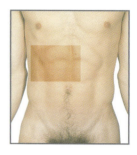

1	横隔膜 Diaphragm
2	［肝］鎌状間膜 Falciform ligament
3	胆嚢底 Fundus of gallbladder
4	大網 Greater omentum
5	下葉〔右肺〕 Inferior lobe〔Right lung〕
6	（肝臓の）左葉 Left lobe of liver
7	心臓周囲の脂肪
8	（肝臓の）右葉 Right lobe of liver
9	胃 Stomach
10	横行結腸 Transverse colon

前方から．

胸腹壁と横隔膜の前部を除去し，内臓がそのままの状態でよく見えるようにしてある．肝臓（6，8）と胃（9）は，横隔膜（1）の直下にある．大網（4）は，胃（9）の大弯（下縁）から吊り下げられ，横行結腸（10）の一部を残して小腸と大腸の大部分を覆っている．胆嚢底（3）の先端が，肝臓の右葉（8）と横行結腸（10）の間に見えている．矢印は，次頁で肝臓を翻転している方向を示す．

● 腹膜の説明は236，240頁の図を参照．

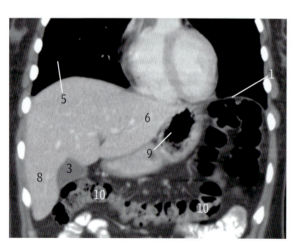

上腹部の CT 冠状断画像

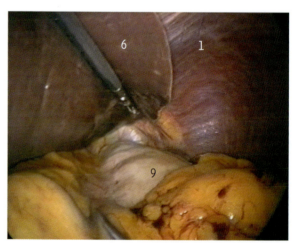

上腹部の腹腔鏡写真

肝硬変

肝臓の外傷

肝臓

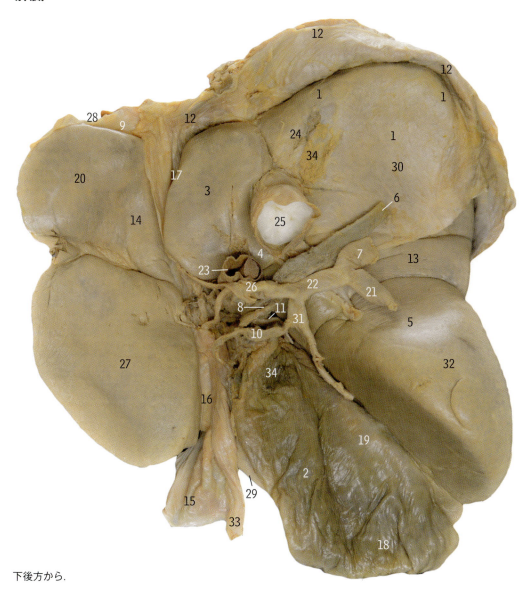

下後方から.

1	無漿膜野 Bare area	12	横隔膜（[肝]冠状間膜とともに翻転してある） Diaphragm
2	胆嚢体 Body of gallbladder	13	十二指腸圧痕 Duodenal impression
3	尾状葉 Caudate lobe	14	食道圧痕 Esophageal impression
4	尾状突起 Caudate process	15	[肝]鎌状間膜 Falciform ligament
5	結腸圧痕 Colic impression	16	肝円索裂 Fissure for round ligament：Fissure for ligamentum teres
6	総胆管 Bile duct	17	静脈管索裂 Fissure for ligamentum venosum
7	総肝動脈 Common hepatic artery	18	胆嚢底 Fundus of gallbladder
8	総肝管 Common hepatic duct	19	胆嚢 Gallbladder
9	[肝]冠状間膜 Coronary ligament	20	胃圧痕 Gastric impression
10	胆嚢動脈 Cystic artery	21	胃十二指腸動脈 Gastroduodenal artery
11	胆嚢管 Cystic duct	22	固有肝動脈 Hepatic artery proper
23	[肝]門脈 Hepatic portal vein		
24	[肝]冠状間膜（肝腎部） Coronary ligament		
25	下大静脈 Inferior vena cava		
26	左枝〔固有肝動脈〕 Left branch [Hepatic artery proper]		
27	（肝臓の）左葉 Left lobe of liver		
28	左三角間膜 Left triangular ligament		
29	方形葉 Quadrate lobe		
30	腎圧痕 Renal impression		
31	右枝〔固有肝動脈〕 Right branch [Hepatic artery proper]		
32	（肝臓の）右葉 Right lobe of liver		
33	肝円索 Round ligament of liver		
34	副腎圧痕 Suprarenal impression		

肝膿瘍

Riedel 葉

肝臓，肝外胆道と関連する血管系

鋳型標本

（黄：胆嚢と胆道．赤：肝動脈とその枝．淡青：[肝]門脈とその支流．濃青：下大静脈，肝静脈ならびにその支流．）

1	総胆管 Bile duct	13	左枝〔固有肝動脈〕（門脈の左枝の前方を通る） Left branch〔Hepatic artery proper〕
2	胆嚢体 Body of gallbladder	14	左胃静脈 Left gastric vein
3	尾状葉 Caudate lobe	15	左肝管 Left hepatic duct
4	尾状突起 Caudate process	16	左肝静脈 Left hepatic vein
5	総肝管 Common hepatic duct	17	（肝臓の）左葉 Left lobe of liver
6	胆嚢動／静脈 Cystic artery/vein	18	胆嚢頸 Neck of gallbladder
7	胆嚢管 Cystic duct	19	[肝]門脈 Hepatic portal vein
8	肝円索裂 Fissure for round ligament：Fissure for ligamentum teres	20	方形葉 Quadrate lobe
9	静脈管索裂 Fissure for ligamentum venosum	21	右枝〔固有肝動脈〕（門脈の右枝の前方を通る） Right branch〔Hepatic artery proper〕
10	胆嚢底 Fundus of gallbladder	22	右胃静脈 Right gastric vein
11	固有肝動脈 Hepatic artery proper	23	（肝臓の）右葉 Right lobe of liver
12	下大静脈 Inferior vena cava		

A B 胆道と膵管

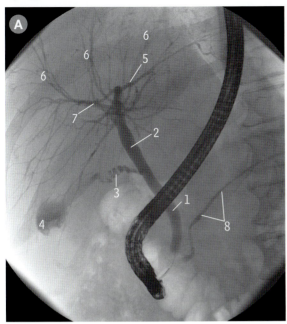
内視鏡的逆行性胆道膵管造影画像（ERCP）

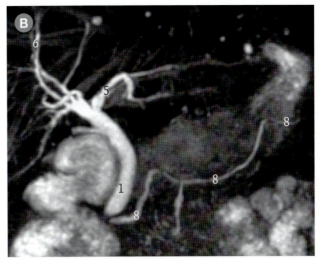
MR 胆道膵管撮影画像（MRCP）

ERCPは，内視鏡を口から咽頭，食道，胃を経由して十二指腸へ挿入し，内視鏡内部のカニューレを大十二指腸乳頭の内部（253頁B）と総胆管に導入するものである．そのため，胆道に造影剤が注入される（同様に，膵管にも導入することができる，B参照）．

1	総胆管 Bile duct	5	左肝管 Left hepatic duct
2	総肝管 Common hepatic duct	6	肝臓の陰影と肝管の支流
3	胆嚢管 Cystic duct	7	右肝管 Right hepatic duct
4	胆嚢 Gallbladder	8	膵管 Pancreatic duct

C 膵管

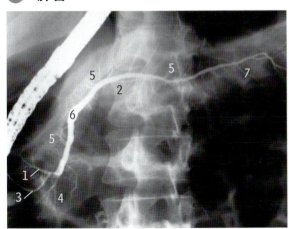
内視鏡的逆行性胆道膵管造影画像（ERCP）

1	副膵管：Santorini 管* Accessory pancreatic duct：Santorini's duct *
2	膵体 Body of pancreas
3	胆膵管膨大部に挿入したカニューレ
4	膵頭 Head of pancreas
5	膵内部を通過する膵管
6	主膵管*：Wirsung 管* Main pancreatic duct *：Wirsung's canal *
7	膵尾 Tail of pancreas

膵癌

胆嚢切除術

胆石

［肝］門脈とその支流ならびに腸間膜の血管

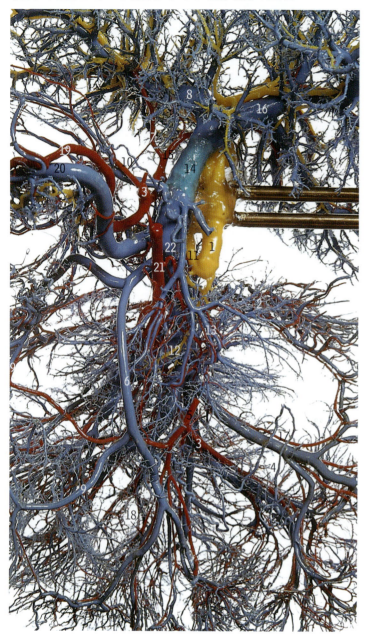

鋳型標本

後方から．（黄：胆道と膵管．赤：動脈．青：門脈系．）

前方から見ると，腸の多くの細かな血管が，太い血管に隠れてしまうおそれがあるので，後方から観察することにする．上腸間膜静脈（22）が上行を続け，脾静脈（20）を受け入れた後に門脈（14）となっている．肝門で，［肝］門脈は右枝（16）と左枝（8）に分かれる．大動脈を除去したため，下腸間膜動脈（5）の上部の位置が少し右へずれ，この動脈から回結腸動脈（4）が起始しているように見える．しかし，これは2つの動脈が単に重なっているにすぎない．回結腸動脈の起始は，上腸間膜動脈から起こっているのだが，この図では見えていない．

1	総胆管	Bile duct
2	中結腸動／静脈（の枝）	Middle colic artery/vein
3	腹腔動脈	Celiac trunk
4	回結腸動／静脈	Ileocolic artery/vein
5	下腸間膜動脈	Inferior mesenteric artery
6	下腸間膜静脈	Inferior mesenteric vein
7	左枝〔固有肝動脈〕	Left branch (Hepatic artery proper)
8	左枝〔［肝］門脈〕	Left branch (Hepatic portal vein)
9	左結腸動／静脈	Left colic artery/vein
10	左胃動／静脈	Left gastric artery/vein
11	膵管	Pancreatic duct
12	膵頭内部の膵管	
13	膵十二指腸動／静脈	Pancreaticoduodenal arteries/veins
14	［肝］門脈	Hepatic portal vein
15	右枝〔固有肝動脈〕	Right branch (Hepatic artery proper)
16	右枝〔［肝］門脈〕	Right branch (Hepatic portal vein)
17	右結腸動／静脈	Right colic artery/vein
18	S状結腸動／静脈	Sigmoid arteries/veins
19	脾動脈	Splenic artery
20	脾静脈	Splenic vein
21	上腸間膜動脈	Superior mesenteric artery
22	上腸間膜静脈	Superior mesenteric vein

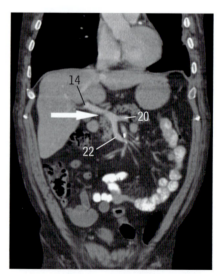

腹部のCT冠状断画像

A B 脾臓

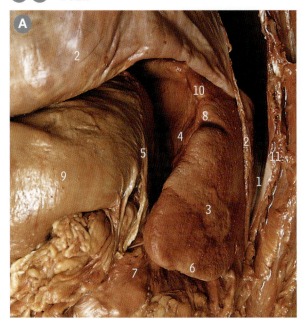

前方から.

左の上前腹壁と下前胸壁を除去し，横隔膜(2)の一部を上方へ翻転して，脾臓をそのままの位置に残してある．脾臓は胃(9)と結腸の左結腸曲(7)に接している．また，脾臓の下部は左の腎臓にも接している(260頁 D16, D9)．

- 胃脾間膜には，脾動静脈の分枝である，短胃動静脈と左胃大網動静脈が含まれる．
- 脾腎ヒダには，膵尾と脾動静脈が含まれている．

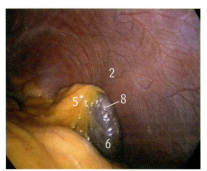

脾臓の腹腔鏡写真

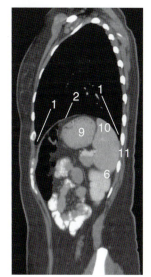

胸部と上腹部の CT 矢状断画像

1	肋骨横隔洞 Costodiaphragmatic recess	5	胃脾間膜 Gastrosplenic ligament	9	胃 Stomach
2	横隔膜 Diaphragm	6	下縁〔脾臓〕 Inferior border〔Spleen〕	10	上縁〔脾臓〕 Superior border〔Spleen〕
3	横隔面 Diaphragmatic surface	7	左結腸曲：脾曲* Left colic flexure：Splenic flexure	11	胸壁* Thoracic wall *
4	胃面 Gastric impression	8	脾臓上縁の切痕 Splenic notch *		

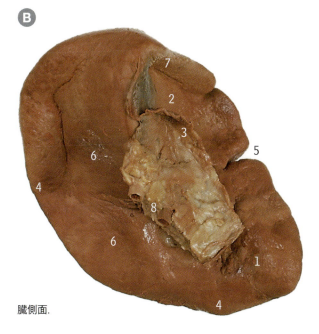

臓側面．

B では脾臓を摘出し，臓側面(内側面)を示してある．胃脾間膜(3)と脾腎ヒダ(8)の一部を脾臓に付着させたままにしてある．

1 結腸面
　Colic impression
2 胃面
　Gastric impression
3 胃脾間膜(短胃動／静脈と左胃大網動／静脈が走る)
　Gastrosplenic ligament
4 下縁
　Inferior border
5 脾臓上縁の切痕
　Splenic notch *
6 腎面
　Renal impression
7 上縁
　Superior border
8 膵尾と脾動／静脈(脾腎ヒダの中を走る)
　Tail of pancreas and Splenic artery/vein

脾臓破裂

脾摘出術

脾嚢胞

脾臓梗塞

脾腫(巨脾症)

副脾

C 脾臓［左上腹部の横断標本］

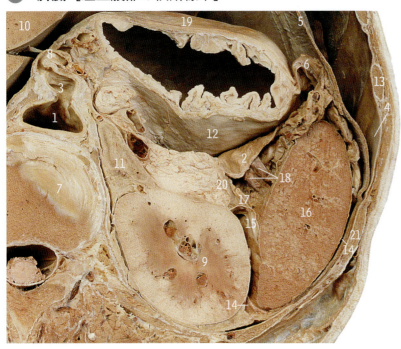

第十二胸椎と第一腰椎間の椎間円板(7)の高さで横断した標本を，下方から胸部の方を見上げている．

1 腹大動脈 Abdominal aorta
2 脾腎ヒダ（前葉） Splenorenal ligament：Lienorenal ligament
3 腹腔動脈 Celiac trunk
4 肋骨横隔洞〔胸膜洞〕 Costodiaphragmatic recess〔Pleural recesses〕
5 横隔膜 Diaphragm
6 胃脾間膜 Gastrosplenic ligament
7 椎間円板 Intervertebral disc
8 左胃動脈 Left gastric artery
9 （左の）腎臓 Kidney
10 （肝臓の）左葉 Left lobe of liver
11 （左の）副腎 Suprarenal gland：Adrenal gland
12 網嚢 Omental bursa：Lesser sac
13 第九肋骨 9th rib：Rib IX
14 腹膜〔大〔腹膜〕嚢〕 Peritoneum〔Greater sac〕
15 脾腎ヒダ（後葉） Splenorenal ligament：Lienorenal ligament
16 脾臓 Spleen
17 脾動脈 Splenic artery
18 脾静脈 Splenic vein
19 胃 Stomach
20 膵尾 Tail of pancreas
21 第十肋骨 10th rib：Rib X

D 盲腸

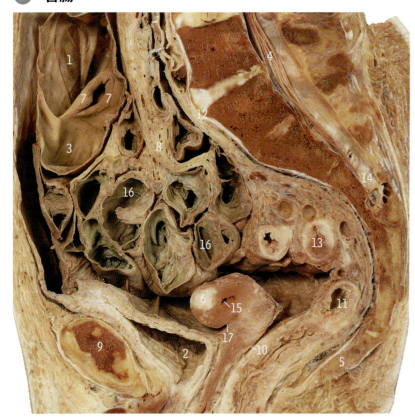

これは女性の骨盤を正中矢状断した標本で，右半を左側方から見たところである．盲腸の前壁を切開し，回腸口の上唇と下唇(7)が見えるように翻転してある．

1 上行結腸 Ascending colon
2 膀胱 Urinary bladder
3 盲腸 Cecum
4 馬尾 Cauda equina
5 尾骨 Coccyx
6 子宮底にある子宮筋腫
7 上唇と下唇〔回腸口〕 Superior lip and Inferior lip〔Ileal orifice：Orifice of ileal papilla〕
8 腸間膜〔小腸〕 Mesentery〔Small intestine〕
9 恥骨結合 Pubic symphysis
10 直腸子宮窩：Douglas窩* Recto-uterine pouch：Pouch of Douglas *
11 直腸 Rectum
12 岬角〔仙骨〕 Promontory〔Sacrum〕
13 S状結腸 Sigmoid colon
14 髄膜嚢*（終末部） Thecal sac *
15 子宮腔 Uterine cavity
16 輪状ヒダ Circular fold：Valvulae conniventes *
17 膀胱子宮窩 Vesico-uterine pouch

矢状断面．内側方から．

膀胱癌

腸重積症

A 虫垂，回結腸動脈ならびに隣接器官

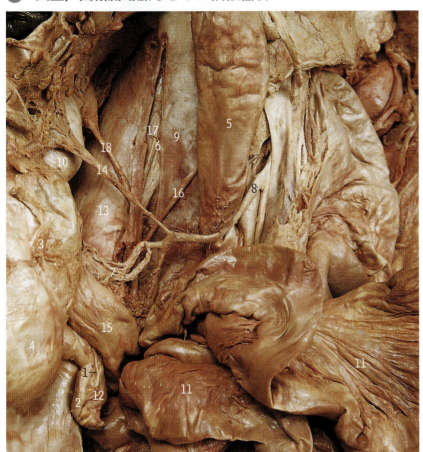

腸間膜と後腹壁の腹膜の大部分を除去し，小腸ループ(11)をこの図の右側に転位させたので，回結腸動脈(8)，回腸終末部(15)ならびに虫垂(2)と虫垂動脈(1)が見える．

1	虫垂動脈（虫垂間膜の内部を走る） Appendicular artery	10	下端〔腎臓〕 Inferior pole：Inferior extremity〔Kidney〕
2	虫垂 Appendix：Vermiform appendix	11	腸間膜と空腸・回腸（のループ） Mesentery, Jejunum and Ileum
3	上行結腸 Ascending colon	12	虫垂間膜 Meso-appendix
4	盲腸 Cecum	13	大腰筋 Psoas major
5	下行部〔十二指腸〕 Descending part〔Duodenum〕	14	右結腸動脈 Right colic artery
6	陰部大腿神経 Genitofemoral nerve	15	回腸終末部 Terminal ileum
7	回腸と盲腸の動／静脈	16	精巣動脈 Testicular artery
8	回結腸動脈 Ileocolic artery	17	精巣静脈 Testicular vein
9	下大静脈 Inferior vena cava	18	尿管 Ureter

前方から．

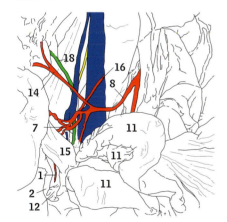

B 盲腸と虫垂

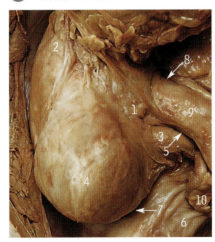

回腸終末部(9)が，盲腸(4)と上行結腸(2)の移行部で大腸に入るのがわかる．虫垂(3)は回腸口のすぐ下で盲腸に開いている．

1	自由ヒモ〔結腸ヒモ〕 Free coli〔Taenia coli〕
2	上行結腸 Ascending colon
3	虫垂（基部） Appendix：Vermiform appendix
4	盲腸 Cecum
5	下回盲陥凹 Inferior ileocaecal recess
6	腹膜（外腸骨動／静脈を覆う） Peritoneum
7	盲腸後陥凹 Retrocaecal recess
8	上回盲陥凹 Superior ileocaecal recess
9	回腸終末部 Terminal ileum
10	虫垂（先端） Appendix：Vermiform appendix

前方から．

虫垂炎

小腸 [C 空腸ループ, D 回腸ループ, E 空腸の血管, F 回腸の血管]

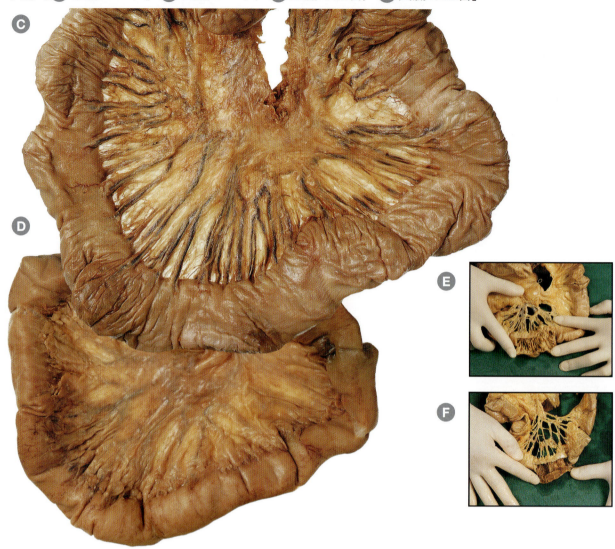

空腸(C)を支える腸間膜の内部において、空腸の血管(E)は吻合して、一重または二重の血管弓を形成する。この血管弓から、まっすぐで長い枝(直枝)が起こり、腸管壁に向かって走る。腸間膜の内部の脂肪は腸間膜根付近に集中する傾向がある。腸管壁の近くは、脂肪を欠いて血管による"窓"のような領域が残る。回腸の血管(F)は、数重にもなる血管弓(F)をつくるので、直枝は空腸に比べて短い。回腸には脂肪を欠く領域はない。空腸(C)の壁は、回腸(D)壁より厚く、内腔も広い。空腸は、粘膜のヒダの数が多いので、回腸より厚いと感じられる。

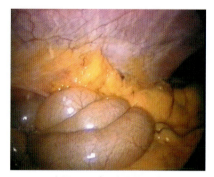

小腸ループの腹腔鏡写真

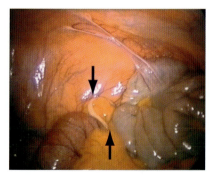

虫垂の腹腔鏡写真

小児の腸重積症

第5章　腹部と骨盤：腎臓と副腎　263

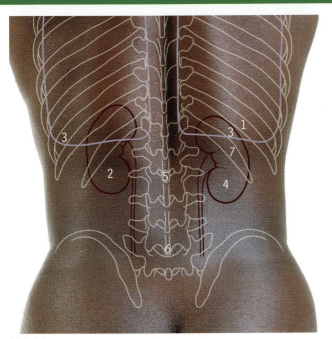

後方から．

A　腎臓と尿管［体表解剖］

左の腎臓の上端は第十一肋骨の高さになっているが，大きな肝臓の存在により，右の腎臓は左の腎臓よりやや低くなっている．左右の腎臓の腎門は，正中線から5cm離れている．胸膜の肋骨横隔洞の下縁が第十二肋骨を横切っている様子を実際の剖出標本（B6）と比較せよ．

1	第十一肋骨 11th rib：Rib XI	5	棘突起〔第一腰椎〕 Spinous process〔L I〕
2	（左の）腎臓 Kidney	6	棘突起〔第四腰椎〕 Spinous process〔L IV〕
3	下縁〔胸膜〕 Lower edge〔Pleura〕	7	第十二肋骨 12th rib：Rib XII
4	（右の）腎臓 Kidney		

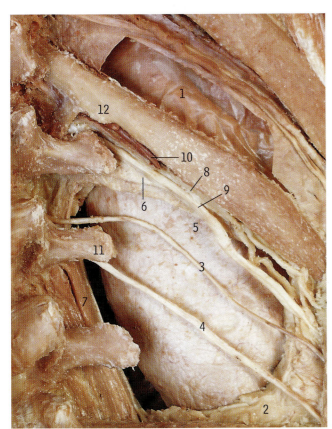

後方から．

B　腎臓（右）

胸壁と腹壁の筋の大部分を除去し，腎臓(5)の後ろを走る3本の神経(9, 3, 4)を示してある．さらに重要なのは，腎臓の上部と胸膜との位置関係である．第十二肋骨(12)の上で，壁側胸膜の一部を切除して肋骨横隔洞(1)を開いてある．肋骨横隔洞の下端(6)は，斜走する第十二肋骨の前面と腎臓の後面の間を横走している．

1	肋骨横隔洞〔胸膜洞〕 Costodiaphragmatic recess〔Pleural recesses〕	7	大腰筋 Psoas major
2	腹膜外組織＊ Extraperitoneal tissue＊	8	肋下動脈 Subcostal artery
3	腸骨下腹神経 Iliohypogastric nerve	9	肋下神経 Subcostal nerve
4	腸骨鼠径神経 Ilio-inguinal nerve	10	肋下静脈 Subcostal vein
5	腎臓 Kidney	11	肋骨突起〔第二腰椎〕 Costal process〔L II〕
6	胸膜（の下縁） Pleura	12	第十二肋骨 12th rib：Rib XII

腰ヘルニア

腎生検

C 腎臓と副腎（左）ならびに関連する血管

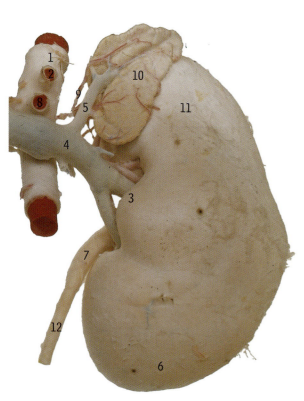

前方から．

血管は，注入された樹脂により拡張している．腎筋膜はすべて除去されているが，副腎（10）は，腎臓上端（11）の内側に，正常の位置のまま残してある．

1	腹大動脈 Abdominal aorta
2	腹腔動脈 Celiac trunk
3	腎門 Hilum of kidney
4	（左の）腎静脈（腎動脈の前方を走る） Renal vein
5	左副腎静脈 Left suprarenal vein
6	下端〔腎臓〕 Inferior pole：Inferior extremity〔Kidney〕
7	腎盂：腎盤 Renal pelvis
8	上腸間膜動脈 Superior mesenteric artery
9	副腎動脈 Suprarenal arteries
10	副腎 Suprarenal gland：Adrenal gland
11	上端〔腎臓〕 Superior pole：Superior extremity〔Kidney〕
12	尿管 Ureter

D 腎臓と副腎（右）ならびに関連する血管

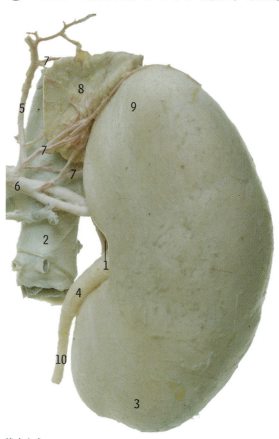

後方から．

一見Cに似ているが，右の腎臓の後面であり，左の腎臓ではない．左右の腎臓とも，腎門は内側に面している．

1	腎門 Hilum of kidney
2	下大静脈 Inferior vena cava
3	下端〔腎臓〕 Inferior pole：Inferior extremity〔Kidney〕
4	腎盂：腎盤 Renal pelvis
5	（右の）下横隔動脈 Inferior phrenic artery
6	（右の）腎動脈 Renal artery
7	副腎動脈 Suprarenal arteries
8	副腎 Suprarenal gland：Adrenal gland
9	上端〔腎臓〕 Superior pole：Superior extremity〔Kidney〕
10	尿管 Ureter

副腎の病変

A 腎臓

腎臓の中心部を通る縦断面である．腎盤(9)と尿管(10)の起始部が含まれている．腎門(2)を出入りする主な血管は除去してある．

1	［腎］皮質 Renal cortex	5	腎錐体 Renal pyramid
2	腎門 Hilum of kidney	6	小腎杯 Minor calyx
3	大腎杯 Major calyx	7	腎柱 Renal column
4	［腎］髄質 Renal medulla	8	腎乳頭 Renal papilla
9	腎盂：腎盤 Renal pelvis	10	尿管 Ureter

● 2つないし3つの大腎杯(3)が合して腎盂(腎盤，9)を形成し，腎門(2)を通り抜けて尿管(10)となる．しばしば，腎盂と尿管の移行部に，わずかに狭窄部が認められる．これは腎盂尿管移行部(Pelviureteric junction：PUJ)として知られており，腎結石で塞がれる場所である．

縦断面．

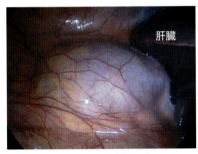

腎臓(右)の腹腔鏡写真
腹膜に覆われている．

B 腎臓(右)

腎動脈(9)の後枝(8)は，この標本では，腎盂(7)と上腎杯(5の上)の後方を通っているが，他のすべての動脈は尿路の前を走る．したがって，この図は右の腎臓を前から見たもので，左の腎臓を後ろから見たものではないことがわかる(静脈，動脈，尿管の順に前方から後方へ並び，腎門が内側にある．264頁参照)．

1	前枝〔腎動脈〕 Anterior branch〔Renal artery〕	7	腎盂：腎盤 Renal pelvis
2	下前区動脈 Anterior inferior segmental artery	8	後枝〔腎動脈〕(後区動脈を形成) Posterior branch〔Renal artery〕
3	上前区動脈(重複) Anterior superior segmental artery	9	腎動脈 Renal artery
4	下区動脈 Inferior segmental artery	10	上区動脈 Superior segmental artery
5	大腎杯 Major calyx	11	尿管 Ureter
6	小腎杯 Minor calyx		

鋳型標本
前方から．（赤：腎動脈．黄：尿管．）

C 大動脈と腎臓

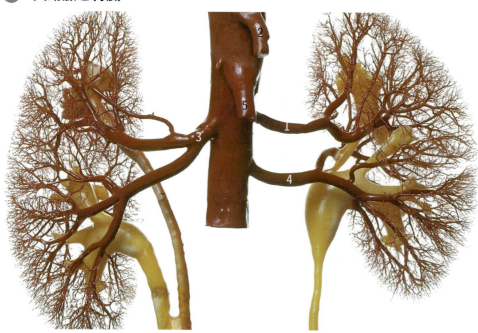

1	（左の）副-腎動脈 Accessory renal artery
2	腹腔動脈 Celiac trunk
3	（右の）腎動脈（近位で分岐する） Renal artery
4	（左の）腎動脈 Renal artery
5	上腸間膜動脈 Superior mesenteric artery

● 副-腎動脈は，大動脈から直接起始する分節的血管である．この標本では，左の副-腎動脈（C1）は上区と前上区に分布し，"正常の"動脈は後区，前下区および下区に分布している．

鋳型標本

前方から．（赤：動脈．黄：尿路．）

右側では尿管（番号は付けられていない）が重複し，別の腎杯から起始している．左側では腎動脈が重複している（1，4）．

D 腎臓と大血管

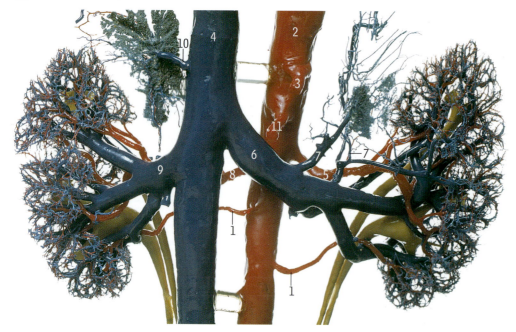

1	副-腎動脈 Accessory renal artery
2	大動脈 Aorta
3	腹腔動脈 Celiac trunk
4	下大静脈 Inferior vena cava
5	（左の）腎動脈 Renal artery
6	（左の）腎静脈 Renal vein
7	左副腎静脈 Left suprarenal vein
8	（右の）腎動脈 Renal artery
9	（右の）腎静脈 Renal vein
10	右副腎静脈 Right suprarenal vein
11	上腸間膜動脈 Superior mesenteric artery

鋳型標本

前方から．（赤：動脈．青：静脈．黄：尿路．）

この標本では，両側とも尿管が重複している（番号は付けられていない）．また，両腎の下端に入る過剰な腎動脈（1）が認められる．副腎（こちらも番号はつけられていない）の輪郭が，静脈の分布からわかる．短い右副腎静脈（10）が，下大静脈（4）に直接流入している．左側には2本の副腎静脈（7）が認められ，いずれも左の腎静脈（6）に流入している．267頁A12，A14も参照．

先天性腎奇形

A 腎臓と副腎（左）

前方から．

後腹壁にある左の腎臓(10)と左の副腎(13)が見える．横隔膜の大部分を除去したが，食道裂孔はそのまま残し，食道の下端(16)が胃の噴門に開口するところを示している．また，この標本では2本ある前迷走神経幹(2)の下に赤色マーカーを挿入してある．後迷走神経幹(18)は食道の右後方にある見える．胸膜(17)の一部を切除し，下位胸椎の側面を走る交感神経幹(22)を示してある．左の腹腔神経節と腹腔神経叢(6)が，腹腔動脈(3)の根部にある．

1	腹大動脈 Abdominal aorta	12	（左の）腎静脈 Renal vein
2	前迷走神経幹（重複，赤色マーカーの前方） Anterior vagal trunk	13	（左の）副腎 Suprarenal gland：Adrenal gland
3	腹腔動脈 Celiac trunk	14	左副腎静脈 Left suprarenal vein
4	総肝動脈 Common hepatic artery	15	（左の）尿管 Ureter
5	下横隔動／静脈 Inferior phrenic artery/vein	16	食道（下端） Esophagus
6	（左の）腹腔神経節と腹腔神経叢 Celiac ganglion and Celiac plexus	17	胸膜（切断縁） Pleura
7	左脚〔横隔膜〕 Left crus〔Diaphragm〕	18	後迷走神経幹 Posterior vagal trunk
8	左胃動脈 Left gastric artery	19	大腰筋 Psoas major
9	左精巣（卵巣）静脈 Left testicular (ovarian) vein	20	脾動脈 Splenic artery
10	（左の）腎臓 Kidney	21	上腸間膜動脈 Superior mesenteric artery
11	（左の）腎動脈 Renal artery	22	交感神経幹 Sympathetic trunk
		23	胸大動脈 Thoracic aorta

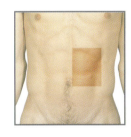

B 腎臓（右）と腎被膜

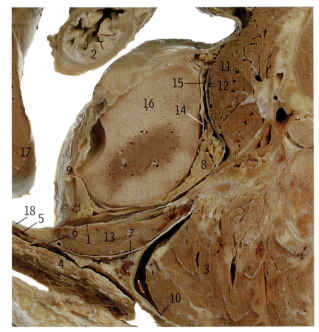

横断面．下方から．

右の腎臓(16)の下部を通る横断面を，下から胸部に向かって見ている．腎周囲の脂肪被膜(8)と腎の線維被膜(14)から，腎被膜(15)を剖出している（本例では，腎の表面に小さな囊胞が認められる）．胸腰筋膜(6)を構成する3葉(1, 7, 10)もこの横断面に明瞭に現れている．

1	前葉：深葉〔胸腰筋膜（腰部）〕 Anterior layer〔Thoracolumbar fascia〕	10	後葉：浅葉〔胸腰筋膜（腰部）〕 Posterior layer〔Thoracolumbar fascia〕
2	小腸 Small intestine	11	大腰筋 Psoas major
3	脊柱起立筋 Erector spinae	12	腰筋筋膜 Psoas fascia
4	外腹斜筋 External oblique	13	腰方形筋 Quadratus lumborum
5	内腹斜筋 Internal oblique	14	線維被膜 Fibrous capsule
6	胸腰筋膜（腰部） Thoracolumbar fascia	15	腎被膜 Renal fascia
7	中葉〔胸腰筋膜（腰部）〕 Middle layer〔Thoracolumbar fascia〕	16	（右の）腎臓 Kidney
8	脂肪被膜 Perinephric fat：Perirenal fat capsule	17	（肝臓の）右葉 Right lobe of liver
9	腹膜 Peritoneum	18	腹横筋 Transversus abdominis

● 腎の固有被膜（線維被膜, 14）の外に脂肪の層（脂肪被膜, 8）があり，その量は個体差が著しい．さらにその外側方には結合組織が凝縮して腎被膜(15)を形成する．

腹腔内出血

腎摘出術

後腹腹気腫

上腸間膜動脈症候群

腎臓と副腎

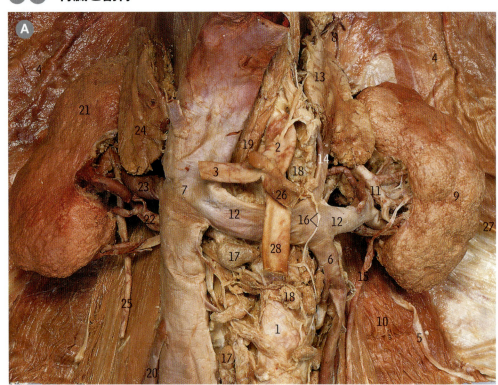

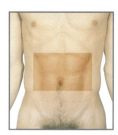

1	腹大動脈と腹大動脈神経叢	Abdominal aorta and Abdominal aortic plexus
2	腹腔動脈	Celiac trunk
3	総肝動脈	Common hepatic artery
4	横隔膜	Diaphragm
5	第一腰神経	1st lumbar nerve
6	左精巣（卵巣）静脈	Left testicular (ovarian) vein
7	下大静脈	Inferior vena cava
8	（左の）下横隔動／静脈	Inferior phrenic artery/veins
9	（左の）腎臓	Kidney
10	（左の）大腰筋	Psoas major
11	（左の）腎動脈	Renal artery
12	（左の）腎静脈	Renal vein
13	（左の）副腎	Suprarenal gland：Adrenal gland
14	左副腎静脈	Left suprarenal vein
15	（左の）尿管	Ureter
16	リンパ管	Lymphatic vessel
17	大動脈傍リンパ節*	Para-aortic nodes*
18	大動脈前リンパ節	Pre-aortic nodes
19	右脚〔横隔膜〕	Right crus (Diaphragm)
20	右精巣（卵巣）静脈	Right testicular (ovarian) vein
21	（右の）腎臓	Kidney
22	（右の）腎動脈	Renal artery
23	（右の）腎静脈	Renal vein
24	（右の）副腎	Suprarenal gland：Adrenal gland
25	（右の）尿管	Ureter
26	脾動脈	Splenic artery
27	（左の）肋下神経	Subcostal nerve
28	上腸間膜動脈	Superior mesenteric artery

後腹壁にある左右の腎臓（9, 21）と左右の副腎（13, 24）を剖出してある．他の内臓は除去してある．左の腎静脈（12）には，左副腎静脈（14）と左精巣（卵巣）静脈（6）が流入し，上腸間膜動脈（28）の後ろで腹大動脈（1）を乗り越えて右へ走り下大静脈（7）に達する．右の腎臓（21）の腎門には，腎動脈（22）の太い枝が見られ，この枝は右の腎静脈（23）の前を通っている．腹大動脈からの左右の腎動脈の起始部は，左の腎静脈（12）と下大静脈（7）の下に隠れているため見えていない．

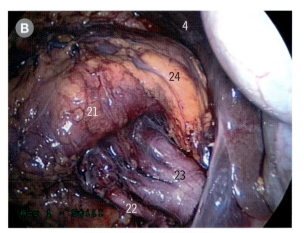

腎臓と副腎（右）の腹腔鏡写真

大動脈の雑音

重複下大静脈

腎癌

後腹膜線維症

C 尿管

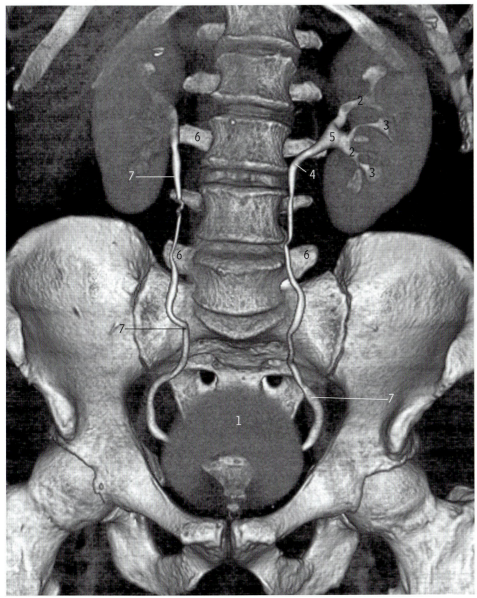

静脈尿路画像（CT画像からの三次元構築画像）

静脈内に注射した造影剤が腎臓から排泄され，腎杯(2, 3)，腎盂(5)および尿管(7)の輪郭が明らかとなっている．尿管が膀胱(1)に入っている．

1	膀胱	Urinary bladder
2	大腎杯	Major calyx
3	小腎杯	Minor calyx
4	腎盂尿管移行部	Pelviureteric junction
5	腎盂：腎盤	Renal pelvis
6	肋骨突起〔腰椎〕	Costal process〔Lumbar vertebra〕
7	尿管	Ureter

● 尿管は，通常，腰椎の肋骨突起の尖端近くに見える．しかしボート選手や競輪選手のように大腰筋が過度に発達していると，この筋の表面でねじれることがある．

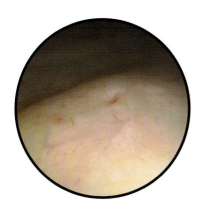

尿管口の膀胱鏡写真

腹部大動脈瘤

腎外傷

尿管瘤

尿路結石

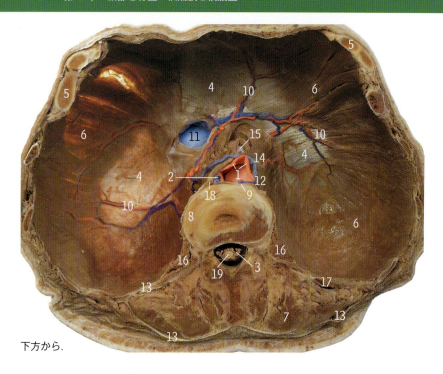

A 横隔膜

1	大動脈 Aorta	10	下横隔動／静脈 Inferior phrenic artery/vein
2	奇静脈 Azygos vein	11	大静脈孔 Caval opening
3	馬尾 Cauda equina	12	左脚 Left crus
4	腱中心〔横隔膜〕 Central tendon〔Diaphragm〕	13	胸腰筋膜（腰部） Thoracolumbar fascia
5	肋骨弓 Costal margin：Costal arch	14	正中弓状靱帯 Median arcuate ligament
6	横隔膜 Diaphragm	15	食道裂孔〔横隔膜〕 Esophageal hiatus〔Diaphragm〕
7	脊柱起立筋 Erector spinae	16	大腰筋 Psoas major
8	椎間円板（第一・第二腰椎間） Intervertebral disc	17	腰方形筋 Quadratus lumborum
9	半奇静脈 Hemi-azygos vein	18	右脚 Right crus
		19	脊髄 Spinal cord

● 横隔膜の右脚(18)は，繊維が左右に分かれて食道裂孔(15)を囲む．

下方から．

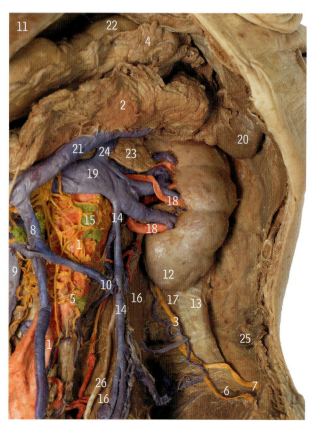

B 後腹壁（左）

後腹壁の構造物を前方から見ている．膵体(2)を上方に翻転し，脾静脈(21)を明らかにしている．副腎(23)が，腎臓の上端から引き離されている（267頁のA10，13と比較）．

1	腹大動脈と腹大動脈神経叢 Abdominal aorta and Abdominal aortic plexus	14	左卵巣静脈 Left ovarian vein
2	膵体 Body of pancreas	15	大動脈傍リンパ節* Para-aortic nodes*
3	第一腰神経 1st lumbar nerve	16	大腰筋 Psoas major
4	大網 Greater omentum	17	腰方形筋 Quadratus lumborum
5	上下腹神経叢 Superior hypogastric plexus	18	腎動脈 Renal artery
6	腸骨鼠径神経 Ilio-inguinal nerve	19	腎静脈 Renal vein
7	腸骨下腹神経 Iliohypogastric nerve	20	脾臓 Spleen
8	下腸間膜静脈 Inferior mesenteric vein	21	脾静脈 Splenic vein
9	下大静脈 Inferior vena cava	22	胃 Stomach
10	左結腸静脈 Left colic vein	23	副腎 Suprarenal gland：Adrenal gland
11	肝臓 Liver	24	左副腎静脈 Left suprarenal vein
12	下端〔腎臓〕 Inferior pole：Inferior extremity〔Kidney〕	25	腹横筋 Transversus abdominis
13	胸腰筋膜（腰部） Thoracolumbar fascia	26	尿管 Ureter

髄質海綿腎

後腹膜出血

後腹壁と骨盤壁

腹膜のすべてと，膀胱(2)，尿管(40)および精管(6)以外の内臓を除去し，血管と神経を剖出してある．

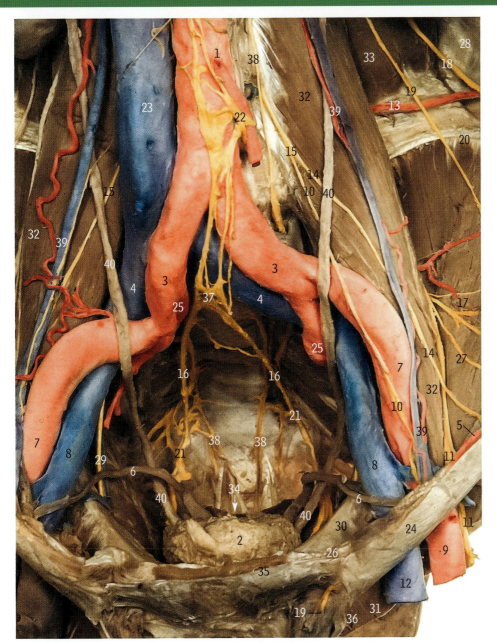

1	腹大動脈と腹大動脈神経叢 Abdominal aorta and Abdominal aortic plexus	15	陰部大腿神経 Genitofemoral nerve	27	外側大腿皮神経（この例では大腿神経から起こっている） Lateral femoral cutaneous nerve
2	膀胱 Urinary bladder	16	下腹神経 Hypogastric nerve	28	胸腰筋膜〔腰部〕 Thoracolumbar fascia
3	総腸骨動脈 Common iliac artery	17	腸骨筋，腰神経叢の枝と腸腰動脈の枝 Iliacus and Branches from Lumbar plexus and Iliolumbar artery	29	閉鎖神経と閉鎖動／静脈 Obturator nerve and Obturator artery/vein
4	総腸骨静脈 Common iliac vein	18	腸骨下腹神経 Iliohypogastric nerve	30	恥骨櫛靱帯 Pectineal ligament
5	深腸骨回旋動脈 Deep circumflex iliac artery	19	腸骨鼠径神経 Ilio-inguinal nerve	31	大腿管の位置
6	精管 Ductus deferens	20	腸腰靱帯 Iliolumbar ligament	32	大腰筋 Psoas major
7	外腸骨動脈 External iliac artery	21	下下腹神経叢：骨盤神経叢と骨盤内臓神経 Inferior hypogastric plexus：Pelvic plexus and Pelvic splanchnic nerves	33	腰方形筋 Quadratus lumborum
8	外腸骨静脈 External iliac vein	22	下腸間膜動脈と下腸間膜動脈神経叢 Inferior mesenteric artery and Inferior mesenteric plexus	34	直腸（切断縁） Rectum
9	大腿動脈 Femoral artery	23	下大静脈 Inferior vena cava	35	腹直筋 Rectus abdominis
10	大腿枝〔陰部大腿神経〕 Femoral branch〔Genitofemoral nerve〕	24	鼠径靱帯 Inguinal ligament	36	精索 Spermatic cord
11	大腿神経 Femoral nerve	25	内腸骨動脈 Internal iliac artery	37	上下腹神経叢 Superior hypogastric plexus
12	大腿静脈 Femoral vein	26	裂孔靱帯 Lacunar ligament	38	交感神経幹と交感神経節 Sympathetic trunk and Sympathetic ganglia
13	第四腰動脈 4th lumbar artery			39	精巣動／静脈 Testicular artery/vein
14	陰部枝〔陰部大腿神経〕 Genital branch〔Genitofemoral nerve〕			40	尿管 Ureter

腸腰筋膿瘍

後腹壁

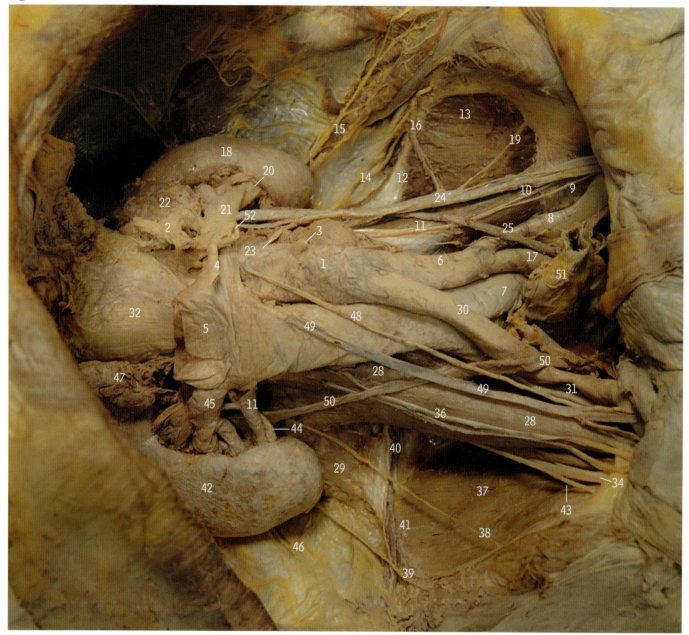

前方から（やや右側方から見ている）.

1	腹大動脈	Abdominal aorta
2	腹腔動脈	Celiac trunk
3	下腸間膜動脈	Inferior mesenteric artery
4	下膵十二指腸動脈	Inferior pancreaticoduodenal artery
5	下大静脈	Inferior vena cava
6	（左の）総腸骨動脈	Common iliac artery
7	（左の）総腸骨静脈	Common iliac vein
8	（左の）外腸骨動脈	External iliac artery
9	（左の）大腿枝〔陰部大腿神経〕	Femoral branch〔Genitofemoral nerve〕
10	（左の）陰部枝〔陰部大腿神経〕	Genital branch〔Genitofemoral nerve〕
11	（左の）陰部大腿神経	Genitofemoral nerve
12	（左の）腸骨稜	Iliac crest
13	（左の）腸骨筋	Iliacus
14	（左の）腸骨鼠径神経	Ilio-inguinal nerve
15	（左の）腸骨下腹神経	Iliohypogastric nerve
16	（左の）腸腰動脈	Iliolumbar artery
17	（左の）内腸骨動脈	Internal iliac artery
18	（左の）腎臓	Kidney
19	外側大腿皮神経	Lateral femoral cutaneous nerve
20	（左の）腎動脈	Renal artery
21	（左の）腎静脈	Renal vein
22	（左の）副腎	Suprarenal gland；Adrenal gland
23	（左の）精巣動脈	Testicular artery
24	左精巣静脈	Left testicular vein
25	（左の）尿管	Ureter

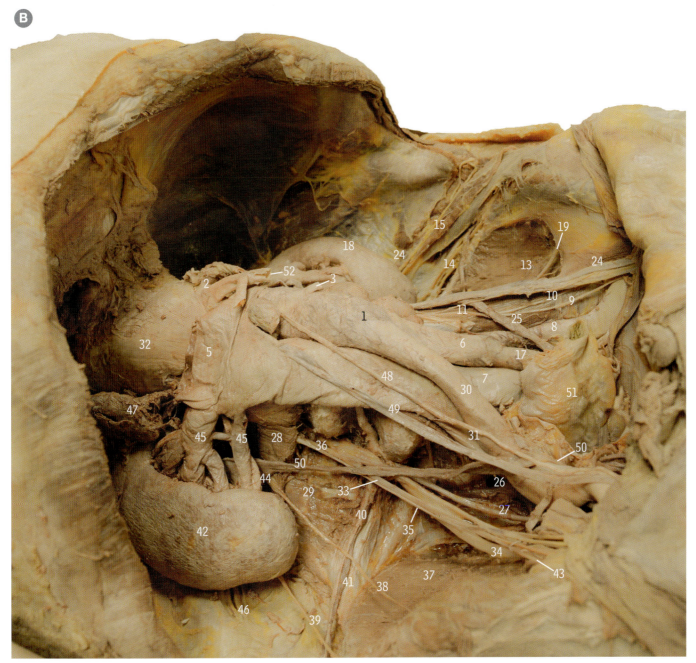

右側前方から．

26 腰仙骨神経幹 Lumbosacral trunk	35 （右の）陰部枝〔陰部大腿神経〕 Genital branch〔Genitofemoral nerve〕	44 （右の）腎動脈 Renal artery
27 閉鎖神経 Obturator nerve	36 （右の）陰部大腿神経 Genitofemoral nerve	45 （右の）腎静脈 Renal vein
28 大腰筋 Psoas major	37 （右の）腸骨筋 Iliacus	46 （右の）肋下神経 Subcostal nerve
29 腰方形筋 Quadratus lumborum	38 （右の）腸骨鼠径神経 Ilio-inguinal nerve	47 （右の）副腎 Suprarenal gland：Adrenal gland
30 （右の）総腸骨動脈 Common iliac artery	39 （右の）腸骨下腹神経 Iliohypogastric nerve	48 （右の）精巣動脈 Testicular artery
31 （右の）総腸骨静脈 Common iliac vein	40 （右の）腸腰動脈 Iliolumbar artery	49 右精巣静脈 Right testicular vein
32 右脚〔横隔膜〕 Right crus〔Diaphragm〕	41 （右の）腸腰静脈 Iliolumbar vein	50 （右の）尿管 Ureter
33 （右の）大腿枝〔陰部大腿神経〕 Femoral branch〔Genitofemoral nerve〕	42 （右の）腎臓 Kidney	51 S状結腸 Sigmoid colon
34 （右の）大腿神経 Femoral nerve	43 （右の）外側大腿皮神経 Lateral femoral cutaneous nerve	52 上腸間膜動脈 Superior mesenteric artery

腹部の自律神経系

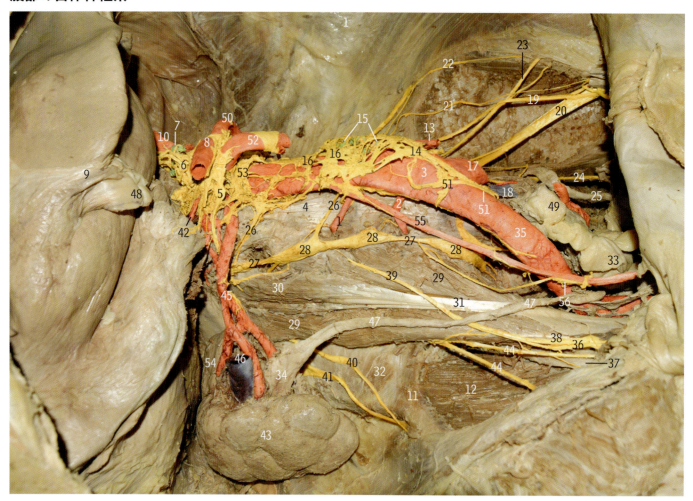

1	第三腰動脈	3rd lumbar artery
2	第四腰動脈	4th lumbar artery
3	腹大動脈	Abdominal aorta
4	前縦靱帯	Anterior longitudinal ligament
5	大動脈腎動脈神経節	Aorticorenal ganglia
6	腹腔神経節	Celiac ganglia
7	腹腔リンパ節と大動脈前リンパ節	Celiac nodes and Pre-aortic nodes
8	腹腔動脈	Celiac trunk
9	〔肝〕鎌状間膜	Falciform ligament
10	固有肝動脈（変異）	Hepatic artery proper
11	腸骨稜	Iliac crest
12	腸骨筋	Iliacus
13	下腸間膜動脈	Inferior mesenteric artery
14	下腸間膜動脈神経節	Inferior mesenteric ganglion
15	下腸間膜動脈リンパ節と大動脈前リンパ節	Inferior mesenteric nodes and Pre-aortic nodes
16	腸間膜動脈間神経叢	Intermesenteric plexus
17	（左の）総腸骨動脈	Common iliac artery
18	（左の）総腸骨静脈	Common iliac vein
19	（左の）大腿枝〔陰部大腿神経〕	Femoral branch（Genitofemoral nerve）
20	（左の）大腿神経	Femoral nerve
21	（左の）陰部枝〔陰部大腿神経〕	Genital branch（Genitofemoral nerve）
22	（左の）腸骨鼠径神経	Ilio-inguinal nerve
23	（左の）外側大腿皮神経（近位で分岐する）	Lateral femoral cutaneous nerve
24	（左の）閉鎖神経	Obturator nerve
25	（左の）尿管	Ureter
26	腰内臓神経	Lumbar splanchnic nerves
27	交感神経幹	Sympathetic trunk
28	幹神経節：交感神経幹神経節	Sympathetic ganglia
29	大腰筋	Psoas major
30	小腰筋	Psoas minor
31	小腰筋（の腱）	Psoas minor
32	腰方形筋	Quadratus lumborum
33	直腸	Rectum
34	腎盂：腎盤	Renal pelvis
35	（右の）総腸骨動脈	Common iliac artery
36	（右の）大腿枝〔陰部大腿神経〕	Femoral branch（Genitofemoral nerve）
37	（右の）大腿神経	Femoral nerve
38	（右の）陰部枝〔陰部大腿神経〕	Genital branch（Genitofemoral nerve）
39	（右の）陰部大腿神経	Genitofemoral nerve
40	（右の）腸骨鼠径神経	Ilio-inguinal nerve
41	（右の）腸骨下腹神経	Iliohypogastric nerve
42	（右の）下横隔動脈	Inferior phrenic artery
43	（右の）腎臓	Kidney
44	（右の）外側大腿皮神経（近位で分岐する）	Lateral femoral cutaneous nerve
45	（右の）腎動脈	Renal artery
46	（右の）腎静脈	Renal vein
47	（右の）尿管	Ureter
48	肝円索	Round ligament of liver
49	S状結腸	Sigmoid colon
50	脾動脈	Splenic artery
51	上下腹神経叢	Superior hypogastric plexus
52	上腸間膜動脈	Superior mesenteric artery
53	上腸間膜動脈神経節	Superior mesenteric ganglion
54	副腎	Suprarenal gland：Adrenal gland
55	精巣動脈	Testicular artery
56	精巣動脈神経叢	Testicular plexus

腰神経叢（左）

大腰筋を除去して，この筋の中を走る腰神経叢の構成を明らかにしている．前外側腹壁の大部分を除去したため，外腹斜筋(1)，内腹斜筋(9)および腹横筋(18)の各最下部だけしか残っていない．また，腸骨下腹神経(6)と腸骨鼠径神経(7)は，実際の位置よりもずっと内側に転位しており，腸骨筋(5)の表面を走っているのではない．

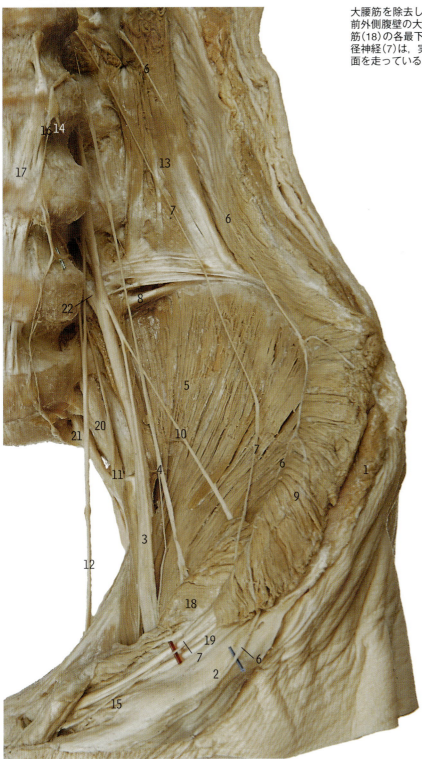

1	外腹斜筋	External oblique
2	腱膜〔外腹斜筋〕	Aponeurosis〔External oblique〕
3	大腿神経	Femoral nerve
4	陰部大腿神経	Genitofemoral nerve
5	腸骨筋	Iliacus
6	腸骨下腹神経	Iliohypogastric nerve
7	腸骨鼠径神経	Ilio-inguinal nerve
8	腸腰靱帯	Iliolumbar ligament
9	内腹斜筋	Internal oblique
10	外側大腿皮神経	Lateral femoral cutaneous nerve
11	腰仙骨神経幹	Lumbosacral trunk
12	閉鎖神経	Obturator nerve
13	腰方形筋	Quadratus lumborum
14	交通枝	Rami communicantes
15	浅鼠径輪	Superficial inguinal ring
16	交感神経幹と交感神経節	Sympathetic trunk and Sympathetic ganglia
17	第三腰椎と前縦靱帯	L III and Anterior longitudinal ligament
18	腹横筋	Transversus abdominis
19	鼠径靱帯（の上面）	Inguinal ligament
20	前枝〔第五腰神経〕	Ventral ramus〔L5〕
21	前枝〔第一仙骨神経〕	Ventral ramus〔S1〕
22	前枝〔第四腰神経〕	Ventral ramus〔L4〕

前方から．

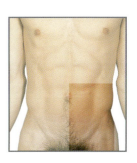

腰部交感神経切除術

A B 男性の骨盤と大腿近位部の筋（左）

A

1	短内転筋 Adductor brevis	14	腰仙骨神経幹 Lumbosacral trunk
2	長内転筋 Adductor longus	15	内閉鎖筋 Obturator internus
3	上前腸骨棘 Anterior superior iliac spine	16	閉鎖神経 Obturator nerve
4	［坐骨］尾骨筋 [Ischio] coccygeus	17	恥骨筋 Pectineus
5	椎間円板（第五腰椎・第一仙椎間） Intervertebral disc	18	梨状筋 Piriformis
6	外腸骨動脈 External iliac artery	19	大腰筋 Psoas major
7	大腿動脈 Femoral artery	20	大腿直筋 Rectus femoris
8	大腿神経 Femoral nerve	21	仙骨神経叢 Sacral plexus
9	大腿静脈 Femoral vein	22	縫工筋 Sartorius
10	薄筋 Gracilis	23	肛門挙筋腱弓 Tendinous arch of levator ani
11	腸骨筋 Iliacus	24	大腿筋膜張筋 Tensor fasciae latae
12	下腹壁動脈（起始部） Inferior epigastric artery	25	外側広筋 Vastus lateralis
13	鼠径靱帯 Inguinal ligament		

少し斜め内側前方から．

前腹壁，内臓と筋膜の大半を除去してある．位置がわかるように，外腸骨動静脈と大腿動静脈の一部，外腹斜筋の腱膜の下縁（鼠径靱帯）は残してある．

- 上前腸骨棘(3)と恥骨結節には，鼠径靱帯(13)の両端が付着し，鼠径部で触知しうる重要な目印である(234頁参照).
- 肛門挙筋と靱帯の付着部よりも上方にある内閉鎖筋(15)の部分は骨盤の壁の一部となる．またこの付着部より下方にある部分は，会陰部で，坐骨肛門窩（坐骨直腸窩）の外側壁の一部を形成する(290, 292頁).
- 梨状筋(18)は坐骨棘より上方の大坐骨孔を通り，また内閉鎖筋(15)は坐骨棘より下方の小坐骨孔を通り，骨盤を出て殿部に至る．

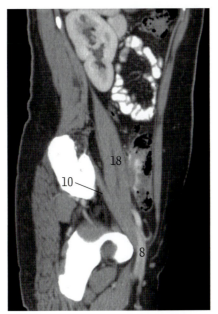

内閉鎖筋を覆う筋膜を，肛門挙筋(11, 20)の腱性起始部まで除去してある．尿道カテーテル(矢印)は尿道括約筋の位置を示している．切断面は，球海綿体筋(※)を通過している．

1	長内転筋	Adductor longus
2	大内転筋	Adductor magnus
3	上前腸骨棘	Anterior superior iliac spine
4	第四仙骨神経の枝	Branch of S4
5	［坐骨］尾骨筋	[Ischio] coccygeus
6	尾骨	Coccyx
7	閉鎖筋膜	Obturator fascia
8	大腿静脈	Femoral vein
9	薄筋	Gracilis
10	腸骨筋	Iliacus
11	腸骨尾骨筋〔肛門挙筋〕	Iliococcygeus (Levator ani)
12	鼠径靱帯	Inguinal ligament
13	坐骨棘	Ischial spine
14	裂孔靱帯	Lacunar ligament
15	内閉鎖筋(閉鎖神経が貫いている)	Obturator internus
16	梨状筋	Piriformis
17	岬角〔仙骨〕	Promontory (Sacrum)
18	大腰筋	Psoas major
19	恥骨結合	Pubic symphysis
20	恥骨尾骨筋〔肛門挙筋〕	Pubococcygeus (Levator ani)
21	直腸	Rectum
22	仙骨管(嚢胞がある)	Sacral canal
23	縫工筋	Sartorius
24	肛門挙筋腱弓	Tendinous arch of levator ani

内側方から．

腹部と骨盤(左)のCT傍矢状断画像

鼠径リンパ節の腫脹

278　第5章　腹部と骨盤：男性の鼠径部，外生殖器

A 精索と精巣（右）

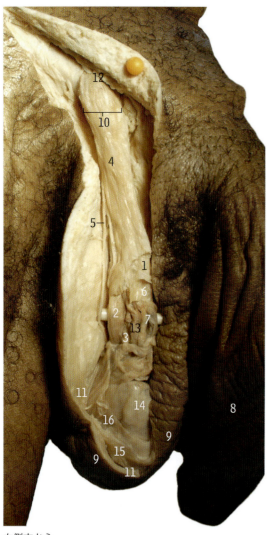

右側方から．

B 精巣，精巣上体および陰茎（右）

右側方から．

1	精巣挙筋膜 Cremasteric fascia	
2	精管 Ductus deferens	
3	精管動脈 Artery to ductus deferens	
4	外精筋膜 External spermatic fascia	
5	腸骨鼠径神経 Ilio-inguinal nerve	
6	内精筋膜 Internal spermatic fascia	
7	蔓状静脈叢 Pampiniform plexus	
8	陰茎 Penis	
9	陰嚢 Scrotum	
10	精索 Spermatic cord	
11	肉様膜 Dartos fascia：Superficial fascia of scrotum	
12	浅鼠径輪 Superficial inguinal ring	
13	精巣動脈 Testicular artery	
14	白膜 Tunica albuginea	
15	壁側板〔精巣鞘膜〕 Parietal layer (Tunica vaginalis)	
16	臓側板〔精巣鞘膜〕 Visceral layer (Tunica vaginalis)	

1	精巣上体垂 Appendix of epididymis	
2	［精巣上体］体 Body of epididymis	
3	陰茎体 Body of penis	
4	亀頭冠 Corona of glans	
5	精管 Ductus deferens	
6	外尿道口 External urethral orifice	
7	包皮 Prepuce：Foreskin	
8	陰茎亀頭 Glans penis	
9	［精巣上体］頭 Head of epididymis	
10	外側浅陰茎背静脈* Lateral superficial dorsal vein of penis *	
11	蔓状静脈叢 Pampiniform plexus	
12	（精巣鞘膜の）嚢 Sac of tunica vaginalis	
13	陰嚢 Scrotum	
14	精索 Spermatic cord	
15	浅陰茎背動脈* Superficial dorsal artery of penis *	
16	陰茎背神経 Dorsal nerve of penis	
17	浅陰茎背静脈 Superficial dorsal vein of penis	
18	肉様膜 Dartos fascia：Superficial fascia of scrotum	
19	［精巣上体］尾 Tail of epididymis	
20	精巣 Testis	
21	壁側板〔精巣鞘膜〕 Parietal layer (Tunica vaginalis)	
22	臓側板〔精巣鞘膜〕（白膜を覆っている） Visceral layer (Tunica vaginalis)	

陰茎の包皮環状切除術

Fournier 症候群

陰嚢水腫

包茎と嵌頓包茎

陰嚢腫脹

精索静脈瘤

精管切除術

男性の骨盤（左）

正中矢状断面．内側方から．

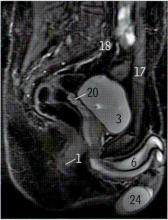

骨盤のMR傍矢状断画像

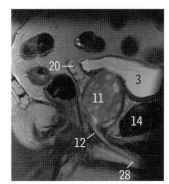

骨盤のMR矢状断画像

1 肛門管 Anal canal	8 精管 Ductus deferens	16 直腸膀胱窩〔腹膜〕 Recto-vesical pouch (Peritoneum)	23 空腸動／静脈と回腸動／静脈〔上腸間膜動／静脈〕 Jejunal arteries/veins and Ileal arteries/veins (Superior mesenteric artery/vein)
2 線維輪 Anulus fibrosus	9 下大静脈 Inferior vena cava	17 腹直筋 Rectus abdominis	24 精巣 Testis
3 膀胱 Urinary bladder	10 壁側腹膜 Parietal peritoneum	18 岬角〔仙骨〕 Promontory (Sacrum)	25 白膜 Tunica albuginea
4 尾骨 Coccyx	11 前立腺 Prostate	19 精丘 Seminal colliculus	26 壁側板〔精巣鞘膜〕 Parietal layer (Tunica vaginalis)
5 総腸骨動脈 Common iliac artery	12 (尿道の)前立腺部 Prostatic urethra	20 精嚢 Seminal vesicle	27 臓側板〔精巣鞘膜〕 Visceral layer (Tunica vaginalis)
6 陰茎海綿体 Corpus cavernosum penis	13 前立腺静脈叢 Prostatic venous plexus	21 S状結腸 Sigmoid colon	28 (尿道の)海綿体部 Spongy urethra
7 深陰茎背静脈 Deep dorsal vein of penis	14 恥骨結合 Pubic symphysis	22 小腸ループ Small intestine	
	15 直腸とS状結腸の接合部		

尿溢出

直腸鏡検査とS状結腸鏡検査

精巣捻転症

骨盤，右鼠径部と陰茎

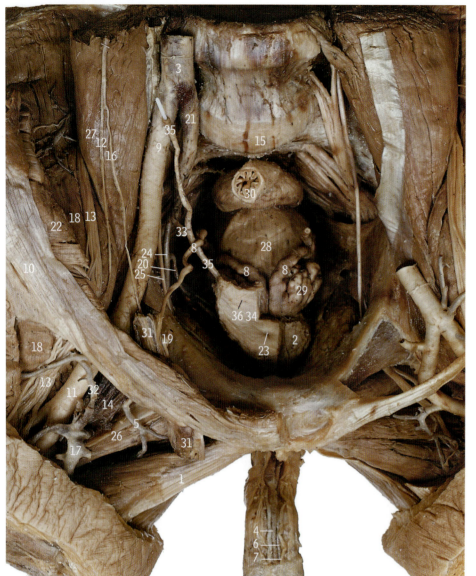

上方から．

膀胱の大部分を除去し，骨盤内の前立腺底(2)の一部と左の精嚢(29)ならびにその内側にある精管(8)を示してある．精管は，骨盤内では尿管(35)の浅側を交叉する．外腸骨動脈(9)は，鼠径靱帯(10)の下を通って大腿動脈(11)となる．陰茎背部の筋膜を剝離し，正中線を走る不対性の深陰茎背静脈(4)とその左右を伴行する陰茎背動脈(6)，陰茎背神経(7)を示している．

● 膀胱三角(34)は，膀胱底の下部または後面にあり，滑らかな粘膜をもった比較的堅い領域である．この三角は内尿道口(23)と左右の尿管口(右は36)の間にある．

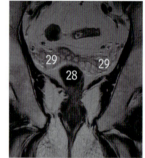

骨盤の MR 冠状断画像

1 長内転筋 Adductor longus	10 腱膜〔外腹斜筋〕と鼠径靱帯 Aponeurosis (External oblique) and Inguinal ligament	18 腸骨筋 Iliacus	28 直腸 Rectum
2 〔前立腺〕底 Base of prostate	11 大腿動脈 Femoral artery	19 下腹壁動脈 Inferior epigastric artery	29 精嚢 Seminal vesicle
3 総腸骨動脈 Common iliac artery	12 大腿枝〔陰部大腿神経〕 Femoral branch (Genitofemoral nerve)	20 下膀胱動脈 Inferior vesical artery	30 S 状結腸（下端で切断） Sigmoid colon
4 深陰茎背静脈 Deep dorsal vein of penis	13 大腿神経 Femoral nerve	21 内腸骨動脈 Internal iliac artery	31 精索 Spermatic cord
5 深外陰部動脈 Deep external pudendal artery	14 大腿静脈 Femoral vein	22 内腹斜筋 Internal oblique	32 浅腸骨回旋静脈 Superficial circumflex iliac vein
6 陰茎背動脈 Dorsal artery of penis	15 椎間円板（第五腰椎・第一仙椎間） Intervertebral disc	23 内尿道口 Internal urethral orifice	33 上膀胱動脈 Superior vesical artery
7 陰茎背神経 Dorsal nerve of penis	16 陰部枝〔陰部大腿神経〕 Genital branch (Genitofemoral nerve)	24 閉鎖動脈 Obturator artery	34 膀胱三角 Trigone of bladder
8 精管 Ductus deferens	17 大伏在静脈 Great saphenous vein：Long saphenous vein	25 閉鎖神経 Obturator nerve	35 尿管 Ureter
9 外腸骨動脈 External iliac artery		26 恥骨筋 Pectineus	36 尿管口 Ureteric orifice
		27 大腰筋 Psoas major	

大腸癌

膀胱炎

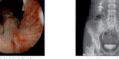

膀胱鏡検査

尿管の奇形

第5章 腹部と骨盤：男性の骨盤

A 膀胱と前立腺

1 膀胱底 Fundus of bladder
2 精管 Ductus deferens
3 (左の)射精管 Ejaculatory duct
4 後面〔前立腺〕 Posterior surface〔Prostate〕
5 精囊 Seminal vesicle
6 尿管 Ureter

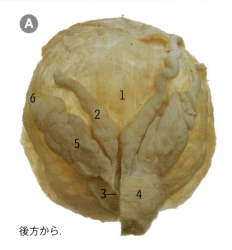

後方から．

B 男性の骨盤（左）

正中断した標本において，前立腺(24)が肥大し，尿道の前立腺部(25)が長くなっている．膀胱の粘膜を除去し(36に膀胱三角を示してある)，膀胱壁の筋層の小柱状のしわを示してある．内腸骨動脈(14)の分枝の変異はまれではない．本例では，閉鎖動脈(22)から中直腸動脈(20)が起こり，さらに上膀胱動脈(34)と下膀胱動脈(13)も起こっている．

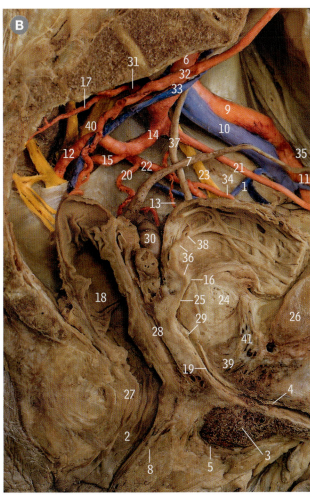

内側方から．

C 精管

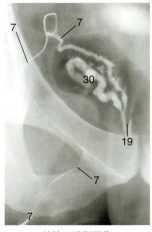 

精管の造影画像　　　前立腺の膀胱鏡写真

1	副閉鎖静脈 Accessory obturator vein	16	内尿道口 Internal urethral orifice	29	精丘 Seminal colliculus
2	肛門管 Anal canal	17	外側仙骨動脈 Lateral sacral artery	30	精囊 Seminal vesicle
3	尿道球 Bulb of penis	18	直腸（下端） Rectum	31	上殿動脈 Superior gluteal artery
4	(尿道の)海綿体部 Spongy urethra	19	(尿道の)隔膜部 Membranous part	32	上直腸動脈 Superior rectal artery
5	球海綿体筋 Bulbospongiosus	20	中直腸動脈 Middle rectal artery	33	上直腸静脈 Superior rectal vein
6	総腸骨動脈 Common iliac artery	21	臍動脈索（臍動脈の遺残） Cord of umbilical artery	34	上膀胱動脈 Superior vesical artery
7	精管 Ductus deferens	22	閉鎖動脈 Obturator artery	35	精巣動／静脈と深鼠径輪 Testicular artery/vein and Deep inguinal ring
8	外肛門括約筋 External anal sphincter	23	閉鎖神経 Obturator nerve	36	膀胱三角 Trigone of bladder
9	外腸骨動脈 External iliac artery	24	前立腺（肥大している） Prostate	37	尿管 Ureter
10	外腸骨静脈 External iliac vein	25	(尿道の)前立腺部 Prostatic urethra	38	尿管口 Ureteric orifice
11	下腹壁動／静脈 Inferior epigastric artery/vein	26	恥骨結合 Pubic symphysis	39	尿生殖隔膜 Urogenital diaphragm
12	下殿動脈 Inferior gluteal artery	27	恥骨直腸筋〔肛門挙筋〕 Puborectalis〔Levator ani〕	40	前枝〔第二仙骨神経〕 Ventral ramus〔S2〕
13	下膀胱動脈 Inferior vesical artery	28	直腸前立腺筋膜：直腸膀胱中隔 Rectoprostatic fascia：Rectovesical septum	41	前立腺静脈叢と膀胱静脈叢 Prostatic venous plexus and Vesical venous plexus
14	内腸骨動脈 Internal iliac artery				
15	内陰部動脈 Internal pudendal artery				

前立腺肥大　　前立腺癌　　経尿道的前立腺切除術　　尿道狭窄症

A 骨盤の動脈と神経（左）

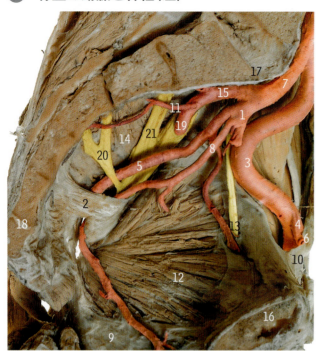

内側方から．

正中断された骨盤の左半において，腹膜の全部，筋膜，静脈ならびに動脈の臓側枝を左の肛門挙筋とともに除去してある．そのため，内閉鎖筋（12）の内面の全体が明らかになっている．骨盤壁の後部では，一般に血管は神経よりも浅いところを走る．

本例において，外腸骨動脈（3）は蛇行が異常に強い．内腸骨動脈の前幹（1）も通常とは異なり，非常に高いところで内陰部動脈（8）と下殿動脈（5）の2本の終枝に分岐している．上殿動脈（19）は腰仙骨神経幹を貫通している．

1	前幹〔内腸骨動脈〕 Anterior trunk〔Internal iliac artery〕	
2	［坐骨］尾骨筋と仙棘靱帯 [Ischio] coccygeus and Sacrospinous ligament	
3	外腸骨動脈 External iliac artery	
4	下腹壁動脈 Inferior epigastric artery	
5	下殿動脈 Inferior gluteal artery	
6	鼠径靱帯 Inguinal ligament	
7	内腸骨動脈 Internal iliac artery	
8	内陰部動脈 Internal pudendal artery	
9	坐骨結節 Ischial tuberosity	
10	裂孔靱帯 Lacunar ligament	
11	外側仙骨動脈 Lateral sacral artery	
12	内閉鎖筋 Obturator internus	
13	閉鎖神経と閉鎖動脈 Obturator nerve and Obturator artery	
14	梨状筋 Piriformis	
15	後幹〔内腸骨動脈〕 Posterior trunk〔Internal iliac artery〕	
16	恥骨結合 Pubic symphysis	
17	岬角〔仙骨〕 Promontory〔Sacrum〕	
18	仙尾関節 Sacrococcygeal joint	
19	上殿動脈（腰仙骨神経幹を貫いている） Superior gluteal artery	
20	第二・第三仙骨神経の前枝の吻合枝	
21	前枝〔第一仙骨神経〕 Ventral ramus〔S1〕	

B 下下腹神経叢：骨盤神経叢（左）

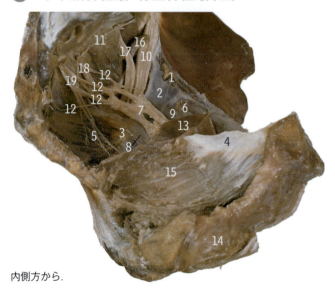
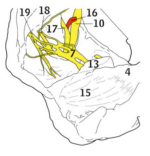

内側方から．

骨盤腔の左半を内側方から見ている．右の骨盤壁は，骨盤底（骨盤隔膜）の一部をつくる右の肛門挙筋（15）以外を除去し，その右側（会陰側）面を見えるようにしてある．骨盤内臓神経（12）は，第二および第三仙骨神経の前枝（18，19）から起こり，下下腹神経叢（7）の形成に関わる．

1	弓状線〔腸骨〕 Arcuate line〔Ilium〕	10	腰仙骨神経幹 Lumbosacral trunk
2	閉鎖筋膜 Obturator fascia	11	（左の）交感神経幹 Sympathetic trunk
3	坐骨棘 Ischial spine	12	骨盤内臓神経（勃起神経） Pelvic splanchnic nerves
4	（右の）閉鎖筋膜（の外側面） Obturator fascia	13	直腸 Rectum
5	（左の）［坐骨］尾骨筋と肛門挙筋神経* [Ischio] coccygeus and Nerves to levator ani*	14	（右の）坐骨枝と恥骨下枝 Ramus of ischium and Inferior pubic ramus
6	（左の）精管 Ductus deferens	15	（右の）肛門挙筋と坐骨肛門窩：坐骨直腸窩 Levator ani and Ischio-anal fossa: Ischiorectal fossa
7	（左の）下下腹神経叢：骨盤神経叢 Inferior hypogastric plexus: Pelvic plexus	16	上殿動脈 Superior gluteal artery
8	（左の）肛門挙筋 Levator ani	17	前枝〔第一仙骨神経〕 Ventral ramus〔S1〕
9	（左の）精嚢 Seminal vesicle	18	前枝〔第二仙骨神経〕 Ventral ramus〔S2〕
		19	前枝〔第三仙骨神経〕 Ventral ramus〔S3〕

内腸骨動脈［その枝と位置関係．女性の骨盤の左半部］

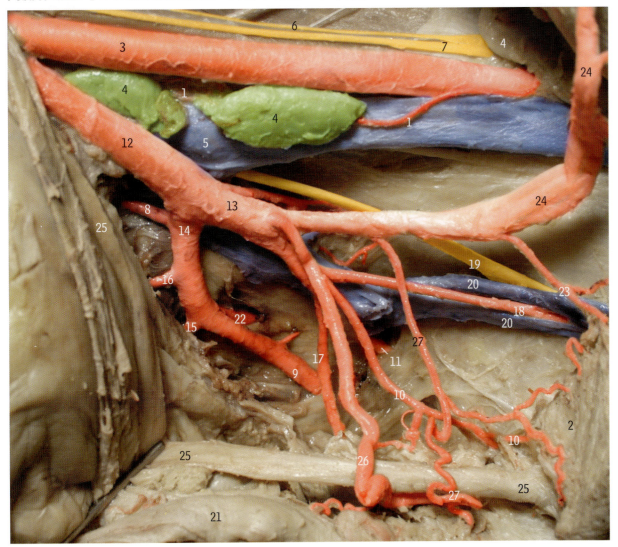

1 腸骨リンパ節への動脈	10 下膀胱動脈 Inferior vesical artery	19 閉鎖神経 Obturator nerve
2 膀胱 Urinary bladder	11 内陰部動脈 Internal pudendal artery	20 閉鎖静脈 Obturator veins
3 外腸骨動脈 External iliac artery	12 内腸骨動脈 Internal iliac artery	21 子宮円索（翻転してある） Round ligament of uterus
4 外腸骨リンパ節（腫大している） External iliac nodes	13 前幹〔内腸骨動脈〕 Anterior trunk〔Internal iliac artery〕	22 上殿動脈 Superior gluteal artery
5 外腸骨静脈 External iliac vein	14 後幹〔内腸骨動脈〕 Posterior trunk〔Internal iliac artery〕	23 上膀胱動脈 Superior vesical artery
6 大腿枝〔陰部大腿神経〕 Femoral branch〔Genitofemoral nerve〕	15 外側仙骨動脈（下枝*） Lateral sacral artery	24 臍動脈索（臍動脈の遺残） Cord of umbilical artery
7 陰部枝〔陰部大腿神経〕 Genital branch〔Genitofemoral nerve〕	16 外側仙骨動脈（上枝*） Lateral sacral artery	25 尿管（牽引してある） Ureter
8 腸腰動脈 Iliolumbar artery	17 中直腸動脈 Middle rectal artery	26 子宮動脈 Uterine artery
9 下殿動脈 Inferior gluteal artery	18 閉鎖動脈 Obturator artery	27 腟動脈 Vaginal artery

内腸骨動脈塞栓術

A 骨盤の骨格と靱帯（左）

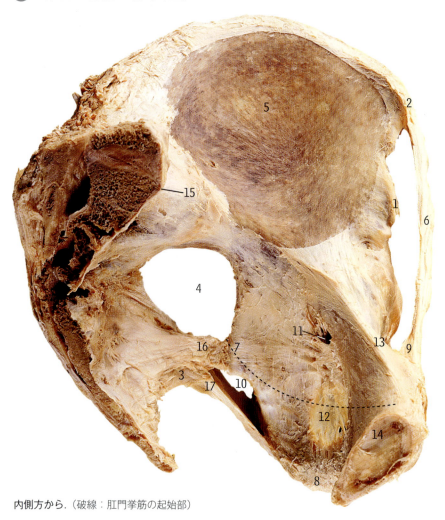

1	下前腸骨棘と直頭〔大腿直筋〕（の起始部） Anterior inferior iliac spine and Straight head〔Rectus femoris〕	
2	上前腸骨棘 Anterior superior iliac spine	
3	鎌状突起〔仙結節靱帯〕 Falciform process〔Sacrotuberous ligament〕	
4	大坐骨孔 Greater sciatic foramen	
5	腸骨窩 Iliac fossa	
6	鼠径靱帯 Inguinal ligament	
7	坐骨棘 Ischial spine	
8	坐骨結節 Ischial tuberosity	
9	裂孔靱帯 Lacunar ligament	
10	小坐骨孔 Lesser sciatic foramen	
11	閉鎖孔（閉鎖神経と閉鎖動/静脈が残っている） Obturator foramen	
12	閉鎖膜 Obturator membrane	
13	恥骨櫛靱帯 Pectineal ligament	
14	恥骨結合 Pubic symphysis	
15	岬角〔仙骨〕 Promontory〔Sacrum〕	
16	仙棘靱帯 Sacrospinous ligament	
17	仙結節靱帯 Sacrotuberous ligament	

- "骨盤の靱帯"（脊柱と骨盤を結ぶ靱帯）に属する靱帯は，仙結節靱帯（17），仙棘靱帯（16）ならびに腸腰靱帯である（腸腰靱帯は334頁C7で後方から見える）．
- 裂孔靱帯（9）は鼠径靱帯（6）の内側端から後方へ走り，恥骨櫛の内側端に達する．恥骨櫛には恥骨櫛靱帯（13）が付着している．

内側方から．（破線：肛門挙筋の起始部）

この骨盤の正中断標本において，靱帯以外の軟組織をすべて除去し，やや上内側方から見ている．

B 大坐骨孔，仙骨神経叢，肛門挙筋（左）

1	大坐骨孔 Greater sciatic foramen	9	前縦靱帯（仙骨の前面を覆う） Anterior longitudinal ligament
2	肛門挙筋 Levator ani	10	陰部神経 Pudendal nerve
3	腰仙骨神経幹（第一仙骨神経を含む） Lumbosacral trunk	11	第二仙骨神経 2nd sacral nerve
4	肛門挙筋神経* Nerves to levator ani *	12	第三・第四仙骨神経 3rd and 4th sacral nerve (S3 and S4)
5	閉鎖筋膜（内閉鎖筋の筋膜） Obturator fascia	13	第五仙骨神経 5th sacral nerve (S5)
6	内閉鎖筋 Obturator internus	14	仙棘靱帯 Sacrospinous ligament
7	閉鎖神経 Obturator nerve	15	肛門挙筋腱弓（肛門挙筋の起始部） Tendinous arch of levator ani
8	梨状筋（筋の大半を除去してある） Piriformis		

内側方から．

骨髄穿刺

閉鎖孔ヘルニア

仙骨神経の刺激

女性の骨盤（左）

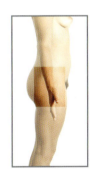

内側方から．動脈に色素を注入してある．この例のように，後傾した子宮はしばしば見られる．

1 前部〔腟円蓋〕 Anterior part〔Vaginal fornix〕	10 子宮底 Fundus of uterus	19 恥骨結合 Pubic symphysis	28 上膀胱動脈 Superior vesical artery
2 膀胱頸 Neck of bladder	11 下腹壁動／静脈 Inferior epigastric artery/vein	20 直腸とS状結腸の接合部	29 膀胱三角 Trigone of bladder
3 子宮頸 Cervix of uterus	12 小陰唇 Labium minus	21 直腸子宮窩：Douglas窩* Recto-uterine pouch：Pouch of Douglas*	30 臍動脈索（臍動脈の遺残） Cord of umbilical artery
4 外子宮口 External os of uterus	13 固有卵巣索 Ligament of ovary	22 直腸 Rectum	31 尿管 Ureter
5 内子宮口 Internal os of uterus	14 臍動脈索：内側臍索* Cord of umbilical artery：Medial umbilical ligament*	23 腹直筋 Rectus abdominis	32 子宮腔 Uterine cavity
6 陰核 Clitoris	15 正中臍索（尿膜管の遺残） Median umbilical ligament	24 恥骨後隙：Retzius腔* Retropubic space：Space of Retzius*	33 腟 Vagina
7 陰核脚 Crus of clitoris	16 閉鎖神経 Obturator nerve	25 子宮円索 Round ligament of uterus	34 第五腰椎 5th lumbar vertebra（L V）
8 外腸骨動脈 External iliac artery	17 閉鎖動／静脈 Obturator artery/veins	26 岬角〔仙骨〕 Promontory〔Sacrum〕	35 膀胱子宮窩 Vesico-uterine pouch
9 外腸骨静脈 External iliac vein	18 後部〔腟円蓋〕 Posterior part〔Vaginal fornix〕	27 S状結腸 Sigmoid colon	36 腟前庭 Vestibule of vagina

便失禁

痔

卵管結紮

直腸診

直腸脱

子宮筋腫

子宮の奇形

女性の骨盤

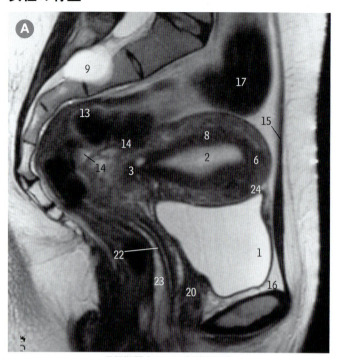

月経期間中の MR 矢状断画像

1	膀胱 Urinary bladder	13	直腸と S 状結腸の接合部
2	子宮腔（の血塊） Uterine cavity	14	直腸子宮窩：Douglas 窩* Recto-uterine pouch：Pouch of Douglas*
3	子宮頸 Cervix of uterus	15	腹直筋 Rectus abdominis
4	黄体 Corpus luteum	16	恥骨後隙：Retzius 腔* Retropubic space：Space of Retzius*
5	子宮腔 Uterine cavity	17	S 状結腸 Sigmoid colon
6	子宮底 Fundus of uterus	18	小腸 Small intestine
7	肛門挙筋 Levator ani	19	膀胱三角 Trigone of bladder
8	［子宮］筋層 Myometrium	20	尿道 Urethra
9	神経根嚢胞：Tarlov 嚢胞 Perineural cyst：Tarlov's cyst	21	卵管：Fallopius 管* Uterine tube：Fallopian tube*
10	卵巣 Ovary	22	腟 Vagina
11	会陰筋 Perineal muscles	23	腟壁* Vaginal wall*
12	後部〔腟円蓋〕 Posterior part〔Vaginal fornix〕	24	膀胱子宮窩 Vesico-uterine pouch

側方から骨盤を見た MR 画像である．子宮底(6)が膀胱(1)の上に載っており，それらの間に膀胱子宮窩(24)の腹膜が介在している．これらの位置関係は，MR 画像(B)でも見られる．

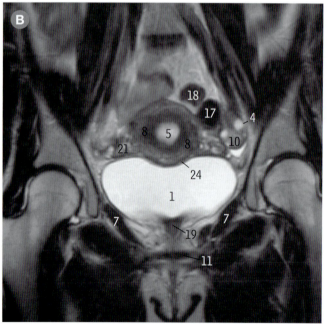

MR 冠状断画像

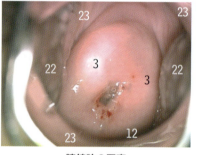

腟鏡診の写真

子宮頸管の塗抹細胞診

膀胱炎

卵巣類皮嚢胞腫

腟内診

女性の骨盤 [A 子宮と卵巣]

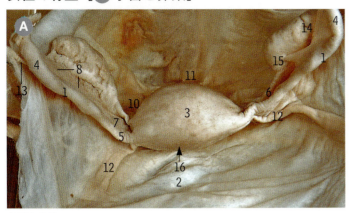

上前方から．

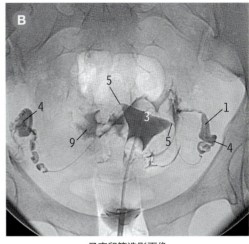

子宮卵管造影画像

1	卵管膨大部 Ampulla of uterine tube	10	子宮広間膜（の後面） Broad ligament of uterus
2	膀胱 Urinary bladder	11	直腸子宮窩：Douglas 窩* Recto-uterine pouch：Pouch of Douglas*
3	子宮底 Fundus of uterus	12	子宮円索 Round ligament of uterus
4	卵管漏斗 Infundibulum of uterine tube	13	卵巣提靱帯：卵巣提索（卵巣動／静脈を含む） Suspensory ligament of ovary
5	卵管峡部 Isthmus of uterine tube	14	卵管端〔卵巣〕 Tubal extremity〔Ovary〕
6	固有卵巣索 Ligament of ovary	15	子宮端〔卵巣〕 Uterine extremity〔Ovary〕
7	卵管間膜 Mesosalpinx	16	膀胱子宮窩 Vesico-uterine pouch
8	卵巣間膜 Mesovarium		
9	腹腔内に漏れた造影剤		

Aでは上前方から骨盤を覗き込んでおり，子宮底(3)が膀胱(2)の上に載っており，それらの間に膀胱子宮窩(16)の腹膜が介在している．Bでは，造影剤が子宮と卵管(3，5，1，4)を満たし，さらに腹膜腔にも漏れ出ている(9)．

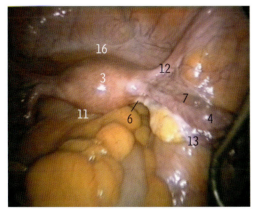

女性の骨盤の腹腔鏡写真

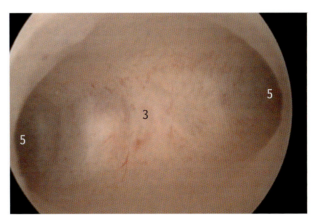

子宮腔と卵管の子宮鏡写真

急性卵管炎

卵巣癌

子宮外妊娠の破裂

子宮内避妊器具

卵管結紮

女性の骨盤（左）

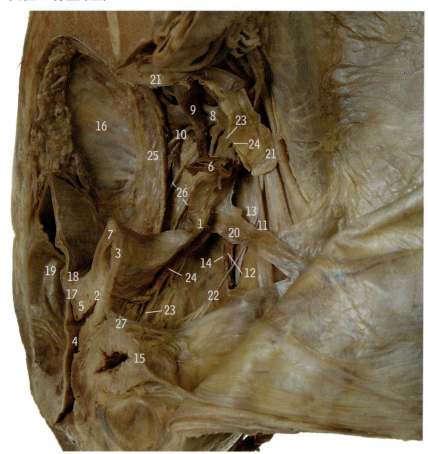

上斜め後方から．

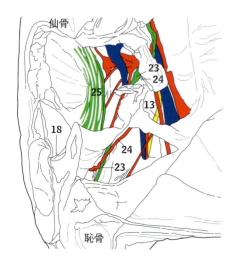

1	卵管膨大部	Ampulla of uterine tube
2	前部〔腟円蓋〕	Anterior part〔Vaginal fornix〕
3	子宮体	Body of uterus
4	腟	Vagina
5	子宮頸	Cervix of uterus
6	卵管采	Fimbriae of uterine tube
7	子宮底	Fundus of uterus
8	内腸骨動脈	Internal iliac artery
9	内腸骨静脈	Internal iliac vein
10	中直腸動脈	Middle rectal artery
11	臍動脈索（臍動脈の遺残）	Cord of umbilical artery
12	閉鎖動脈	Obturator artery
13	閉鎖神経	Obturator nerve
14	閉鎖静脈	Obturator vein
15	腹膜（膀胱を覆っている）	Peritoneum
16	腹膜（梨状筋を覆っている）	Peritoneum
17	後部〔腟円蓋〕	Posterior part〔Vaginal fornix〕
18	直腸子宮窩：Douglas窩*	Recto-uterine pouch：Pouch of Douglas*
19	直腸	Rectum
20	子宮円索	Round ligament of uterus
21	S状結腸間膜	Sigmoid mesocolon
22	上膀胱動脈	Superior vesical artery
23	尿管	Ureter
24	子宮動脈	Uterine artery
25	子宮仙骨靱帯	Uterosacral ligament
26	腟動脈（重複）	Vaginal artery
27	膀胱子宮窩	Vesico-uterine pouch

前腹壁を前へ翻転し，骨盤の左半を斜め前方から見ている．膀胱子宮窩(27)の腹膜に切開を加え，子宮を後方へ牽引してある．それにより，尿管(23)が膀胱へ向かって走りながら子宮動脈(24)の下を交叉しているのが見える．子宮仙骨靱帯(25)は直腸(19)の側面を後方へ走り，仙骨の前面に向かっている．S状結腸間膜(21)の根はもとの位置のままにしてあり，左の尿管(23)が腹部から骨盤へ入るときにこの箇所を通ることを強調してある．

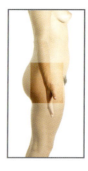

肛門直腸膿瘍

子宮癌

子宮摘出術

骨盤内臓の支持装置

危険な妊娠中絶

女性の会陰　[A 体表解剖，B 坐骨直腸窩]

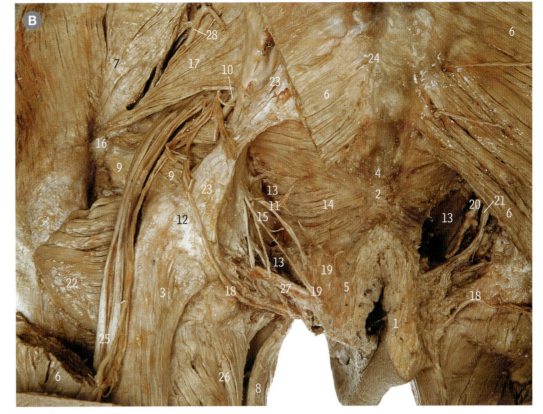

後方から.

1	前陰唇交連〔大陰唇〕 Anterior commissure〔Labium majus〕		
2	陰核 Clitoris		
3	膣脱		
4	外尿道口 External urethral orifice		
5	大陰唇 Labium majus		
6	小陰唇 Labium minus		
7	恥丘 Mons pubis		
8	会陰腱中心：会陰体 Perineal body		
9	後陰唇交連〔大陰唇〕 Posterior commissure〔Labium majus〕		
10	陰核包皮 Prepuce of clitoris		
11	膣口 Vaginal orifice		
12	膣前庭 Vestibule of vagina		

1	肛門縁* Margin of anus*	15	内閉鎖筋と閉鎖筋膜 Obturator internus and Obturator fascia
2	肛門尾骨靱帯 Anococcygeal body：Anococcygeal ligament	16	内閉鎖筋（の腱） Obturator internus
3	長頭〔大腿二頭筋〕 Long head〔Biceps femoris〕	17	梨状筋 Piriformis
4	尾骨 Coccyx	18	会陰枝〔後大腿皮神経〕 Perineal branches〔Posterior femoral cutaneous nerve〕
5	外肛門括約筋 External anal sphincter	19	後陰唇神経 Posterior labial nerve
6	大殿筋 Gluteus maximus	20	内陰部動脈 Internal pudendal artery
7	中殿筋 Gluteus medius	21	陰部神経 Pudendal nerve
8	薄筋 Gracilis	22	大腿方形筋 Quadratus femoris
9	下双子筋 Gemellus inferior：Inferior gemellus	23	仙結節靱帯 Sacrotuberous ligament
10	下殿動脈 Inferior gluteal artery	24	仙骨 Sacrum
11	下直腸神経 Inferior rectal nerves	25	坐骨神経 Sciatic nerve
12	坐骨結節 Ischial tuberosity	26	半膜様筋と半腱様筋 Semimembranosus and Semitendinosus
13	坐骨肛門窩：坐骨直腸窩（脂肪を除去してある） Ischio-anal fossa：Ischiorectal fossa	27	浅会陰横筋 Superficial transverse perineal muscle
14	肛門挙筋 Levator ani	28	上殿動脈 Superior gluteal artery

● 坐骨直腸窩は，窩の下内側が直腸ではなく肛門管であるため，現在では坐骨肛門窩とよばれており，このほうが適切で正しい名称といえる．壁の構成と内容物は，男女いずれも同様である．

Bartholin 腺膿瘍

会陰切開

女性性器切除（割礼）

陰部神経ブロック

女性の会陰と坐骨直腸窩（砕石位）

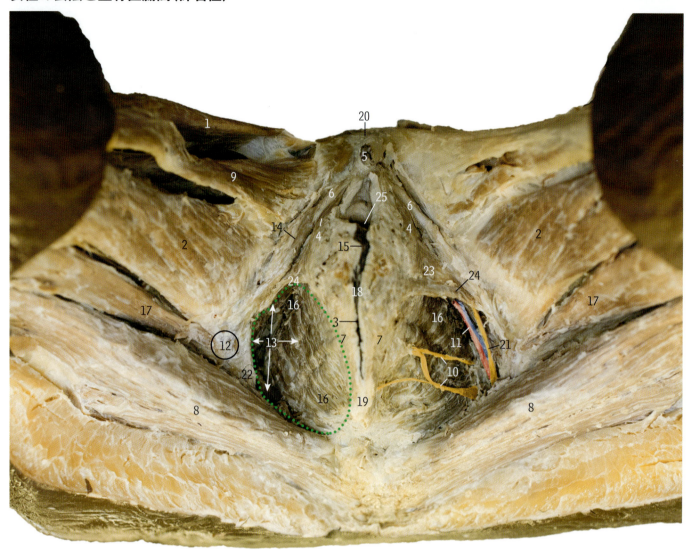

下方から．

1　長内転筋　Adductor longus	9　薄筋　Gracilis	17　長頭〔大腿二頭筋〕と半腱様筋　Long head (Biceps femoris) and Semitendinosus
2　大内転筋　Adductor magnus	10　下直腸神経の枝　Branch of Inferior rectal nerve	18　会陰腱中心：会陰体　Perineal body
3　肛門　Anus	11　内陰部動／静脈　Internal pudendal artery/vein	19　[会陰] 縫線　Perineal raphe
4　球海綿体筋　Bulbospongiosus	12　坐骨結節（○で囲んである）　Ischial tuberosity	20　恥骨結合　Pubic symphysis
5　陰核（横切してある）　Clitoris	13　坐骨肛門窩：坐骨直腸窩（緑色の破線で囲んである）　Ischio-anal fossa：Ischiorectal fossa	21　陰部神経　Pudendal nerve
6　陰核脚　Crus of clitoris	14　坐骨海綿体筋　Ischiocavernosus	22　仙結節靱帯　Sacrotuberous ligament
7　外肛門括約筋　External anal sphincter	15　小陰唇　Labium minus	23　除去された会陰膜の位置
8　大殿筋　Gluteus maximus	16　肛門挙筋　Levator ani	24　浅会陰横筋　Superficial transverse perineal muscle
		25　腟前庭（小陰唇の間のスペース）　Vestibule of vagina

腟壁のGartner（管）嚢胞

性器の発達異常

坐骨肛門窩膿瘍

A 男性の会陰

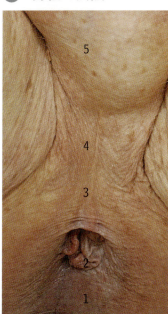

陰嚢(5)を上前方に引き上げ，会陰の中心部を示した．

1	肛門尾骨靱帯	Anococcygeal body：Anococcygeal ligament
2	肛門縁＊（肛門皮膚垂が見られる）	Margin of anus＊
3	会陰腱中心：会陰体	Perineal body
4	［会陰］縫線（尿道球を覆っている）	Perineal raphe
5	陰嚢（右の精巣を覆っている）	Scrotum

● 肛門皮膚垂は，痔の既往を示すことがある．

B 陰茎根

陰茎を横切して前部を除去し，陰茎根を示してある．陰茎根は，背側にある左右2つの陰茎海綿体(2)と腹側にある1つの尿道海綿体(3．尿道(14)を通す)から形成されている．

1	球海綿体筋 Bulbospongiosus		9	坐骨海綿体筋 Ischiocavernosus
2	陰茎海綿体 Corpus cavernosum penis		10	坐骨枝と恥骨下枝 Ramus of ischium and Inferior pubic ramus
3	尿道海綿体 Corpus spongiosum of penis		11	会陰腱中心：会陰体 Perineal body
4	深陰茎背静脈 Deep dorsal vein of penis		12	恥骨結合 Pubic symphysis
5	陰茎背動脈 Dorsal artery of penis		13	浅会陰横筋（会陰膜を覆っている） Superficial transverse perineal muscle
6	陰茎背神経 Dorsal nerve of penis		14	尿道 Urethra
7	外肛門括約筋 External anal sphincter			
8	下直腸動／静脈と下直腸神経（坐骨肛門窩を横切っている） Inferior rectal artery/veins and Inferior rectal nerves			

尿道の膀胱鏡写真

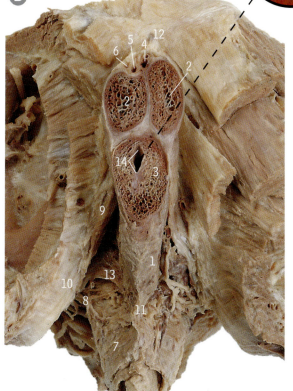

前下方から．

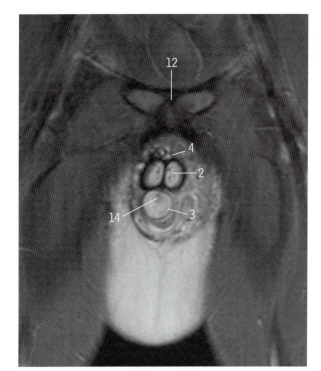

陰茎のMR画像

尿道球腺

肛門癌

陰嚢水腫

尿道下裂

鎖肛

男性の会陰と坐骨肛門（直腸）窩

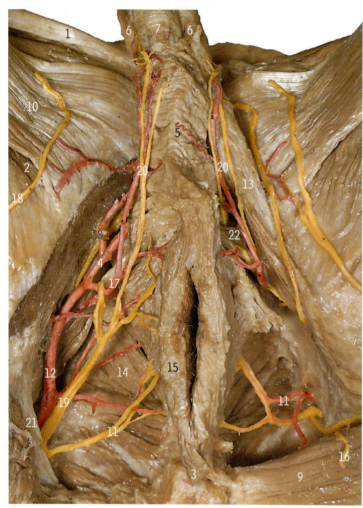

下方から．

坐骨肛門窩の脂肪をすべて除去した結果，肛門挙筋(14)の会陰面と坐骨肛門窩の内部を走る血管と神経が明らかになっている．左側（図の向かって右側）の会陰膜(22)はそのまま残してあるが，右側ではこの膜と下層の筋（尿生殖隔膜）を除去してある．

1	長内転筋	Adductor longus
2	大内転筋	Adductor magnus
3	肛門尾骨靱帯	Anococcygeal body：Anococcygeal ligament
4	尿道球動脈	Artery of bulb of penis
5	球海綿体筋（尿道球を覆っている）	Bulbospongiosus
6	陰茎海綿体	Corpus cavernosum penis
7	尿道海綿体	Corpus spongiosum of penis
8	陰茎背神経と陰茎背動脈	Dorsal nerve of penis and Dorsal artery of penis
9	大殿筋	Gluteus maximus
10	薄筋	Gracilis
11	下直腸動／静脈と下直腸神経（坐骨肛門窩を走る）	Inferior rectal artery/veins and Inferior rectal nerves
12	内陰部動脈	Internal pudendal artery
13	坐骨海綿体筋（陰茎脚を覆っている）	Ischiocavernosus
14	肛門挙筋	Levator ani
15	肛門縁*	Margin of anus *
16	貫通皮神経	Perforating cutaneous nerve
17	会陰動脈	Perineal artery
18	会陰枝〔後大腿皮神経〕	Perineal branches〔Posterior femoral cutaneous nerve〕
19	会陰神経	Perineal nerve
20	後陰嚢動／静脈と後陰嚢神経	Posterior scrotal arteries/veins and Posterior scrotal nerves
21	仙結節靱帯	Sacrotuberous ligament
22	浅会陰横筋（会陰膜の後縁を覆っている）	Superficial transverse perineal muscle

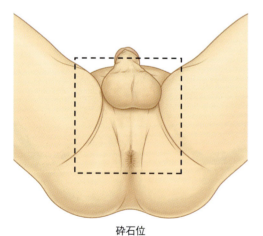

砕石位

● 男女両性とも，坐骨肛門窩の側壁には陰部神経管がある．この管を開放して内容物を露出してある．陰部神経管には，内陰部動脈(12)ならびに陰部神経の終枝である会陰神経(19)と陰茎背神経(8)または陰核背神経が含まれている．

会陰瘻

持続勃起症

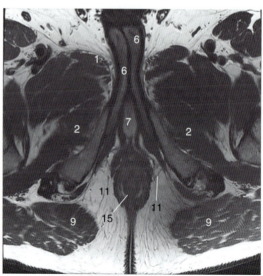

尿生殖三角のMR横断画像

下肢

 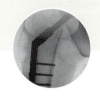

下肢 [**A** 体表解剖, **B**〜**D** 浅層, **E** 骨格]

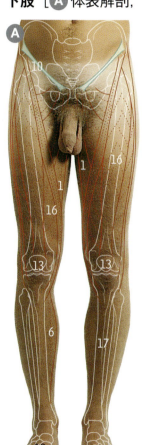    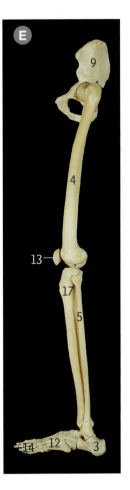

A・B：前方から．C：後方から．D・E：外側方から．

1 内転筋群*　Adductor muscles *
2 大腿二頭筋　Biceps femoris
3 踵骨　Calcaneus
4 大腿骨　Femur
5 腓骨　Fibula
6 腓腹筋　Gastrocnemius
7 大殿筋　Gluteus maximus
8 大腿部膝屈筋*（ハムストリング）　Hamstrings *
9 寛骨　Hip bone：Coxal bone
10 鼠径靱帯　Inguinal ligament
11 腸脛靱帯　Iliotibial tract
12 中足骨　Metatarsals
13 膝蓋骨　Patella
14 趾［節］骨　Phalanges
15 長腓骨筋と短腓骨筋　Peroneus (fibularis) longus and Peroneus (fibularis) brevis
16 大腿四頭筋　Quadriceps femoris
17 脛骨　Tibia

寛骨（左）

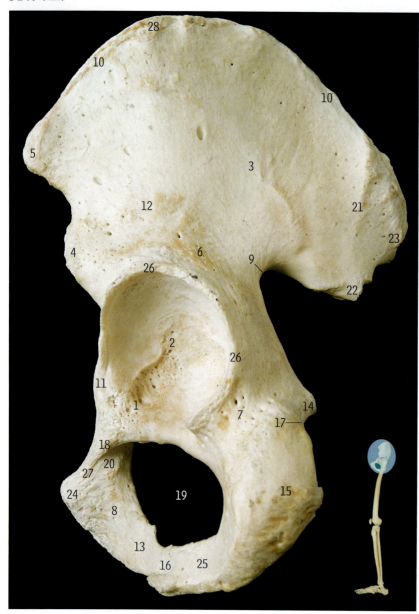

外側面．

1	寛骨臼切痕	Acetabular notch
2	寛骨臼	Acetabulum
3	前殿筋線	Anterior gluteal line
4	下前腸骨棘	Anterior inferior iliac spine
5	上前腸骨棘	Anterior superior iliac spine
6	腸骨体	Body of ilium
7	坐骨体	Body of ischium
8	恥骨体	Body of pubis
9	大坐骨切痕	Greater sciatic notch
10	腸骨稜	Iliac crest
11	腸恥隆起	Iliopubic eminence
12	下殿筋線	Inferior gluteal line
13	恥骨下枝	Inferior pubic ramus
14	坐骨棘	Ischial spine
15	坐骨結節	Ischial tuberosity
16	恥骨下枝と坐骨枝の接合部	
17	小坐骨切痕	Lesser sciatic notch
18	閉鎖稜	Obturator crest
19	閉鎖孔	Obturator foramen
20	閉鎖溝	Obturator groove
21	後殿筋線	Posterior gluteal line
22	下後腸骨棘	Posterior inferior iliac spine
23	上後腸骨棘	Posterior superior iliac spine
24	恥骨結節	Pubic tubercle
25	坐骨枝	Ramus of ischium
26	寛骨臼縁	Acetabular margin
27	恥骨上枝	Superior pubic ramus
28	腸骨結節	Tuberculum of iliac crest

- 寛骨は腸骨，坐骨および恥骨が合して形成される．
- 左右の寛骨は，前方では正中線の恥骨結合で連結する．また，後方では仙骨によって分けられ，それぞれ仙腸関節を形成する．左右の寛骨は，仙骨と尾骨とともに骨盤を構成する（96頁参照）．

寛骨（左）［筋と靱帯の付着部］

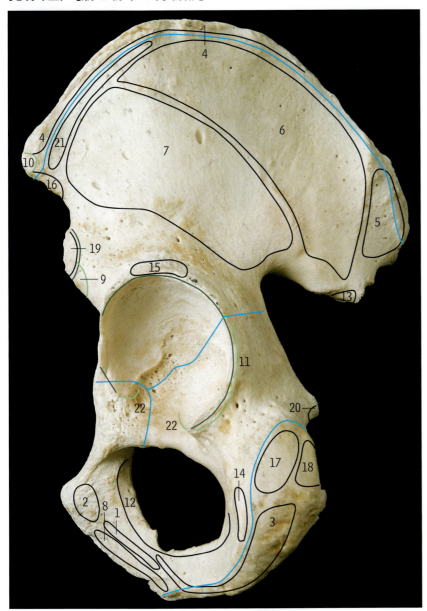

外側面．（青線：骨端線．緑線：股関節包の付着部．淡緑線：靱帯の付着部．）

1	短内転筋	Adductor brevis
2	長内転筋	Adductor longus
3	大内転筋	Adductor magnus
4	外腹斜筋	External oblique
5	大殿筋	Gluteus maximus
6	中殿筋	Gluteus medius
7	小殿筋	Gluteus minimus
8	薄筋	Gracilis
9	腸骨大腿靱帯	Iliofemoral ligament
10	鼠径靱帯	Inguinal ligament
11	坐骨大腿靱帯	Ischiofemoral ligament
12	外閉鎖筋	Obturator externus
13	梨状筋	Piriformis
14	大腿方形筋	Quadratus femoris
15	反転頭〔大腿直筋〕	Reflected head〔Rectus femoris〕
16	縫工筋	Sartorius
17	半膜様筋	Semimembranosus
18	長頭〔大腿二頭筋〕と半腱様筋	Long head〔Biceps femoris〕and Semitendinosus
19	直頭〔大腿直筋〕	Straight head〔Rectus femoris〕
20	上双子筋	Gemellus superior：Superior gemellus
21	大腿筋膜張筋	Tensor fasciae latae
22	寛骨臼横靱帯	Transverse acetabular ligament

寛骨（左）

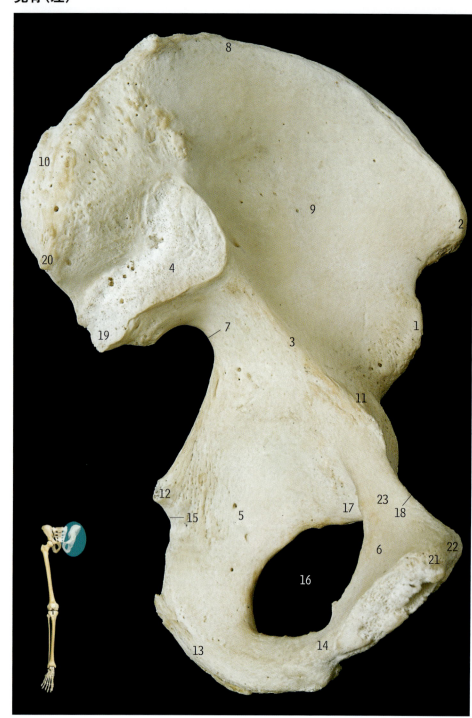

内側面．

1	下前腸骨棘	Anterior inferior iliac spine
2	上前腸骨棘	Anterior superior iliac spine
3	弓状線	Arcuate line
4	耳状面	Auricular surface
5	坐骨体	Body of ischium
6	恥骨体	Body of pubis
7	大坐骨切痕	Greater sciatic notch
8	腸骨稜	Iliac crest
9	腸骨窩	Iliac fossa
10	腸骨粗面	Iliac tuberosity
11	腸恥隆起	Iliopubic eminence
12	坐骨棘	Ischial spine
13	坐骨結節	Ischial tuberosity
14	坐骨枝と恥骨下枝	Ramus of ischium and Inferior pubic ramus
15	小坐骨切痕	Lesser sciatic notch
16	閉鎖孔	Obturator foramen
17	閉鎖溝	Obturator groove
18	恥骨櫛	Pecten pubis
19	下後腸骨棘	Posterior inferior iliac spine
20	上後腸骨棘	Posterior superior iliac spine
21	恥骨稜	Pubic crest
22	恥骨結節	Pubic tubercle
23	恥骨上枝	Superior pubic ramus

- 腸骨の耳状面（4）は，仙腸関節の関節面である．
- 大坐骨切痕（7）は，男性ではより鉤形（J状）になるのに対し，女性ではより直角（L状）になる．

寛骨(左)［筋と靱帯の付着部］

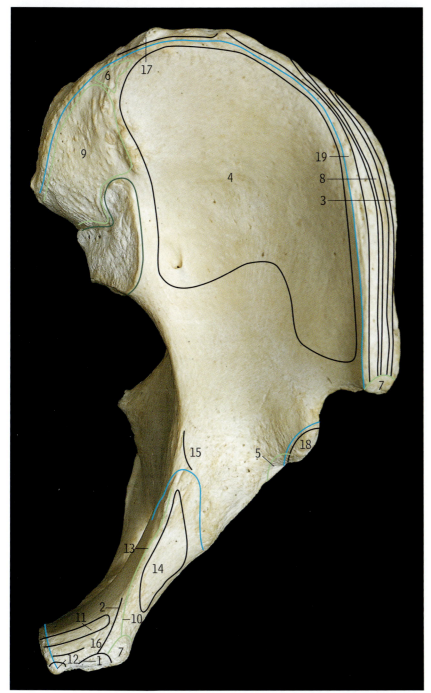

1	前葉〔腹直筋鞘〕	Anterior layer〔Rectus sheath〕
2	結合腱：鼠径鎌	Conjoint tendon：Inguinal falx
3	外腹斜筋	External oblique
4	腸骨筋	Iliacus
5	腸骨大腿靱帯	Iliofemoral ligament
6	腸腰靱帯	Iliolumbar ligament
7	鼠径靱帯	Inguinal ligament
8	内腹斜筋	Internal oblique
9	骨間仙腸靱帯	Interosseous sacro-iliac ligament
10	裂孔靱帯	Lacunar ligament
11	腹直筋（外側腱*）	Rectus abdominis
12	腹直筋（内側腱*）	Rectus abdominis
13	恥骨櫛靱帯	Pectineal ligament
14	恥骨筋	Pectineus
15	小腰筋	Psoas minor
16	錐体筋	Pyramidalis
17	腰方形筋	Quadratus lumborum
18	直頭〔大腿直筋〕	Straight head〔Rectus femoris〕
19	腹横筋	Transversus abdominis

- 鼠径靱帯(7)は外腹斜筋の腱膜の下縁によって形成され，上前腸骨棘と恥骨結節との間に張っている．
- 裂孔靱帯(10．しばしば"鼠径靱帯の恥骨櫛部"とよばれる)は，鼠径靱帯の内側端から後方へ延びて恥骨櫛に付着した部分である．
- 恥骨櫛靱帯(13)は，裂孔靱帯が恥骨櫛に沿って外側へ延びたものである．恥骨櫛靱帯は鼠径靱帯の一部ではないので，裂孔靱帯の別名の"鼠径靱帯の恥骨櫛部"と混同してはならない．
- 結合腱(鼠径鎌，2)は，内腹斜筋と腹横筋の腱膜から形成され，恥骨稜および恥骨櫛に隣接する領域に着き，内側で腹直筋鞘の前葉と癒合する．

上方から．（青線：骨端線．緑線：仙腸関節包の付着部．淡緑線：靱帯の付着部．）

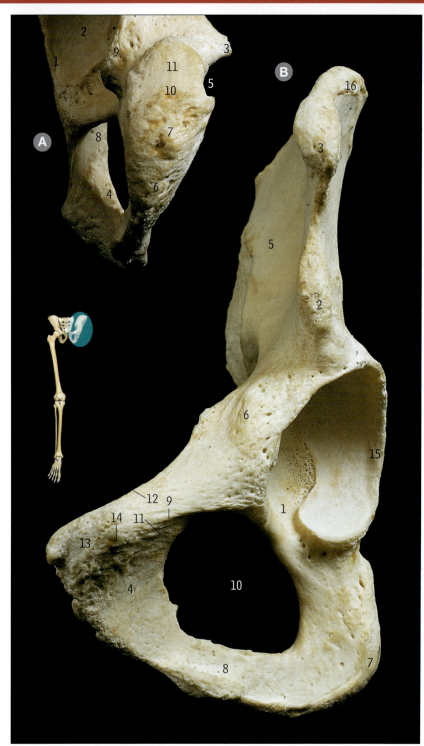

A 寛骨（左）[坐骨結節]

1. 寛骨臼切痕 Acetabular notch
2. 寛骨臼 Acetabulum
3. 坐骨棘 Ischial spine
4. 恥骨下枝と坐骨枝 Inferior ramus of pubis and Ramus of ischium
5. 小坐骨切痕 Lesser sciatic notch
6. 縦稜＊〔坐骨結節〕 Longitudinal ridge＊〔Ischial tuberosity〕
7. 下部＊〔坐骨結節〕 Lower part＊〔Ischial tuberosity〕
8. 閉鎖溝 Obturator groove
9. 寛骨臼縁 Acetabular margin
10. 横稜＊〔坐骨結節〕 Transverse ridge＊〔Ischial tuberosity〕
11. 上部＊〔坐骨結節〕 Upper part＊〔Ischial tuberosity〕

B 寛骨（左）

1. 寛骨臼切痕 Acetabular notch
2. 下前腸骨棘 Anterior inferior iliac spine
3. 上前腸骨棘 Anterior superior iliac spine
4. 恥骨体 Body of pubis
5. 腸骨窩 Iliac fossa
6. 腸恥隆起 Iliopubic eminence
7. 坐骨結節 Ischial tuberosity
8. 恥骨下枝と坐骨枝 Inferior ramus of pubis and Ramus of ischium
9. 閉鎖稜 Obturator crest
10. 閉鎖孔 Obturator foramen
11. 閉鎖溝 Obturator groove
12. 恥骨櫛 Pecten pubis
13. 恥骨稜 Pubic crest
14. 恥骨結節 Pubic tubercle
15. 寛骨臼縁 Acetabular margin
16. 腸骨結節 Tuberculum of iliac crest

A：後下方から．B：前方から．

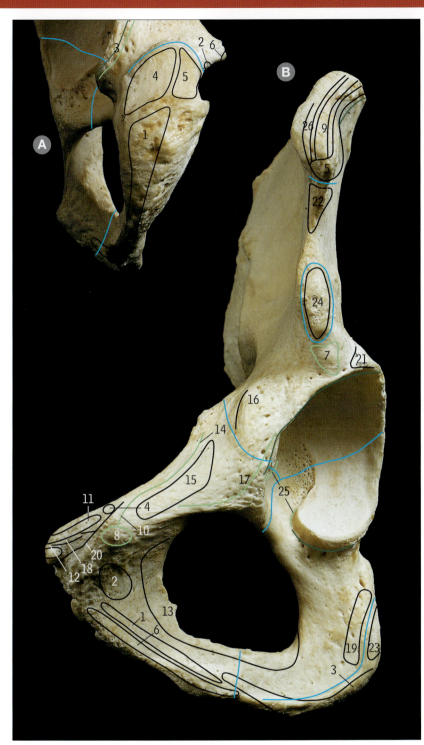

Ⓐ 寛骨（左）［坐骨結節，筋と靱帯の付着部］

1. 大内転筋 Adductor magnus
2. 下双子筋 Gemellus inferior：Inferior gemellus
3. 坐骨大腿靱帯 Ischiofemoral ligament
4. 半膜様筋 Semimembranosus
5. 長頭〔大腿二頭筋〕と半腱様筋 Long head〔Biceps femoris〕and Semitendinosus
6. 上双子筋 Gemellus superior：Superior gemellus

● 坐骨結節の大内転筋(1)の起始部より内側の領域は，線維脂肪組織と大殿筋の下にある坐骨包によって覆われている．

Ⓑ 寛骨（左）［筋と靱帯の付着部］

1. 短内転筋 Adductor brevis
2. 長内転筋 Adductor longus
3. 大内転筋 Adductor magnus
4. 結合腱：鼠径鎌 Conjoint tendon：Inguinal falx
5. 外腹斜筋と鼠径靱帯 External oblique and Inguinal ligament
6. 薄筋 Gracilis
7. 腸骨大腿靱帯 Iliofemoral ligament
8. 鼠径靱帯 Inguinal ligament
9. 内腹斜筋 Internal oblique
10. 裂孔靱帯 Lacunar ligament
11. 腹直筋（外側頭） Rectus abdominis
12. 腹直筋（内側頭） Rectus abdominis
13. 外閉鎖筋 Obturator externus
14. 恥骨櫛靱帯 Pectineal ligament
15. 恥骨筋 Pectineus
16. 小腰筋 Psoas minor
17. 恥骨大腿靱帯 Pubofemoral ligament
18. 錐体筋 Pyramidalis
19. 大腿方形筋 Quadratus femoris
20. 腹直筋鞘 Rectus sheath
21. 反転頭〔大腿直筋〕 Reflected head〔Rectus femoris〕
22. 縫工筋 Sartorius
23. 半膜様筋 Semimembranosus
24. 直頭〔大腿直筋〕 Straight head〔Rectus femoris〕
25. 寛骨臼横靱帯 Transverse acetabular ligament
26. 腹横筋 Transversus abdominis

Ａ：後下方から．Ｂ：前方から．（青線：骨端線．緑線：股関節包の付着部．淡緑線：靱帯の付着部．）

大腿骨（左）［上端］

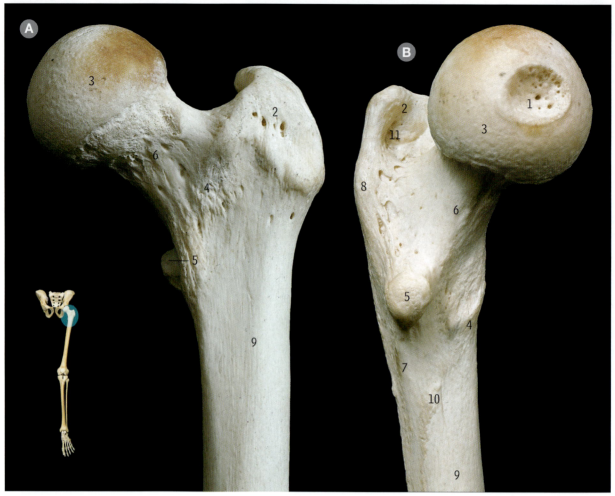

A：前方から．B：内側方から．

1	大腿骨頭窩 Fovea for ligament of head
2	大転子 Greater trochanter
3	大腿骨頭 Head of femur
4	転子間線 Intertrochanteric line
5	小転子 Lesser trochanter
6	大腿骨頸 Neck of femur
7	恥骨筋線 Pectineal line
8	方形結節〔転子間稜〕 Quadrate tubercle〔Intertrochanteric crest〕
9	大腿骨体 Shaft of femur：Body of femur
10	内側広筋の起始線＊
11	転子窩 Trochanteric fossa

- 転子間線(4)は，大腿骨前面の大腿骨体(9)と大腿骨頸(6)の結合部にある．転子間稜(8, 304頁A5)は，大腿骨後面の結合部の稜線である．
- 大腿骨体と大腿骨頸とのなす角は成人では約125°である．
- 大腿骨の恥骨筋線(7)を恥骨の恥骨櫛(298頁9)と混同してはいけない[訳注1]．また，大腿骨の恥骨筋線(7)と内側広筋の起始線(10)を混同してはならない[訳注2]．一般に大腿骨においては，内側広筋の起始線のほうが，恥骨筋線より明瞭である[訳注3]．
- ［訳注1］英語圏ではしばしばこれらの2つに，ともにPectineal lineという用語を使う．
- ［訳注2］英語圏ではしばしばこれらの2つに，ともにSpiral lineという用語を使う．
- ［訳注3］「解剖学用語」では，日本語の恥骨筋線に対してPectineal line：Spiral lineという2つの英語名を与えている．よって，混同をさけるため，本書では恥骨櫛はPecten pubis，恥骨筋線はPectineal lineとしている．なお，内側広筋の起始線には，「解剖学用語」に適切な用語が与えられていない．

剥離骨折

大腿骨（左）［上端，筋と靱帯の付着部］

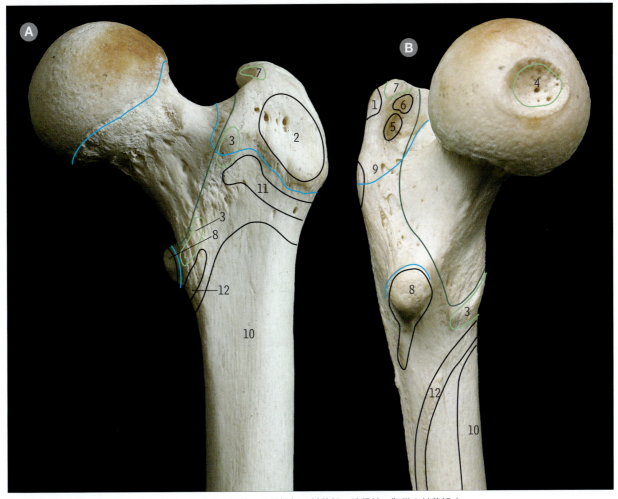

A：前方から．**B**：内側方から．（青線：骨端線．緑線：股関節包の付着部．淡緑線：靱帯の付着部．）

1 中殿筋
　Gluteus medius
2 小殿筋
　Gluteus minimus
3 腸骨大腿靱帯
　Iliofemoral ligament
4 大腿骨頭靱帯
　Ligament of head of femur
5 外閉鎖筋
　Obturator externus
6 内閉鎖筋，上双子筋，下双子筋
　Obturator internus, Gemellus superior：Superior gemellus，
　Gemellus inferior：Inferior gemellus
7 梨状筋
　Piriformis
8 大腰筋と腸骨筋
　Psoas major and Iliacus
9 大腿方形筋
　Quadratus femoris
10 中間広筋
　Vastus intermedius
11 外側広筋
　Vastus lateralis
12 内側広筋
　Vastus medialis

- 腸骨大腿靱帯（301頁B7）は逆V字形の靱帯である．V字の幹は寛骨の下前腸骨棘に付き，外側束と内側束は股関節包に癒合して転子間線（304頁6）の上（外側）端と下（内側）端に付着する．
- 大腰筋の腱は小転子（304頁8）に着く．腸骨筋の筋束の多くは大腰筋腱に着くが，一部は大腿骨の小転子の下方にまで達する．

大腿骨転子間骨折

大腿骨(左) [上端]

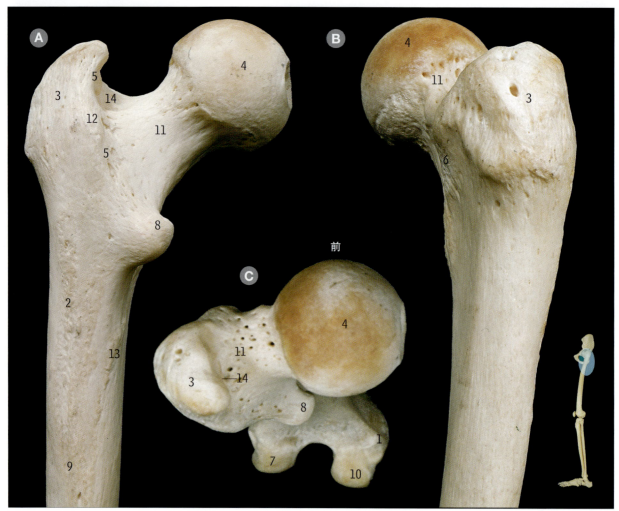

A：後方から．B：外側方から．C：上方から．

1	内転筋結節(大腿骨の下端) Adductor tubercle	8	小転子 Lesser trochanter
2	殿筋粗面 Gluteal tuberosity	9	粗線 Linea aspera
3	大転子 Greater trochanter	10	内側顆(大腿骨の下端) Medial condyle
4	大腿骨頭 Head of femur	11	大腿骨頸 Neck of femur
5	転子間稜 Intertrochanteric crest	12	方形結節 Quadrate tubercle
6	転子間線 Intertrochanteric line	13	内側広筋の起始線*
7	外側顆(大腿骨の下端) Lateral condyle	14	転子窩 Trochanteric fossa

- 大腿骨頸(C11)は，上内側方向はもちろんのこと，前方へも突出している．その角度(大腿骨の捻転角または前捻角)は，成人では大腿骨下端の横軸に対して約15°である．
- 小転子(8)は，後内側方向に突出している．

大腿骨頸部骨折

大腿骨（左）［上端，筋と靱帯の付着部］

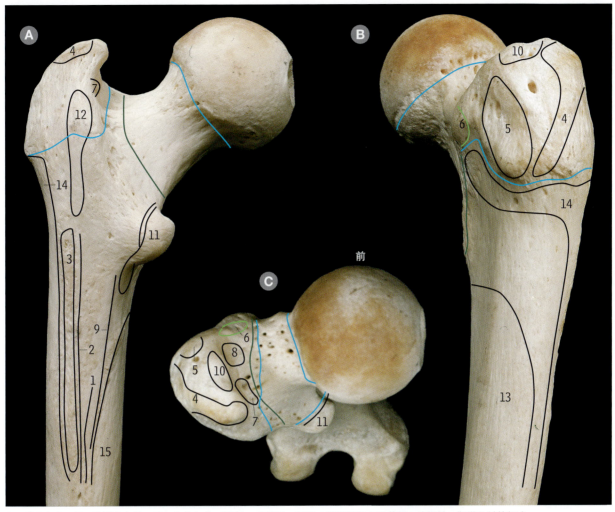

A：後方から．B：外側方から．C：上方から．（青線：骨端線．緑線：股関節包の付着部．淡緑線：靱帯の付着部．）

1	短内転筋	Adductor brevis
2	大内転筋	Adductor magnus
3	大殿筋	Gluteus maximus
4	中殿筋	Gluteus medius
5	小殿筋	Gluteus minimus
6	横部〔腸骨大腿靱帯〕	Transverse part〔Iliofemoral ligament〕
7	外閉鎖筋	Obturator externus
8	内閉鎖筋，上双子筋，下双子筋	Obturator internus, Gemellus superior：Superior gemellus, Gemellus inferior：Inferior gemellus
9	恥骨筋	Pectineus
10	梨状筋	Piriformis
11	大腰筋と腸骨筋	Psoas major and Iliacus
12	大腿方形筋	Quadratus femoris
13	中間広筋	Vastus intermedius
14	外側広筋	Vastus lateralis
15	内側広筋	Vastus medialis

● 大腿骨前面（303 頁）では股関節包は転子間線に付着する．しかし後面では大腿骨頸に付き，外側は転子間稜（304 頁 A5）まで達しない．

外骨腫による
大腿骨の骨棘

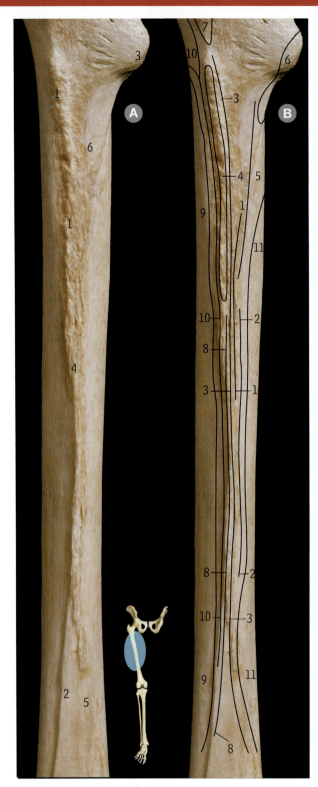

A 大腿骨（左）［大腿骨体］

1	殿筋粗面 Gluteal tuberosity	4	粗線 Linea aspera
2	外側顆上線 Lateral supracondylar line	5	内側顆上線 Medial supracondylar line
3	小転子 Lesser trochanter	6	恥骨筋線 Pectineal line

● ざらざらした粗線(4)には，しばしば明瞭な内側唇ならびに外側唇が認められる．外側唇は上方で殿筋粗面(1)まで続いている．

B 大腿骨（左）［大腿骨体，筋と靱帯の付着部］

1	短内転筋 Adductor brevis	7	大腿方形筋 Quadratus femoris
2	長内転筋 Adductor longus	8	短頭〔大腿二頭筋〕 Short head〔Biceps femoris〕
3	大内転筋 Adductor magnus	9	中間広筋 Vastus intermedius
4	大殿筋 Gluteus maximus	10	外側広筋 Vastus lateralis
5	恥骨筋 Pectineus	11	内側広筋 Vastus medialis
6	大腰筋と腸骨筋〔腸腰筋〕 Psoas major and Iliacus〔Iliopsoas〕		

● 明瞭に図示するために，粗線への筋の付着は，相互にやや離して描いてある．

C 大腿骨［上端］

骨梁の主なものを示すように，大腿骨を透明化し，縦に2つに割ったものの後ろの半分である．

1. 大腿骨距* Calcar femorale *
2. 大腿骨体の外側面から大転子に至る骨梁
3. 大腿骨体の外側面から大腿骨頭に至る骨梁
4. 大腿骨体の内側面から大転子に至る骨梁
5. 大腿骨体の内側面から大腿骨頭に至る骨梁
6. 骨梁が乏しい三角域

● 大腿骨距(1)は，小結節領域から大腿骨頭の下面へ向かう骨梁が集中して緻密化したところである．

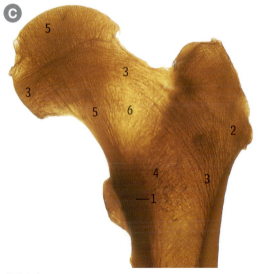

前方から．

A：後方から．B：後方から．

大腿骨の骨幹の骨折

第6章 下肢：下肢骨　307

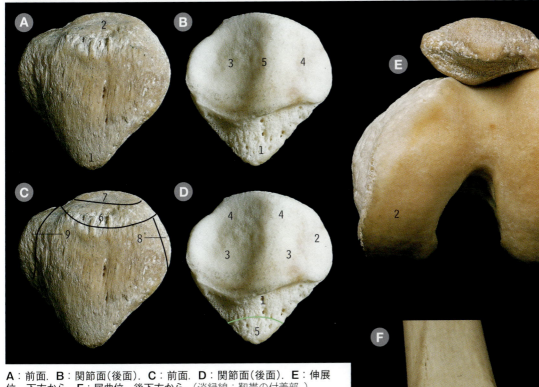

A：前面．B：関節面（後面）．C：前面．D：関節面（後面）．E：伸展位，下方から．F：屈曲位，後下方から．（淡緑線：靱帯の付着部．）

A B 膝蓋骨（左）

1 膝蓋骨尖　Apex of patella
2 膝蓋骨底　Base of patella
3 大腿骨の外側顆に対向する関節面
4 大腿骨の内側顆に対向する関節面
5 垂直稜＊　Vertical ridge＊

C D 膝蓋骨（左）［筋と靱帯の付着部］

1 膝蓋下脂肪体と接する部分
2 最大屈曲時に大腿骨の内側顆に対向する部分
3 伸展時に大腿骨に対向する面
4 屈曲時に大腿骨に対向する面
5 膝蓋靱帯　Patellar ligament
6 大腿直筋〔大腿四頭筋〕　Rectus femoris〔Quadriceps femoris〕
7 中間広筋〔大腿四頭筋〕　Vastus intermedius〔Quadriceps femoris〕
8 外側広筋〔大腿四頭筋〕　Vastus lateralis〔Quadriceps femoris〕
9 内側広筋〔大腿四頭筋〕　Vastus medialis〔Quadriceps femoris〕

E F 大腿骨と膝蓋骨（左）［骨を組み合わせてある］

屈曲位では，大腿骨の内側顆（2）と膝蓋骨の接触域が広がることに注意せよ．

1 外側顆　Lateral condyle
2 内側顆　Medial condyle

● 膝蓋骨の関節面の最内側部（D2）は，最大限に屈曲したときにのみ内側顆と接する（F）．

二分膝蓋骨

膝蓋骨の脱臼

膝蓋骨骨折

大腿骨(左) [下端]

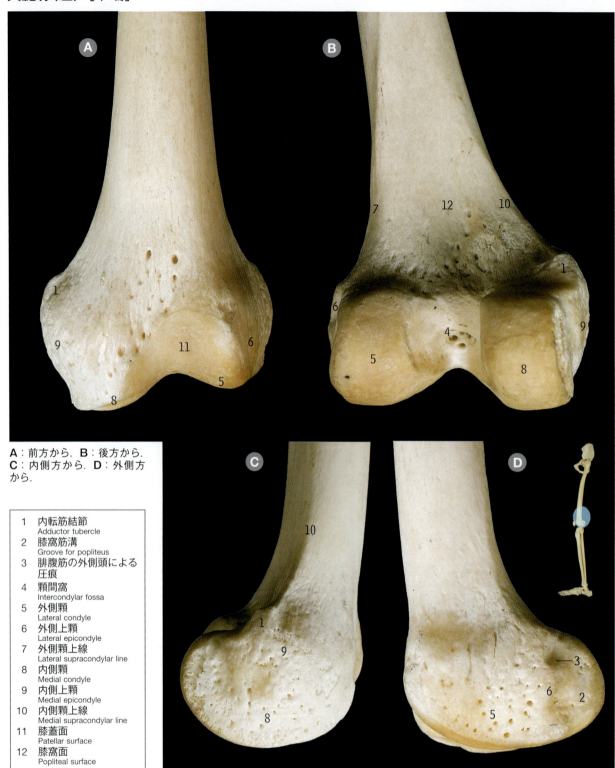

A：前方から. B：後方から.
C：内側方から. D：外側方から.

1	内転筋結節	Adductor tubercle
2	膝窩筋溝	Groove for popliteus
3	腓腹筋の外側頭による圧痕	
4	顆間窩	Intercondylar fossa
5	外側顆	Lateral condyle
6	外側上顆	Lateral epicondyle
7	外側顆上線	Lateral supracondylar line
8	内側顆	Medial condyle
9	内側上顆	Medial epicondyle
10	内側顆上線	Medial supracondylar line
11	膝蓋面	Patellar surface
12	膝窩面	Popliteal surface

大腿骨（左）［下端，筋と靱帯の付着部］

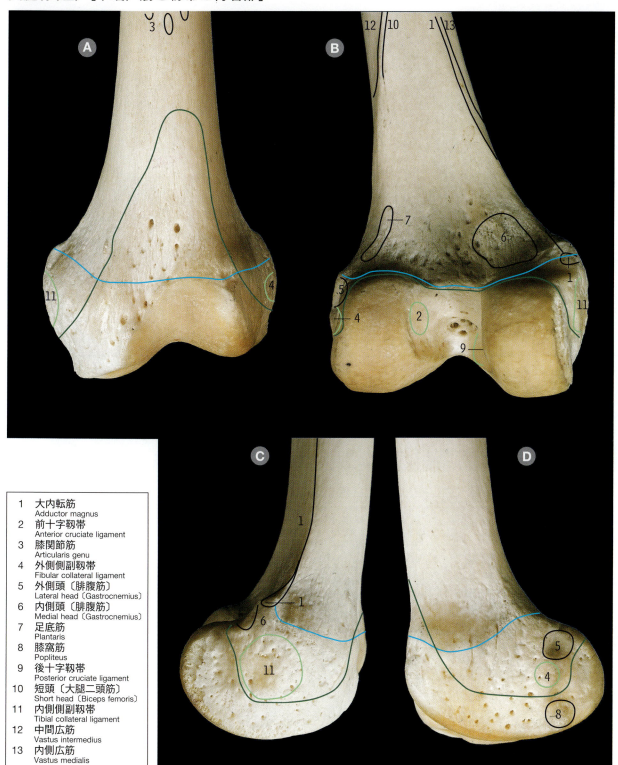

1	大内転筋 Adductor magnus
2	前十字靱帯 Anterior cruciate ligament
3	膝関節筋 Articularis genu
4	外側側副靱帯 Fibular collateral ligament
5	外側頭〔腓腹筋〕 Lateral head〔Gastrocnemius〕
6	内側頭〔腓腹筋〕 Medial head〔Gastrocnemius〕
7	足底筋 Plantaris
8	膝窩筋 Popliteus
9	後十字靱帯 Posterior cruciate ligament
10	短頭〔大腿二頭筋〕 Short head〔Biceps femoris〕
11	内側側副靱帯 Tibial collateral ligament
12	中間広筋 Vastus intermedius
13	内側広筋 Vastus medialis

A：前方から．**B**：後方から．**C**：内側方から．**D**：外側方から．（青線：骨端線．緑線：膝関節包の付着部．淡緑線：靱帯の付着部．）

脛骨（左）［上端］

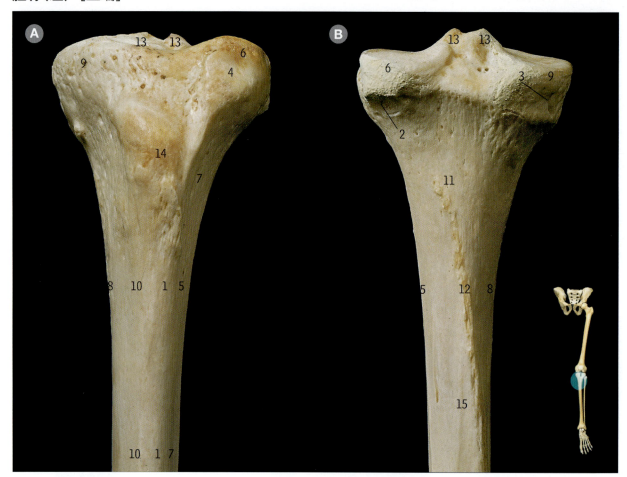

A：前方から．B：後方から．

1	前縁 Anterior border
2	腓骨関節面 Fibular articular facet
3	半膜様筋の腱が着く溝
4	腸脛靱帯による圧痕
5	骨間縁 Interosseous border
6	外側顆 Lateral condyle
7	外側面 Lateral surface
8	内側縁 Medial border
9	内側顆 Medial condyle
10	内側面 Medial surface
11	後面 Posterior surface
12	ヒラメ筋線 Soleal line
13	内側顆間結節と外側顆間結節〔顆間隆起〕 Medial intercondylar tubercle and Lateral intercondylar tubercle〔Intercondylar eminence〕
14	脛骨粗面 Tibial tuberosity
15	長趾屈筋と後脛骨筋との間の筋間中隔が着く垂直線

- 脛骨体には，前縁(1)，内側縁(8)，骨間縁(5)の3縁が認められ，また内側面(10)，外側面(7)，後面(11)の3面が認められる．
- 前縁(1)の大部分は，軽く曲がった稜を形成し，一般に"向こう脛（ずね）"とよばれる．滑らかな内側面(10)の大部分は，皮下にある．後面には，ヒラメ筋線(12)と垂直線(15)がある．
- 脛骨粗面(14)は前縁の上端にある．

A B 脛骨（左）［上端，筋と靱帯の付着部］

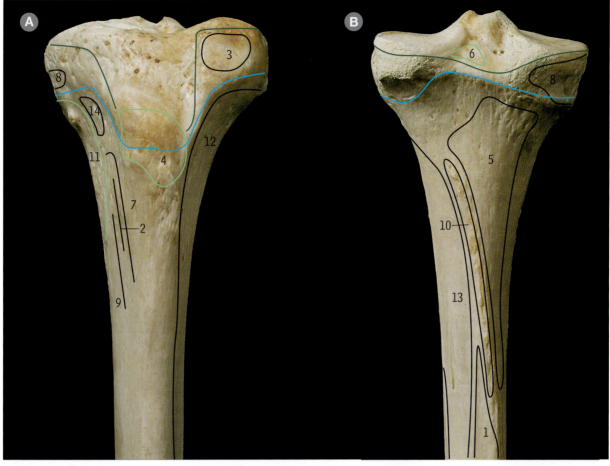

A：前方から．B：後方から．（青線：骨端線．緑線：膝関節包の付着部．淡緑線：靱帯の付着部．）

1	長趾屈筋 Flexor digitorum longus	8	半膜様筋 Semimembranosus
2	薄筋 Gracilis	9	半腱様筋 Semitendinosus
3	腸脛靱帯 Iliotibial tract	10	ヒラメ筋 Soleus
4	膝蓋靱帯 Patellar ligament	11	内側側副靱帯 Tibial collateral ligament
5	膝窩筋 Popliteus	12	前脛骨筋 Tibialis anterior
6	後十字靱帯 Posterior cruciate ligament	13	後脛骨筋 Tibialis posterior
7	縫工筋 Sartorius	14	内側広筋 Vastus medialis

C 脛骨，下腿骨間膜，腓骨

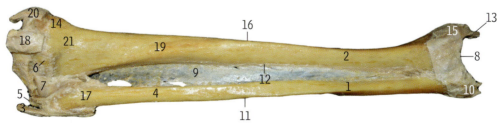

1	前縁〔腓骨〕 Anterior border〔Fibula〕	7	腸脛靱帯 Iliotibial tract	13	内側靱帯：三角靱帯 Medial ligament : Deltoid ligament	19	脛骨 Tibia
2	前縁〔脛骨〕 Anterior border〔Tibia〕	8	下関節面 Inferior articular surface	14	内側顆 Medial condyle	20	内側側副靱帯 Tibial collateral ligament
3	大腿二頭筋（の腱） Biceps femoris	9	下腿骨間膜 Interosseous membrane of leg	15	内果 Medial malleolus	21	脛骨粗面 Tibial tuberosity
4	腓骨 Fibula	10	外果 Lateral malleolus	16	内側面〔脛骨〕 Medial surface〔Tibia〕		
5	外側側副靱帯 Fibular collateral ligament	11	外側面〔腓骨〕 Lateral surface〔Fibula〕	17	腓骨頸 Neck of fibula		
6	Gerdy 結節* Gerdy's tubercle *	12	外側面〔脛骨〕 Lateral surface〔Tibia〕	18	膝蓋靱帯 Patellar ligament		

脛骨(左)［上端］

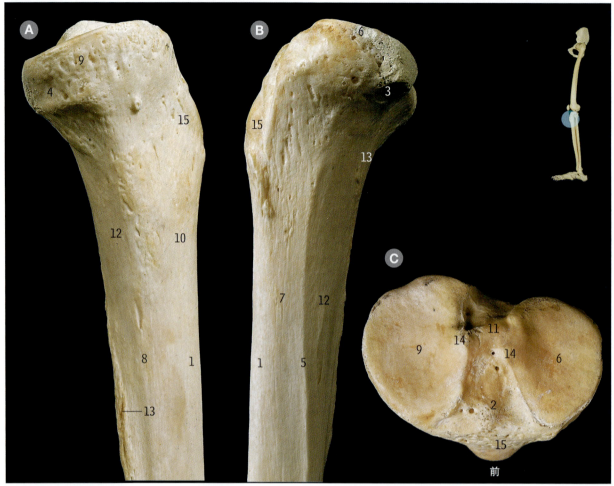

A：内側方から．B：外側方から．C：上方から．

1	前縁 Anterior border	9	内側顆 Medial condyle
2	前顆間区 Anterior intercondylar area	10	内側面 Medial surface
3	腓骨関節面 Fibular articular facet	11	後顆間区 Posterior intercondylar area
4	半膜様筋の腱が着く溝	12	後面 Posterior surface
5	骨間縁 Interosseous border	13	ヒラメ筋線 Soleal line
6	外側顆 Lateral condyle	14	内側顆間結節と外側顆間結節〔顆間隆起〕Medial intercondylar tubercle and Lateral intercondylar tubercle〔Intercondylar eminence〕
7	外側面 Lateral surface		
8	内側縁 Medial border	15	脛骨粗面 Tibial tuberosity

- 内側顆(C9)は外側顆(C6)より大きい．
- 脛骨の腓骨関節面(B3)は，外側顆(B6)の後下方にある．

Osgood-Schlatter病

脛骨(左)［上端，筋と靱帯の付着部］

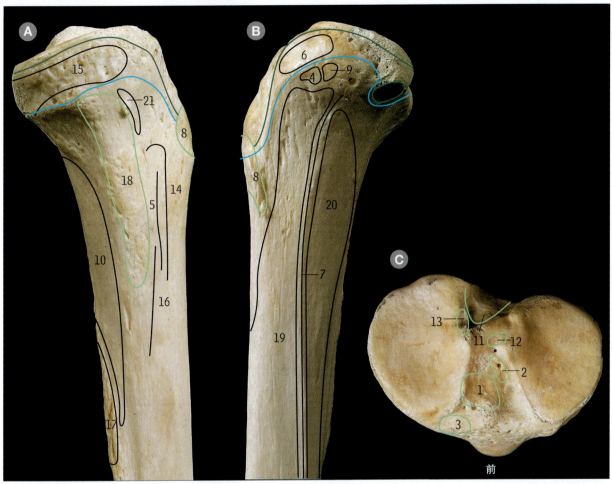

A：内側方から．B：外側方から．C：上方から．（青線：骨端線．緑線：膝関節包と脛腓関節包の付着部．淡緑線：靱帯の付着部．）

1 前十字靱帯 Anterior cruciate ligament	12 後角*〔外側半月〕 Posterior horn *〔Lateral meniscus〕
2 前角*〔外側半月〕 Anterior horn *〔Lateral meniscus〕	13 後角*〔内側半月〕 Posterior horn *〔Medial meniscus〕
3 前角*〔内側半月〕 Anterior horn *〔Medial meniscus〕	14 縫工筋 Sartorius
4 長趾伸筋 Extensor digitorum longus	15 半膜様筋 Semimembranosus
5 薄筋 Gracilis	16 半腱様筋 Semitendinosus
6 腸脛靱帯 Iliotibial tract	17 ヒラメ筋 Soleus
7 下腿骨間膜 Interosseous membrane of leg	18 内側側副靱帯 Tibial collateral ligament
8 膝蓋靱帯 Patellar ligament	19 前脛骨筋 Tibialis anterior
9 長腓骨筋 Fibularis (Peroneus) longus	20 後脛骨筋 Tibialis posterior
10 膝窩筋 Popliteus	21 内側広筋 Vastus medialis
11 後十字靱帯 Posterior cruciate ligament	

314　第6章　下肢：下肢骨

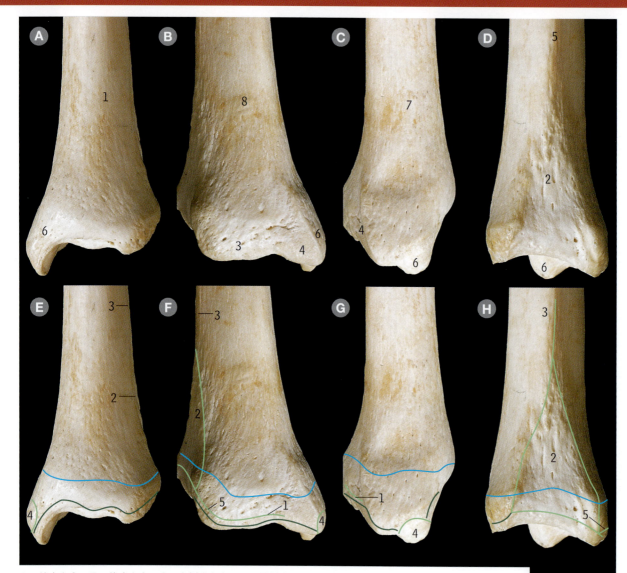

A：前方から．B：後方から．C：内側方から．D：外側方から．E：前方から．F：後方から．G：内側方から．H：外側方から．（青線：骨端線．緑線：距腿関節包の付着部．淡緑線：靱帯の付着部．）

Ⓐ〜Ⓓ　脛骨（左）［下端］

1. 前縁　Anterior border
2. 腓骨切痕　Fibular notch
3. 長母趾屈筋が通る溝
4. 後脛骨筋が通る溝
5. 骨間縁　Interosseous border
6. 内果　Medial malleolus
7. 内側面　Medial surface
8. 後面　Posterior surface

Ⓔ〜Ⓗ　脛骨（左）［下端，筋と靱帯の付着部］

1. 下横靱帯*　Inferior transverse ligament *
2. 骨間靱帯*　Interosseous ligament *
3. 下腿骨間膜　Interosseous membrane of leg
4. 内側靱帯：三角靱帯　Medial ligament：Deltoid ligament
5. 後脛腓靱帯　Posterior tibiofibular ligament

● 内側靱帯（G4）は，一般に三角靱帯とよばれる．

脛骨骨折

脛骨と腓骨（左）［骨を組み合わせてある］

A：上端，後方から．B：上端，上方から．C：腓骨の上端，上方から．D：下端，後方から．E：下端，下方から．

1. 腓骨頭尖
   Apex of head of fibula
2. 腓骨頭関節面（脛腓関節）
   Articular facet of fibula
3. 外果関節面〔腓骨〕（距腿関節）
   Articular facet of lateral malleolus〔Fibula〕
4. 腓骨頭
   Head of fibula
5. 下関節面〔脛骨〕（距腿関節）
   Inferior articular surface〔Tibia〕
6. 脛腓靱帯結合：下脛腓関節*
   Tibiofibular syndesmosis：Inferior tibiofibular joint
7. 内果関節面〔脛骨〕（距腿関節）
   Articular facet of medial malleolus〔Tibia〕
8. 外側顆〔脛骨〕
   Lateral condyle〔Tibia〕
9. 外果
   Lateral malleolus
10. 外果窩
    Malleolar fossa
11. 内果
    Medial malleolus
12. 脛腓関節
    Tibiofibular joint：Superior tibiofibular joint

- 脛腓関節（A12）は滑膜性の連結である．
- 脛腓靱帯結合（D6）は靱帯結合である．
- 外果（D9）は，内果（D11）よりも下方に延びている．

足根骨脱臼

A：前方から．B：後方から．C：内側方から．
D：外側方から．

Ⓐ〜Ⓓ 腓骨（左）［上端］

1 前縁 Anterior border
2 腓骨頭尖 Apex of head of fibula
3 腓骨頭関節面（脛腓関節） Articular facet of fibula
4 腓骨頭 Head of fibula
5 骨間縁 Interosseous border
6 外側面 Lateral surface
7 内側稜 Medial crest
8 内側面 Medial surface
9 腓骨頸 Neck of fibula
10 後縁 Posterior border
11 後面 Posterior surface

- 腓骨には前縁（A1），骨間縁（A5），後縁（B10）の3縁が認められる．また，内側面（A8），外側面（A6），後面（B11）の3面が認められる．
- 腓骨体は，一見，4縁と4面があるように見える．しかし，これは内側稜（B7）が後面（B11）を内側部と外側部に分けているからである．

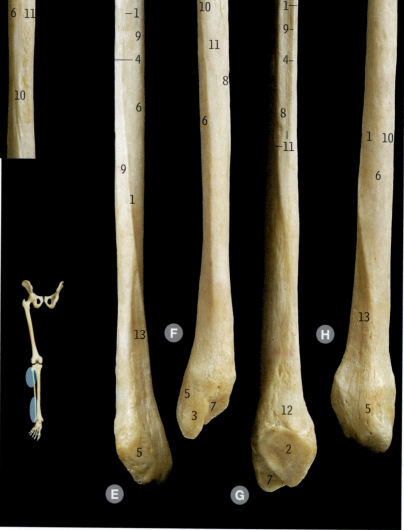

E：前方から．F：後方から．G：内側方から．H：外側方から．

Ⓔ〜Ⓗ 腓骨（左）［下端］

1 前縁 Anterior border
2 外果関節面〔腓骨〕 Articular facet of lateral malleolus〔Fibula〕
3 短腓骨筋が通る溝
4 骨間縁 Interosseous border
5 外果 Lateral malleolus
6 外側面 Lateral surface
7 外果窩 Malleolar fossa
8 内側稜 Medial crest
9 内側面 Medial surface
10 後縁 Posterior border
11 後面 Posterior surface
12 骨間靱帯*（の付着面） Interosseous ligament*
13 皮下に接する三角形の領域

第6章 下肢：下肢骨　317

A〜D 腓骨（左）[上端，筋と靱帯の付着部]

1 大腿二頭筋 Biceps femoris
2 長趾伸筋 Extensor digitorum longus
3 長母趾伸筋 Extensor hallucis longus
4 外側側副靱帯 Fibular collateral ligament
5 長母趾屈筋 Flexor hallucis longus
6 下腿骨間膜 Interosseous membrane of leg
7 短腓骨筋 Fibularis (Peroneus) brevis
8 長腓骨筋 Fibularis (Peroneus) longus
9 ヒラメ筋 Soleus
10 後脛骨筋 Tibialis posterior

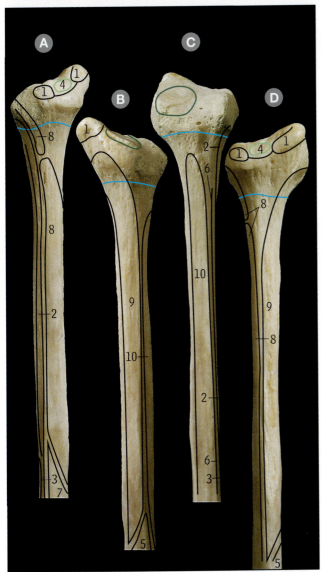

A：前方から．B：後方から．C：内側方から．D：外側方から．（青線：骨端線．緑線：脛腓関節包の付着部．淡緑線：靱帯の付着部．）

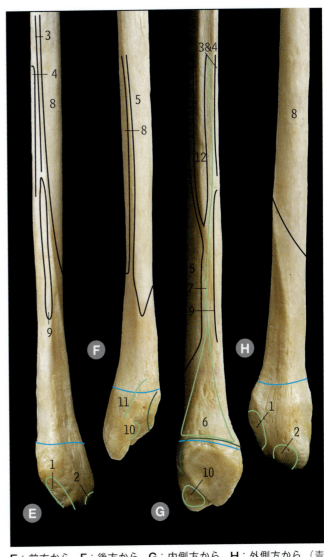

E：前方から．F：後方から．G：内側方から．H：外側方から．（青線：骨端線．緑線：距腿関節包の付着部．淡緑線：靱帯の付着部．）

E〜H 腓骨（左）[下端，筋と靱帯の付着部]

1 前距腓靱帯 Anterior talofibular ligament
2 踵腓靱帯 Calcaneofibular ligament
3 長趾伸筋 Extensor digitorum longus
4 長母趾伸筋 Extensor hallucis longus
5 長母趾屈筋 Flexor hallucis longus
6 骨間靱帯* Interosseous ligament *
7 下腿骨間膜 Interosseous membrane of leg
8 短腓骨筋 Fibularis (Peroneus) brevis
9 第三腓骨筋 Fibularis (Peroneus) tertius
10 後距腓靱帯 Posterior talofibular ligament
11 後脛腓靱帯 Posterior tibiofibular ligament
12 後脛骨筋 Tibialis posterior

足の骨（左）［Ⓐ 足背，Ⓑ 足底］

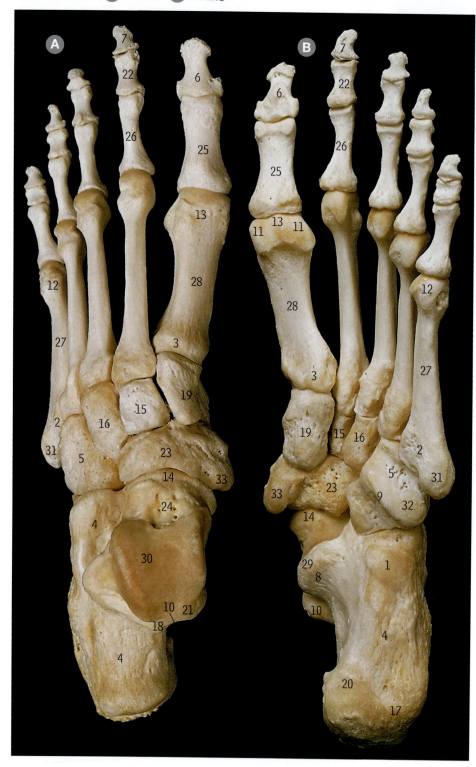

1	踵骨結節	Calcaneal tubercle
2	第五中足骨底	Base of 5th metatarsal bone
3	第一中足骨底	Base of 1st metatarsal bone
4	踵骨	Calcaneus
5	立方骨	Cuboid
6	末節骨〔母趾（第一趾）〕	Distal phalanx〔Great toe [I]〕
7	末節骨〔第二趾〕	Distal phalanx〔2nd toe [II]〕
8	長母趾屈筋腱溝〔踵骨〕	Groove for tendon of flexor hallucis longus〔Calcaneus〕
9	長腓骨筋腱溝〔立方骨〕	Groove for tendon of fibularis (peroneus) longus〔Cuboid〕
10	長母趾屈筋腱溝〔距骨〕	Groove for tendon of flexor hallucis longus〔Talus〕
11	短母趾屈筋の腱の種子骨による溝	
12	第五中足骨頭	Head of 5th metatarsal bone
13	第一中足骨頭	Head of 1st metatarsal bone
14	距骨頭	Head of talus
15	中間楔状骨	Intermediate cuneiform
16	外側楔状骨	Lateral cuneiform
17	踵骨隆起外側突起	Lateral process of calcaneal tuberosity
18	外側結節〔距骨〕	Lateral tubercle〔Talus〕
19	内側楔状骨	Medial cuneiform
20	踵骨隆起内側突起	Medial process of calcaneal tuberosity
21	内側結節〔距骨〕	Medial tubercle〔Talus〕
22	中節骨〔第二趾〕	Middle phalanx〔2nd toe [II]〕
23	舟状骨	Navicular
24	距骨頸	Neck of talus
25	基節骨〔母趾（第一趾）〕	Proximal phalanx〔Great toe [I]〕
26	基節骨〔第二趾〕	Proximal phalanx〔2nd toe [II]〕
27	第五中足骨体	Shaft of 5th metatarsal bone：Body of 5th metatarsal bone
28	第一中足骨体	Shaft of 1st metatarsal bone：Body of 1st metatarsal bone
29	載距突起〔踵骨〕	Sustentaculum tali〔Calcaneus〕
30	上面〔距骨滑車〕	Superior facet〔Trochlea of talus〕
31	第五中足骨粗面	Tuberosity of 5th metatarsal bone
32	立方骨粗面	Tuberosity of cuboid
33	舟状骨粗面	Tuberosity of navicular

趾関節脱臼

外反母趾

足の骨（左）［Ⓐ 足背，筋と靱帯の付着部，Ⓑ 足底，筋と靱帯の付着部］

関節包と小さな靱帯は省略してある．

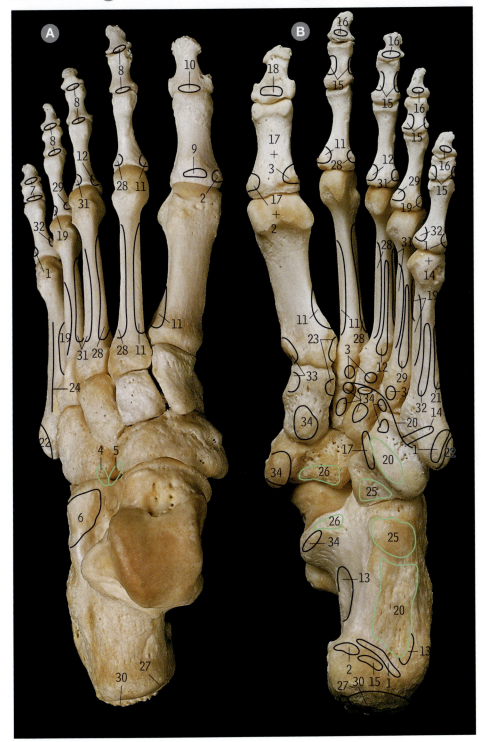

（淡緑線：靱帯の付着部．）

1	小趾外転筋	Abductor digiti minimi
2	母趾外転筋	Abductor hallucis
3	母趾内転筋	Adductor hallucis
4	踵立方靱帯〔二分靱帯〕	Calcaneocuboid ligament〔Bifurcate ligament〕
5	踵舟靱帯〔二分靱帯〕	Calcaneonavicular ligament〔Bifurcate ligament〕
6	短趾伸筋	Extensor digitorum brevis
7	長趾伸筋	Extensor digitorum longus
8	長趾伸筋と短趾伸筋	Extensor digitorum longus and Extensor digitorum brevis
9	短母趾伸筋	Extensor hallucis brevis
10	長母趾伸筋	Extensor hallucis longus
11	第一背側骨間筋	1st dorsal interosseous
12	第一底側骨間筋	1st plantar interosseous
13	足底方形筋	Quadratus plantae：Flexor accessorius
14	短小趾屈筋	Flexor digiti minimi brevis
15	短趾屈筋	Flexor digitorum brevis
16	長趾屈筋	Flexor digitorum longus
17	短母趾屈筋	Flexor hallucis brevis
18	長母趾屈筋	Flexor hallucis longus
19	第四背側骨間筋	4th dorsal interosseous
20	長足底靱帯	Long plantar ligament
21	小趾対立筋（短小趾屈筋の一部）	Opponens digiti minimi
22	短腓骨筋	Fibularis (Peroneus) brevis
23	長腓骨筋	Fibularis (Peroneus) longus
24	第三腓骨筋	Fibularis (Peroneus) tertius
25	底側踵立方靱帯：短足底靱帯	Plantar calcaneocuboid ligament：Short plantar ligament
26	底側踵舟靱帯	Plantar calcaneonavicular ligament：Spring ligament
27	足底筋	Plantaris
28	第二背側骨間筋	2nd dorsal interosseous
29	第二底側骨間筋	2nd plantar interosseous
30	踵骨腱：Achilles 腱	Calcaneal tendon：Achilles tendon *
31	第三背側骨間筋	3rd dorsal interosseous
32	第三底側骨間筋	3rd plantar interosseous
33	前脛骨筋	Tibialis anterior
34	後脛骨筋	Tibialis posterior

母趾の種子骨骨折

中足骨骨折

足の骨（左）

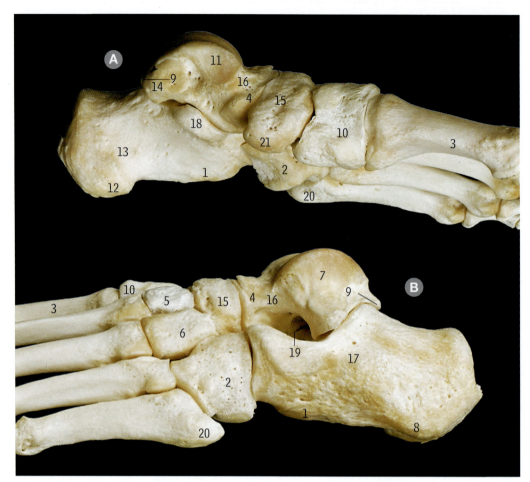

A：内側方から． B：外側方から．

1	踵骨結節 Calcaneal tubercle	8	踵骨隆起外側突起 Lateral process of calcaneal tuberosity	15	舟状骨 Navicular
2	立方骨 Cuboid	9	外側結節〔距骨〕 Lateral tubercle〔Talus〕	16	距骨頭 Neck of talus
3	第一中足骨 1st metatarsal bone	10	内側楔状骨 Medial cuneiform	17	腓骨筋滑車〔踵骨〕 Fibular (Peroneal) trochlea〔Calcaneus〕
4	距骨頭 Head of talus	11	内果面〔距骨〕 Medial malleolar facet〔Talus〕	18	載距突起〔踵骨〕 Sustentaculum tali〔Calcaneus〕
5	中間楔状骨 Intermediate cuneiform	12	踵骨隆起内側突起 Medial process of calcaneal tuberosity	19	足根洞 Tarsal sinus
6	外側楔状骨 Lateral cuneiform	13	内側面*〔踵骨〕 Medial surface *〔Calcaneus〕	20	第五中足骨粗面 Tuberosity of 5th metatarsal bone
7	外果面〔距骨〕 Lateral malleolar facet〔Talus〕	14	内側結節〔距骨〕 Medial tubercle〔Talus〕	21	舟状骨粗面 Tuberosity of navicular

踵骨骨折

ハンマー趾：槌趾

三角骨症候群

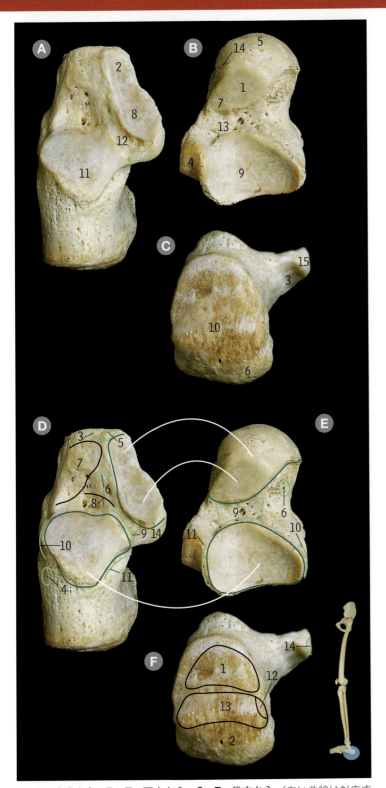

A~C 足の骨(左) [A C 踵骨, B 距骨]

1. 前踵骨関節面〔距骨〕 Anterior facet for calcaneus〔Talus〕
2. 前距骨関節面〔踵骨〕 Anterior talar articular surface〔Calcaneus〕
3. 長母趾屈筋腱溝〔踵骨〕 Groove for tendon of flexor hallucis longus〔Calcaneus〕
4. 長母趾屈筋腱溝〔距骨〕 Groove for tendon of flexor hallucis longus〔Talus〕
5. 距骨頭 Head of talus
6. 踵骨隆起内側突起 Medial process of calcaneal tuberosity
7. 中踵骨関節面〔距骨〕 Middle facet for calcaneus〔Talus〕
8. 中距骨関節面〔踵骨〕 Middle talar articular surface〔Calcaneus〕
9. 後踵骨関節面〔距骨〕 Posterior calcaneal articluar facet〔Talus〕
10. 後面*〔踵骨〕 Posterior surface *〔Calcaneus〕
11. 後距骨関節面〔踵骨〕 Posterior talar articular surface〔Calcaneus〕
12. 踵骨溝 Calcaneal sulcus
13. 距骨溝 Sulcus tali
14. 底側踵舟靱帯：ばね靱帯*（の距骨への付着面） Plantar calcaneonavicular ligament : Spring ligament
15. 載距突起〔踵骨〕 Sustentaculum tali〔Calcaneus〕

D~F 足の骨(左) [D F 踵骨, 筋と靱帯の付着部, E 距骨, 靱帯の付着部]

1. 踵骨腱(Achilles 腱)の滑液包 Bursa of calcaneal (achilles) tendon : Retrocalcaneal bursa
2. 線維脂肪組織と接する領域
3. 踵立方靱帯〔二分靱帯〕 Calcaneocuboid ligament〔Bifurcate ligament〕
4. 踵腓靱帯 Calcaneofibular ligament
5. 踵舟靱帯〔二分靱帯〕 Calcaneonavicular ligament〔Bifurcate ligament〕
6. 距踵頸靱帯* Cervical ligament * : External talocalcaneal ligament *
7. 短趾伸筋 Extensor digitorum brevis
8. 下伸筋支帯 Inferior extensor retinaculum
9. 骨間距踵靱帯 Talocalcaneal interosseous ligament
10. 外側距踵靱帯 Lateral talocalcaneal ligament
11. 内側距踵靱帯 Medial talocalcaneal ligament
12. 足底筋 Plantaris
13. 踵骨腱：Achilles 腱 Calcaneal tendon : Achilles tendon *
14. 脛踵部〔内側靱帯：三角靱帯〕 Tibiocalcaneal part〔Medial ligament : Deltoid ligament〕

A・D：上方から．B・E：下方から．C・F：後方から．（白い曲線は対応する関節面を表す．緑線：距踵（距骨下）関節包と距踵舟関節包の付着部．淡緑線：靱帯の付着部．）

- 骨間距踵靱帯(9)は，隣り合う距骨下関節と距踵舟関節の関節包が肥厚して形成される．
- "距骨下関節"という用語の解釈の違いについては358頁の解説を参照．

Ⓐ～Ⓙ 下肢の骨（左）［二次骨化中心］

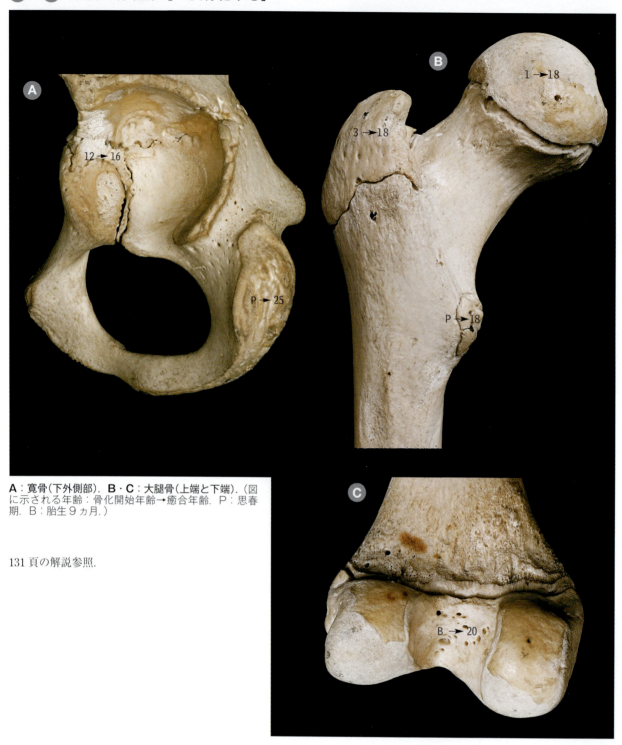

A：寛骨（下外側部）．**B・C**：大腿骨（上端と下端）．（図に示される年齢：骨化開始年齢→癒合年齢．P：思春期．B：胎生9ヵ月．）

131頁の解説参照．

大腿骨頭すべり症

第6章 下肢：下肢骨の成長　323

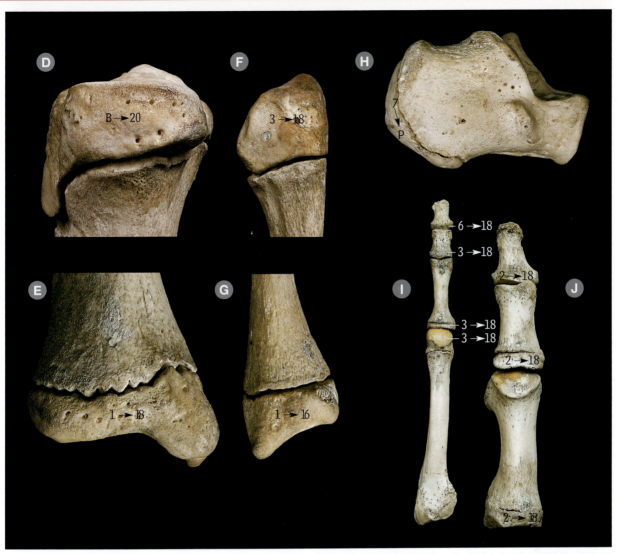

D・E：脛骨（上端と下端）．F・G：腓骨（上端と下端）．H：踵骨．I：第二趾の中足骨と趾節骨．J：母趾の中足骨と趾節骨．（図に示される年齢：骨化開始年齢→癒合年齢．P：思春期．B：胎生9ヵ月．）

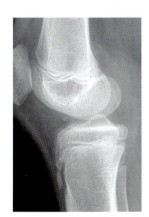 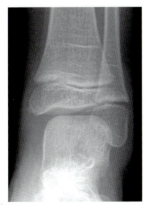

膝関節と距腿関節の単純X線画像

- 寛骨（A）では，腸骨，坐骨，恥骨間のY字状の軟骨に，1個あるいはそれ以上の二次性骨化中心が現れる．他の骨化中心（ここには描かれていない）は，通常，腸骨稜，下前腸骨棘，恥骨結節（まれに），恥骨稜に現れる（すべて思春期→25歳）．
- 膝蓋骨（描かれていない）は，3～6歳の間に1個かそれ以上の骨化中心が生じ，骨化が始まる．
- 趾節骨ならびに第一中足骨は，近位端に二次骨化中心が生じる．他の中足骨は，遠位端に1個の骨化中心が生じる．
- 足根骨においては，最大である踵骨は妊娠3ヵ月で骨化し始め，距骨はそれより約3ヵ月後から骨化する．立方骨は，出生前後から骨化し始めるが，外側楔状骨は1歳時，内側楔状骨は2歳時，中間楔状骨と舟状骨は3歳時に骨化し始める．
- 踵骨（H）は，二次骨化中心のある唯一の足根骨である．

A 殿部［体表解剖］

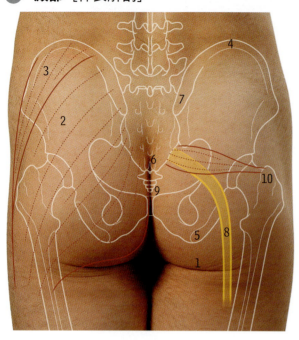

腸骨稜(4)と上後腸骨棘(7), 尾骨の先端(9), 坐骨結節(5), 大腿骨の大転子の尖端(10)は, 触知できる体表の目印である. 上後腸骨棘(7)と尾骨の先端(9)の中点から大腿骨の大転子の尖端(10)を結んだ線は, 梨状筋の下縁(右殿部に図示してある)を示す. 梨状筋は, 殿部において鍵となる最も重要な構造物である坐骨神経が通るところを示す(黄色部分(8). 次頁を参照).

1 殿溝 Gluteal fold ; Gluteal sulcus
2 大殿筋 Gluteus maximus
3 中殿筋 Gluteus medius
4 腸骨稜 Iliac crest
5 坐骨結節 Ischial tuberosity
6 殿裂 Intergluteal cleft ; Natal cleft
7 上後腸骨棘 Posterior superior iliac spine
8 坐骨神経 Sciatic nerve
9 尾骨(先端) Coccyx
10 大転子〔大腿骨〕(尖端) Greater trochanter〔Femur〕

B 殿部(右)［皮神経］

皮膚と皮下組織を除去し, 第一～第三腰神経と第一～第三仙骨神経の皮枝(3, 4), ならびに後大腿皮神経(5)と貫通皮神経(11)を解剖してある. 写真の下端に示す曲線は殿溝の位置を示す. 大殿筋(7)の筋束は下外側方へ走るので, 大殿筋の下縁と殿溝とは一致しない.

1 大内転筋 Adductor magnus
2 尾骨 Coccyx
3 上殿皮神経(第一～第三腰神経後枝の皮枝) Superior clunial nerves
4 中殿皮神経(第一～第三仙骨神経後枝の皮枝) Medial clunial nerves
5 下殿皮神経〔後大腿皮神経〕 Inferior clunial nerves〔Posterior femoral cutaneous nerve〕
6 殿筋筋膜*(中殿筋を覆う) Gluteal fascia *
7 大殿筋 Gluteus maximus
8 薄筋 Gracilis
9 腸骨稜 Iliac crest
10 坐骨肛門窩と肛門挙筋 Ischio-anal fossa and Levator ani
11 貫通皮神経 Perforating cutaneous nerve
12 後葉：浅葉〔胸腰筋膜(腰部)〕(脊柱起立筋を覆う) Posterior layer〔Thoracolumbar fascia〕
13 半腱様筋 Semitendinosus

- 殿部はしばしば筋肉内注射が行われる部位である. 適切な部位は, 腸骨稜の最上部を上縁, 殿溝を下縁とする殿部上外側の四半部である. 殿部の下縁は殿溝とする.
- 上縁と下縁の間の領域を正中線と体の外側面の中間点を通る垂直線で分けた上外側の四半部は, Bの"7"の位置よりもかなり上方でかつ外側である. ここは, 注射をしても安全な領域である. 次頁で示されるこの領域は, 坐骨神経よりも十分に上方で右に位置している.

殿部の筋肉内注射

A 殿部（左）[浅層]

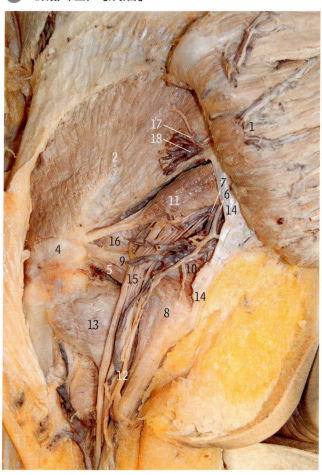

B 殿部（左）[深層]

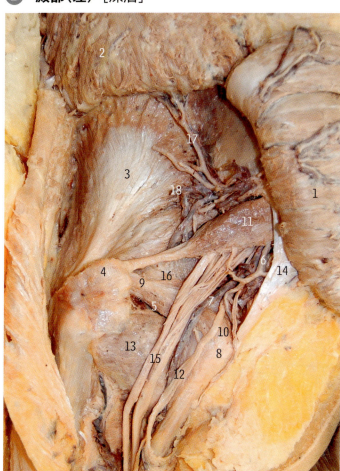

1	大殿筋（翻転してある） Gluteus maximus	10	内閉鎖筋 Obturator internus
2	中殿筋（Bでは翻転してある） Gluteus medius	11	梨状筋 Piriformis
3	小殿筋 Gluteus minimus	12	後大腿皮神経 Posterior cutaneous nerve of thigh； Posterior femoral cutaneous nerve
4	大転子〔大腿骨〕 Greater trochanter〔Femur〕	13	大腿方形筋 Quadratus femoris
5	下双子筋 Gemellus inferior；Inferior gemellus	14	仙結節靱帯 Sacrotuberous ligament
6	下殿動脈 Inferior gluteal artery	15	坐骨神経 Sciatic nerve
7	下殿静脈 Inferior gluteal vein	16	上双子筋 Gemellus superior；Superior gemellus
8	坐骨結節 Ischial tuberosity	17	上殿動脈 Superior gluteal artery
9	内閉鎖筋（の腱） Obturator internus	18	上殿静脈 Superior gluteal vein

● 坐骨神経の2部（総腓骨神経と脛骨神経）は，通常，膝窩の頂点で互いに分かれる（344頁B）．しかし，しばしば梨状筋の下から現れるときから分かれていることもある．また，総腓骨神経が梨状筋を貫くことさえある．

A B 大腿（右）［A 殿部とハムストリング（膝屈筋）の近位部，B 深層］

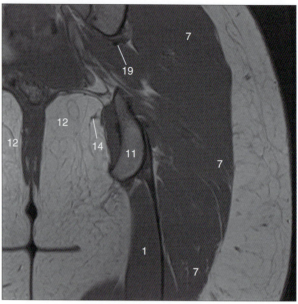

股関節と大腿上部のMR冠状断画像

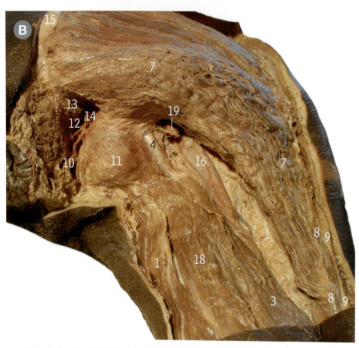

A：後方から．B：後下方から．坐骨肛門窩を明らかにしている．

1	大内転筋 Adductor magnus
2	肛門 Anus
3	大腿二頭筋 Biceps femoris
4	長頭〔大腿二頭筋〕（の腱） Long head〔Biceps femoris〕
5	外肛門括約筋 External anal sphincter
6	殿筋筋膜*（中殿筋を覆う） Gluteal fascia *
7	大殿筋 Gluteus maximus
8	大殿筋の腸脛靱帯への付着部
9	腸脛靱帯（大腿筋膜の肥厚部） Iliotibial tract
10	下直腸動／静脈 Inferior rectal artery/veins
11	坐骨結節 Ischial tuberosity
12	坐骨肛門窩：坐骨直腸窩 Ischio-anal fossa : Ischiorectal fossa
13	肛門挙筋 Levator ani
14	内陰部動／静脈と陰部神経 Internal pudendal artery/vein and Pudendal nerve
15	仙骨後面の筋膜
16	坐骨神経（筋膜鞘に包まれている） Sciatic nerve
17	陰嚢（の皮膚） Scrotum
18	半腱様筋 Semitendinosus
19	上殿動／静脈 Superior gluteal artery/veins

ハムストリング の断裂（肉離れ）

ⓒ 大腿上部（右）

後方から．

大殿筋(5)を外側へ翻転してある．半腱様筋(22)と大腿二頭筋(9)の間隙を開き，坐骨神経(19)とその筋枝を示してある．

1	大内転筋 Adductor magnus	13	半腱様筋への枝 Nerve to Semitendinosus
2	下殿動脈との吻合枝	14	短頭〔大腿二頭筋〕への枝 Nerve to Short head〔Biceps femoris〕
3	第一貫通動脈 1st perforating artery	15	内転筋腱裂孔 Adductor hiatus
4	第四貫通動脈 4th perforating artery	16	膝窩動脈 Popliteal artery
5	大殿筋 Gluteus maximus	17	膝窩静脈 Popliteal vein
6	薄筋 Gracilis	18	大腿方形筋 Quadratus femoris
7	腸脛靭帯（外側広筋を覆う） Iliotibial tract	19	坐骨神経 Sciatic nerve
8	坐骨結節 Ischial tuberosity	20	第二貫通動脈 2nd perforating artery
9	長頭〔大腿二頭筋〕 Long head〔Biceps femoris〕	21	半膜様筋 Semimembranosus
10	長頭〔大腿二頭筋〕への枝 Nerve to Long head〔Biceps femoris〕	22	半腱様筋 Semitendinosus
11	半膜様筋への枝 Nerve to Semimembranosus	23	短頭〔大腿二頭筋〕 Short head〔Biceps femoris〕
12	半膜様筋と大内転筋への枝 Nerve to Semimembranosus and Adductor magnus	24	第三貫通動脈 3rd perforating artery
		25	小内転筋（大内転筋の上部） Adductor minimus

● 坐骨神経の外側部（3つのうち，一番上の19），すなわち総腓骨神経から起こる唯一の筋枝は，大腿二頭筋短頭への枝(14)である．他のすべての筋枝，すなわち大腿二頭筋長頭への枝(10)，半膜様筋への枝(11)，半膜様筋および大内転筋への共通枝(12)，半腱様筋への枝(13)は，坐骨神経の内側部（中央の19）の脛骨神経から起こる．

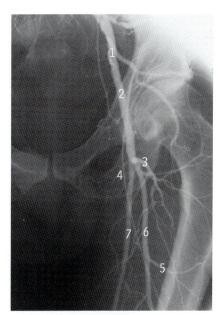

大腿の血管造影画像

1	右大腿動脈から腹大動脈の遠位部に挿入されたカテーテル
2	大腿動脈 Femoral artery
3	外側大腿回旋動脈 Lateral circumflex femoral artery
4	内側大腿回旋動脈 Medial circumflex femoral artery
5	貫通動脈 Perforating artery
6	大腿深動脈 Deep artery of thigh
7	大腿動脈 Femoral artery

A 大腿前面と下腹部

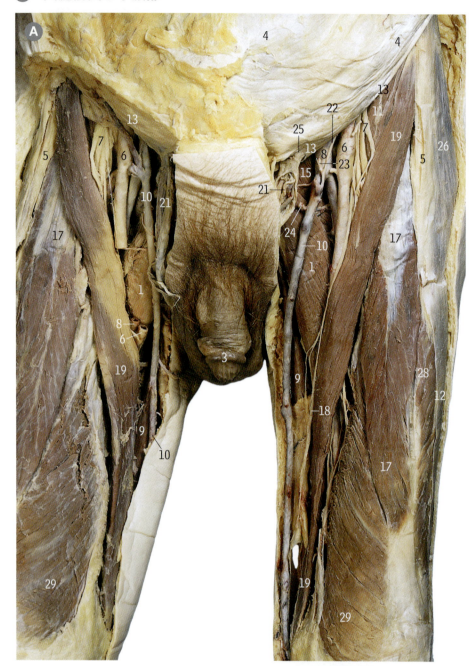

1	長内転筋 Adductor longus
2	内側広筋への動脈枝 Arterial branch to vastus medialis
3	亀頭冠〔陰茎〕 Corona of glans〔Penis〕
4	腱膜〔外腹斜筋〕 Aponeurosis〔External oblique〕
5	大腿筋膜（切断縁） Fascia lata
6	大腿動脈 Femoral artery
7	大腿神経 Femoral nerve
8	大腿静脈 Femoral vein
9	薄筋 Gracilis
10	大伏在静脈 Great saphenous vein：Long saphenous vein
11	腸骨筋 Iliacus
12	腸脛靱帯 Iliotibial tract
13	鼠径靱帯 Inguinal ligament
14	内側広筋への枝 Nerve to Vastus medialis
15	恥骨筋 Pectineus
16	大腿深動脈の貫通枝 Perforating artery〔Deep artery of thigh〕
17	大腿直筋 Rectus femoris
18	伏在神経 Saphenous nerve
19	縫工筋 Sartorius
20	縫工筋下筋膜＊（腱膜が厚くなったもの） Subsartorial fascia＊
21	精索 Spermatic cord
22	浅腸骨回旋静脈 Superficial circumflex iliac vein
23	浅腹壁静脈 Superficial epigastric vein
24	浅外陰部静脈＊ Superficial external pudendal vein＊
25	浅鼠径輪 Superficial inguinal ring
26	大腿筋膜張筋（大腿筋膜よりも深い） Tensor fasciae latae
27	静脈弁のふくらみ
28	外側広筋 Vastus lateralis
29	内側広筋 Vastus medialis

腰神経叢ブロック

下肢の帯状疱疹

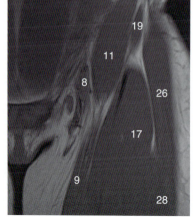
大腿上部のMR冠状断画像

B 大腿前面の上部

- 大腿三角の境界は，鼠径靱帯(13)，縫工筋(19)の内側縁，長内転筋(1)である．
- 大腿血管鞘(すでに除去してある)の内側部は大腿管であり，中間部は大腿静脈(8)を，外側部は大腿動脈(6)を包む．大腿神経(7)は，大腿血管鞘の外側にあり，鞘には含まれない．

縫工筋を内側へ引き寄せ，縫工筋下の(血管および神経の通る)管を示す．
（番号は前頁の用語表を参照．）

大腿神経麻痺

閉鎖神経麻痺

大腿動脈（右）

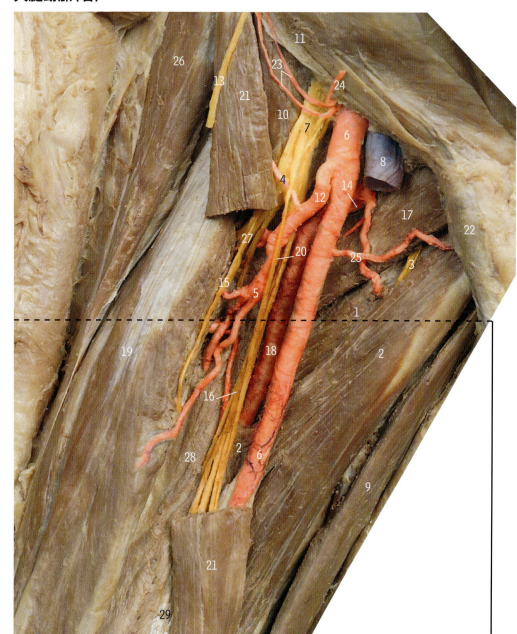

1	短内転筋 Adductor brevis
2	長内転筋 Adductor longus
3	前枝〔閉鎖神経〕 Anterior branch (Obturator nerve)
4	上行枝〔外側大腿回旋動脈〕 Ascending branch (Lateral circumflex femoral artery)
5	下行枝〔外側大腿回旋動脈〕 Descending branch (Lateral circumflex femoral artery)
6	大腿動脈 Femoral artery
7	大腿神経 Femoral nerve
8	大腿静脈 Femoral vein
9	薄筋 Gracilis
10	腸骨筋 Iliacus
11	鼠径靱帯 Inguinal ligament
12	外側大腿回旋動脈 Lateral circumflex femoral artery
13	外側大腿皮神経 Lateral femoral cutaneous nerve
14	内側大腿回旋動脈 Medial circumflex femoral artery
15	大腿直筋への枝 Nerve to Rectus femoris
16	内側広筋への枝 Nerve to Vastus medialis
17	恥骨筋 Pectineus
18	大腿深動脈 Deep artery of thigh
19	大腿直筋 Rectus femoris
20	伏在神経 Saphenous nerve
21	縫工筋 Sartorius
22	精索 Spermatic cord
23	浅腸骨回旋動脈（重複） Superficial circumflex iliac artery
24	浅腹壁動脈 Superficial epigastric artery
25	浅外陰部動脈（起始位置が低い） Superficial external pudendal artery
26	大腿筋膜張筋 Tensor fasciae latae
27	横枝〔外側大腿回旋動脈〕 Transverse branch (Lateral circumflex femoral artery)
28	中間広筋 Vastus intermedius
29	内側広筋 Vastus medialis

大腿動脈穿刺

知覚異常性大腿神経痛

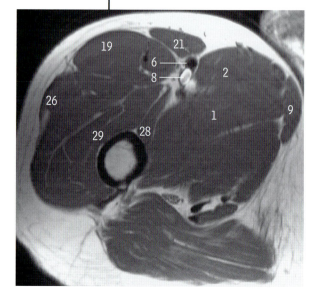
大腿上部のMR横断画像

Ⓐ Ⓑ 大腿三角の境界と底

A：前外側方から．B：前方から．○印は鼠径靱帯の両端を示す．

1	長内転筋 Adductor longus	10	閉鎖神経 Obturator nerve
2	上前腸骨棘 Anterior superior iliac spine	11	恥骨筋 Pectineus
3	大腿筋膜 Fascia lata	12	陰茎 Penis
4	大腿動脈 Femoral artery	13	貫通する動脈枝
5	大腿神経 Femoral nerve	14	大腰筋 Psoas major
6	腸骨筋 Iliacus	15	恥骨結節 Pubic tubercle
7	腸腰筋 Iliopsoas	16	縫工筋 Sartorius
8	腸脛靱帯 Iliotibial tract	17	陰嚢 Scrotum
9	鼠径靱帯 Inguinal ligament	18	大腿筋膜張筋 Tensor fasciae latae

C 大腿下部（右）

縫工筋(13)の下部を内側へずらして内転筋管の下部を開き，大腿動脈(2)を明らかにしてある．この動脈は，内転筋腱裂孔(7)を通り抜け，膝の後ろの膝窩に入って膝窩動脈となる(344頁)．

1	大内転筋 Adductor magnus	8	膝蓋骨 Patella
2	大腿動脈 Femoral artery	9	大腿四頭筋（の腱） Quadriceps femoris
3	薄筋 Gracilis	10	大腿直筋 Rectus femoris
4	腸脛靱帯 Iliotibial tract	11	伏在枝〔下行膝動脈〕 Saphenous branch〔Descending genicular artery〕
5	内側広筋（最下端の水平筋束） Vastus medialis	12	伏在神経 Saphenous nerve
6	内側膝蓋支帯 Medial patellar retinaculum	13	縫工筋 Sartorius
7	内転筋腱裂孔 Adductor hiatus	14	内側広筋への枝 Nerve to Vastus medialis

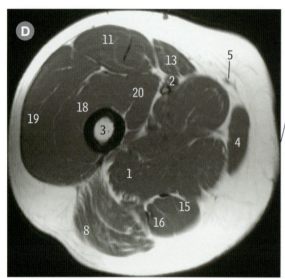

MR 横断画像

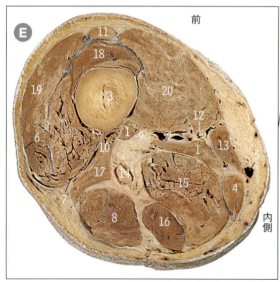

横断面

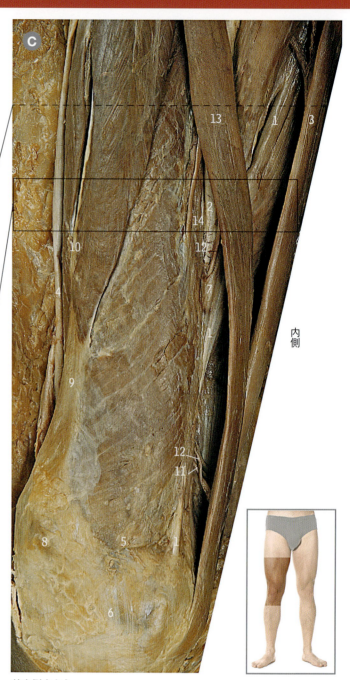

前内側方から．

D E 大腿の下部（右）

1	大内転筋 Adductor magnus	11	大腿直筋 Rectus femoris
2	大腿動／静脈 Femoral artery/vein	12	伏在神経 Saphenous nerve
3	大腿骨 Femur	13	縫工筋 Sartorius
4	薄筋 Gracilis	14	坐骨神経 Sciatic nerve
5	大伏在静脈 Great saphenous vein；Long saphenous vein	15	半膜様筋 Semimembranosus
6	腸脛靱帯 Iliotibial tract	16	半腱様筋 Semitendinosus
7	外側大腿筋間中隔 Lateral femoral intermuscular septum	17	短頭〔大腿二頭筋〕 Short head〔Biceps femoris〕
8	長頭〔大腿二頭筋〕 Long head〔Biceps femoris〕	18	中間広筋 Vastus intermedius
9	内転筋腱裂孔 Adductor hiatus	19	外側広筋 Vastus lateralis
10	大腿深動／静脈 Deep artery/vein of thigh	20	内側広筋 Vastus medialis

大腿膝窩動脈バイパス

間欠性跛行

筋移行術

大腿四頭筋の腱断裂

股関節（右）

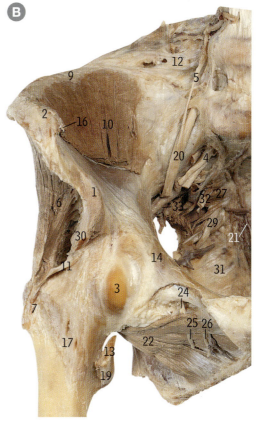

A：前下方から．B：前上方から．

● 坐骨大腿靱帯の線維束の一部は，輪帯の形成に加わる．輪帯は大腿骨頸の周りの首輪を形成し，関節包の輪状線維束をつくる．

1	下前腸骨棘	Anterior inferior iliac spine
2	上前腸骨棘	Anterior superior iliac spine
3	腸恥包	Iliopectineal bursa
4	前枝〔第一仙骨神経〕	Ventral ramus〔S1〕
5	前枝〔第四腰神経〕	Ventral ramus〔L4〕
6	小殿筋	Gluteus minimus
7	大転子	Greater trochanter
8	大腿部膝屈筋*（ハムストリング）（の起始部）	Hamstring *
9	腸骨稜	Iliac crest
10	腸骨筋	Iliacus
11	腸骨大腿靱帯	Iliofemoral ligament
12	腸腰靱帯	Iliolumbar ligament
13	腸腰筋（の腱）	Iliopsoas
14	腸恥隆起	Iliopubic eminence
15	下双子筋	Gemellus inferior；Inferior gemellus
16	鼠径靱帯	Inguinal ligament
17	転子間線（と関節包の付着部）	Intertrochanteric line
18	坐骨結節	Ischial tuberosity
19	小転子	Lesser trochanter
20	腰仙骨神経幹	Lumbosacral trunk
21	正中仙骨動脈	Median sacral artery
22	外閉鎖筋	Obturator externus
23	内閉鎖筋（の腱）	Obturator internus
24	前枝〔閉鎖神経〕	Anterior branch〔Obturator nerve〕
25	後枝〔閉鎖神経〕	Posterior branch〔Obturator nerve〕
26	閉鎖動／静脈	Obturator artery/veins
27	梨状筋	Piriformis
28	恥骨大腿靱帯	Pubofemoral ligament
29	陰部神経	Pudendal nerve
30	大腿直筋	Rectus femoris
31	仙棘靱帯	Sacrospinous ligament
32	前枝〔第二仙骨神経〕	Ventral ramus〔S2〕
33	上殿動脈	Superior gluteal artery

Trendelenburg 徴候

後方から.

C 脊柱と骨盤の間ならびに仙骨と腸骨の間の靱帯（右）

1	関節唇 Acetabular labrum	9	坐骨結節 Ischial tuberosity
2	尾骨 Coccyx	10	小坐骨切痕 Lesser sciatic notch
3	後仙腸靱帯 Posterior sacro-iliac ligament	11	上後腸骨棘 Posterior superior iliac spine
4	鎌状突起〔仙結節靱帯〕 Falciform process〔Sacrotuberous ligament〕	12	仙棘靱帯と坐骨棘 Sacrospinous ligament and Ischial spine
5	大坐骨切痕 Greater sciatic notch	13	仙結節靱帯 Sacrotuberous ligament
6	腸骨稜 Iliac crest	14	上関節突起〔第五腰椎〕 Superior articular process〔L V〕
7	腸腰靱帯 Iliolumbar ligament	15	肋骨突起〔第五腰椎〕 Costal process〔L V〕
8	下関節突起〔第五腰椎〕 Inferior articular process〔L V〕		

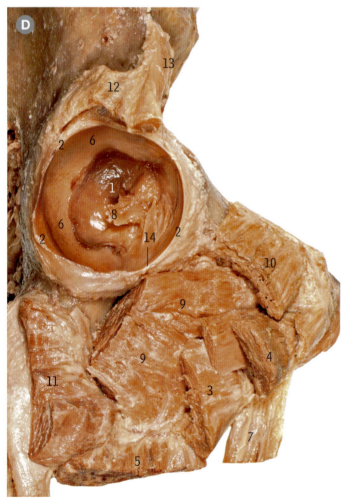

右側方から.

D 大腿骨を除去した股関節（右）

大腿骨を，関節唇，寛骨臼横靱帯および大腿骨頭靱帯を残して寛骨臼からはずし，除去してある.

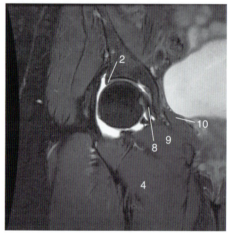

股関節のMR関節造影冠状断画像

1	寛骨臼窩 Acetabular fossa	8	大腿骨頭靱帯 Ligament of head of femur
2	関節唇 Acetabular labrum	9	外閉鎖筋 Obturator externus
3	短内転筋 Adductor brevis	10	恥骨筋 Pectineus
4	長内転筋 Adductor longus	11	大腿方形筋 Quadratus femoris
5	大内転筋 Adductor magnus	12	反転頭〔大腿直筋〕 Reflected head〔Rectus femoris〕
6	月状面 Lunate surface	13	直頭〔大腿直筋〕 Straight head〔Rectus femoris〕
7	薄筋 Gracilis	14	寛骨臼横靱帯 Transverse acetabular ligament

大腿骨頭壊死

A B 股関節（左）

切断面は，おおよそ大腿骨頭(8)の中心ならびに大転子(7)の中心を通過している．大腿骨頸(14)の上方で，小殿筋(6)とその上を覆っている中殿筋(5)が大転子(7)に停止する．一方，大腰筋(17)の腱と腸骨筋(12)の筋束は，大腿骨頭の下方を通って後方へ走り，小転子に向かう．輪帯(22)の輪走線維は，関節内にある大腿骨頸の関節包(3)を締めつけている．

1	関節唇	Acetabular labrum
2	長内転筋	Adductor longus
3	関節包〔股関節〕	Articular capsule〔Hip joint〕
4	外腸骨動脈	External iliac artery
5	中殿筋	Gluteus medius
6	小殿筋	Gluteus minimus
7	大転子	Greater trochanter
8	大腿骨頭	Head of femur
9	寛骨臼（の硝子軟骨）	Acetabulum
10	大腿骨頭（の硝子軟骨）	Head of femur
11	腸骨稜	Iliac crest
12	腸骨筋	Iliacus
13	内側大腿回旋動／静脈	Medial circumflex femoral artery/veins
14	大腿骨頸	Neck of femur
15	恥骨筋	Pectineus
16	大腿深動／静脈	Deep artery/vein of thigh
17	大腰筋	Psoas major
18	寛骨臼縁	Acetabular margin
19	大腿骨体	Shaft of femur：Body of femur
20	外側広筋	Vastus lateralis
21	内側広筋	Vastus medialis
22	輪帯	Zona orbicularis

冠状断面．前方から．

● 中殿筋(5)と小殿筋(6)が大転子に集中していることが，この断面標本でよく示されている．これらの筋は，股関節の外転筋として大腿骨に働くと分類される．しかし，より重要な働きは，歩行時に内転するのを防ぐことである．つまり，対側の下肢が地面を離れているときに，骨盤が傾かないようにしているのである（Trendelenburg 徴候参照，333 頁）．

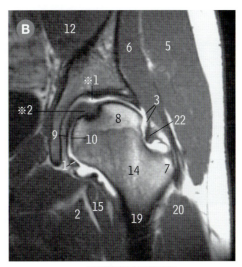

MR 関節造影冠状断画像
（※1：造影剤による関節腔の輪郭．※2：大腿骨頭靱帯．）

股関節置換術

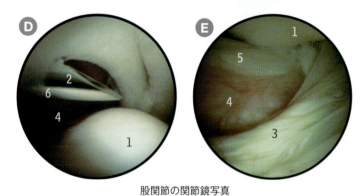

CT画像からの三次元構築画像

C 股関節と仙腸関節（左）

1	上前腸骨棘	Anterior superior iliac spine
2	第一尾椎	1st coccygeal vertebra (Co I)
3	大転子〔大腿骨〕	Greater trochanter〔Femur〕
4	大腿骨頭	Head of femur
5	恥骨下枝	Inferior pubic ramus
6	坐骨	Ischium
7	坐骨結節	Ischial tuberosity
8	小転子〔大腿骨〕	Lesser trochanter〔Femur〕
9	大腿骨頸	Neck of femur
10	閉鎖孔	Obturator foramen
11	恥骨櫛	Pecten pubis
12	岬角〔仙骨〕	Promontory〔Sacrum〕
13	恥骨結合	Pubic symphysis
14	恥骨結節	Pubic tubercle
15	寛骨臼縁	Acetabular margin
16	仙腸関節	Sacro-iliac joint
17	仙骨	Sacrum
18	恥骨上枝	Superior pubic ramus
19	肋骨突起〔第五腰椎〕	Costal process〔L V〕

股関節の関節鏡写真

D E 股関節

1	大腿骨頭	Head of femur
2	洗浄針	
3	大腿骨頭靱帯	Ligament of head of femur
4	滑膜	Synovial membrane
5	寛骨臼横靱帯	Transverse acetabular ligament
6	輪帯	Zona orbicularis

股関節の後方脱臼

A B 膝（右）［半屈曲位］

1. 大腿二頭筋 Biceps femoris
2. 総腓骨神経 Common fibular (peroneal) nerve
3. 腓骨頭 Head of fibula
4. 腸脛靱帯 Iliotibial tract
5. 外側頭〔腓腹筋〕 Lateral head〔Gastrocnemius〕
6. 外側顆〔大腿骨〕（の輪郭） Lateral condyle〔Femur〕
7. 外側顆〔脛骨〕（の輪郭） Lateral condyle〔Tibia〕
8. 膝蓋骨 Patella
9. 膝蓋靱帯 Patellar ligament
10. 膝窩 Popliteal fossa
11. 半膜様筋 Semimembranosus
12. 半腱様筋 Semitendinosus
13. 脛骨粗面 Tibial tuberosity
14. 内側広筋 Vastus medialis

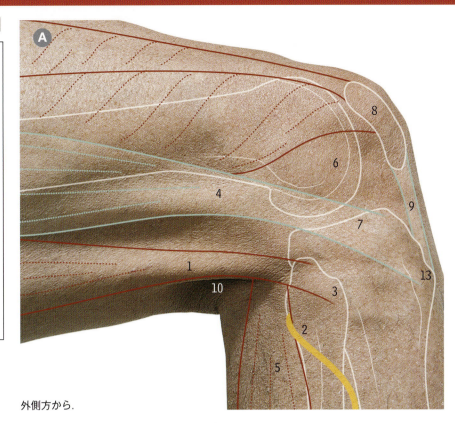

外側方から．

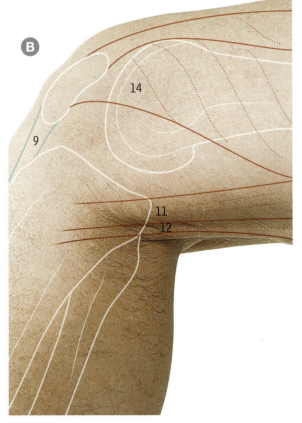

内側方から．

外側では，膝の後ろに丸みを帯びた大腿二頭筋の腱(1)が，その前には幅広い帯状の腸脛靱帯(4)が，そしてそれらの間に溝が，容易に触知できる．内側では，丸みを帯びた細い半腱様筋(12)と，そのすぐ前に幅の広い半膜様筋(11)の2つの腱が触知できる．前方では，膝蓋靱帯(9)が，膝蓋骨(8)と脛骨粗面(13)の距離を一定に保っている．側方では，大腿骨と脛骨の外側顆(6，7)の辺縁同士が隣接しているのがわかる．

外反膝，内反膝

膝蓋腱反射

外側方から．

C 膝（右）［浅層］

大腿二頭筋（2）の後ろの筋膜を除去し，大腿二頭筋の腱のすぐ後ろを下行する総腓骨神経（3）を明らかにしてある．この神経は，ヒラメ筋（12）と長腓骨筋（5）が隣接するところの間を走った後，長腓骨筋に覆われながら腓骨頸に沿って走る．この標本では，細い皮下の血管や神経は，除去してある．

1	腸脛靱帯（の脛骨への付着部） Iliotibial tract
2	大腿二頭筋 Biceps femoris
3	総腓骨神経 Common fibular (peroneal) nerve
4	下腿筋膜（下腿伸筋群を覆う） Deep fascia of leg
5	下腿筋膜（長腓骨筋を覆う） Deep fascia of leg
6	大腿筋膜 Fascia lata
7	腓骨頭 Head of fibula
8	腸脛靱帯 Iliotibial tract
9	外側腓腹皮神経 Lateral sural cutaneous nerve
10	外側頭〔腓腹筋〕 Lateral head〔Gastrocnemius〕
11	膝蓋骨 Patella
12	ヒラメ筋 Soleus

- 腸脛靱帯（8）は，大腿筋膜（6）の肥厚した外側部である．この靱帯の上部には，大腿筋膜張筋と大殿筋の大部分が停止する．
- 総腓骨神経（3）は，下肢の神経の中で最も損傷を受けやすい．それは，皮下に位置するところや腓骨頸と接しているところにおいてである．

内側方から．

D 膝（右）［浅層］

大伏在静脈（3）は，膝蓋骨（7）の内側縁から手の幅ほどの距離だけ後方を上行する．伏在神経（8）は，縫工筋（9）と薄筋（2）の腱の間から皮下に現れる．伏在神経の膝蓋下枝（4）は，脛骨の内側顆の上縁の少し下方をカーブを描いて前方へ走る．

1	内側大腿皮神経の枝*，訳注 Branches of Medial femoral cutaneous nerve *
2	薄筋 Gracilis
3	大伏在静脈 Great saphenous vein：Long saphenous vein
4	膝蓋下枝〔伏在神経〕 Infrapatellar branch〔Saphenous nerve〕
5	脛骨の内側顆の上縁の高さ
6	内側頭〔腓腹筋〕 Medial head〔Gastrocnemius〕
7	膝蓋骨 Patella
8	伏在神経 Saphenous nerve
9	縫工筋 Sartorius
10	半腱様筋 Semitendinosus
11	内側広筋 Vastus medialis

［訳注］大腿神経の前皮枝の内側部．

A〜D 膝関節（左）［靱帯］

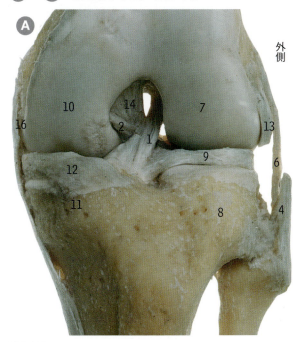

前方から．

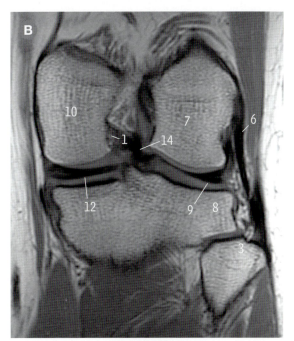

MR冠状断画像

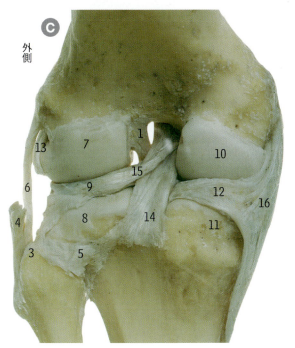

後方から．

膝関節包と周囲のすべての組織を除去し，膝関節の靱帯だけを残してある．関節は軽く屈曲させてある．

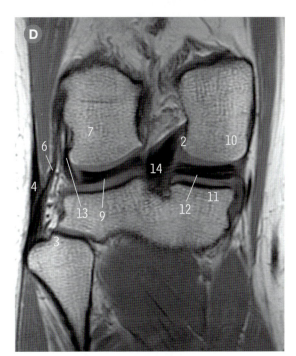

MR冠状断画像

1	前十字靱帯 Anterior cruciate ligament	9	外側半月 Lateral meniscus
2	前半月大腿靱帯 Anterior meniscofemoral ligament	10	内側顆〔大腿骨〕 Medial condyle〔Femur〕
3	腓骨頭尖 Apex of head of fibula	11	内側顆〔脛骨〕 Medial condyle〔Tibia〕
4	大腿二頭筋（の腱） Biceps femoris	12	内側半月 Medial meniscus
5	関節包〔脛腓関節〕 Articular capsule（Tibiofibular joint： Superior tibiofibular joint）	13	膝窩筋（の腱） Popliteus
6	外側側副靱帯 Fibular collateral ligament	14	後十字靱帯 Posterior cruciate ligament
7	外側顆〔大腿骨〕 Lateral condyle〔Femur〕	15	後半月大腿靱帯 Posterior meniscofemoral ligament
8	外側顆〔脛骨〕 Lateral condyle〔Tibia〕	16	内側側副靱帯 Tibial collateral ligament

- 外側側副靱帯(A6)は，断面が丸い約5cmの靱帯であり，大腿骨の外側上顆と腓骨頭尖(C3)のすぐ前に付着する．この靱帯は，大腿二頭筋の腱(C4)に大部分が覆われている．
- 内側半月は，内側側副靱帯の深部に付着する．このことは半月の固定には役立つが，脛骨と大腿骨の間の回旋運動によって，半月がはさみ込まれたり裂けたりしやすい．
- 外側半月(A9)は，外側側副靱帯(A6)に付着していない．しかし，後方では膝窩筋に付着している．
- 内側側副靱帯は，長さが約12cmである幅の広い平らな線維束であり，上方は大腿骨の内側上顆，下方は脛骨の内側顆ならびに内側顆より下方の脛骨内側面の広い領域に付着する．
- "十字靱帯"は，脛骨への付着の前後関係から名前が付けられている．
- 前十字靱帯(A1)は，後外側方に上行し，大腿骨の外側顆(C7)の内側部に付着する．
- 後十字靱帯(C14)は，前内側方に上行し，大腿骨の内側顆(A10)の外側面に付着する．

E 膝関節-脛骨の上面(左)

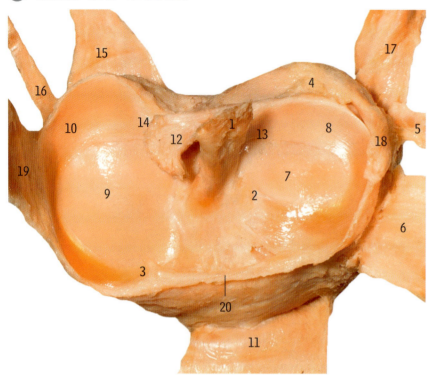

上方から．

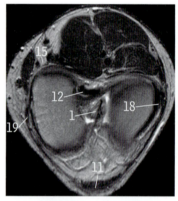

膝関節のMR横断画像

1 前十字靱帯 Anterior cruciate ligament	8 外側半月 Lateral meniscus	15 半膜様筋(の腱) Semimembranosus
2 前角*〔外側半月〕 Anterior horn*〔Lateral meniscus〕	9 内側顆〔脛骨〕 Medial condyle〔Tibia〕	16 半腱様筋(の腱) Semitendinosus
3 前角*〔内側半月〕 Anterior horn*〔Medial meniscus〕	10 内側半月 Medial meniscus	17 大腿二頭筋(の腱) Biceps femoris
4 外側半月の膝窩筋への付着部	11 膝蓋靱帯 Patellar ligament	18 膝窩筋(の腱) Popliteus
5 外側側副靱帯 Fibular collateral ligament	12 後十字靱帯 Posterior cruciate ligament	19 内側側副靱帯(内側半月に付着している) Tibial collateral ligament
6 腸脛靱帯 Iliotibial tract	13 後角*〔外側半月〕 Posterior horn*〔Lateral meniscus〕	20 膝横靱帯 Transverse ligament of knee
7 外側顆〔脛骨〕 Lateral condyle〔Tibia〕	14 後角*〔内側半月〕 Posterior horn*〔Medial meniscus〕	

半月板断裂

前十字靱帯の断裂

A B 膝関節（右）

大腿骨の下端部の内側半を除去し，十字靱帯がX状に交叉しているのが見える．前十字靱帯(1)は後外側へ，後十字靱帯(13)は前内側へ上行する．BのMR画像では，膝蓋下脂肪体(3)が明らかになっている．

内側方から．大腿骨の内側顆を除去してある．

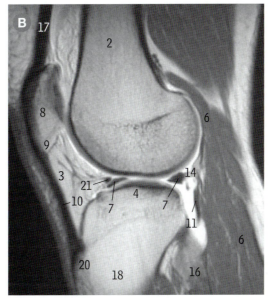

MR 矢状断画像

1	前十字靱帯 Anterior cruciate ligament	8	膝蓋骨 Patella	15	半膜様筋 Semimembranosus
2	大腿骨 Femur	9	膝蓋骨尖 Apex of patella	16	ヒラメ筋 Soleus
3	膝蓋下脂肪体 Infrapatellar fat pad：Hoffa*	10	膝蓋靱帯 Patellar ligament	17	大腿四頭筋（の腱） Quadriceps femoris
4	顆間隆起 Intercondylar eminence	11	膝窩筋 Popliteus	18	脛骨 Tibia
5	外側顆〔大腿骨〕 Lateral condyle〔Femur〕	12	関節包の後部	19	内側側副靱帯 Tibial collateral ligament
6	外側頭〔腓腹筋〕 Lateral head〔Gastrocnemius〕	13	後十字靱帯 Posterior cruciate ligament	20	脛骨粗面 Tibial tuberosity
7	外側半月 Lateral meniscus	14	後半月大腿靱帯 Posterior meniscofemoral ligament	21	膝横靱帯 Transverse ligament of knee

C D 膝関節（左）

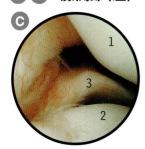
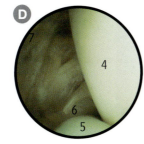

1	外側顆〔大腿骨〕 Lateral condyle〔Femur〕
2	外側顆〔脛骨〕 Lateral condyle〔Tibia〕
3	外側半月 Lateral meniscus
4	内側顆〔大腿骨〕 Medial condyle〔Femur〕
5	内側半月 Medial meniscus
6	後十字靱帯 Posterior cruciate ligament
7	関節包（の後部） Articular capsule

膝関節の関節鏡写真
C：前外側アプローチ．D：後内側アプローチ．

後十字靱帯の断裂

膝蓋上包

E 膝関節（左）

1	前十字靱帯 Anterior cruciate ligament	11	膝蓋骨 Patella
2	腱膜〔外側広筋〕（切断縁） Aponeurosis〔Vastus lateralis〕	12	膝蓋骨の関節軟骨
3	（脛骨上面の）関節軟骨 Articular cartilage	13	膝蓋靱帯 Patellar ligament
4	深膝蓋下包 Deep infrapatellar bursa	14	膝窩筋（の腱）（外側脛骨上顆への付着部） Popliteus
5	大腿筋膜 Fascia lata	15	後十字靱帯 Posterior cruciate ligament
6	外側側副靱帯 Fibular collateral ligament	16	大腿四頭筋（の腱） Quadriceps femoris
7	腓骨頭 Head of fibula	17	膝蓋上包 Suprapatellar bursa
8	腸脛靱帯（切断縁） Iliotibial tract	18	膝蓋上脂肪体* Suprapatellar fat pad*
9	膝蓋下脂肪体 Infrapatellar fat pad：Hoffa*	19	脛骨粗面 Tibial tuberosity
10	外側半月 Lateral meniscus		

外側から開き，関節内部の構造を示してある．

F 膝関節（左）

樹脂の注入により関節包(3)が膨らんでいる．樹脂は膝蓋上包(10)，膝窩筋下陥凹(2)および半膜様筋の滑液包(9)にも広がっている．

1	膝関節筋 Articularis genu	7	大腿四頭筋（の腱） Quadriceps femoris
2	膝窩筋下陥凹 Subpopliteal recess	8	半膜様筋 Semimembranosus
3	関節包 Articular capsule	9	半膜様筋の滑液包 Semimembranosus bursa
4	内側半月 Medial meniscus	10	膝蓋上包 Suprapatellar bursa
5	膝蓋骨 Patella	11	内側側副靱帯 Tibial collateral ligament
6	膝蓋靱帯 Patellar ligament		

● 膝蓋上包(F10)は関節包(F3)と常に交通する．膝窩筋下陥凹(F2)は関節包(F3)に通常交通し，半膜様筋の滑液包(F9)とも交通することがありうる．

内側方から．関節包と滑液包に樹脂を注入してある．

G 前十字靱帯

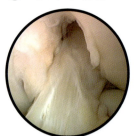

前十字靱帯の関節鏡写真
前方から．

膝関節の吸引ならびに注射

下肢の滑液包炎

膝蓋前滑液包炎

膝関節（X線画像と関節鏡写真）

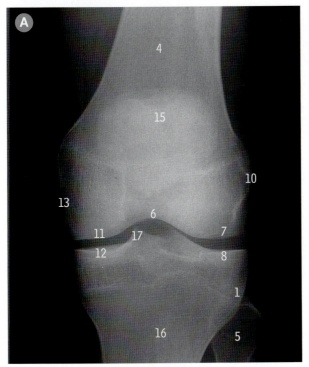
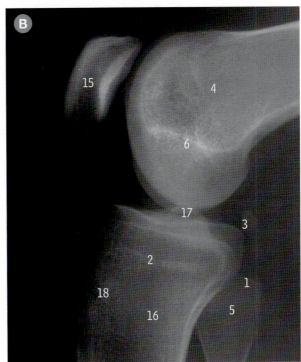

A：前方から．**B**：外側方から（屈曲させてある）．

Aでは，膝蓋骨の陰影（15）が大腿骨に重なっている．大腿骨と脛骨の外側顆同士ならびに内側顆同士の間隙（7と8の間，11と12の間）は，関節面の表面の硝子軟骨の厚さ，ならびに辺縁では関節半月によって生じる．膝を屈曲したCを307頁のEの骨標本と比較するとよい．また，膝蓋骨の外側縁（9）は，この頁のEの関節鏡写真で見えている．

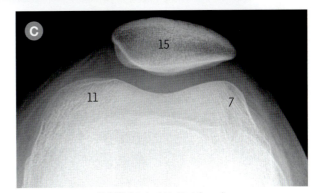

軸射像（スカイラインビュー）

1	腓骨頭尖 Apex of head of fibula	10	外側上顆〔大腿骨〕 Lateral epicondyle〔Femur〕
2	骨端線 Epiphysial line	11	内側顆〔大腿骨〕 Medial condyle〔Femur〕
3	ファベラ*（腓腹筋の外側頭腱の種子骨） Fabella*	12	内側顆〔脛骨〕 Medial condyle〔Tibia〕
4	大腿骨 Femur	13	内側上顆〔大腿骨〕 Medial epicondyle〔Femur〕
5	腓骨頭 Head of fibula	14	内側半月 Medial meniscus
6	顆間窩 Intercondylar fossa	15	膝蓋骨 Patella
7	外側顆〔大腿骨〕 Lateral condyle〔Femur〕	16	脛骨 Tibia
8	外側顆〔脛骨〕 Lateral condyle〔Tibia〕	17	内側顆間結節と外側顆間結節〔顆間隆起〕 Medial intercondylar tubercle and Lateral intercondylar tubercle〔Intercondylar eminence〕
9	膝蓋骨（の外側縁） Patella	18	脛骨粗面 Tibial tuberosity

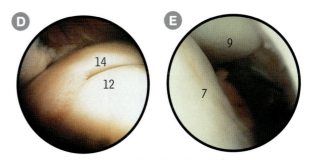

D：前外側アプローチ．**E**：膝蓋骨（外側方から）．

膝関節置換術

A B 膝窩（右）［浅層］

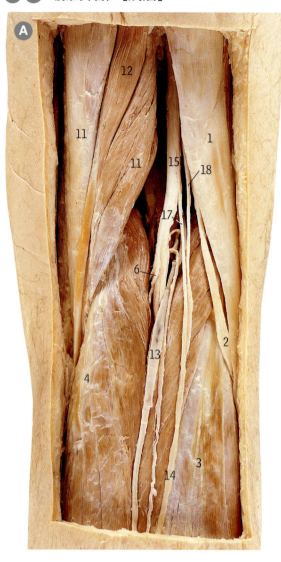

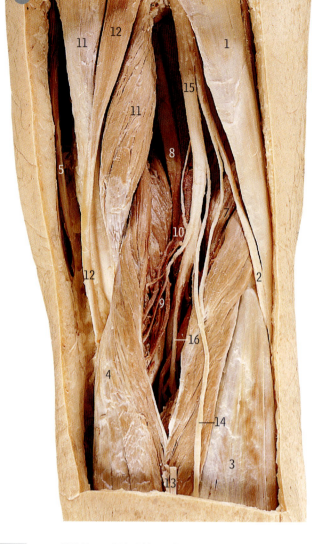

菱形の膝窩の屋根をつくる皮膚と筋膜，膝窩を埋めた脂肪を除去してあるが，筋膜を貫く小伏在静脈は残してある．外側腓腹皮神経と内側腓腹皮神経が通常よりも高いところで合しているため，腓腹神経がこの領域で見えている．

腓腹筋の二頭を分離してあるので，深部の構造が見える．

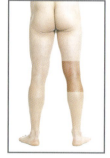

1	大腿二頭筋 Biceps femoris	7	足底筋 Plantaris	13	小伏在静脈 Small saphenous vein：Short saphenous vein
2	総腓骨神経 Common fibular (peroneal) nerve	8	膝窩動脈 Popliteal artery	14	腓腹神経 Sural nerve
3	外側頭〔腓腹筋〕 Lateral head〔Gastrocnemius〕	9	腓腹筋への枝〔膝窩動／静脈〕 Branches to Gastrocnemius〔Popliteal artery/vein〕	15	脛骨神経 Tibial nerve
4	内側頭〔腓腹筋〕 Medial head〔Gastrocnemius〕	10	膝窩静脈 Popliteal vein	16	筋枝〔脛骨神経〕 Muscular branches〔Tibial nerve〕
5	薄筋 Gracilis	11	半膜様筋 Semimembranosus	17	内側腓腹皮神経〔脛骨神経〕 Medial sural cutaneous nerve〔Tibial nerve〕
6	内側頭〔腓腹筋〕への枝 Nerve to Medial head〔Gastrocnemius〕	12	半腱様筋 Semitendinosus	18	外側腓腹皮神経〔総腓骨神経〕 Lateral sural cutaneous nerve〔Common fibular (peroneal) nerve〕

C D 膝窩［深層］

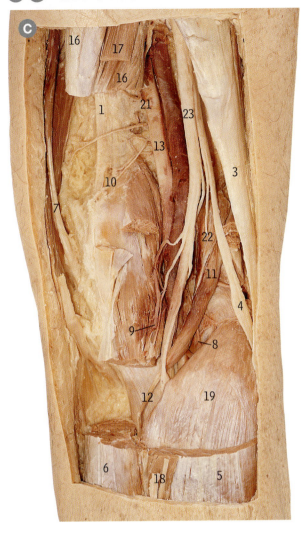

半腱様筋と半膜様筋および腓腹筋の起始部のほとんどを除去し，足底筋ならびに深部を走る膝窩動脈の枝とヒラメ筋を明らかにしてある．

膝窩の輪郭をつくる筋群を除去し，膝窩動脈とその膝関節周囲の吻合枝や終枝，前脛骨動脈，後脛骨動脈を明らかにしてある．

1	大内転筋 Adductor magnus	7	薄筋 Gracilis	13	膝窩動脈 Popliteal artery	19	ヒラメ筋 Soleus
2	前脛骨動脈 Anterior tibial artery	8	外側下膝動脈 Inferior lateral genicular artery	14	膝窩筋 Popliteus	20	外側上膝動脈 Superior lateral genicular artery
3	大腿二頭筋 Biceps femoris	9	内側下膝動脈 Inferior medial genicular artery	15	後脛骨動脈 Posterior tibial artery	21	内側上膝動脈 Superior medial genicular artery
4	総腓骨神経 Common fibular (peroneal) nerve	10	中膝動脈 Middle genicular artery	16	半膜様筋 Semimembranosus	22	腓腹神経 Sural nerve
5	外側頭〔腓腹筋〕 Lateral head〔Gastrocnemius〕	11	足底筋 Plantaris	17	半腱様筋 Semitendinosus	23	脛骨神経 Tibial nerve
6	内側頭〔腓腹筋〕 Medial head〔Gastrocnemius〕	12	足底筋（の腱） Plantaris	18	小伏在静脈 Small saphenous vein；Short saphenous vein		

膝窩囊胞（Baker 囊胞）

膝窩動脈瘤

腓腹神経移植

A 下腿（左）

1	前脛骨動脈（下腿骨間膜の前方を通る）	Anterior tibial artery
2	前脛骨筋への枝〔深腓骨神経〕	Branch to Tibialis anterior (Deep fibular (peroneal) nerve)
3	深腓骨神経	Deep fibular (peroneal) nerve
4	長趾伸筋	Extensor digitorum longus
5	長母趾伸筋	Extensor hallucis longus
6	腓骨頭	Head of fibula
7	中間足背皮神経〔浅腓骨神経〕	Intermediate dorsal cutaneous nerve (Superficial fibular (peroneal) nerve)
8	内側足背皮神経〔浅腓骨神経〕	Medial dorsal cutaneous nerve (Superficial fibular (peroneal) nerve)
9	長腓骨筋	Fibularis (Peroneus) longus
10	反回枝*〔総腓骨神経〕	Recurrent branch* (Common fibular (peroneal) nerve)
11	浅腓骨神経	Superficial fibular (peroneal) nerve
12	前脛骨筋と下腿筋膜（前脛骨筋を覆う）	Tibialis anterior and Deep fascia of leg
13	脛骨粗面と膝蓋靱帯	Tibial tuberosity and Patellar ligament

B 膝（左）

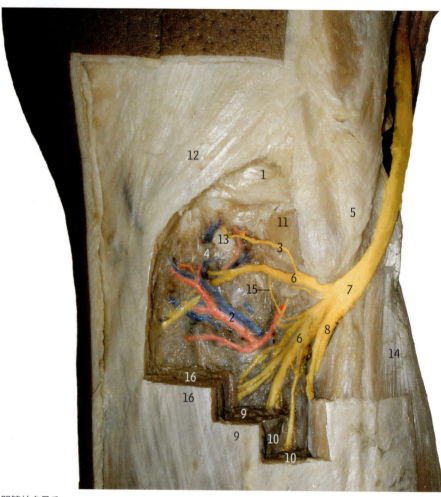

A：前外側方から．B：外側方から．総腓骨神経と関節枝を見る．

1	前腓骨頭靱帯	Anterior ligament of fibular head
2	前脛骨反回動／静脈	Anterior tibial recurrent artery/vein
3	関節枝〔総腓骨神経〕	Articular branch (Common fibular (peroneal) nerve)
4	関節への動／静脈	
5	大腿二頭筋（の腱）	Biceps femoris
6	深腓骨神経	Deep fibular (peroneal) nerve
7	総腓骨神経（腓骨頭をまわる）	Common fibular (peroneal) nerve
8	浅腓骨神経	Superficial fibular (peroneal) nerve
9	長趾伸筋	Extensor digitorum longus
10	長腓骨筋	Fibularis (Peroneus) longus
11	腓骨頭	Head of fibula
12	腸脛靱帯	Iliotibial tract
13	下腿骨間膜	Interosseous membrane of leg
14	外側頭〔腓腹筋〕	Lateral head (Gastrocnemius)
15	反回枝*〔深腓骨神経〕	Recurrent branch* (Deep fibular (peroneal) nerve)
16	前脛骨筋	Tibialis anterior

総腓骨神経麻痺

膝と下腿（左）

A：後内側方から． B：外側方から．

膝関節包に小さな窓を開け，大腿骨の内側顆(7)と内側半月(1の番号が付けられているところ)の一部を示した．

1	伏在枝の枝〔下行膝動脈〕（内側半月の内側を横切る） Branch of Saphenous branch〔Descending genicular artery〕
2	内側上膝動脈の枝 Branches of Superior medial genicular artery
3	薄筋 Gracilis
4	大伏在静脈 Great saphenous vein：Long saphenous vein
5	膝蓋下枝〔伏在神経〕 Infrapatellar branch〔Saphenous nerve〕
6	膝蓋下脂肪体 Infrapatellar fat pad：Hoffa *
7	内側顆〔大腿骨〕（関節包の一部を除去してある） Medial condyle〔Femur〕
8	内側頭〔腓腹筋〕 Medial head〔Gastrocnemius〕
9	内側面〔脛骨〕 Medial surface〔Tibia〕
10	膝蓋靱帯 Patellar ligament
11	伏在神経と（それに伴行する）動脈* Saphenous nerve and artery *
12	縫工筋 Sartorius
13	半膜様筋 Semimembranosus
14	半腱様筋 Semitendinosus
15	内側側副靱帯 Tibial collateral ligament

膝関節包に小さな窓を開け，膝窩筋(14)の腱が外側側副靱帯(5)の下層を通るところを示している．総腓骨神経(2)は，大腿二頭筋(1)の後方を走り，長腓骨筋(13)とヒラメ筋(15)の間隙を通り抜ける．浅腓骨神経は，長腓骨筋(13)と長趾伸筋(3)の間を通って浅層に現れる．

1	大腿二頭筋 Biceps femoris	9	外側腓腹皮神経 Lateral sural cutaneous nerve
2	総腓骨神経 Common fibular (peroneal) nerve	10	外側頭〔腓腹筋〕 Lateral head〔Gastrocnemius〕
3	長趾伸筋 Extensor digitorum longus	11	外側半月 Lateral meniscus
4	下腿筋膜（前脛骨筋を覆う） Deep fascia of leg	12	膝蓋靱帯 Patellar ligament
5	外側側副靱帯 Fibular collateral ligament	13	長腓骨筋 Fibularis (Peroneus) longus
6	腓骨頭 Head of fibula	14	膝窩筋 Popliteus
7	腸脛靱帯 Iliotibial tract	15	ヒラメ筋 Soleus
8	膝蓋下脂肪体 Infrapatellar fat pad：Hoffa *	16	浅腓骨神経 Superficial fibular (peroneal) nerve

A B 下腿と足根（左）［皮静脈と皮神経］

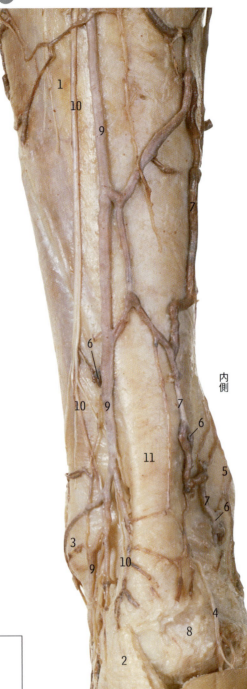

A：内側方から．B：後方から．

Bの標本（Aの標本とは異なる）では，内側の後弓静脈（7）は太く拡張している．

1	下腿筋膜	Deep fascia of leg
2	踵の線維脂肪組織	
3	外果	Lateral malleolus
4	内側踵骨枝〔脛骨神経〕	Medial calcaneal branches〔Tibial nerve〕
5	内果	Medial malleolus
6	筋膜を貫通する静脈	
7	後弓静脈*	Posterior arch vein*
8	後面*〔踵骨〕	Posterior surface*〔Calcaneus〕
9	小伏在静脈	Small saphenous vein：Short saphenous vein
10	腓腹神経	Sural nerve
11	踵骨腱：Achilles腱（下腿筋膜に包まれている）	Calcaneal tendon：Achilles tendon*

● 筋膜を貫通する静脈は，皮静脈（下腿筋膜より表層）と深部の静脈（下腿筋膜より深層）を交通している．交通がよく見られる場所は，脛骨のすぐ後ろ，腓骨の後ろ，内転筋管の内部である．交通する静脈には，血液が浅層から深層へ流れるようにする弁がある．下肢の静脈還流は（下腿筋膜より奥にある）筋群のポンプ作用によって起こる．弁が機能不全になったり静脈が閉塞すると，皮静脈の圧が上がり，静脈瘤（拡張して曲がりくねる）となる．

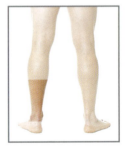

1	下腿筋膜（ヒラメ筋を覆う）	Deep fascia of leg
2	大伏在静脈	Great saphenous vein：Long saphenous vein
3	内果	Medial malleolus
4	内側面〔脛骨〕（皮下に触れることができる）	Medial surface〔Tibia〕
5	筋膜を貫通する静脈	
6	後弓静脈*	Posterior arch vein*
7	伏在神経	Saphenous nerve
8	踵骨腱：Achilles腱	Calcaneal tendon：Achilles tendon*

下腿静脈瘤による足根の潰瘍形成

下肢の深部静脈血栓症

C D 下肢の静脈

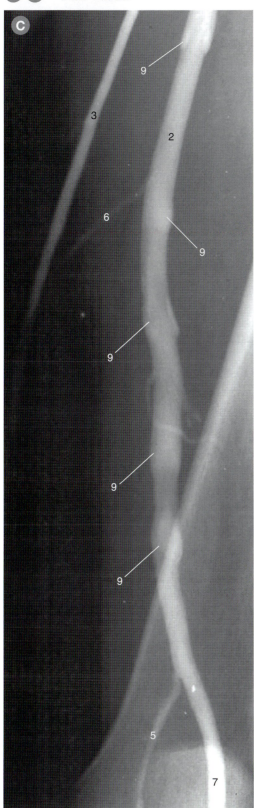

大腿部の造影画像

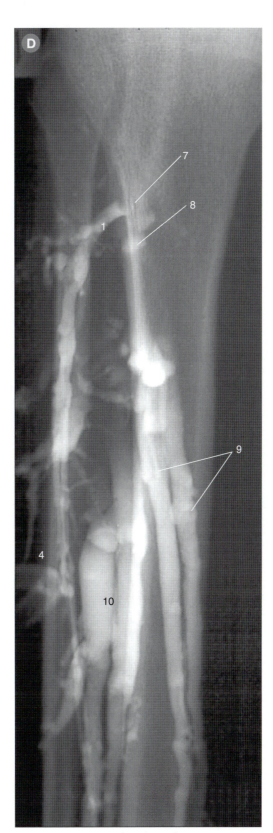

下腿部の造影画像

● 腓腹深部の静脈（ヒラメ筋より深部または内部）は，命にもかかわる静脈塞栓を起こすことがある．

1 前脛骨静脈
　Anterior tibial vein
2 大腿静脈
　Femoral vein
3 大伏在静脈
　Great saphenous vein：Long saphenous vein
4 外側下腿回旋静脈*
　Lateral circumflex calf vein*
5 筋からの静脈〔大腿静脈〕
　Muscular tributary〔Femoral vein〕
6 筋膜を貫通する静脈
7 膝窩静脈
　Popliteal vein
8 後脛骨静脈
　Posterior tibial vein
9 静脈弁
　Venous valve
10 下腿静脈叢*
　Calf venous plexus*

E 腓腹(左) [浅層]

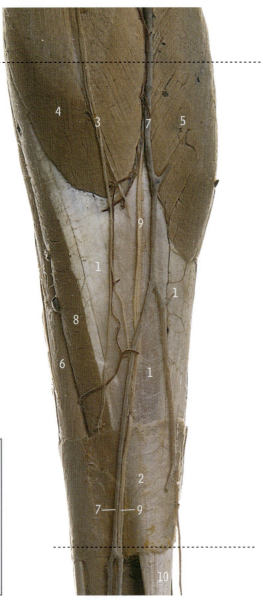
後方から．

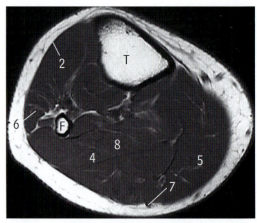
腓腹の MR 横断 T1 強調画像

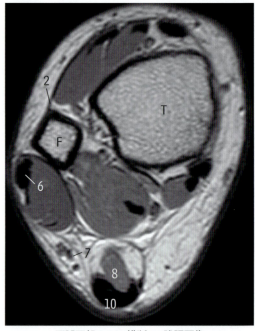
下腿下部の MR 横断 T1 強調画像

- 膝より下方では，大伏在静脈(348頁, A2)は伏在神経(348頁, A7)と並走する．
- 腓腹(ふくらはぎ)では，小伏在静脈(7)は腓腹神経(9)と並走する．

1	腓腹筋の腱膜 Aponeurosis of Gastrocnemius
2	下腿筋膜 Deep fascia of leg
3	外側腓腹皮神経 Lateral sural cutaneous nerve
4	外側頭〔腓腹筋〕 Lateral head〔Gastrocnemius〕
5	内側頭〔腓腹筋〕 Medial head〔Gastrocnemius〕
6	長腓骨筋 Fibularis (Peroneus) longus
7	小伏在静脈 Small saphenous vein：Short saphenous vein
8	ヒラメ筋 Soleus
9	腓腹神経 Sural nerve
10	踵骨腱：Achilles 腱 Calcaneal tendon：Achilles tendon *

冠動脈バイパス術のための静脈採取

A 膝窩と腓腹の上部（左）

B 腓腹の下部と足根（左）

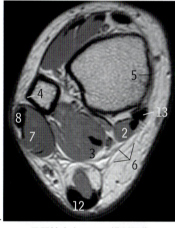

足関節直上のMR横断画像

1	下腿筋膜（後脛骨筋を覆う） Deep fascia of leg
2	長趾屈筋 Flexor digitorum longus
3	長母趾屈筋 Flexor hallucis longus
4	外果 Lateral malleolus
5	内果 Medial malleolus
6	屈筋支帯（の一部） Flexor retinaculum
7	短腓骨筋 Fibularis（Peroneus）brevis
8	長腓骨筋 Fibularis（Peroneus）longus
9	後脛骨動／静脈と脛骨神経の通る位置
10	後距腓靱帯 Posterior talofibular ligament
11	上腓骨筋支帯 Superior fibular（peroneal）retinaculum
12	踵骨腱：Achilles 腱 Calcaneal tendon：Achilles tendon *
13	後脛骨筋 Tibialis posterior

1	膝窩筋の外側半月への付着部	11	長腓骨筋 Fibularis（Peroneus）longus
2	大腿二頭筋 Biceps femoris	12	足底筋 Plantaris
3	関節包〔膝関節〕 Articular capsule〔Knee joint〕	13	膝窩筋 Popliteus
4	外側側副靱帯 Fibular collateral ligament	14	後面〔腓骨〕（ヒラメ筋を除去してある） Posterior surface〔Fibula〕
5	長趾屈筋 Flexor digitorum longus	15	縫工筋 Sartorius
6	長母趾屈筋 Flexor hallucis longus	16	半膜様筋 Semimembranosus
7	薄筋 Gracilis	17	半腱様筋 Semitendinosus
8	外側頭〔腓腹筋〕 Lateral head〔Gastrocnemius〕	18	ヒラメ筋 Soleus
9	内側顆〔大腿骨〕 Medial condyle〔Femur〕	19	内側側副靱帯 Tibial collateral ligament
10	内側頭〔腓腹筋〕 Medial head〔Gastrocnemius〕	20	後脛骨筋 Tibialis posterior

後脛骨筋腱炎

A 下腿(右)［膝窩］

後方から．

1 大腿二頭筋 Biceps femoris	10 膝窩静脈 Popliteal vein
2 総腓骨神経 Common fibular (peroneal) nerve	11 縫工筋 Sartorius
3 外側頭〔腓腹筋〕 Lateral head〔Gastrocnemius〕	12 半膜様筋 Semimembranosus
4 内側頭〔腓腹筋〕 Medial head〔Gastrocnemius〕	13 半腱様筋 Semitendinosus
5 薄筋 Gracilis	14 小伏在静脈 Small saphenous vein：Short saphenous vein
6 薄筋（の腱） Gracilis	15 ヒラメ筋 Soleus
7 大伏在静脈 Great saphenous vein：Long saphenous vein	16 踵骨腱：Achilles 腱 Calcaneal tendon：Achilles tendon *
8 外側腓腹皮神経 Lateral sural cutaneous nerve	17 踵骨腱：Achilles 腱（の上端） Calcaneal tendon：Achilles tendon *
9 内側腓腹皮神経 Medial sural cutaneous nerve	18 脛骨神経 Tibial nerve
	19 小伏在静脈を形成する静脈網

B 腓腹(右)［筋，神経，静脈］

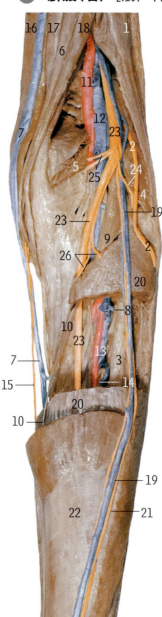

後方から．

1 大腿二頭筋 Biceps femoris	14 ヒラメ筋に出入りする血管
2 総腓骨神経 Common fibular (peroneal) nerve	15 伏在神経 Saphenous nerve
3 後面〔腓骨〕 Posterior surface〔Fibula〕	16 縫工筋 Sartorius
4 外側頭〔腓腹筋〕 Lateral head〔Gastrocnemius〕	17 半膜様筋 Semimembranosus
5 内側頭〔腓腹筋〕 Medial head〔Gastrocnemius〕	18 半腱様筋 Semitendinosus
6 薄筋 Gracilis	19 小伏在静脈（外側に引いてある） Small saphenous vein：Short saphenous vein
7 大伏在静脈 Great saphenous vein：Long saphenous vein	20 ヒラメ筋 Soleus
8 腓骨静脈 Fibular (Peroneal) vein	21 腓腹神経（外側に引いてある） Sural nerve
9 足底筋 Plantaris	22 踵骨腱：Achilles 腱（の上端） Calcaneal tendon：Achilles tendon *
10 足底筋（の腱） Plantaris	23 脛骨神経 Tibial nerve
11 膝窩動脈 Popliteal artery	24 腓腹筋の外側頭への枝〔脛骨神経〕 Branches to Lateral head of Gastrocnemius〔Tibial nerve〕
12 膝窩静脈 Popliteal vein	25 腓腹筋の内側頭への枝〔脛骨神経〕 Branches to Medial head of Gastrocnemius〔Tibial nerve〕
13 後脛骨動／静脈 Posterior tibial artery/vein	26 ヒラメ筋への枝〔脛骨神経〕 Branches to Soleus〔Tibial nerve〕

コンパートメント症候群

第6章 下肢：下腿　353

C 下腿の下部（右）[深層]

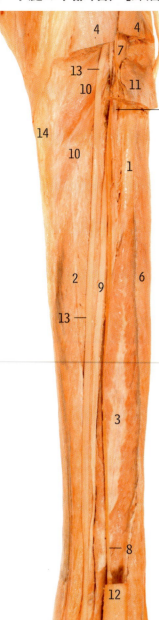

D 膝窩動脈

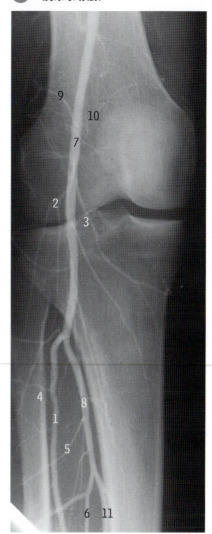

1	前脛骨動脈 Anterior tibial artery
2	外側下膝動脈 Inferior lateral genicular artery
3	内側下膝動脈 Inferior medial genicular artery
4	筋枝〔前脛骨動脈〕 Muscular branches〔Anterior tibial artery〕
5	筋枝〔脛骨腓骨動脈幹*〕 Muscular branches〔Tibiofibular trunk*〕
6	腓骨動脈 Fibular (Peroneal) artery
7	膝窩動脈 Popliteal artery
8	脛骨腓骨動脈幹*（後脛骨動脈と腓骨動脈の共同幹） Tibiofibular trunk*
9	外側上膝動脈 Superior lateral genicular artery
10	内側上膝動脈 Superior medial genicular artery
11	後脛骨動脈 Posterior tibial artery

動脈の造影画像

1	後面〔腓骨〕 Posterior surface〔Fibula〕	8	足底筋（の腱） Plantaris
2	長趾屈筋 Flexor digitorum longus	9	後脛骨動脈 Posterior tibial artery
3	長母趾屈筋 Flexor hallucis longus	10	膝窩筋 Popliteus
4	腓腹筋 Gastrocnemius	11	ヒラメ筋 Soleus
5	腓骨動脈 Fibular (Peroneal) artery	12	踵骨腱：Achilles腱 Calcaneal tendon：Achilles tendon*
6	長腓骨筋 Fibularis (Peroneus) longus	13	脛骨神経 Tibial nerve
7	足底筋 Plantaris	14	後面〔脛骨〕 Posterior surface〔Tibia〕

A 足根と足（右）

1. 短趾伸筋 Extensor digitorum brevis
2. 外果 Lateral malleolus
3. 長腓骨筋と短腓骨筋 Fibularis (Peroneus) longus and Fibularis (Peroneus) brevis
4. 小伏在静脈 Small saphenous vein：Short saphenous vein
5. 踵骨腱：Achilles 腱 Calcaneal tendon：Achilles tendon*
6. 前脛骨筋 Tibialis anterior
7. 第五中足骨粗面 Tuberosity of 5th metatarsal bone

- 大伏在静脈（B7）は，内果（B9）の前を上行する．
- 小伏在静脈（A4）は，外果（A2）の後ろを上行する．

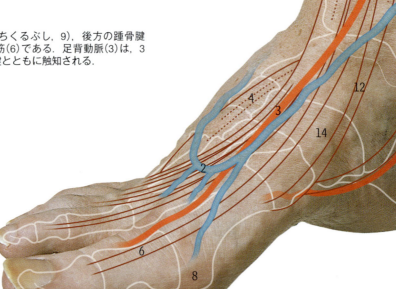

外側方から．

B 足根と足（右）

明らかに特徴的な体表の形態は，内果（うちくるぶし，9），後方の踵骨腱（Achilles 腱，11）ならびに前方の長母趾伸筋（6）である．足背動脈（3）は，3 の番号が付けられている位置で，長趾伸筋腱とともに触知される．

1. 踵骨 Calcaneus
2. 足背静脈弓 Dorsal venous arch of foot
3. 足背動脈 Dorsalis pedis artery
4. 短趾伸筋 Extensor digitorum brevis
5. 長趾伸筋 Extensor digitorum longus
6. 長母趾伸筋 Extensor hallucis longus
7. 大伏在静脈 Great saphenous vein：Long saphenous vein
8. 第一中足骨頭 Head of 1st metatarsal bone
9. 内果 Medial malleolus
10. 後脛骨動脈 Posterior tibial artery
11. 踵骨腱：Achilles 腱 Calcaneal tendon：Achilles tendon*
12. 前脛骨筋 Tibialis anterior
13. 後脛骨筋 Tibialis posterior
14. 舟状骨粗面 Tuberosity of navicular

前内側方から．

Achilles 腱反射

Achilles 腱断裂

内反尖足（内反足）

静脈切開

第6章　下肢：足根と足　355

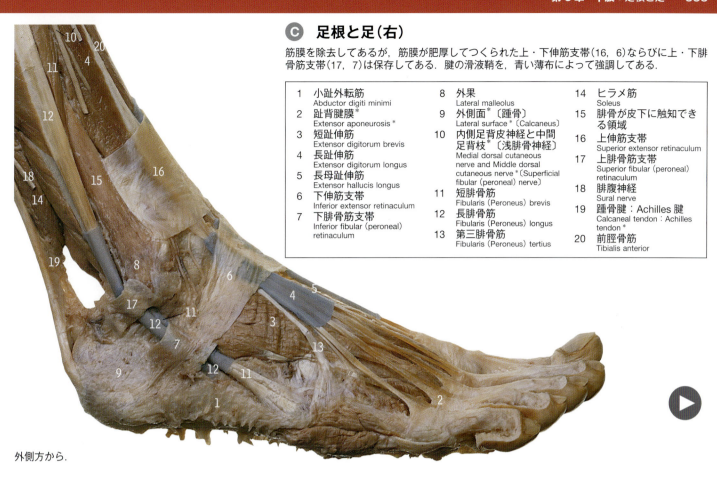

C　足根と足（右）

筋膜を除去してあるが，筋膜が肥厚してつくられた上・下伸筋支帯（16，6）ならびに上・下腓骨筋支帯（17，7）は保存してある．腱の滑液鞘を，青い薄布によって強調してある．

1	小趾外転筋 Abductor digiti minimi	8	外果 Lateral malleolus	14	ヒラメ筋 Soleus
2	趾背腱膜* Extensor aponeurosis*	9	外側面*〔踵骨〕 Lateral surface*〔Calcaneus〕	15	腓骨が皮下に触知できる領域
3	短趾伸筋 Extensor digitorum brevis	10	内側足背皮神経と中間足背枝*〔浅腓骨神経〕 Medial dorsal cutaneous nerve and Middle dorsal cutaneous nerve *〔Superficial fibular (peroneal) nerve〕	16	上伸筋支帯 Superior extensor retinaculum
4	長趾伸筋 Extensor digitorum longus			17	上腓骨筋支帯 Superior fibular (peroneal) retinaculum
5	長母趾伸筋 Extensor hallucis longus			18	腓腹神経 Sural nerve
6	下伸筋支帯 Inferior extensor retinaculum	11	短腓骨筋 Fibularis (Peroneus) brevis	19	踵骨腱：Achilles 腱 Calcaneal tendon：Achilles tendon*
7	下腓骨筋支帯 Inferior fibular (peroneal) retinaculum	12	長腓骨筋 Fibularis (Peroneus) longus	20	前脛骨筋 Tibialis anterior
		13	第三腓骨筋 Fibularis (Peroneus) tertius		

外側方から．

D　足根と足（右）

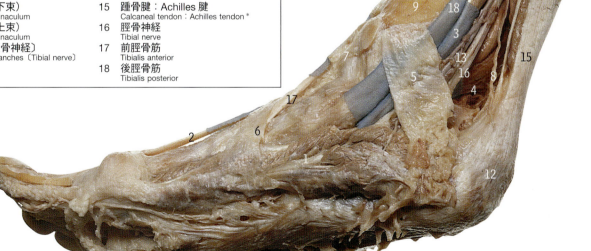

1	母趾外転筋 Abductor hallucis	10	内側面〔脛骨〕 Medial surface〔Tibia〕
2	長母趾伸筋 Extensor hallucis longus	11	足底筋（の腱） Plantaris
3	長趾屈筋 Flexor digitorum longus	12	後面*〔踵骨〕 Posterior surface*〔Calcaneus〕
4	長母趾屈筋 Flexor hallucis longus	13	後脛骨動／静脈 Posterior tibial artery/vein
5	屈筋支帯 Flexor retinaculum	14	ヒラメ筋 Soleus
6	下伸筋支帯（の下束） Inferior extensor retinaculum	15	踵骨腱：Achilles 腱 Calcaneal tendon：Achilles tendon*
7	下伸筋支帯（の上束） Inferior extensor retinaculum	16	脛骨神経 Tibial nerve
8	内側踵骨枝〔脛骨神経〕 Medial calcaneal branches〔Tibial nerve〕	17	前脛骨筋 Tibialis anterior
9	内果 Medial malleolus	18	後脛骨筋 Tibialis posterior

内側方から．

足関節の関節鏡

趾の先天異常

A 下腿の下部と足根（右）

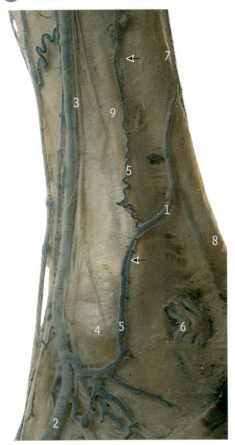

内側後方から．

下腿筋膜はそのまま残し，内果の後ろに小さな窓を開けて後脛骨動静脈と脛骨神経（6）を明らかにしてある．大伏在静脈（3）は，内果（4）の前を上行し，後ろを後弓静脈（5）が走っている．筋膜を貫通する静脈がよく認められる高さを矢印で示してある（348頁A5，B6）．

1	小伏在静脈との吻合
2	足背静脈弓 Dorsal venous arch of foot
3	大伏在静脈と伏在神経 Great saphenous vein：Long saphenous vein and Saphenous nerve
4	内果 Medial malleolus
5	後弓静脈* Posterior arch vein*
6	後脛骨動／静脈と脛骨神経 Posterior tibial artery/vein and Tibial nerve
7	小伏在静脈 Small saphenous vein：Short saphenous vein
8	踵骨腱：Achilles 腱 Calcaneal tendon：Achilles tendon*
9	後脛骨筋と長趾屈筋（下腿筋膜に覆われている） Tibialis posterior and Flexor digitorum longus

B 足根（右）

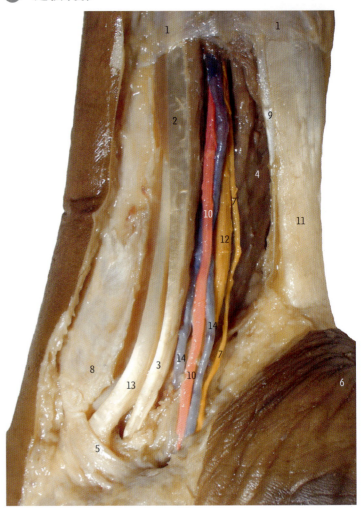

内側方から．

1	下腿筋膜 Deep fascia of leg
2	長趾屈筋 Flexor digitorum longus
3	長趾屈筋（の腱） Flexor digitorum longus
4	長母趾屈筋 Flexor hallucis longus
5	屈筋支帯 Flexor retinaculum
6	踵 Heel
7	内側踵骨枝〔脛骨神経〕 Medial calcaneal branches〔Tibial nerve〕
8	内果〔脛骨〕 Medial malleolus〔Tibia〕
9	足底筋（の腱） Plantaris
10	後脛骨動脈 Posterior tibial artery
11	踵骨腱：Achilles 腱 Calcaneal tendon：Achilles tendon*
12	脛骨神経 Tibial nerve
13	後脛骨筋（の腱） Tibialis posterior
14	後脛骨動／静脈 Posterior tibial artery/vein

下肢の潰瘍形成　　下肢静脈瘤

第6章　下肢：足根と足　357

C　足根と足（左）

足を底屈位とし，距腿関節の関節包の一部を除去して距骨（1 の番号の付けられているところ）を示してある．第三腓骨筋（12）と長趾伸筋（5）の各腱は，短趾伸筋（4）の浅層を通る．小伏在静脈と腓腹神経（13）は，外果（8）の後ろを通る．

1	前外果動脈（距骨の前方を通る：距腿関節包は除去してある） Anterior lateral malleolar artery	9	貫通枝〔腓骨動脈〕 Perforating branch〔Fibular (Peroneal) artery〕
2	前脛骨動／静脈と深腓骨神経 Anterior tibial artery/veins and Deep fibular (peroneal) nerve	10	短腓骨筋 Fibularis (Peroneus) brevis
3	下腿筋膜（上伸筋支帯を形成している） Deep fascia of leg	11	長腓骨筋 Fibularis (Peroneus) longus
4	短趾伸筋 Extensor digitorum brevis	12	第三腓骨筋 Fibularis (Peroneus) tertius
5	長趾伸筋 Extensor digitorum longus	13	小伏在静脈と腓腹神経 Small saphenous vein and Sural nerve
6	長母趾伸筋 Extensor hallucis longus	14	浅腓骨神経 Superficial fibular (peroneal) nerve
7	下伸筋支帯（一部を除去してある） Inferior extensor retinaculum	15	足根洞 Tarsal sinus
8	外果 Lateral malleolus	16	踵骨腱：Achilles 腱 Calcaneal tendon：Achilles tendon *
		17	前脛骨筋 Tibialis anterior

D　足根（左）

横断面を上方から見たところであり，足根（足くび）の領域の腱，血管および神経の位置を強調してある．距骨（18）を中心に，左に内果（9），右に外果（8）がある．内果の前に大伏在静脈（7）と伏在神経（15）があり，内果のすぐ後ろに後脛骨筋（22）の腱がある．外果の後ろに小伏在静脈（16）と腓腹神経（17）があり，それらと外果との間に長腓骨筋（11）と短腓骨筋（10）の腱が介在する．足根の前には足背動静脈（2）と深腓骨神経（1）があり，長母趾伸筋（4）と長趾伸筋（3）の各腱の間にはさまれている．内果（9）と後脛骨筋（22）の後で，後脛骨動静脈（14）と脛骨神経（20）が，長趾屈筋（5）と長母趾屈筋（6）の各腱にはさまれて走っている．

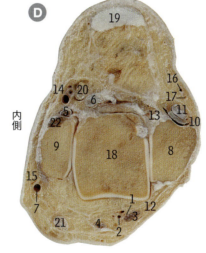

横断面．

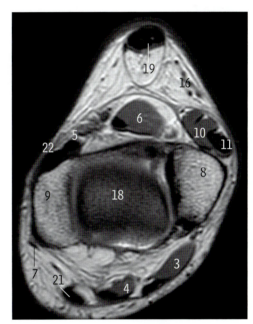

足関節の MR 横断画像

1	深腓骨神経 Deep fibular (peroneal) nerve	12	第三腓骨筋 Fibularis (Peroneus) tertius
2	足背動／静脈* Dorsalis pedis artery/vein*	13	後距腓靱帯 Posterior talofibular ligament
3	長趾伸筋 Extensor digitorum longus	14	後脛骨動／静脈 Posterior tibial artery/vein
4	長母趾伸筋 Extensor hallucis longus	15	伏在神経 Saphenous nerve
5	長趾屈筋 Flexor digitorum longus	16	小伏在静脈 Small saphenous vein：Short saphenous vein
6	長母趾屈筋 Flexor hallucis longus	17	腓腹神経 Sural nerve
7	大伏在静脈 Great saphenous vein：Long saphenous vein	18	距骨 Talus
8	外果〔腓骨〕 Lateral malleolus〔Fibula〕	19	踵骨腱：Achilles 腱 Calcaneal tendon：Achilles tendon *
9	内果〔脛骨〕 Medial malleolus〔Tibia〕	20	脛骨神経 Tibial nerve
10	短腓骨筋 Fibularis (Peroneus) brevis	21	前脛骨筋 Tibialis anterior
11	長腓骨筋 Fibularis (Peroneus) longus	22	後脛骨筋 Tibialis posterior

Charcot 関節症

第6章 下肢：足根と足

A 足背（足のこう）（右）

1	弓状動脈 Arcuate artery	10	第一中足趾節関節 1st metatarsophalangeal joint
2	背側趾動脈 Dorsal digital arteries	11	第四背側骨間筋 4th dorsal interosseous
3	足背動脈 Dorsalis pedis artery	12	第三腓骨筋 Fibularis (Peroneus) tertius
4	短趾伸筋 Extensor digitorum brevis	13	第二背側骨間筋 2nd dorsal interosseous
5	長趾伸筋 Extensor digitorum longus	14	第二背側中足動脈 2nd dorsal metatarsal artery
6	短母趾伸筋 Extensor hallucis brevis	15	内側足根動脈 Medial tarsal arteries
7	長母趾伸筋 Extensor hallucis longus	16	第三背側骨間筋 3rd dorsal interosseous
8	第一背側骨間筋 1st dorsal interosseous	17	前脛骨筋 Tibialis anterior
9	第一背側中足動脈 1st dorsal metatarsal artery	18	第五中足骨粗面と短腓骨筋 Tuberosity of 5th metatarsal bone and Fibularis (Peroneus) brevis

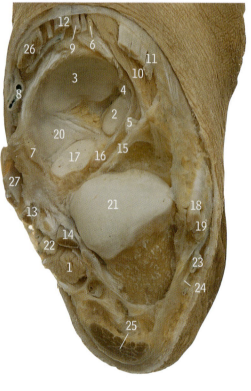

B 距骨下関節と距踵舟関節（右）

距骨を除去し、踵骨の各関節面（21, 17, 2）、舟状骨の関節面（3）ならびに底側踵舟靱帯（ばね靱帯, 20）を示してある．

1	母趾外転筋 Abductor hallucis	15	下伸筋支帯 Inferior extensor retinaculum
2	前距骨関節面〔踵骨〕 Anterior talar articular surface〔Calcaneus〕	16	骨間距踵靱帯 Talocalcaneal interosseous ligament
3	舟状骨（の距骨との関節面） Navicular	17	中距骨関節面〔踵骨〕 Middle talar articular surface〔Calcaneus〕
4	踵舟靱帯〔二分靱帯〕 Calcaneonavicular ligament〔Bifurcate ligament〕	18	短腓骨筋 Fibularis (Peroneus) brevis
5	距踵頸靱帯* Cervical ligament* : External talocalcaneal ligament*	19	長腓骨筋 Fibularis (Peroneus) longus
6	深腓骨神経 Deep fibular (peroneal) nerve	20	底側踵舟靱帯：ばね靱帯* Plantar calcaneonavicular ligament : Spring ligament
7	内側靱帯：三角靱帯 Medial ligament : Deltoid ligament	21	後距骨関節面〔踵骨〕 Posterior talar articular surface〔Calcaneus〕
8	足背静脈弓 Dorsal venous arch of foot	22	後脛骨動／静脈と内側足底神経・外側足底神経 Posterior tibial artery/vein, Medial plantar nerve and Lateral plantar nerve
9	足背動／静脈* Dorsalis pedis artery/vein*	23	小伏在静脈 Small saphenous vein : Short saphenous vein
10	短趾伸筋 Extensor digitorum brevis	24	腓腹神経 Sural nerve
11	長趾伸筋 Extensor digitorum longus	25	踵骨腱：Achilles腱 Calcaneal tendon : Achilles tendon*
12	長母趾伸筋 Extensor hallucis longus	26	前脛骨筋 Tibialis anterior
13	長趾屈筋 Flexor digitorum longus	27	後脛骨筋 Tibialis posterior
14	長母趾屈筋 Flexor hallucis longus		

●臨床では、"距骨下関節"という用語を、距踵関節（解剖学における距骨下関節）と距踵舟関節の距踵部の両者を含めた名称として使用することがある．足の内がえし、外がえしの運動の大部分が、距骨頸靱帯の軸上で、距骨の下のこれらの両関節で行われるからである．

足関節の神経ブロック

悪性黒色腫

足根管症候群

C〜E 足根と足（左）［靱帯］

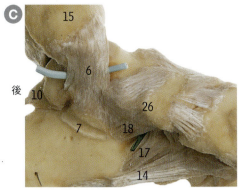
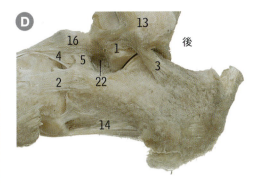

Cでは，内果（15）の下方で，内側靱帯（三角靱帯，6）の浅部と深部の間にマーカーを通してある．舟状骨粗面（26）の下方で，底側踵舟靱帯（18）と底側踵立方靱帯（17）の間にマーカーを通してある．

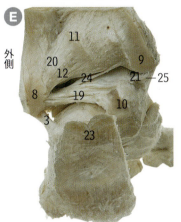

1	前距腓靱帯 Anterior talofibular ligament	9	後脛骨筋腱溝＊〔内果〕 Groove for tibialis posterior＊〔Medial malleolus〕	18	底側踵舟靱帯 Plantar calcaneonavicular ligament：Spring ligament
2	踵立方靱帯〔二分靱帯〕 Calcaneocuboid ligament〔Bifurcate ligament〕	10	長母趾屈筋腱溝 Groove for tendon of flexor hallucis longus	19	後距腓靱帯 Posterior talofibular ligament
3	踵腓靱帯 Calcaneofibular ligament	11	長母趾屈筋腱溝＊〔脛骨〕 Groove for tendon of flexor hallucis longus〔Tibia〕	20	後脛腓靱帯 Posterior tibiofibular ligament
4	踵舟靱帯〔二分靱帯〕 Calcaneonavicular ligament〔Bifurcate ligament〕	12	下横靱帯 Inferior transverse ligament＊	21	後距部〔内側靱帯：三角靱帯〕 Posterior tibiotalar part〔Medial ligament：Deltoid ligament〕
5	距踵頸靱帯＊ Cervical ligament＊：External talocalcaneal ligament＊	13	外果 Lateral malleolus	22	足根洞 Tarsal sinus
6	内側靱帯：三角靱帯 Medial ligament：Deltoid ligament	14	長足底靱帯 Long plantar ligament	23	踵骨腱：Achilles 腱 Calcaneal tendon：Achilles tendon＊
7	長母趾屈筋腱溝〔載距突起〕 Groove for tendon of flexor hallucis longus〔Sustentaculum tali〕	15	内果 Medial malleolus	24	後距腓靱帯（の脛骨への線維束） Posterior talofibular ligament
8	短腓骨筋腱溝＊〔外果〕 Groove for fibularis(peroneus)brevis＊〔Lateral malleolus〕	16	距骨頸 Neck of talus	25	脛踵部〔内側靱帯：三角靱帯〕 Tibiocalcaneal part〔Medial ligament：Deltoid ligament〕
		17	底側踵立方靱帯：短足底靱帯 Plantar calcaneocuboid ligament：Short plantar ligament	26	舟状骨粗面 Tuberosity of navicular

C：内側方から． D：外側方から．
E：後方から．

F 足（左）

1	小趾外転筋 Abductor digiti minimi	11	短趾屈筋 Flexor digitorum brevis	19	内側足底動脈 Medial plantar artery	27	距舟部＊〔距踵舟関節〕 Talonavicular part＊〔Talocalcaneonavicular joint〕
2	母趾外転筋 Abductor hallucis	12	短母趾屈筋 Flexor hallucis brevis	20	第一中趾節関節 1st metatarsophalangeal joint	28	距骨 Talus
3	踵骨 Calcaneus	13	長母趾屈筋 Flexor hallucis longus	21	舟状骨 Navicular	29	踵骨腱：Achilles 腱 Calcaneal tendon：Achilles tendon＊
4	楔舟関節 Cuneonavicular joint	14	大伏在静脈 Great saphenous vein：Long saphenous vein	22	足底腱膜 Plantar aponeurosis	30	長母趾屈筋（の腱） Flexor hallucis longus
5	末節骨 Distal phalanx	15	骨間距踵靱帯 Talocalcaneal interosseous ligament	23	底側踵舟靱帯 Plantar calcaneonavicular ligament：Spring ligament	31	脛骨 Tibia
6	長母趾伸筋 Extensor hallucis longus	16	（足の）趾節間関節 Interphalangeal joint of foot	24	基節骨 Proximal phalanx	32	後脛骨筋 Tibialis posterior
7	脂肪体＊ Fat pad＊	17	外側足底神経と外側足底動／静脈 Lateral plantar nerve and Lateral plantar artery/vein	25	ヒラメ筋 Soleus	33	脛距部＊〔距腿関節〕 Tibiotalar part＊〔Ankle joint〕
8	第一中足骨 1st metatarsal bone	18	内側楔状骨 Medial cuneiform	26	距骨下関節 Subtalar joint：Talocalcanean joint		
9	第一足根中足関節 1st tarsometatarsal joint						
10	足底方形筋 Quadratus plantae：Flexor accessorius						

内側方から．矢状断．

足関節の捻挫

A〜D 足底（左）［A 足底腱膜，B 浅い神経および筋の層］

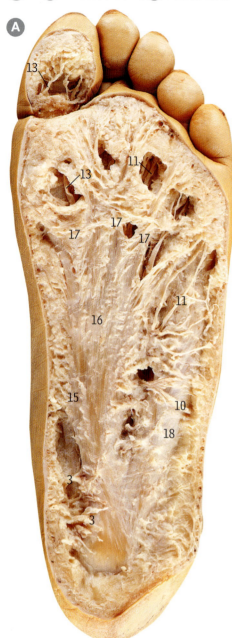
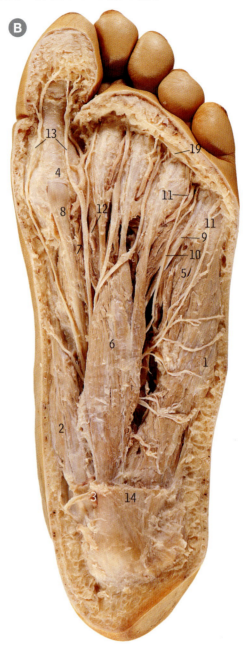

足底の皮膚を除去し，足底腱膜を示してある．足底腱膜は厚い中央部と趾への腱束と，薄い外側部と内側部からなる．

足底腱膜の深部の，足底の浅い層には，足底の神経，足底の動脈および筋がある．

1 小趾外転筋 Abductor digiti minimi	8 長母趾屈筋 Flexor hallucis longus	14 足底腱膜 Plantar aponeurosis
2 母趾外転筋 Abductor hallucis	9 外側足底動脈 Lateral plantar artery	15 足底腱膜（母趾外転筋を覆う部分） Plantar aponeurosis
3 踵骨内側の神経血管束	10 外側足底神経 Lateral plantar nerve	16 足底腱膜（短趾屈筋を覆う部分） Plantar aponeurosis
4 趾の線維鞘 Fibrous sheaths of toes	11 総底側趾神経および固有底側趾神経〔外側足底神経〕 Common plantar digital nerve and Proper plantar digital nerve〔Lateral plantar nerve〕	17 足底腱膜（趾へ向かう線維束） Plantar aponeurosis
5 短小趾屈筋 Flexor digiti minimi brevis		18 足底腱膜（小趾外転筋を覆う部分） Plantar aponeurosis
6 短趾屈筋 Flexor digitorum brevis	12 虫様筋 Lumbrical	19 浅横中足靱帯 Superficial transverse metatarsal ligament
7 短母趾屈筋 Flexor hallucis brevis	13 固有底側趾神経〔内側足底神経〕 Proper plantar digital nerve〔Medial plantar nerve〕	

扁平足

足底筋膜炎

C: 短趾屈筋を除去してある. D: 長趾屈筋を除去してある.

1	小趾外転筋 Abductor digiti minimi	8	短趾屈筋（切断してある） Flexor digitorum brevis	15	総底側趾神経〔外側足底神経〕 Common plantar digital nerve〔Lateral plantar nerve〕
2	母趾外転筋 Abductor hallucis	9	長趾屈筋 Flexor digitorum longus	16	深枝〔外側足底神経〕 Deep branch〔Lateral plantar nerve〕
3	斜頭〔母趾内転筋〕 Oblique head〔Adductor hallucis〕	10	短母趾屈筋 Flexor hallucis brevis	17	虫様筋 Lumbrical
4	横頭〔母趾内転筋〕 Transverse head〔Adductor hallucis〕	11	長母趾屈筋 Flexor hallucis longus	18	内側足底動脈 Medial plantar artery
5	趾の線維鞘 Fibrous sheaths of toes	12	底側骨間筋 Plantar interossei	19	内側足底神経 Medial plantar nerve
6	足底方形筋 Quadratus plantae : Flexor accessorius	13	外側足底動脈 Lateral plantar artery	20	総底側趾神経〔内側足底神経〕 Common plantar digital nerves〔Medial plantar nerve〕
7	短小趾屈筋 Flexor digiti minimi brevis	14	外側足底神経 Lateral plantar nerve		

Babinski 反射：
伸展性足底反射

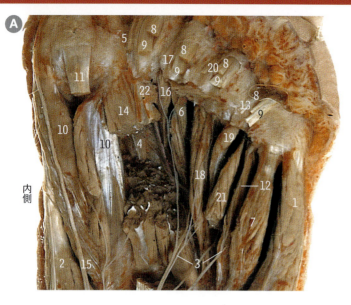

内側

A 足底（左）[深層，骨間筋]

1	小趾外転筋 Abductor digiti minimi	12	第四背側骨間筋 4th dorsal interosseous
2	母趾外転筋 Abductor hallucis	13	第四虫様筋 4th lumbrical
3	深枝の枝〔外側足底神経〕Branches of Deep branch〔Lateral plantar nerve〕	14	斜頭〔母趾内転筋〕Oblique head〔Adductor hallucis〕
4	第一背側骨間筋 1st dorsal interosseous	15	（母趾の）固有底側趾神経 Plantar digital nerve of great toe
5	第一虫様筋 1st lumbrical	16	第二背側骨間筋 2nd dorsal interosseous
6	第一底側骨間筋 1st plantar interosseous	17	第二虫様筋 2nd lumbrical
7	短小趾屈筋 Flexor digiti minimi brevis	18	第二底側骨間筋 2nd plantar interosseous
8	短趾屈筋 Flexor digitorum brevis	19	第三背側骨間筋 3rd dorsal interosseous
9	長趾屈筋 Flexor digitorum longus	20	第三虫様筋 3rd lumbrical
10	短母趾屈筋 Flexor hallucis brevis	21	第三底側骨間筋 3rd plantar interosseous
11	長母趾屈筋 Flexor hallucis longus	22	横頭〔母趾内転筋〕Transverse head〔Adductor hallucis〕

B 足底（右）[足底動脈弓]

屈筋とその腱の大半を除去してある．外側足底動脈(8)が足底方形筋(3)と交叉し，屈筋腱の深層にある深足底動脈弓(12)に続く．

1	小趾外転筋 Abductor digiti minimi	10	内側足底動脈と内側足底神経 Medial plantar artery and Medial plantar nerve
2	母趾外転筋 Abductor hallucis	11	斜頭〔母趾内転筋〕Oblique head〔Adductor hallucis〕
3	足底方形筋 Quadratus plantae; Flexor accessorius	12	深足底動脈弓 Deep plantar arch
4	短小趾屈筋 Flexor digiti minimi brevis	13	固有底側趾動脈 Plantar digital arteries proper
5	短趾屈筋 Flexor digitorum brevis	14	底側中足動脈 Plantar metatarsal artery
6	短母趾屈筋 Flexor hallucis brevis	15	第二底側骨間筋 2nd plantar interosseous
7	第四背側骨間筋 4th dorsal interosseous	16	第三底側骨間筋 3rd plantar interosseous
8	外側足底動脈 Lateral plantar artery	17	横頭〔母趾内転筋〕Transverse head〔Adductor hallucis〕
9	虫様筋 Lumbrical	18	舟状骨粗面 Tuberosity of navicular

C 足

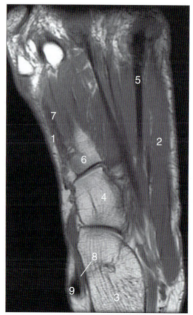

MR 横断画像

1	小趾外転筋 Abductor digiti minimi
2	母趾外転筋 Abductor hallucis
3	踵骨 Calcaneus
4	立方骨 Cuboid
5	長母趾屈筋 Flexor hallucis longus
6	中足骨底 Base of metatarsal bone
7	小趾対立筋 Opponens digiti minimi
8	短腓骨筋（の腱）Fibularis (Peroneus) brevis
9	長腓骨筋（の腱）Fibularis (Peroneus) longus

D 足底（左）［靱帯と腱］

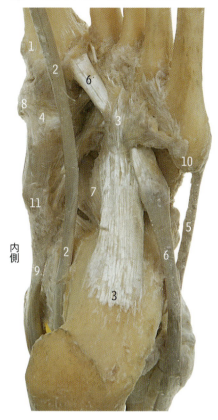

長足底靱帯(3)の前端部が，立方骨(E6)の溝に架橋してトンネルをつくる．ここを長腓骨筋腱(6)が通り，内側楔状骨(4)と第一中足骨底(1)に達する．

1	第一中足骨底	Base of 1st metatarsal bone
2	長母趾屈筋	Flexor hallucis longus
3	長足底靱帯	Long plantar ligament
4	内側楔状骨	Medial cuneiform
5	短腓骨筋	Fibularis (Peroneus) brevis
6	長腓骨筋	Fibularis (Peroneus) longus
7	底側踵立方靱帯：短足底靱帯	Plantar calcaneocuboid ligament : Short plantar ligament
8	前脛骨筋	Tibialis anterior
9	後脛骨筋	Tibialis posterior
10	第五中足粗面	Tuberosity of 5th metatarsal bone
11	舟状骨粗面	Tuberosity of navicular

● 底側踵舟靱帯(E9)は，一般にばね靱帯(Spring ligament)とよばれ，足の最も重要な靱帯の1つである．この靱帯は，載距突起(E7)と舟状骨粗面(E16)の間に張り，内側では距腿関節の内側靱帯（三角靱帯）と混じり合う．また，この靱帯は距骨頭の一部を載せて支えている．

E 足底（左）［靱帯］

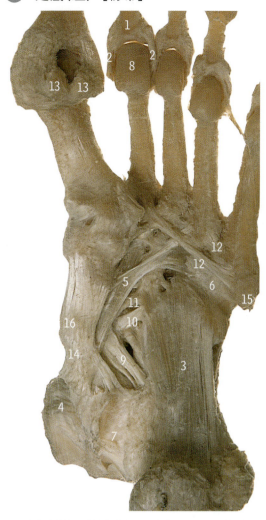

長足底靱帯(3)の前端を除去し，立方骨の長腓骨筋腱溝(6)を示してある．

1	基節骨底	Base of proximal phalanx
2	側副靱帯〔中足趾節関節〕	Collateral ligaments〔Metatarsophalangeal joint〕
3	長足底靱帯（の深束）	Long plantar ligament
4	内側靱帯：三角靱帯	Medial ligament : Deltoid ligament
5	後脛骨筋からの線維束	
6	長腓骨筋腱溝〔立方骨〕	Groove for tendon of fibularis (peroneus) longus〔Cuboid〕
7	長母趾屈筋腱溝〔載距突起〕	Groove for tendon of flexor hallucis longus〔Sustentaculum tali〕
8	第二中足骨頭	Head of 2nd metatarsal bone
9	底側踵舟靱帯	Plantar calcaneonavicular ligament : Spring ligament
10	底側立方舟靱帯	Plantar cuboideonavicular ligament
11	底側楔舟靱帯	Plantar cuneonavicular ligament
12	底側中足靱帯	Plantar metatarsal ligament
13	種子骨	Sesamoid bone
14	後脛骨筋	Tibialis posterior
15	第五中足骨粗面	Tuberosity of 5th metatarsal bone
16	舟状骨粗面	Tuberosity of navicular

A B 足根

1	踵骨	Calcaneus
2	立方骨	Cuboid
3	腓骨	Fibula
4	距骨頭	Head of talus
5	外側楔状骨	Lateral cuneiform
6	外果〔腓骨〕	Lateral malleolus〔Fibula〕
7	距骨後突起〔距骨〕	Posterior process〔Talus〕
8	内果〔脛骨〕	Medial malleolus〔Tibia〕
9	内側結節〔距骨〕	Medial tubercle〔Talus〕
10	舟状骨	Navicular
11	脛腓靭帯結合：下脛腓関節*	Tibiofibular syndesmosis：Inferior tibiofibular joint
12	載距突起〔踵骨〕	Sustentaculum tali〔Calcaneus〕
13	距骨	Talus
14	脛骨	Tibia
15	第五中足骨粗面	Tuberosity of 5th metatarsal bone

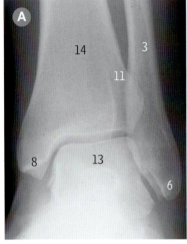

X線前後方向画像

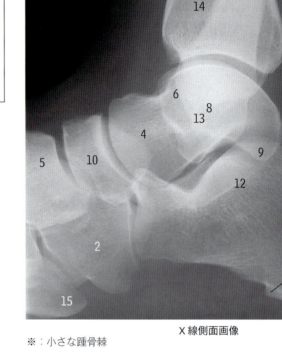

※：小さな踵骨棘

X線側面画像

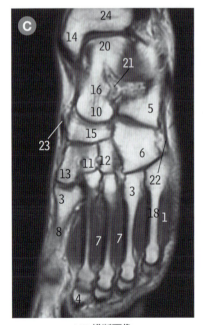

MR 横断画像

C D 足

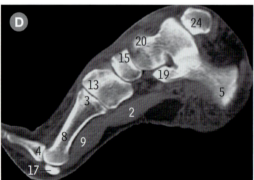

母趾(指)を通る CT 矢状断画像

1	小趾外転筋	Abductor digiti minimi
2	母趾外転筋	Abductor hallucis
3	中足骨底	Base of metatarsal bone
4	基節骨底	Base of proximal phalanx
5	踵骨	Calcaneus
6	立方骨	Cuboid
7	背側骨間筋	Dorsal interossei
8	第一中足骨	1st metatarsal bone
9	短趾屈筋	Flexor digitorum brevis
10	距骨頭	Head of talus
11	中間楔状骨	Intermediate cuneiform
12	外側楔状骨	Lateral cuneiform
13	内側楔状骨	Medial cuneiform
14	内果	Medial malleolus
15	舟状骨	Navicular
16	距骨頸	Neck of talus
17	短母趾屈筋腱内の種子骨	
18	中足骨体	Shaft of metatarsal bone：Body of metatarsal bone
19	載距突起〔踵骨〕	Sustentaculum tali〔Calcaneus〕
20	距骨	Talus
21	足根洞（距踵頸靭帯）	Tarsal sinus (Talocalcaneal cervical ligament)
22	短腓骨筋（の腱）	Fibularis (Peroneus) brevis
23	前脛骨筋（の腱）	Tibialis anterior
24	脛骨	Tibia

Pott 骨折（足関節果部骨折）と他の足関節の骨折

リンパ系

リンパ系

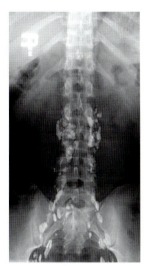

腰部の前後画像：
造影剤後期充満画像

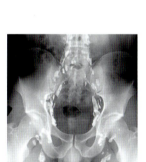

骨盤の前後画像：
リンパ節の造影剤後期充満画像

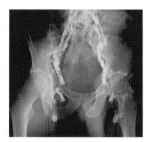

骨盤の前後画像：
リンパ管の造影剤注入直後画像

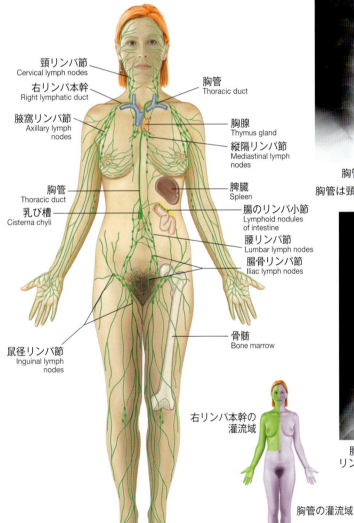

- 頸リンパ節 Cervical lymph nodes
- 右リンパ本幹 Right lymphatic duct
- 腋窩リンパ節 Axillary lymph nodes
- 胸管 Thoracic duct
- 乳び槽 Cisterna chyli
- 鼠径リンパ節 Inguinal lymph nodes
- 胸管 Thoracic duct
- 胸腺 Thymus gland
- 縦隔リンパ節 Mediastinal lymph nodes
- 脾臓 Spleen
- 腸のリンパ小節 Lymphoid nodules of intestine
- 腰リンパ節 Lumbar lymph nodes
- 腸骨リンパ節 Iliac lymph nodes
- 骨髄 Bone marrow

右リンパ本幹の灌流域

胸管の灌流域

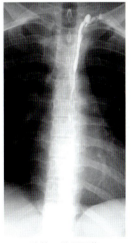

胸管の造影画像
胸管は頸部で終わる．

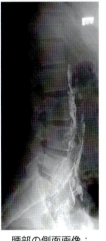

腰部の側面画像：
リンパ管の造影剤注入直後画像

リンパ系
（メチレンブルー検査）

● 造影剤注入当日（第一期）の撮影はリンパ管の造影に最適であるのに対し，48時間後（第二期）の撮影はリンパ節の描出に最も適している．

A B 胸腺

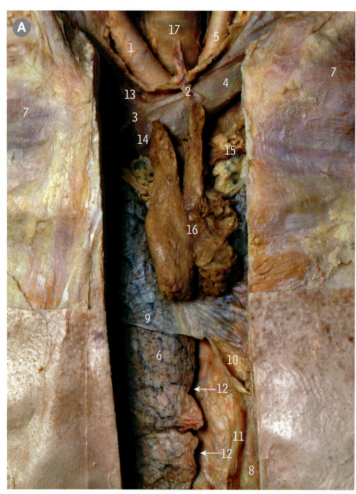

胸骨を縦に割って開いたため，胸腺が縦隔の前方上部にあるのが見えている．

- 口蓋扁桃（一般に"扁桃腺"とよばれる）はリンパ組織の塊であり，子どものときはしばしば大きくなるが成長に従って小さくなる．舌の後方（舌扁桃）と，〔咽頭〕鼻部と耳管扁桃の後壁（咽頭扁桃）にあるリンパ組織が共に気管と食道の上端でリンパ組織の輪（Waldeyer扁桃輪）を形づくる．

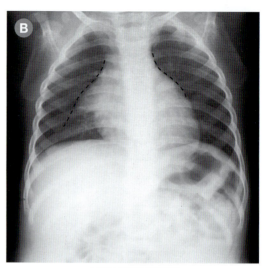

小児の胸部X線画像

- 小児の胸腺は2歳以下で胸部単純X線撮影で見ることができる．破線で輪郭を描いたように，ヨットの大三角帆（Sail sign）として現れる．

C 口蓋扁桃

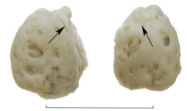

2cm

14歳の患者から摘出した標本の内側面に見られる穴は，扁桃陰窩の開口部である．矢印は，扁桃内裂（発生時の第二咽頭嚢の遺残）を示している．口蓋扁桃は，口を開けた時，口蓋垂の左右にある咽頭弓の間で容易に確認できる．

1	腕頭動脈 Brachiocephalic trunk	6	上葉〔右肺〕 Superior lobe〔Right lung〕	11	胸膜（右胸膜の切断縁） Pleura	15	胸腺静脈（内胸静脈へ流入する） Thymic vein
2	下甲状腺静脈 Inferior thyroid vein	7	大胸筋 Pectoralis major	12	胸膜腔 Pleural cavity	16	胸腺（2葉になっている） Thymus
3	（右の）内胸静脈 Internal thoracic vein	8	線維性心膜 Fibrous pericardium	13	右腕頭静脈 Right brachiocephalic vein	17	気管 Trachea
4	左腕頭静脈 Left brachiocephalic vein	9	胸膜 Pleura	14	上大静脈 Superior vena cava		
5	（左の）総頸動脈 Common carotid artery	10	胸膜（左胸膜の切断縁） Pleura				

胸腺

扁桃炎

頸部

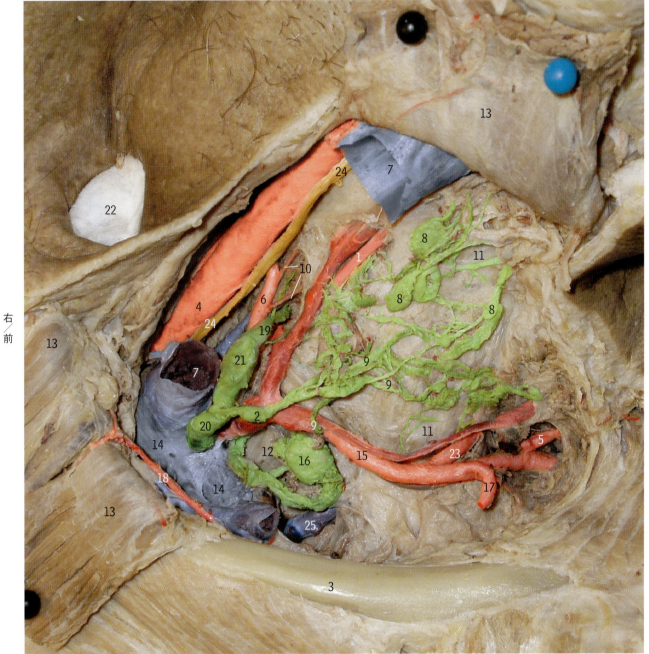

頸部の基底部で左鎖骨下静脈に注ぐ胸管の終末部を解剖した．左側から見ている．

1. 上行頸動脈とその伴行静脈
   Ascending cervical artery and venae comitantes
2. 頸リンパ本幹
   Jugular trunk
3. （左の）鎖骨
   Clavicle
4. 総頸動脈
   Common carotid artery
5. 肩甲背動脈
   Dorsal scapular artery
6. 下甲状腺動脈
   Inferior thyroid artery
7. 内頸静脈
   Internal jugular vein
8. リンパ節（鎖状に連なる深頸リンパ節群）
   Lymph node
9. リンパ管（リンパ節から頸リンパ本幹へ注ぐ）
   Lymphatic vessel
10. 頸長筋への枝〔下甲状腺動脈〕
    Branches to Longus colli〔Inferior thyroid artery〕
11. 椎前葉〔頸筋膜〕
    Prevertebral layer〔Cervical fascia〕
12. 前斜角筋
    Anterior scalene
13. 胸鎖乳突筋（翻転し，ピンで留めてある）
    Sternocleidomastoid
14. 鎖骨下静脈
    Subclavian vein
15. 浅頸動脈
    Superficial cervical artery
16. 鎖骨上リンパ節：Virchow リンパ節＊（腫大している）
    Supraclavicular node：Virchow node＊
17. 肩甲上動脈
    Suprascapular artery
18. 鎖骨枝〔胸肩峰動脈〕
    Clavicular branch〔Thoraco-acromial artery〕
19. 胸管
    Thoracic duct
20. 胸管（終末部）
    Thoracic duct
21. 胸管（膨大している）
    Thoracic duct
22. 気管切開をした部位
23. 頸横動脈
    Transverse cervical artery
24. 迷走神経［X］
    Vagus nerve［X］
25. 椎骨静脈
    Vertebral vein

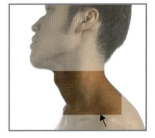

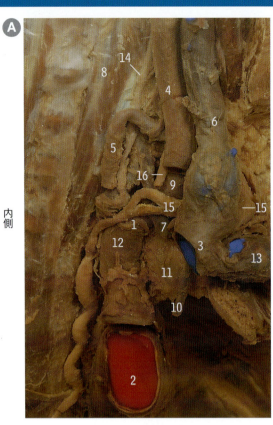

左側

A 胸管［頸部］

この頸部の基部と上胸部の左側深部の解剖では，内頸静脈(6)と鎖骨下静脈(13)が合流し，左腕頭静脈(3)となる．胸管(15)は，椎骨動脈(9)の前ならびに総頸動脈(4)の後ろを通る直前の少しの間，2条に分かれている（総頸動脈の下端は，胸管を見せるために切断してある）．そこから胸管は，内頸静脈(6)と鎖骨下静脈(13)の合流部に流入する手前まで，内頸静脈の後ろを走っている．

1	鎖骨下ワナ Ansa subclavia	9	椎骨動脈（の起始部） Vertebral artery
2	大動脈弓 Arch of aorta：Aortic arch	10	横隔神経 Phrenic nerve
3	腕頭静脈 Brachiocephalic vein	11	胸膜 Pleura
4	総頸動脈 Common carotid artery	12	鎖骨下動脈 Subclavian artery
5	下甲状腺動脈 Inferior thyroid artery	13	鎖骨下静脈 Subclavian vein
6	内頸静脈 Internal jugular vein	14	交感神経幹 Sympathetic trunk
7	内胸動脈 Internal thoracic artery	15	胸管 Thoracic duct
8	頸長筋 Longus colli	16	迷走神経［X］ Vagus nerve [X]

B 胸管の下胸部と腹部

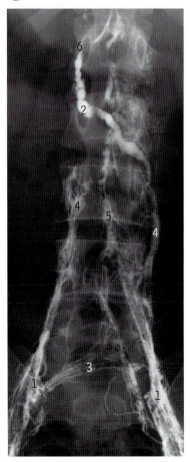

腹部リンパ管ならびに胸管の造影画像

Virchow リンパ節

C 胸管［頸部の終末部］

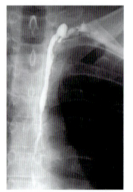

胸管の造影画像

1	総腸骨リンパ管* Common iliac vessels *
2	乳び槽 Cisterna chyli：Chyle cistern
3	腰部のリンパ鎖の交叉
4	大動脈傍リンパ管* Para-aortic vessels *
5	大動脈前リンパ管* Pre-aortic vessels *
6	胸管 Thoracic duct

D 腹部リンパ管

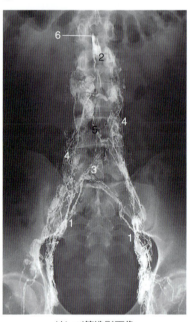

リンパ管造影画像
（腹部への造影剤注入直後）

後縦隔

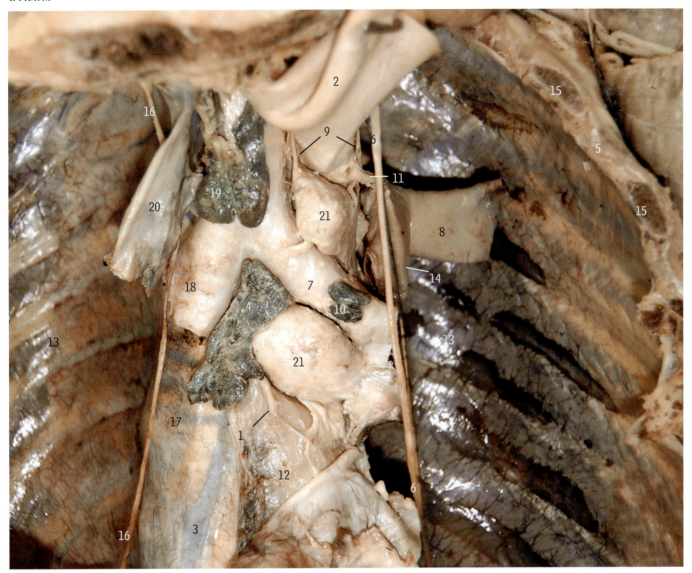

中等度のリンパ節腫脹を伴う.

1 食道神経叢（の前部） Esophageal plexus	7 左主気管支 Left main bronchus	13 壁側胸膜 Parietal pleura	19 （右の）上気管気管支リンパ節 Superior tracheobronchial nodes
2 大動脈弓（翻転してある） Arch of aorta : Aortic arch	8 左肺動脈 Left pulmonary artery	14 肺動脈［幹］ Pulmonary trunk	20 上大静脈（翻転してある） Superior vena cava
3 奇静脈 Azygos vein	9 （左の）反回神経 Recurrent laryngeal nerve	15 肋骨（切断縁） Ribs	21 腫瘍 Tumor
4 下気管気管支リンパ節 Inferior tracheobronchial nodes	10 （左の）気管気管支リンパ節 Tracheobronchial nodes	16 （右の）横隔神経 Phrenic nerve	
5 肋間隙 Intercostal space	11 動脈管索 Ligamentum arteriosum	17 （右の）肋間静脈 Posterior intercostal vein	
6 （左の）横隔神経 Phrenic nerve	12 食道 Esophagus	18 右主気管支 Right main bronchus	

第7章 リンパ系：腋窩

リンパ節がやや腫脹している腋窩（右）

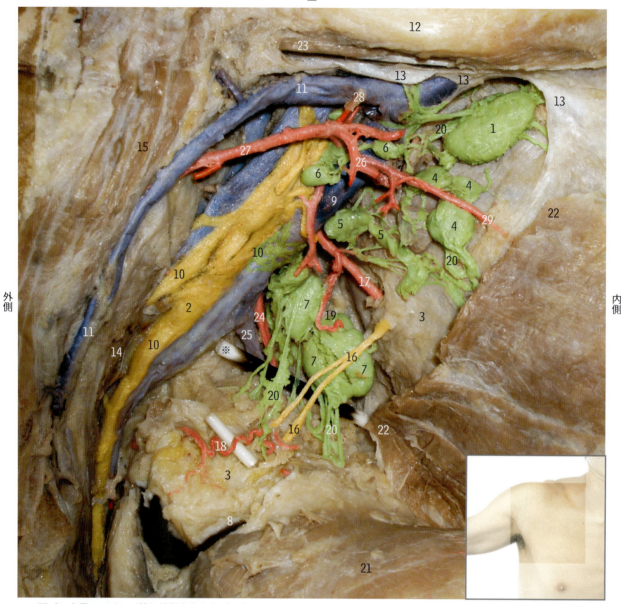

※：羽ペンを置いてリンパ管と神経をもち上げてある．

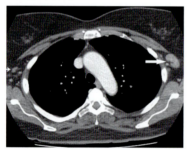

腋窩のCT横断画像
矢印は，肥大した腋窩リンパ節を示す．

1	三角筋胸筋リンパ節〔上〔腋窩〕リンパ節〕（腫大している） Infraclavicular nodes〔Apical nodes〕
2	腋窩筋膜鞘 Axillary fascial sheath
3	腋窩の脂肪
4	前〔腋窩〕リンパ節〔腋窩リンパ節〕 Anterior nodes〔Axillary lymph nodes〕
5	中心〔腋窩〕リンパ節〔腋窩リンパ節〕 Central nodes〔Axillary lymph nodes〕
6	外側〔腋窩〕リンパ節〔腋窩リンパ節〕（正常） Lateral nodes〔Axillary lymph nodes〕
7	後〔腋窩〕リンパ節〔腋窩リンパ節〕（腫大している） Posterior nodes〔Axillary lymph nodes〕
8	腋窩の皮膚
9	腋窩静脈 Axillary vein
10	腕神経叢（腋窩鞘に包まれている） Brachial plexus
11	橈側皮静脈 Cephalic vein
12	鎖骨 Clavicle
13	鎖骨胸筋筋膜（切断縁） Clavipectoral fascia
14	烏口腕筋 Coracobrachialis
15	三角筋 Deltoid
16	肋間上腕神経 Intercostobrachial nerves
17	外側胸動脈 Lateral thoracic artery
18	外側胸動脈（腋窩の皮膚および汗腺への枝） Lateral thoracic artery
19	外側胸動脈（リンパ節への枝） Lateral thoracic artery
20	リンパ管 Lymphatic vessel
21	大胸筋（翻転してある） Pectoralis major
22	小胸筋 Pectoralis minor
23	鎖骨下筋 Subclavius
24	肩甲下動脈 Subscapular artery
25	肩甲下静脈 Subscapular vein
26	胸肩峰動脈 Thoraco-acromial artery
27	三角筋枝〔胸肩峰動脈〕 Deltoid branch〔Thoraco-acromial artery〕
28	鎖骨枝〔胸肩峰動脈〕 Clavicular branch〔Thoraco-acromial artery〕
29	胸筋枝〔胸肩峰動脈〕 Pectoral branches〔Thoraco-acromial artery〕

乳癌の腋窩リンパ節（センチネルリンパ節）郭清

リンパ管炎

リンパ浮腫

A 右腋窩とリンパ節

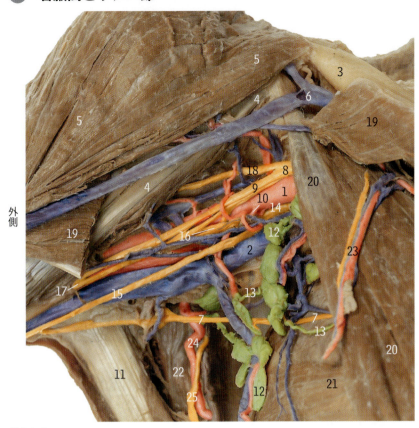

大胸筋(19)を翻転し，腋窩動脈と腕神経叢を包んでいる腋窩鞘とともに鎖骨胸筋筋膜を取り除いてある．

1	腋窩動脈 Axillary artery	14	内側神経束〔腕神経叢〕 Medial cord〔Brachial plexus〕
2	腋窩静脈 Axillary vein	15	内側上腕皮神経 Medial cutaneous nerve of arm：Medial brachial cutaneous nerve
3	鎖骨 Clavicle	16	正中神経内側根 Medial root of median nerve
4	烏口腕筋 Coracobrachialis	17	正中神経 Median nerve
5	三角筋 Deltoid	18	筋皮神経 Musculocutaneous nerve
6	橈側皮静脈(三角筋静脈への合流部) Cephalic vein	19	大胸筋 Pectoralis major
7	肋間上腕神経 Intercostobrachial nerves	20	小胸筋 Pectoralis minor
8	外側神経束〔腕神経叢〕 Lateral cord〔Brachial plexus〕	21	前鋸筋 Serratus anterior
9	正中神経外側根 Lateral root of median nerve	22	肩甲下筋 Subscapularis
10	外側胸動脈 Lateral thoracic artery	23	胸肩峰動／静脈と外側胸筋神経 Thoraco-acromial artery/ vein and Lateral pectoral nerve
11	広背筋 Latissimus dorsi	24	胸背動脈 Thoracodorsal artery
12	リンパ節 Lymph node	25	胸背神経 Thoracodorsal nerve
13	リンパ管 Lymphatic vessel		

前方から．

B 肘窩(右)［リンパ節］

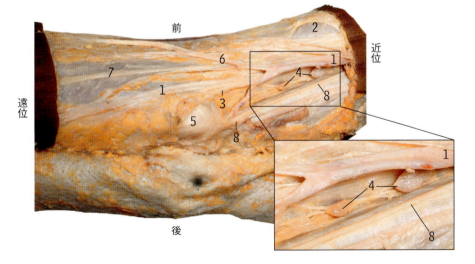

1	尺側皮静脈 Basilic vein	5	内側上顆〔上腕骨〕 Medial epicondyle〔Humerus〕
2	上腕二頭筋 Biceps brachii	6	肘正中皮静脈 Median cubital vein
3	内側前腕皮神経 Medial cutaneous nerve of forearm：Medial antebrachial cutaneous nerve	7	前腕正中皮静脈 Median antebrachial vein
4	肘リンパ節 Cubital lymph nodes	8	尺骨神経 Ulnar nerve

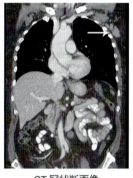

CT 冠状断画像

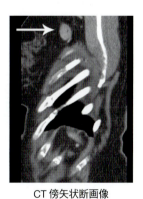

CT 傍矢状断画像

矢印は，腋窩のリンパ節腫大を示す．

後上腹壁の乳び槽

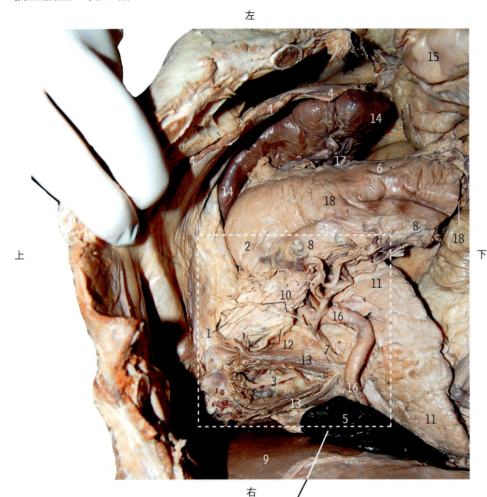

横隔膜の右脚を裂いて乳び槽を示してある.

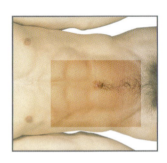

1	前迷走神経幹	Anterior vagal trunk
2	噴門〔胃〕	Cardia〔Stomach〕
3	乳び槽	Cisterna chyli
4	横隔膜	Diaphragm
5	胆嚢	Gallbladder
6	大弯〔胃〕	Greater curvature〔Stomach〕
7	左胃動脈	Left gastric artery
8	小弯〔胃〕	Lesser curvature〔Stomach〕
9	肝臓	Liver
10	食道動脈〔左胃動脈〕	Esophageal branches〔Left gastric artery〕
11	膵臓	Pancreas
12	後迷走神経幹	Posterior vagal trunk
13	右脚〔横隔膜〕(裂いてある)	Right crus〔Diaphragm〕
14	脾臓	Spleen
15	左結腸曲：脾曲*	Left colic flexure：Splenic flexure
16	脾動脈	Splenic artery
17	脾門と脾動／静脈	Splenic hilum with Splenic artery/vein
18	胃(切断してある)	Stomach

女性骨盤［正中断した左骨盤］

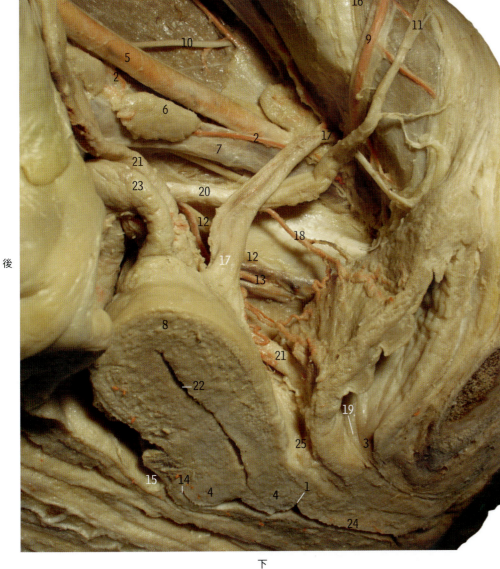

子宮後屈（正常変異）．リンパ節が腫脹している．

1　前部〔腟円蓋〕 　　Anterior part〔Vaginal fornix〕	10　外側大腿皮神経 　　Lateral femoral cutaneous nerve	18　上膀胱動脈 　　Superior vesical arteries
2　リンパ節への動脈	11　臍動脈索：内側臍索* 　　Cord of umbilical artery：Medial umbilical ligament*	19　膀胱三角 　　Trigone of bladder
3　膀胱頸 　　Neck of bladder	12　閉鎖神経 　　Obturator nerve	20　臍動脈索（臍動脈の遺残） 　　Cord of umbilical artery
4　子宮頸 　　Cervix of uterus	13　閉鎖動／静脈 　　Obturator artery/veins	21　尿管 　　Ureter
5　外腸骨動脈 　　External iliac artery	14　後部〔腟円蓋〕 　　Posterior part〔Vaginal fornix〕	22　子宮腔 　　Uterine cavity
6　外腸骨リンパ節（腫脹している） 　　External iliac nodes	15　直腸子宮窩：Douglas窩* 　　Recto-uterine pouch：Pouch of Douglas*	23　卵管：Fallopius管* 　　Uterine tube：Fallopian tube*
7　外腸骨静脈 　　External iliac vein	16　腹直筋 　　Rectus abdominis	24　腟 　　Vagina
8　子宮底 　　Fundus of uterus	17　子宮円索 　　Round ligament of uterus	25　膀胱子宮窩 　　Vesico-uterine pouch
9　下腹壁動／静脈 　　Inferior epigastric artery/vein		

骨盤のリンパ管系

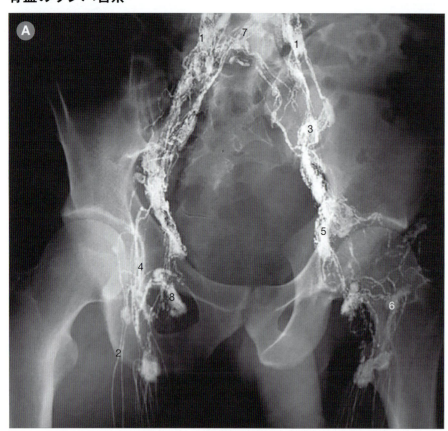

1	上行する腰リンパ鎖
2	求心性鼠径リンパ鎖
3	総腸骨リンパ節 Common iliac nodes
4	遠心性鼠径リンパ鎖
5	外腸骨リンパ節 External iliac nodes
6	浅鼠径リンパ節 Superficial inguinal nodes
7	腰部のリンパ鎖の交叉
8	深鼠径リンパ節 Deep inguinal nodes

A 骨盤のリンパ管造影画像（造影剤注入直後）

B 骨盤のリンパ管造影画像（造影剤後期充満期）

骨盤のリンパ節の大きな腫脹

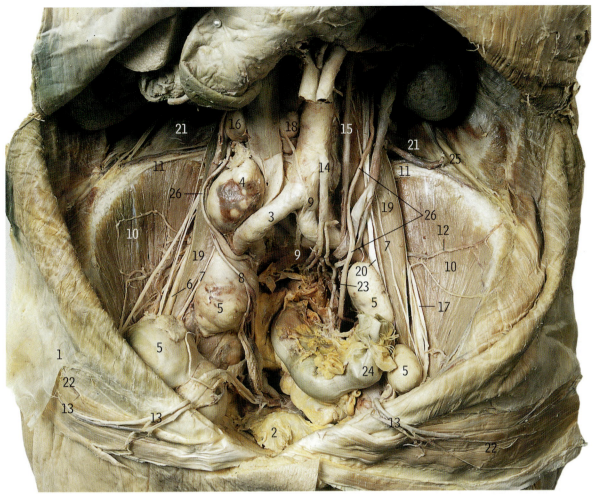

リンパ節群の位置関係を示す．

1	弓状線〔腹直筋鞘後面〕 Arcuate line〔Posterior rectus sheath〕	14	下腸間膜動脈 Inferior mesenteric artery
2	膀胱 Urinary bladder	15	下腸間膜静脈 Inferior mesenteric vein
3	総腸骨動脈 Common iliac artery	16	（右の）外側大静脈リンパ節（腫大している） Lateral caval nodes
4	総腸骨リンパ節（かなり腫大している） Common iliac nodes	17	外側大腿皮神経 Lateral femoral cutaneous nerve
5	外腸骨リンパ節（かなり腫大している） External iliac nodes	18	大動脈大静脈間リンパ節（腫大している） Aortocaval node
6	大腿神経 Femoral nerve	19	大腰筋 Psoas major
7	陰部大腿神経 Genitofemoral nerve	20	小腰筋 Psoas minor
8	精巣(卵巣)静脈 Testicular (Ovarian) vein	21	腰方形筋 Quadratus lumborum
9	上下腹神経叢 Superior hypogastric plexus	22	腹直筋 Rectus abdominis
10	腸骨筋 Iliacus	23	S状結腸枝〔左結腸動脈〕 Sigmoid branches〔Left colic artery〕
11	腸腰靱帯 Iliolumbar ligament	24	S状結腸 Sigmoid colon
12	腸腰静脈 Iliolumbar vein	25	肋下神経 Subcostal nerve
13	下腹壁動／静脈 Inferior epigastric artery/vein	26	尿管 Ureter

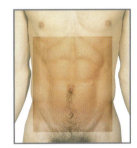

リンパ節腫脹

リンパ腫と巨脾症（脾腫）

大腿のリンパ系と浅鼠径リンパ節　[A 軽度に腫大したリンパ節，B 中等度に腫大したリンパ節]

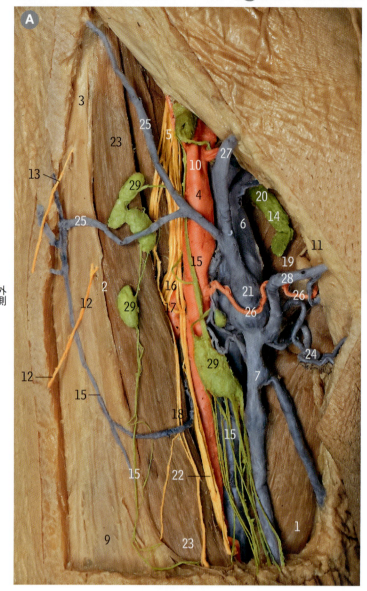

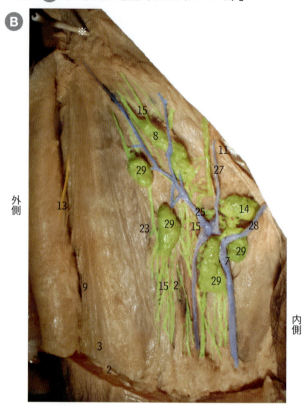

※：右上前腸骨棘の位置．

- 大腿三角は，鼠径靱帯(11)，縫工筋(23)の内側縁，長内転筋(1)の内側縁によってつくられる．
- 大腿管(20)とは，大腿鞘(除去してある)の内側区画であり，中間区画には大腿静脈(6)，外側区画には大腿動脈(4)が含まれる．大腿神経(5)は，大腿鞘の外側にあって，大腿鞘のなかには含まれない．

1	長内転筋 Adductor longus	15	リンパ管 Lymphatic vessel
2	大腿筋膜(切断縁) Fascia lata	16	筋枝〔大腿神経〕(外側大腿回旋動／静脈の表面を通る) Muscular branches〔Femoral nerve〕
3	大腿筋膜(大腿筋膜張筋の表面を覆う部分) Fascia lata	17	縫工筋への枝 Nerve to sartorius
4	大腿動脈 Femoral artery	18	外側広筋への枝 Nerve to Vastus lateralis
5	大腿神経 Femoral nerve	19	恥骨筋 Pectineus
6	大腿静脈 Femoral vein	20	大腿管の位置
7	大伏在静脈 Great saphenous vein：Long saphenous vein	21	伏在静脈の静脈瘤 Saphena varix
8	浅鼠径リンパ節(水平鎖) Superficial inguinal nodes	22	伏在神経 Saphenous nerve
9	腸脛靱帯(外側広筋の表面を覆う) Iliotibial tract	23	縫工筋 Sartorius
10	下腹壁動／静脈 Inferior epigastric artery/vein	24	陰嚢からの静脈
11	鼠径靱帯 Inguinal ligament	25	浅腸骨回旋静脈 Superficial circumflex iliac vein
12	前皮枝〔大腿神経〕：中間大腿皮神経* Anterior cutaneous branches〔Femoral nerve〕	26	浅外陰部動脈 Superficial external pudendal artery
13	外側大腿皮神経 Lateral femoral cutaneous nerve	27	浅腹壁静脈 Superficial epigastric vein
		28	浅外陰部静脈* Superficial external pudendal vein *
14	リンパ節(Cloquetリンパ節) Lymph node	29	浅鼠径リンパ節(縦鎖) Superficial inguinal nodes

遺伝性下腿浮腫（Milroy病）

限局性リンパ管腫

性病性リンパ肉芽種

象皮病

和文索引

【アルファベット】

Achilles 腱　319, 321, 348, 350, 351, 352, 353, 354, 355, 356, 357, 358, 359
　　滑液包　321
Adam のりんご　28, 48
DIPJ：遠位指節間関節　172
Douglas 窩　260, 285, 286, 287, 288, 373
Edinger—Westphal 核　85
Eustachian 管　23
Eustachian 弁　199
Fallopius 管　286, 373
Galen 静脈　60, 68
Galen の吻合　49
Gerdy 結節　311
Hesselbach 三角　232, 233
Lister 結節　124, 126, 155
Louis 角　183, 187, 189
Lower 結節　199
Luschka 関節　112
Magendie 孔　70
McBurney 点　231
MCPJ：中手指節関節　172
Meyer ［の］ループ　79
Morison 窩　243
Petit 腰三角　105
PIPJ：近位指節間関節　172
Retzius 腔　285, 286
Riedel 葉　245
Santorini 管　257
Sylvius 水道　70
S 状結腸　250, 260, 273, 274, 279, 280, 285, 286, 375
S 状結腸間膜　288
S 状結腸枝　375
S 状結腸静脈　258
S 状結腸動脈　249, 258
S 状静脈洞　71
S 状洞溝　11, 17, 23, 24, 27
Tarlov 嚢胞　286
Thebesian 弁　199
Valsalva 洞　197, 202, 203
Virchow リンパ節　185, 367
Winslow 孔　240
Wirsung 管　257

【ア】

趾の線維鞘　360, 361
アブミ骨　57, 58
アブミ骨筋　57, 58
アブミ骨筋神経　58
アブミ骨底　58
鞍結節　11, 25
鞍上槽：視交叉槽　60
鞍背　11, 12, 17, 25, 60

【イ】

胃　84, 226, 238, 241, 246, 250, 251, 254, 259, 260, 270, 372
　小弯　240, 243, 244, 247, 251, 252, 372
　大弯　238, 241, 243, 244, 247, 251, 252, 372
　噴門　372
胃圧痕　255
胃十二指腸動脈　244, 246, 247, 255
胃体　251, 252, 253
一次視覚野　79
胃底　251
イニオン　4, 7
胃脾間膜　259, 260
胃面　259
陰核　285, 289, 290
陰核脚　285, 290
陰核包皮　289
陰茎　278, 280, 331
　亀頭冠　328
陰茎海綿体　279, 291, 292
陰茎亀頭　278
陰茎根　291
陰茎体　278
陰茎提靱帯　230
陰茎背神経　278, 280, 291, 292
陰茎背動脈　280, 291, 292
咽頭　45, 46
咽頭結節　9, 27
［咽頭］喉頭部　60
［咽頭］口部　60, 226
咽頭枝　45, 55, 84
咽頭静脈　45
咽頭静脈叢　47
咽頭神経叢　84
咽頭頭底板　45
［咽頭］鼻部：鼻咽頭　60, 79
咽頭扁桃　60
咽頭縫線　10, 45
陰嚢　278, 291, 326, 331
陰部枝　233, 271, 272, 273, 274, 280, 283
陰部神経　284, 289, 290, 326, 333
陰部大腿神経　261, 271, 272, 273, 274, 275, 375
　陰部枝　233, 271, 272, 273, 274, 280, 283
　大腿枝　233, 271, 272, 273, 274, 280, 283

【ウ】

右胃静脈　256
右胃大網静脈　241, 247, 251, 253
右胃大網動脈　247, 251, 253

右胃動脈　246, 251
　幽門洞枝　244
右縁枝：鋭［角］縁枝　196, 197, 202
迂回槽　60
右下肺静脈　192, 193, 196, 197, 198, 204, 205, 214, 216, 222
右下葉気管支　193, 195, 209, 214, 215
右肝管　246, 247, 257
右冠状動脈　196, 197, 200, 202, 203
　右縁枝：鋭［角］縁枝　196, 202
　右心室枝　197, 198, 200, 203
　右心房枝　197
　円錐枝　197, 200, 202, 203
　後下行枝：後室間枝　203
　後室間枝：後下行枝　197, 200, 202
　房室結節枝　197
右冠状動脈口　200, 201
右脚（横隔膜の）　252, 268, 270, 273, 372
右結腸曲：肝曲　243, 250
右結腸静脈　258
右結腸動脈　248, 253, 258, 261
烏口肩峰靱帯　117, 119, 142
烏口鎖骨靱帯　117
烏口上腕靱帯　119
烏口突起　116, 118, 135, 143
烏口腕筋　117, 119, 121, 135, 142, 145, 146, 147, 148, 149, 150, 151, 370, 371
右枝（［肝］門脈の）　258
右枝（固有肝動脈の）　246, 255, 256, 258
右主気管支　193, 195, 204, 205, 209, 212, 214, 215, 220, 369
右上肺静脈　192, 193, 196, 197, 198, 204, 205, 214, 216, 222
右上葉気管支　193, 195, 204, 205, 209, 212, 214, 215, 216
右上肋間静脈　205, 220
右心耳　191, 196, 197, 198, 199, 201
右心室　196, 197, 198, 199, 200
　動脈円錐　201
右心室枝　197, 198, 200, 202, 203
右心房　196, 197, 199, 200, 201, 203, 208
右心房枝　197
右精巣静脈　245, 268, 273
右線維三角　200, 201
右線維輪　200, 201
右中葉気管支　193, 195, 209, 214, 215, 216
右肺　190, 191, 192, 193, 209, 210, 212, 216
　下葉　254
　上葉　366
右肺静脈　203
右肺動脈　190, 193, 194, 195, 204, 205, 208, 214, 215, 216, 222
　上葉動脈　204, 205

右板　48, 50
右半月弁（大動脈弁の）　200, 201
右半月弁（肺動脈弁の）　201
右副腎静脈　266
右房室口　200
右房室弁：三尖弁　184, 199
　後尖　200, 201
　前尖　199, 200, 201
　中隔尖　200, 201
右葉（肝臓の）　230, 239, 240, 241, 243, 244, 245, 251, 253, 254, 255, 256, 267
右葉（甲状腺の）　29, 30, 33, 35, 36, 45, 48, 192, 195
右卵巣静脈　245, 268
右リンパ本幹　31, 37
右腕頭静脈　30, 36, 37, 190, 191, 208, 217, 218, 219, 224, 366
運動根（顔面神経［Ⅶ］の）　61
運動根（三叉神経［Ⅴ］の）　56

【エ】

鋭［角］縁枝：右縁枝　196, 197, 202
永久歯　13
　犬歯　13
　側切歯　13
　第一小臼歯　13
　第一大臼歯　13
　第二小臼歯　13
　第二大臼歯　13
　中切歯　13
会陰　289, 290, 291, 292
会陰筋　286
会陰腱中心：会陰体　289, 290, 291
会陰枝　289, 292
会陰神経　292
会陰動脈　292
［会陰］縫線　290, 291
腋窩　144, 145, 147, 186
腋窩筋膜鞘　370
腋窩静脈　135, 148, 190, 191, 208, 217, 219, 370, 371
腋窩神経　136, 142, 145, 146, 147, 148, 149, 150, 152
腋窩動脈　142, 144, 147, 148, 149, 190, 191, 192, 193, 194, 195, 208, 219, 371
　胸筋枝　149
腋窩突起：外側突起　184
腋窩リンパ節　135
遠位指節間関節　164, 172
遠位手掌皮線　163
遠位手首皮線　163
円回内筋　127, 151, 156, 157, 158, 159, 160, 161
　尺骨頭　127, 160
　上腕頭　123, 160
縁結節　12, 24
縁枝（左冠状動脈の）　198, 203
縁枝：縁溝（帯状溝の）　64
縁上回　63
延髄：髄脳　60, 61, 62, 66, 67, 68, 70, 84, 100
　オリーブ　66, 76, 78
延髄根　71, 85
円錐枝　197, 200, 202, 203
円錐靱帯　117, 119, 142
円錐靱帯結節　118
延髄錐体　66, 67, 70, 76, 78

【オ】

横隔神経　29, 30, 31, 32, 35, 36, 37, 135, 144, 145, 190, 191, 192, 193, 194, 195, 204, 205, 206, 207, 218, 219, 221, 225, 368, 369
横隔膜　181, 183, 191, 192, 193, 194, 196, 204, 205, 206, 225, 226, 230, 232, 240, 252, 254, 255, 259, 260, 268, 270, 372
　右脚　252, 268, 270, 273, 372
　腱中心　225, 270
　左脚　267, 270
　食道裂孔　227, 251, 270
　大静脈孔　227
　大動脈裂孔　227
横隔面　216, 259
横筋筋膜　235
横口蓋縫線：口蓋上顎縫合　9
横行結腸　230, 237, 238, 239, 241, 242, 243, 246, 247, 248, 249, 250, 253, 254
横行結腸間膜　241
横行部：水平部（十二指腸の）　245, 248, 253
横行部：水平部（僧帽筋の）　105, 106
横静脈洞　59, 61
黄色靱帯　103
横線　94
黄体　286
横頭　130, 171, 361, 362
横洞溝　11, 17, 27
横突起　28, 37, 44, 57, 71, 89, 90, 91, 94, 98, 99, 102, 223
　横突肋骨窩　91
　結節間板　90, 98
　後結節　90, 98
　前結節　90, 98
横突孔　89, 90
横突肋骨窩　90, 91, 181, 223
黄斑
　中心窩　53
横披裂筋　49, 50
横部　305
横稜　300
オトガイ下静脈　32
オトガイ下動脈　31, 32, 34
オトガイ筋　2, 19, 40
オトガイ結節　18
オトガイ孔　1, 4, 13, 16, 18, 38
オトガイ静脈　38
オトガイ神経　38, 40, 81, 82
オトガイ舌筋　19, 43, 48
オトガイ舌骨筋　19, 29, 48, 56, 85
オトガイ動脈　38
オトガイ隆起　1, 4, 17, 18
オリーブ　66, 67, 70, 76, 78
オリーブ後溝　70
オリーブ前溝　70

【カ】

外陰部静脈　230
外果　311, 315, 316, 348, 351, 354, 355, 357, 359, 364
回外筋　127, 159, 161, 162
回外筋稜　125, 154, 161
外果窩　315, 316
外果関節面　315, 316
外果面　320
外頸静脈　28, 32, 33, 190, 191, 217
外頸動脈　29, 30, 31, 32, 33, 34, 35, 36, 44, 56, 71
回結腸静脈　248, 258
回結腸動脈　248, 253, 258, 261
外後頭隆起　4, 7, 9, 17, 27, 110, 111
外後頭稜　9, 27, 110, 111
外肛門括約筋　281, 289, 290, 291, 326
外耳　57
外子宮口　285
外耳道　4, 7, 9, 14, 23, 47, 57, 58
外精筋膜　278
外舌筋　85
回旋枝　197, 198, 200, 202, 203
外側［腋窩］リンパ節　185, 370
外側顆（脛骨の）　310, 312, 315, 337, 339, 340, 341, 343
外側顆（大腿骨の）　304, 307, 308, 337, 339, 341, 343
外側塊　3, 71, 98, 99, 112, 113
　下関節面　89
　上関節面　89
外側顆間結節　310, 312, 343
外側角　27
外側下膝動脈　345, 353
外側顆上線　306, 308
外側顆上稜　122
外側下腿回旋静脈　349
外側環軸関節　71, 98, 99, 112, 113
外側胸筋神経　135, 144, 145, 146, 150, 371
外側胸動脈　135, 145, 146, 147, 148, 370, 371
外側距踵靱帯　321
　浅リンパ節　147, 148
外側楔状骨　318, 320, 364
外側結節　91, 318, 320
外側溝　63
　後枝　63
　上行枝　63
　前枝　63
外側広筋　276, 303, 305, 306, 307, 328, 332, 335
　腱膜　342
外側後頭側頭回：紡錘状回　64
外側骨半規管　57, 58
外側骨膨大部　58
外側臍ヒダ　232, 233
外側枝：対角枝　198, 202, 203
外側膝状体　70, 79
外側手根側副靱帯　173
外側上顆（上腕骨の）　122, 126, 153, 154, 156, 157, 161
外側上顆（大腿骨の）　308, 343
外側上膝動脈　345, 353
外側神経束　144, 145, 146, 150, 371
外側靱帯（母指の手根中手関節の）　172
外側舌喉頭蓋ヒダ　49
外側浅陰茎背静脈　278
外側仙骨動脈　281, 282, 283
外側仙骨稜　94
外側前腕皮神経　151, 156, 157, 158, 160
外側足底静脈　359
外側足底神経　358, 359, 360, 361
　固有底側趾神経　360

和文索引　379

深枝　361, 362
総底側趾神経　361
外側足底動脈　359, 360, 361, 362
外側側副靱帯　154, 161, 309, 311, 317, 339, 340, 342, 347, 351
外側大静脈リンパ節　375
外側大腿回旋動脈　230, 327, 330
　横枝　330
　下行枝　330
　上行枝　330
外側大腿筋間中隔　332
外側大腿皮神経　233, 271, 272, 273, 274, 275, 330, 373, 375, 376
外側中葉区　210, 211, 212
外側中葉枝　209
外側直筋　43, 51, 52, 53, 54, 80
外側頭（上腕三頭筋の）　121, 133, 139, 143, 150, 152
外側頭（腓腹筋の）　309, 337, 338, 341, 344, 345, 346, 347, 350, 351, 352
外側頭直筋　10, 37, 44, 71
外側突起（ツチ骨の）　57
外側突起：腋窩突起（乳腺の）　184
外側肺底区　210, 211, 212, 213
外側肺底枝　209
外側板　7, 9, 12, 17, 25, 44
外側半月　339, 340, 341, 342, 347
　後角　313, 340
　前角　313, 340
外側皮枝　137
外側腓腹皮神経　338, 344, 347, 350, 352
外側部（後頭骨の）　27
外側部（軸椎の）　112
外側部（仙骨の）　93, 94, 101, 102
外側面（脛骨の）　310, 311, 312
外側面（踵骨の）　355
外側面（橈骨の）　124
外側面（腓骨の）　311, 316
外側面（鼻骨の）　21
外側翼突筋　19, 43
　下頭　42, 44
　上頭　10, 42
外側翼突筋神経　82
外側輪状披裂筋　49
外側肋横突靱帯　181, 223
回腸　230, 239, 248, 249, 250, 261, 262
回腸口　250
　下唇　260
　上唇　260
外腸骨静脈　233, 235, 271, 281, 283, 285, 373
外腸骨動脈　233, 235, 271, 272, 276, 280, 281, 282, 283, 285, 335, 373
外腸骨リンパ節　283, 373, 374, 375
回腸終末部　242, 250, 261
回腸静脈　279
回腸動脈　279
回腸ループ　262
外転神経［Ⅵ］　52, 53, 54, 55, 56, 58, 59, 61, 66, 67, 70, 78, 80, 83
回内筋粗面　124
外尿道括約筋　297
外尿道口　278, 289
海馬　72, 73, 76, 77
　海馬足　73
灰白交通枝　221
灰白翼：迷走神経三角　71

灰白隆起　66, 68, 79
海馬采　73
海馬足　73
海馬傍回　64, 66
外鼻孔　38
外腹斜筋　88, 105, 106, 107, 181, 186, 228, 229, 232, 267, 275, 295, 299, 301
　腱膜　228, 229, 230, 234, 275, 280, 328
外閉鎖筋　295, 301, 303, 305, 333, 334
外包　75, 77
解剖学的嗅ぎタバコ入れ　163
解剖頸　120
蓋膜　98
海綿静脈洞　47, 59
海綿体部　279, 281
外肋間筋　106, 107, 145, 146, 181, 187, 188
外肋間膜　187
下咽頭収縮筋　31, 32, 35, 45, 47, 48
　甲状咽頭部　45
　輪状咽頭部　45, 47
下縁（下顎枝の）　18, 38
下縁（下顎体の）　38
下縁（胸膜の）　263
下縁（肺の）　216
下縁（脾臓の）　259
下横隔静脈　267, 268, 270
下横隔動脈　252, 264, 267, 268, 270, 274
下横靱帯　314, 359
下オトガイ棘　18
顆窩　27
下回盲陥凹　261
下角（肩甲骨の）　116, 118, 136, 186
下角（甲状軟骨の）　48
下角：側頭角（側脳室の）　72, 74
　側脳室脈絡叢　76
下顎　13
下顎縁枝　31, 32, 34, 39, 83
下顎窩　7, 9, 23
下顎角　13, 17, 18, 28, 38
下顎管　42
下顎頭　18, 47
下顎結合　14
下顎孔　17, 18
下顎後静脈　32, 33, 40, 42, 82, 217
下顎骨　12, 18, 19, 30, 33, 43, 60
　下顎枝　4, 16
　筋突起　4
下顎枝　1, 4, 13, 14, 16, 17, 18, 29
　下縁　18, 38
　後縁　18
　前縁　18
下顎小舌　17, 18
下顎神経［V₃］　42, 44, 47, 56, 59, 82
　頬神経　40, 42
　筋枝　44
下顎切痕　18
下顎体　1, 4, 13, 16, 17, 18, 32, 39, 40, 42
　下縁　38
下顎底　18
下顎頭　4, 18, 38
踵　356
下下腹神経叢：骨盤神経叢　271, 282
顆管　9
顆間窩　308, 343

下眼窩裂　1, 7, 9, 12
下眼瞼　51
下関節上腕靱帯　143
下関節突起　90, 91, 92, 112, 113, 334
下関節面（脛骨の）　311, 315
下関節面（椎骨の）　89, 112
顆間隆起　341
　外側顆間結節　310, 312, 343
　内側顆間結節　310, 312, 343
下気管気管支リンパ節　369
下脚　57
下丘　68, 70, 71, 76
蝸牛　58, 83
　骨ラセン板　58
蝸牛軸　58
蝸牛小管　23
蝸牛神経　58, 83
蝸牛頂　58
下丘腕　70
下極　251
角回　63
顎下神経節　35, 56
顎下腺　28, 29, 30, 32, 33, 36, 40, 42, 43, 47
顎下腺窩　18
顎下腺管　29, 35, 56
顎関節　6, 10
　関節円板　42
　関節包　29, 40, 42
顎舌骨筋　19, 29, 30, 32, 33, 34, 35, 42, 48, 56
顎舌骨筋神経　29, 42, 56, 81
顎舌骨筋神経溝　17, 18
顎舌骨筋線　17, 18
下区動脈　265
顎動脈　42, 47, 56, 82
　翼突筋枝　43
顎二腹筋
　後腹　10, 29, 31, 32, 33, 35, 37, 42, 47, 56
　前腹　19, 29, 30, 32, 33, 34, 35, 43
角膜縁　51
隔膜部　281
下顎神経節　37
下顎心臓枝　205
下脛腓関節：脛腓靱帯結合　315, 364
下結節　91
下肩甲下神経　147, 148, 149, 150
下後鋸筋　181
窩後結節　23
下行結腸　237, 238, 239, 249, 250
下行枝（外側大腿回旋動脈の）　330
下行膝動脈
　伏在枝　332, 347
下甲状結節　48
下甲状腺静脈　30, 32, 36, 190, 191, 192, 193, 194, 217, 218, 366
下甲状腺動脈　31, 35, 36, 37, 192, 194, 195, 218, 367, 368
　食道枝　37
下項線　7, 9, 27
下行大動脈　208
　胸大動脈　189, 194, 206
下後腸骨棘　294, 296, 298
下部（十二指腸の）　240, 245, 250, 261
下部（僧帽筋の）　105, 106
下根（頸神経ワナの）　29, 31, 33

和文索引

下枝（動眼神経［Ⅲ］の）　54
下矢状静脈洞　61
下歯槽神経　29, 42, 56, 81, 82
下歯槽動脈　42
下斜筋　51, 52, 54, 80
下唇　260
下唇下制筋　2, 6, 19, 39
下伸筋支帯　321, 355, 357, 358
下神経幹　147, 148
下神経節（迷走神経［Ⅹ］の）　37, 45
下膵十二指腸動脈　272
下垂体　55, 60, 61
　後葉　60
　前葉　60
下垂体窩　4, 11, 12, 17, 25
下垂体茎　59, 60, 66, 70, 78, 79
下錐体洞溝　11, 27
下舌区　210, 211, 213
下舌枝（上葉気管支の）　209, 213
下舌枝（肺舌静脈の）　213
下前区動脈　265
下前腸骨棘　96, 284, 294, 296, 298, 300, 333
下前頭回　63
　眼窩部　63
　三角部　63
　弁蓋部：前頭弁蓋　63
下前頭溝　63
下双子筋　289, 297, 301, 303, 305, 325, 333
下側頭回　63, 64
下側頭溝　63, 64
下側頭線　4, 20, 24, 40
下腿筋膜　338, 346, 347, 348, 350, 351, 356, 357
下腿骨間膜　311, 313, 314, 317, 346
下大静脈　103, 192, 193, 194, 196, 197, 199, 200, 203, 204, 208, 222, 225, 231, 240, 243, 245, 252, 255, 256, 261, 264, 266, 268, 270, 271, 272, 279
下大静脈口　197, 199
下腿静脈叢　349
下大静脈弁　199
下大脳静脈　62
下唾液核　85
肩関節　115, 142
　関節包　142
下端（腎臓の）　261, 264, 270
下腸間膜静脈　245, 249, 258, 270, 375
下腸間膜動脈　245, 249, 258, 271, 272, 274, 375
下腸間膜動脈神経節　274
下腸間膜動脈神経叢　271
下腸間膜動脈リンパ節　274
下直腸静脈　291, 292, 326
下直腸神経　289, 291, 292
下直腸動脈　291, 292, 326
下直筋　44, 52, 54, 80
下椎切痕　90, 91, 92
滑車　51, 52
滑車窩　20
滑車下神経　51, 52, 81
滑車上静脈　38
滑車上神経　38, 39, 40, 51, 52, 53, 54, 81, 82
滑車上動脈　38, 51, 53
滑車神経　80

滑車神経［Ⅳ］　51, 52, 53, 54, 56, 59, 61, 66, 70, 76, 78
滑車切痕　125, 126, 154, 155, 156
滑膜　336
下殿筋線　294
下殿静脈　325
下殿動脈　281, 282, 283, 289, 325
下殿皮神経　324
下頭　42, 44
下頭斜筋　109, 110
下橈尺関節　155
　関節円板　172
　嚢状陥凹　172, 173
下頭頂小葉　63
下内側静脈　53
下内側動脈　53
下鼻甲介　1, 12, 16, 26, 43, 55, 56, 79
　後端　26
　篩骨突起　26
　前端　26
　涙骨突起　26
下腓骨筋支帯　355
下鼻道　12, 21, 55
下腹　28, 29, 30, 31, 32, 117, 119, 135, 146, 195
下腹神経　271
下副腎動脈　252
下腹部：恥骨上部　227
下腹壁静脈　229, 231, 232, 233, 235, 281, 285, 373, 375, 376
下腹壁動脈　229, 231, 232, 233, 235, 276, 280, 281, 282, 285, 373, 375, 376
　恥骨枝　235
下膀胱動脈　280, 281, 283
［肝］鎌状間膜　230, 232, 237, 239, 240, 243, 245, 254, 255, 274
鎌状突起　284, 297, 334
下葉（右肺の）　209, 210, 211, 212, 254
下葉（左肺の）　209, 210, 211, 213
下葉気管支　213
下葉動脈　214
下肋部　227
下肋骨窩　90, 91
肝円索　237, 238, 239, 241, 244, 255, 274
肝円索裂　255, 256
眼窩　1, 51, 52, 53, 54
　内側壁　44
眼窩縁　12, 24
眼窩回　64
眼窩下縁　1, 16, 21, 38
眼窩下管　21
眼窩隔膜　51
眼窩下孔　1, 12, 21, 38, 54
眼窩下溝　12, 21
眼窩下静脈　38
眼窩下神経　38, 40, 51, 52, 53, 54, 81, 82
眼窩下動脈　38, 52, 54
眼窩溝　64, 66
眼窩脂肪体　51
眼窩上縁　1, 16, 20, 38
眼窩上孔：眼窩上切痕　1, 12, 20, 38
眼窩上静脈　38
眼窩上神経　38, 39, 40, 51, 52, 53, 54, 81, 82
眼窩上切痕　38

眼窩上動脈　51, 52
眼窩突起　12, 22
眼窩板　4, 12, 26
眼窩部（下前頭回の）　63
眼窩部（前頭骨の）　11, 12, 17, 20
［肝］鎌状間膜　230, 232, 237, 239, 240, 243, 245, 254, 255, 274
眼窩面（頬骨の）　24
眼窩面（上顎骨の）　21
眼窩面（大翼の）　25
眼窩面（涙骨の）　21
［肝］冠状間膜　255
眼球　51, 53, 54, 60
肝曲：右結腸曲　243, 250
寛骨　293, 294, 295, 296, 297, 298, 299, 300, 301
寛骨臼　96, 294, 300, 335
寛骨臼縁　294, 300, 335, 336
寛骨臼横靱帯　295, 301, 334, 336
寛骨臼窩　334
寛骨臼切痕　294, 300
［肝］冠状間膜　255
冠状溝：房室溝　191
冠状静脈口　199, 200
冠状静脈洞　197, 198, 203
冠状静脈弁　199
冠状縫合　4, 8, 14, 17
肝腎陥凹　243
眼神経［V₁］　44, 56, 59, 81
幹神経節：交感神経幹神経節　101, 274
関節円板（顎関節の）　42
関節円板（下橈尺関節の）　172, 173, 177, 178
関節円板（肩鎖関節の）　143
関節窩　116, 118, 142, 143
関節下結節　118
関節腔　223
関節結節　7, 9, 23
関節枝　346
関節上結節　118
関節唇　142, 143, 334, 335
関節包（顎関節の）　29, 40, 42
関節包（肩関節の）　142, 143
関節包（脛腓関節の）　339
関節包（股関節の）　335
関節包（膝関節の）　342, 351
関節包（肘関節の）　154, 156
肝臓　84, 237, 242, 247, 254, 255, 256, 270, 372
　Riedel葉　245
　右葉　230, 239, 240, 241, 243, 244, 245, 251, 253, 254, 255, 256, 267
　左葉　238, 240, 243, 244, 245, 253, 254, 255, 256, 260
　尾状葉　244, 246, 247, 251
　方形葉　240, 244
環椎：第一頸椎　87, 89
　横突起　28, 37, 44, 57, 71, 98, 99
　外側塊　3, 71, 98, 99, 112, 113
　下関節面　112
　後弓　60, 61, 71, 98, 99, 100, 109, 110, 111, 112
　前弓　55, 60, 79, 89, 112, 113
環椎横靱帯（環椎十字靱帯の）　98
環椎後頭関節　10, 71, 98
環椎十字靱帯　98
貫通枝　357

貫通動脈　327
貫通皮神経　292, 324
眼底　53
眼動脈　51, 53, 54, 60
閂（カンヌキ）　71
顔面横動脈　40
顔面静脈　30, 31, 32, 33, 38, 39, 40, 42
顔面神経［Ⅶ］　33, 40, 44, 58, 59, 66, 70, 78, 83, 84
　運動根　61
　下顎縁枝　31, 32, 34, 39
　頰筋枝　39
　頰骨枝　39
　頸枝　32, 42
　膝神経節　44, 58
　側頭枝　39
顔面神経管　57, 58
顔面神経丘　71
顔面動脈　28, 29, 30, 31, 32, 33, 34, 35, 38, 39, 40, 42, 47
［肝］門脈　246, 255, 256, 258
　右枝　258
　左枝　244, 258
岩様部：錐体乳突部　11, 23, 56
眼輪筋　2, 6, 39, 40

【キ】

気管　28, 36, 37, 49, 50, 112, 113, 190, 191, 193, 195, 205, 208, 214, 215, 218, 220, 226, 366
気管気管支リンパ節　369
気管支縦隔リンパ本幹　37
気管支動脈　192, 193, 195, 214, 215, 216
気管支肺リンパ節：肺門リンパ節　216
気管軟骨　48
気管竜骨：気管カリナ　193, 195, 212
奇静脈　204, 208, 214, 221, 224, 225, 270, 369
奇静脈弓　205, 221
基節骨（足の）　318, 359
基節骨（手の）　128, 129, 178
基節骨底（足の）　363, 364
基節骨底（手の）　128, 164, 172
基節骨頭（手の）　128, 164
亀頭冠　278, 328
キヌタ・アブミ関節　58
キヌタ・ツチ関節　58
キヌタ骨　57, 58
　長脚　57
脚間槽　76
脚間裂：水平裂　70
球海綿体筋　281, 290, 291, 292
弓下窩　23
嗅球　59, 66, 78
球形嚢　83
嗅溝　64
嗅索　59, 61, 66, 67, 79
臼歯腺　29
弓状線　96, 232, 282, 296, 298, 375
弓状動脈　358
弓状隆起　11, 23
嗅神経糸　55
嗅脳溝　64
［十二指腸］球部　252
橋　56, 60, 62, 66, 67, 68, 70, 76, 77, 78, 83
胸横筋　183, 189

境界溝　71
胸郭上口　183, 218, 219, 220
胸管　37, 214, 218, 221, 225, 367, 368
［狭義の］大脳脚　66, 78, 79
頰筋　2, 6, 19, 29, 33, 39, 40, 42, 43
胸筋間リンパ節　185
胸筋筋膜　185
胸筋枝（胸肩峰動脈の）　135, 144, 145, 190, 191, 192, 370
胸筋枝（腋窩動脈の）　149
頰筋枝（顔面神経［Ⅶ］の）　39, 83
胸肩峰静脈　217, 371
胸肩峰動脈　370, 371
　胸筋枝　135, 144, 145, 190, 191, 192, 370
　肩峰枝　135, 148
　鎖骨枝　367, 370
　三角筋枝　370
胸骨　182, 183, 193, 208
頰骨　1, 4, 12, 24, 43
　眼窩縁　12
胸骨角　182, 187, 189
頰骨眼窩孔　12, 24
胸骨関節面　118
頰骨顔面孔　24
頰骨弓　4, 7, 9, 16, 29, 38, 40, 42, 43
胸骨剣結合　182, 184
胸骨甲状筋　29, 31, 32, 33, 35, 48, 85, 135, 147, 148, 183
頰骨枝　39, 83
頰骨神経　81
胸骨舌骨筋　29, 30, 31, 32, 33, 34, 35, 36, 48, 85, 119, 135, 144, 147, 148, 183
頰骨側頭孔　24
胸骨体　179, 182, 183, 189
胸骨端　118, 183
胸骨頭　28, 30, 32, 134, 217
頰骨突起（上顎骨の）　21
頰骨突起（前頭骨の）　20
頰骨突起（側頭骨の）　4, 23
胸骨部　133
胸骨柄　36, 48, 179, 182, 183, 217
胸骨柄結合　182, 183, 184, 217
胸鎖関節　28, 36, 183, 184, 208, 217
胸鎖乳突筋　6, 10, 28, 29, 31, 32, 33, 34, 35, 37, 39, 48, 85, 110, 119, 147, 148, 183, 184, 195, 367
　胸骨頭　28, 30, 32, 134, 217
　鎖骨頭　28, 30, 32, 134, 217
胸鎖乳突筋枝（後頭動脈の）　29
橋枝（脳底動脈の）　67
頰脂肪体　32, 40
頰神経（下顎神経［V₃］の）　40, 42, 81
　後枝　107, 137, 223
胸心臓神経　193, 194, 195
胸腺　218, 366
胸腺静脈　207, 217, 218, 366
橋前槽　60
胸腺動脈　218
胸大動脈　189, 194, 206, 207, 215, 224, 225, 267
胸椎　87, 179
胸背静脈　191, 217, 219
胸背神経　144, 146, 147, 148, 149, 150, 371
胸背動脈　145, 146, 147, 148, 149, 191,

371
橋被蓋：橋背側部　60
峡部（舟状骨）　128
胸壁　259
強膜　51
胸膜　98, 188, 205, 207, 225, 263, 267, 366, 368
　下縁　263
胸膜腔　366
胸膜上膜　181
胸膜頂　217
胸膜洞　260, 263
胸腰筋膜　88, 105, 106, 107, 138, 139, 140, 267, 270, 271
　後葉：浅葉　267, 324
　前葉：深葉　103, 267
　中葉　267
胸肋部　134
棘下窩　116, 118, 139, 141
棘間靱帯　101, 102, 103
棘筋　105, 106, 107
棘結節　93
棘孔　9, 11, 25, 58
棘上窩　116, 118, 139, 141
棘上筋　117, 119, 121, 138, 139, 140, 141, 142, 143
棘上靱帯　101, 102, 103
棘突起（胸椎の）　89, 90, 91, 101, 102, 112, 186, 223
棘突起（頸椎の）　71, 90, 99, 100, 110, 112, 113
棘突起（腰椎の）　92, 95, 102, 103, 113, 263
距骨　321, 357, 359, 364
　外果面　320
　外側結節　318, 320
　距骨後突起　364
　後踵骨関節面　321
　前踵骨関節面　321
　中踵骨関節面　321
　長母趾屈筋腱溝　318, 321
　内果面　320
　内側結節　318, 320, 364
距骨下関節　359
距骨滑車
　上面　318
距骨頸　318, 320, 359, 364
距骨溝　321
距骨後突起　364
距骨頭　318, 320, 321, 364
距舟部（距踵舟関節の）　359
距踵頸靱帯　321, 358, 359, 364
距踵舟関節
　距舟部　359
距腿関節
　脛距部　359
棘下筋　104, 105, 106, 117, 119, 121, 136, 138, 139, 140, 141, 142, 152
棘下筋膜　105, 137
近位指節間関節　164, 172
近位手掌皮線　163
近位手首皮線　163
筋横隔動脈　225
筋枝　44, 160, 168, 344, 353, 376
筋性部　200
［子宮］筋層　286
緊張部　57

筋突起（下顎骨の）　4, 18
筋突起（披裂軟骨の）　48
筋皮神経　135, 142, 144, 145, 146, 147, 148, 150, 151, 219, 371

【ク】

区域気管支　209
空腸　239, 241, 242, 245, 248, 249, 250, 261
空腸静脈　248, 279
空腸動脈　248, 253, 279
薬指：第四指　176
　基節骨　128
　基節骨底　128
　基節骨頭　128
　末節骨　128
屈筋支帯　159, 166, 167, 168, 169, 171, 351, 355, 356
クモ膜　71, 98, 100, 111
クモ膜下腔　52
クモ膜顆粒　60, 61, 62
クモ膜顆粒小窩　8

【ケ】

頸横静脈　32, 217
頸横動脈　29, 31, 32, 36, 138, 147, 148, 192, 193, 194, 195, 219, 367
　浅枝：浅頸動脈　218
鶏冠　3, 11, 16, 17, 26, 53
鶏冠翼　26
頸胸神経節：星状神経節　207, 220
頸棘筋　109
脛距部（距腿関節の）　359
頸筋膜
　椎前葉　367
脛骨　293, 310, 311, 312, 313, 314, 315, 341, 343, 359, 364
　外側顆　315, 337, 339, 340, 341, 343
　外側面　311
　下関節面　315
　後面　353
　前縁　311
　長母趾屈筋腱溝　359
　内果　356, 357, 364
　内果関節面　315
　内側顆　339, 340, 343
　内側面　311, 347, 348, 355
脛骨神経　344, 345, 352, 353, 355, 356, 357
　筋枝　344
　内側踵骨枝　348, 355, 356
　内側腓腹皮神経　344
脛骨粗面　310, 311, 312, 337, 341, 342, 343, 346
脛骨腓骨動脈幹　353
　筋枝　353
頸枝（顔面神経［Ⅶ］の）　32, 42, 83
茎状突起（尺骨の）　125, 126, 129, 155, 162, 173, 177, 178
茎状突起（側頭骨の）　4, 7, 9, 23, 57
茎状突起（橈骨の）　124, 126, 129, 155, 163, 173, 177, 178
茎状突起鞘　7, 23
脛踵部　321, 359
頸静脈窩　23
頸静脈結節　27
頸静脈孔　9, 11, 71, 84, 85
頸静脈上球　56, 57
頸静脈切痕　27
頸静脈突起　27
頸静脈二腹筋リンパ節　32, 148
頸静脈面　23
頸神経
頸神経叢　34, 85
頸神経ワナ　31, 85, 147, 148
　下根　29, 31, 33
　上根　29, 31, 32, 33, 35
頸切痕　28, 179, 182, 183, 184, 217
頸長筋　37, 207, 368
頸椎　87
頸動脈管　9, 23, 57
頸動脈溝　11, 25
頸動脈小体枝　45
頸動脈洞　35, 45
頸動脈洞枝　84
茎突咽頭筋　10, 35, 45, 47, 84
茎突下顎靱帯　19
茎突舌筋　10, 29, 35, 47
茎突舌骨筋　10, 29, 31, 32, 34, 35, 47, 48
茎突舌骨筋枝　83
茎突舌骨靱帯　29, 35, 48
茎乳突孔　9, 14, 23, 57
頸半棘筋　109, 110
脛腓関節　315
　関節包　339
脛腓靱帯結合：下脛腓関節　315, 364
頸リンパ本幹　36, 37, 367
外科頸　120
結合腱：鼠径鎌　234, 235, 299, 301
楔舟関節　359
月状溝　74
月状骨　128, 129, 172, 173, 177, 178
楔状束結節　71
楔状軟骨　49
月状面　334
結節間溝　120
結節間板　90, 98, 99
楔前部　64
結腸　242
結腸圧痕　255
結腸ヒモ　261
結腸辺縁弓：結腸辺縁動脈　249
結腸辺縁動脈：結腸辺縁弓　249
結腸膨起　250
結腸面　259
楔部　64
結膜半月ヒダ　51
腱画　228, 229
肩甲回旋静脈　143
肩甲回旋動脈　143, 146, 147, 148, 149, 152
肩甲下窩　116
肩甲下筋　117, 119, 121, 135, 142, 143, 145, 146, 147, 148, 149, 150, 371
　腱下包　142
肩甲下静脈　370
肩甲下動脈　145, 146, 147, 148, 149, 370
肩甲挙筋　29, 31, 33, 37, 106, 117, 119, 138, 139, 140, 141
肩甲棘　104, 105, 106, 116, 118, 136, 138, 139, 141, 186
肩甲頸　116
肩甲骨　115, 116, 117, 118, 119, 208
　外側縁　143
　下角　136, 186
　内側縁　88, 136, 138, 139, 140, 141, 186
肩甲上静脈　30, 142, 143, 217
肩甲上神経　31, 32, 135, 139, 140, 141, 142, 143, 144, 219
肩甲上動脈　30, 31, 32, 33, 36, 37, 139, 140, 141, 142, 143, 144, 145, 146, 147, 148, 192, 193, 194, 195, 218, 219, 367
肩甲舌骨筋　31, 34, 48, 85, 139, 141, 144, 145
　下腹　28, 29, 30, 31, 32, 117, 119, 135, 146, 195
　上腹　29, 30, 31, 32, 33, 35, 147, 148
肩甲切痕　116
肩甲背神経　31, 32
肩甲背動脈　37, 138, 367
肩鎖関節　118, 132, 134, 136, 142, 143, 184
　関節円板　143
腱索　199, 200
犬歯　13
犬歯窩　21
腱鞘　172
剣状突起　179, 182, 187, 189, 227
犬歯隆起　21
腱中心　225, 270
肩峰　116, 118, 132, 134, 136, 137, 138, 139, 140, 141, 142, 143, 179
肩峰角　116
肩峰下包　142
肩峰関節面　118
肩峰枝（胸肩峰動脈の）　135, 148
肩峰端　118, 132, 134, 136
腱膜（外側広筋の）　342
腱膜（外腹斜筋の）　228, 229, 230, 234, 275, 328
腱膜（後頭前頭筋の）　5
腱膜（上眼瞼挙筋の）　51
腱膜（内腹斜筋の）　228, 229

【コ】

鉤　64, 66, 77
後陰唇交連　289
後陰唇神経　289
後陰嚢静脈　292
後陰嚢神経　292
後陰嚢動脈　292
後［腋窩］リンパ節　185, 370
後縁（下顎枝の）　18
後縁（尺骨の）　125, 153
後縁（鋤骨の）　9, 25
後縁（橈骨の）　124
後縁（腓骨の）　316
口蓋　43
口蓋咽頭筋　10, 47
口蓋棘　9
口蓋溝　9
口蓋骨　12, 16, 22
　眼窩突起　12
　上顎突起　22
　錐体突起　7, 9
　垂直板　12, 26
　水平板　7, 9, 12, 17, 22, 26
口蓋骨鞘突管　9
口蓋上顎縫合：横口蓋縫合　9

和文索引　383

口蓋垂　47
口蓋垂筋　10
口蓋突起　9, 12, 17, 21, 22, 26
口蓋帆挙筋　10, 47
口蓋帆張筋　10, 44, 56
口蓋扁桃　84, 366
後顆間区　312
口角　38
岬角　57, 93, 94, 96, 260, 277, 279, 282, 284, 285, 336
後角（外側半月の）　313, 340
後角（内側半月の）　313, 340
口角下制筋　2, 6, 19, 33, 39, 40
口角挙筋　2, 6, 39
後下行枝：後室間枝　197, 200, 202, 203
後下小脳動脈　66, 67, 71
後幹　282, 283
交感神経
　　交通枝　205, 207
　　上頸神経節　45
交感神経幹　37, 45, 100, 101, 194, 195, 204, 205, 207, 218, 220, 221, 222, 223, 225, 267, 271, 274, 275, 282, 368
交感神経幹神経節：幹神経節　101, 102, 195, 274
交感神経節　204, 205, 207, 221, 222, 271, 275
後環椎後頭膜　110, 111
［広義の］大脳脚　66, 70
［内包］後脚　74, 75, 76
後弓　60, 61, 71, 89, 98, 99, 100, 109, 110, 111, 112
後弓静脈　348, 356
後距骨関節面　321, 358
後距腓靱帯　317, 351, 357, 359
咬筋　2, 6, 10, 19, 32, 33, 34, 39, 40, 43
　　前縁　28, 38
咬筋神経　81, 82
口腔　43
口腔前庭　43
後脛距部　359
広頸筋　2, 6, 19, 30, 33, 40, 43
後脛骨筋　311, 313, 317, 319, 351, 354, 355, 356, 357, 358, 359, 363
後脛骨筋腱溝　359
後脛骨静脈　349, 352, 355, 356, 357, 358
後脛骨動脈　345, 352, 353, 354, 355, 356, 357, 358
後脛腓靱帯　314, 317, 359
後結節　89, 90, 98, 99
硬口蓋　43, 51, 60
後交通動脈　59, 66, 67, 78
後硬膜動脈　37, 45
後交連　68
後骨間神経　156, 161
後骨間動脈　176
後骨間動脈の枝　161
後骨半規管　58
後根　71, 100
虹彩　51
後枝（外側溝の）　63
後枝（胸神経の）　99, 107, 223
後枝（頸神経の）　71, 99, 100
後枝（左胃動脈の）　244
後枝（尺側反回動脈の）　153, 158, 160
後枝（腎動脈の）　265

後枝（閉鎖神経の）　333
後枝（腰神経の）　102, 106
後耳介静脈　32, 217
後耳介神経　83
後耳介動脈　29
後篩骨孔　12, 20
後篩骨溝　26
後篩骨神経　81
後室間枝：後下行枝　197, 200, 202, 203
後斜角筋　34, 181
後斜走靱帯：後束　154
後縦隔　194, 195, 221, 368
後十字靱帯　309, 311, 313, 339, 340, 341, 342
後縦靱帯　98
甲状咽頭部　45
甲状関節面　48, 50
甲状頸動脈　31, 36, 37, 147, 148, 192, 193, 195, 218
甲状喉頭蓋筋　49
後踵骨関節面　321
後上歯槽枝　81
後上歯槽神経　82
甲状舌骨筋　29, 30, 31, 32, 33, 34, 35, 48, 85, 144
甲状舌骨筋枝　29, 31, 32, 35
甲状舌骨膜　29, 32, 33, 49, 50
甲状腺　144
　　右葉　29, 30, 33, 35, 36, 45, 48, 192, 195
　　左葉　30, 32, 34, 36, 48, 190, 193, 194, 218
甲状腺峡部　28, 36, 48, 50, 190, 192, 193, 194, 195, 217, 218
後床突起　11, 25, 59
鉤状突起：体鉤（頸骨の）　90, 91, 125
鉤状突起（篩骨の）　12, 26
鉤状突起（尺骨の）　126, 154, 155, 156
鉤状突起（膵臓の）　245, 253
甲状軟骨　48, 60
　　右板　50
　　喉頭隆起　48, 217
　　左板　47, 49, 50
　　斜線　33
後小脳延髄槽：大槽　60
甲状披裂筋　49
後上葉区　210, 211, 212
後上葉枝　209
後上腕回旋静脈　143
後上腕回旋動脈　143, 145, 146, 147, 148, 152
後上腕皮神経　137, 139, 140
後神経束　145, 146, 150
項靱帯　108, 109
光錐　57
後正中溝　71
後脊髄静脈　99
後脊髄動脈　71, 98, 99
後尖（三尖弁の）　200, 201
後尖（僧帽弁の）　200, 201
後仙腸靱帯　334
後前腕皮神経　139
後側頭泉門　14
後大腿皮神経　325
　　会陰枝　289, 292
　　下殿皮神経　324
後大脳動脈　59, 66, 67, 76, 78

後端　26
後中心傍回　64
鉤椎関節　112
交通枝　101, 102, 205, 207, 223, 275
後殿筋線　294
喉頭　48, 49, 50, 113
後頭縁　24
後頭顆　7, 9, 17, 27
喉頭蓋　47, 49, 50, 60
後頭蓋窩　61
喉頭蓋軟骨　48
喉頭蓋谷　47, 49, 50, 60, 226
後［頭］角（側脳室の）　72, 73, 74, 75
後頭角（頭頂骨の）　24
後［頭］角球　74
後頭下神経　109
後頭極　62, 63
後頭筋　6, 10, 108, 110, 111
喉頭口　49, 50, 60
後頭骨　4, 7, 8, 14, 17, 27, 100, 109
　　後頭鱗　27
　　小脳窩　11
　　底部　3, 98, 112
喉頭室　50
後頭前切痕　63
喉頭前庭　50
［喉頭］前庭ヒダ　49, 50
後頭前頭筋
　　腱膜　5
　　後頭筋　6, 10, 108, 110, 111
　　前頭筋　5, 39
後頭動脈　29, 34, 35, 37, 44, 108, 109, 110, 111
　　胸鎖乳突筋枝　29
後頭動脈溝　7, 9, 23
［咽頭］喉頭部　60
後頭葉　63, 79
喉頭隆起　28, 30, 48, 217
後頭鱗　27
鉤突窩　122, 123
後乳頭筋　199, 200
広背筋　88, 105, 106, 107, 117, 121, 133, 136, 137, 138, 139, 140, 141, 144, 145, 146, 147, 148, 149, 150, 152, 181, 186, 190, 191, 371
後肺底区　210, 211, 212, 213
後肺底枝　209
後半月大腿靱帯　339, 341
後半月弁　200, 201
後鼻棘　9, 22
後鼻孔　9, 17, 60, 61
後皮枝（頸神経の）　111
［咽頭］口部　60, 226
後部（腔円蓋の）　285, 286, 288, 373
後腹　10, 29, 31, 32, 33, 35, 37, 42, 47, 56
硬膜　5, 62, 71, 82, 98, 99, 100, 101, 110, 111
硬膜枝　81
硬膜鞘　98, 99, 101
後迷走神経幹　251, 267, 372
後毛様体動脈　51, 53
肛門　290, 326
肛門縁　289, 291, 292
肛門管　279, 281
肛門挙筋　235, 282, 284, 286, 289, 290, 292, 297, 324, 326

恥骨直腸筋　281
恥骨尾骨筋　277
腸骨尾骨筋　277
肛門挙筋腱弓　276, 277, 284
肛門挙筋神経　282, 284
肛門尾骨靱帯　289, 291, 292
後有孔質　66, 68, 70, 79
後葉（下垂体の）　60
後葉：浅葉（胸腰筋膜の）　267, 324
後葉（内腹斜筋の腱膜の）　228
後葉（腹直筋鞘の）　229, 232, 233
口輪筋　39, 40
後輪状披裂筋　47, 48, 49
後涙嚢稜　4, 12, 21
後弯　87
股関節　250
　関節包　335
黒質　76, 79
鼓索上陥凹　57
鼓索神経　42, 44, 56, 57, 58, 82, 85
鼓室蓋　11, 23, 57
鼓室蓋稜　9
鼓室神経　57, 84
鼓室神経小管　23
鼓室部　4, 9, 23, 37
鼓室輪　14
鼓室鱗裂　9, 23
古線条体：淡蒼球　74, 75, 76, 77
骨間縁　124, 125, 155, 310, 312, 314, 316
骨間距踵靱帯　321, 358, 359
骨間中手靱帯　172
骨間靱帯　314, 316, 317
骨間仙腸靱帯　297, 299
骨性の蝸牛管　58
骨総脚　58
骨端線　143, 343
骨盤　276, 279, 281, 282, 284, 285, 286, 287, 288, 373, 374, 375
骨盤縁　233
骨盤神経叢：下下腹神経叢　271, 282
骨盤内臓神経　271, 282
骨ラセン板　58
鼓膜　57, 58
鼓膜臍　57
鼓膜張筋　10, 57
鼓膜張筋半管　23
固有肝動脈　244, 246, 247, 255, 256, 274
　右枝　246, 247, 255, 256, 258
　左枝　246, 247, 255, 256, 258
固有掌側指神経　167, 169, 171
固有掌側指動脈　167, 169, 170
固有底側趾神経　360, 362
固有底側趾動脈　362
固有卵巣索　285, 287
小指
　基節骨　128
根糸　67, 71, 98, 99, 100, 101, 111
根静脈　100
根動脈　98, 100

【サ】

最外包　75, 77
載距突起　318, 320, 321, 364
　長母趾屈筋腱溝　359, 363
最上胸動脈　145, 146, 149
最上項線　7, 27

最上鼻甲介　56
左胃静脈　251, 256, 258
臍静脈　232
最上肋間静脈　205, 220, 224
最上肋間動脈　207, 220
左胃大網静脈　241, 246, 251
左胃大網動脈　244, 246, 251
最長筋　105, 106, 107
左胃動脈　244, 246, 247, 251, 258, 260, 267, 372
　後枝　244
　食道枝　244, 251, 372
　前枝　244
臍動脈　232
臍動脈索　281, 283, 285, 288, 373
最内肋間筋　188, 189, 194, 195
臍部　227
左縁枝：鈍［角］縁枝　197, 198, 200, 202, 203
左下肺静脈　192, 193, 196, 197, 198, 206, 207, 213, 214, 216, 222
左下葉気管支　193, 194, 209, 212, 215
左肝管　246, 247, 256, 257
左冠状動脈　198, 200, 202, 203
　縁枝　198, 203
　回旋枝　197, 198, 200, 203
　前下行枝：前室間枝　196, 202, 203
左冠状動脈口　197, 201
左冠状動脈の枝　200
左肝静脈　256
左脚（横隔膜の）　267, 270
左結腸曲：脾曲　250, 259, 372
左結腸静脈　258, 270
左結腸動脈　249, 258
　S状結腸枝　375
鎖骨　28, 30, 48, 118, 119, 133, 134, 135, 142, 143, 147, 148, 149, 179, 184, 208, 217, 219, 367, 370, 371
　胸骨端　118, 183
　肩峰端　118, 132, 134, 136
坐骨　336
坐骨海綿体筋　290, 291, 292, 297
鎖骨下窩　28, 132, 217
鎖骨下筋　30, 119, 135, 147, 149, 181, 370
鎖骨下筋溝　118
鎖骨下静脈　30, 31, 36, 37, 135, 149, 190, 191, 205, 207, 208, 217, 218, 219, 220, 224, 367, 368
鎖骨下静脈溝　181
鎖骨下動脈　30, 36, 37, 144, 145, 146, 192, 193, 194, 195, 204, 205, 207, 208, 214, 218, 219, 220, 224, 368
鎖骨下動脈溝　181
鎖骨下ワナ　36, 207, 368
鎖骨胸筋筋膜　119, 134, 370
坐骨棘　96, 277, 282, 284, 294, 296, 298, 300, 334
坐骨結節　282, 284, 289, 290, 294, 296, 300, 324, 325, 326, 327, 333, 334, 336
　横稜　300
　下部　300
　縦稜　300
　上部　300
坐骨肛門窩：坐骨直腸窩　282, 289, 290, 292, 324, 326
鎖骨枝　367, 370

坐骨枝　282, 291, 294, 296, 300
鎖骨上神経　30, 32, 134
鎖骨上リンパ節　185, 367
坐骨神経　289, 324, 325, 326, 327, 332
鎖骨切痕　182
鎖骨体　118
坐骨体　294, 296
坐骨大腿靱帯　295, 301
鎖骨頭　28, 30, 32, 134, 217
［坐骨］尾骨筋　95, 276, 277, 282, 297
鎖骨部（大胸筋の）　133, 134
左三角間膜　255
左枝（［肝］門脈の）　244, 258
左枝（固有肝動脈の）　246, 255, 256, 258
左主気管支　195, 206, 207, 209, 212, 213, 214, 215, 216, 222, 369
左上肺静脈　193, 196, 197, 198, 206, 207, 213, 214, 216, 222
左上葉気管支　209, 212, 215
左上肋間静脈　206, 207
左心耳　196, 197, 198, 203
左心室　191, 196, 197, 198, 200, 203, 207, 208
左心室後静脈　203
左心房　197, 198, 200, 201, 203, 214
左心房斜静脈　203
左精巣静脈　103, 245, 267, 268, 272
左線維三角　200, 201
左線維輪　200, 201
左肺　190, 191, 192, 193, 209, 210, 211, 212, 213, 216
左肺静脈　203
左肺動脈　193, 194, 206, 207, 213, 214, 215, 216, 222, 369
　上葉動脈　208
［左肺の］小舌　192, 216
［左肺の］心切痕　216
左半月弁（大動脈弁の）　200, 201
左半月弁（肺動脈弁の）　201
左副腎静脈　264, 266, 267, 268, 270
左辺縁静脈　198
左房室口
　左線維輪　200
左房室弁：僧帽弁　184, 200
鞘状突起　25
左葉（肝臓の）　238, 240, 243, 244, 245, 253, 254, 255, 256, 260
左葉（甲状腺の）　30, 32, 34, 36, 48, 190, 193, 194, 218
左卵巣静脈　103, 245, 267, 268, 270
左腕頭静脈　36, 37, 190, 191, 207, 208, 217, 218, 219, 224, 366
三角窩　57
三角間隔　152
三角筋　28, 88, 105, 106, 107, 115, 117, 119, 121, 132, 133, 134, 135, 136, 137, 138, 139, 140, 141, 142, 143, 147, 148, 150, 152, 186, 219, 370, 371
三角筋胸筋溝　132, 179
三角筋胸筋リンパ節　185, 370
三角筋枝　370
三角筋粗面　120
三角骨　128, 129, 173, 177, 178
三角靱帯：内側靱帯　311, 314, 358, 359, 363
　脛踵部　321, 359
　後脛距部　359

和文索引 385

三角線維軟骨複合体　173, 178
三角部　63
三叉神経［Ⅴ］　42, 44, 47, 54, 55, 56,
　　59, 61, 66, 67, 70, 78, 82
　　運動根　56
三叉神経圧痕　11, 23
三叉神経節　44, 56, 59, 80
三尖弁：右房室弁　184, 199, 201
　　後尖　200, 201
　　前尖　199, 200, 201
　　中隔尖　200, 201
山腹前裂：第一裂　70

【シ】

耳介結節　57
耳介枝　84
耳介側頭神経　29, 38, 39, 40, 42, 56, 57,
　　81, 82
四角隙　152
四角膜　49, 50
視覚野　74
耳下腺　28, 30, 32, 33, 34, 39, 40, 43,
　　47, 56, 81, 82, 84
耳下腺管　29, 38, 40
耳下腺枝　81
耳下腺神経叢　83
耳管　56, 58, 84
　　骨部　57
耳管咽頭口　55, 60
耳管半管　23
弛緩部　57
子宮円索　228, 229, 234, 283, 285, 287,
　　288, 373
［子宮］筋層　286
子宮腔　260, 285, 286, 373
子宮頸　285, 286, 288, 373
子宮広間膜　287
子宮仙骨靱帯　288
子宮体　288
子宮端　287
子宮底　285, 286, 287, 288, 373
子宮動脈　283, 288
軸椎：第二頸椎　87, 89, 98, 110, 111
　　外側部　112
　　棘突起　99, 100, 110, 112
　　歯突起　55, 60, 61, 112, 113
　　上関節面　98, 112
　　椎弓根　98
　　椎体　112
指屈筋の総腱鞘　167
歯茎　43
耳甲介　57
視交叉槽：鞍上槽　60
篩骨　12, 26
　　眼窩板　4, 12
　　鶏冠　17
　　鉤状突起　12
　　篩板　11, 12, 51, 53, 55, 59
　　垂直板　17, 55
篩骨棘　25
篩骨神経溝　21
篩骨切痕　20
篩骨突起　26
篩骨胞　12, 26, 55
篩骨蜂巣　3, 12, 16, 60
　　上壁　20
篩骨迷路　26

篩骨稜　21, 22
篩骨漏斗　55
視索　59, 66, 70, 76, 79
視索上陥凹　68, 72
指三角靱帯　176
示指：第二指　167, 172
　　基節骨　128
示指伸筋　127, 161, 162, 163, 174, 175
示指橈側動脈　167, 169, 170, 174
耳珠　38, 40, 42, 57
視床　60, 68, 70, 73, 74, 75, 76, 77
矢状縁　24
視床下溝　68, 70
視床下部　68, 70
視床間橋：中間質　68, 70
篩状筋膜　234
歯状靱帯　71, 98, 100, 111
視床線条体静脈　74, 76
視床枕　79
茸状乳頭　49
矢状縫合　7, 8, 14
耳状面　93, 296, 298
矢状稜　20
［総］指伸筋　162, 168, 175, 176, 177
視神経［Ⅱ］　43, 44, 51, 52, 53, 54, 55,
　　56, 59, 60, 61, 66, 67, 70, 73, 78, 79,
　　81
視神経円板：視神経乳頭　53
視神経外鞘　52
視神経管　11, 12, 25
視神経交叉：視交叉　47, 51, 59, 60, 66,
　　68, 70, 79
耳神経節　44, 82, 84
視神経乳頭：視神経円板　53
支靱帯　176
耳垂　57
指節間関節　115
　　側副靱帯　172
趾節間関節　359
趾［節］骨　293
指節骨体　178
指節骨底　178
指節骨頭　178
歯槽突起　17, 21
歯槽部　18
膝横靱帯　340, 341
膝窩　337, 344, 345, 351
膝蓋下枝　338, 347
膝蓋下脂肪体　341, 342, 347
膝蓋骨　293, 307, 332, 337, 338, 341,
　　342, 343
膝蓋骨尖　307, 341
膝蓋骨底　307
膝蓋上脂肪体　342
膝蓋上包　342
膝蓋靱帯　307, 311, 313, 337, 340, 341,
　　342, 346, 347
膝蓋面　308
膝窩筋　309, 311, 313, 339, 340, 341,
　　342, 345, 347, 351, 353
膝窩筋下陥凹　342
膝窩筋溝　308
膝窩静脈　327, 344, 349, 352
膝窩動脈　327, 344, 345, 352, 353
膝窩面　308
室間孔　68, 72, 74
膝関節

関節包　351
膝関節筋　309, 342
櫛状筋　199, 201
膝神経節　44, 58
歯突起　55, 60, 61, 89, 112, 113
歯突起窩　89
指背腱膜　130, 176
趾背腱膜　355
指背腱膜腱帽　176
篩板　11, 12, 26, 51, 53, 55, 59, 79
視放線　74, 75, 79
脂肪体　359
脂肪被膜　267
尺骨　125, 126, 127, 154, 155
　　回外筋稜　154, 161
　　滑車切痕　126, 154, 155, 156
　　茎状突起　125, 126, 129, 155, 162, 173,
　　　177, 178
　　後縁　153
　　鈎状突起　126, 154, 155, 156
　　肘頭　126, 153, 154, 155, 156
　　橈骨切痕　126
尺骨神経　145, 146, 147, 148, 149, 150,
　　151, 152, 153, 156, 158, 159, 160, 163,
　　166, 167, 168, 169, 171, 219, 371
　　筋枝　168
　　手背枝　174
　　掌枝　159, 167
　　深枝　168, 169, 171
　　浅枝　171
尺骨切痕　124
尺骨粗面　125, 126, 154, 155
尺骨頭　125, 127, 160, 163, 170, 173,
　　178
尺骨動脈　153, 156, 158, 159, 160, 163,
　　166, 167, 168, 169, 170, 171, 177
　　深掌枝　168, 169, 170, 171
尺側手根屈筋　127, 130, 153, 156, 158,
　　159, 160, 163, 166, 167, 168, 169, 170,
　　171, 177
尺側手根伸筋　127, 130, 161, 162, 168,
　　174, 175, 176, 177
尺側正中皮静脈　156, 157
尺側反回動脈
　　後枝　153, 158, 160
　　前枝　160
尺側皮静脈　151, 156, 157, 158, 159, 217,
　　371
斜索　154
射精管　281
斜線　18, 33
斜束：横走靱帯　154
斜台　11, 12, 17, 55, 60, 61, 79, 84
斜頭（母指内転筋の）　130, 171
斜頭（母趾内転筋の）　361, 362
斜披裂筋　47, 49
斜裂　213, 216
縦隔　204
縦隔胸膜　204, 206
終糸　101
舟状骨　128, 129, 173, 177, 178, 318,
　　320, 358, 359, 364
　　峡部　128
舟状骨結節　128, 172
舟状骨粗面　318, 320, 354, 359, 362, 363
縦走手掌皮線　163
縦束　98

十二指腸　245, 246, 253
　　横行部：水平部　245, 248, 253
　　下行部　240, 245, 250, 261
　　上行部　245
　　上部　240, 241, 243, 251
十二指腸圧痕　255
[十二指腸]球部　252
十二指腸空腸曲　241
十二指腸乳頭　253
終板　68
皺眉筋　2, 6
自由ヒモ　261
縦稜　300
珠間切痕　57
手根　168, 173, 175, 178
手根管　171
手根中央関節　177
手根中手関節　172
種子骨　363
手掌　163, 166, 167, 170, 171, 172
手掌腱膜　166
主膵管　257
手背　163, 173, 174, 175, 176
手背枝　174
手背静脈網　168
腫瘍　369
上胃部　227
小陰唇　285, 289, 290
上咽頭枝　47
上咽頭収縮筋　10, 19, 45, 47
上[腋窩]リンパ節　185, 370
上縁（肩甲骨の）　116
上縁（脾臓の）　259
小円筋　106, 117, 119, 121, 137, 138, 139, 140, 141, 152
上オトガイ棘　18
上窩　71
上外側静脈　53
上外側動脈　53
上回盲陥凹　261
小角　48
上角　27, 48, 116
上顎　13
上顎縁　24
上顎間縫合：正中口蓋縫合　9
上顎結節　7, 9, 21
上顎骨　1, 4, 12, 14, 21, 22, 26, 43
　　口蓋突起　9, 12, 17, 22, 26
　　歯槽突起　17
　　前頭突起　1, 4, 12, 26
　　側頭下面　7
上顎神経[V₂]　44, 54, 56, 59, 82
上顎洞　16, 21, 43, 44, 55, 82
上顎洞口　12
上顎洞底　3
上顎洞裂孔　21
上顎突起　22, 26
小角軟骨　49, 50
松果体　68, 75
松果体上陥凹　68, 72
上下腹神経叢　249, 270, 271, 274, 375
上-下葉区　210, 211, 212, 213
上-下葉枝　209
上眼窩裂　1, 11, 12, 16, 25, 80, 81, 85
上眼瞼　51
上眼瞼挙筋　51, 52, 53, 54, 80
　　腱膜　51

小鉗子　74, 75, 76
上関節上腕靱帯　143
上関節突起　90, 91, 92, 93, 94, 95, 101, 112, 113, 334
上関節面　89, 98, 112
上気管気管支リンパ節　369
上脚　57
上丘　68, 70
小胸筋　117, 135, 144, 145, 146, 147, 148, 149, 150, 187, 190, 191, 192, 193, 208, 370, 371
小頬骨筋　2, 6, 39
笑筋　40
上区動脈　265
上頸神経節　37, 45, 47, 85
小結節　120, 142
上結節　91
小結節稜　120
上肩甲横靱帯　117, 119, 139, 141, 142
上肩甲下神経　147, 148, 149, 150
上行咽頭動脈　34, 35, 37, 45
小口蓋管　22
小口蓋孔　9
小口蓋神経　44, 55
上後鋸筋　139, 141, 181
上行頸動脈　36, 37, 195, 218, 367
上行結腸　237, 238, 239, 241, 242, 243, 248, 250, 253, 260, 261
上行口蓋動脈　29, 35
上行枝（外側溝の）　63
上行枝（外側大腿回旋動脈の）　330
上甲状結節　48
上甲状切痕　48
上甲状腺静脈　29, 30, 36
上甲状腺動脈　29, 30, 31, 32, 33, 34, 35, 36, 45
上項線　7, 9, 27, 110, 111
上行大動脈　191, 192, 193, 194, 195, 196, 197, 199, 200, 201, 202, 203, 222
上後腸骨棘　104, 105, 294, 296, 298, 324, 334
小後頭神経　29, 31, 32, 33, 108
上喉頭神経　45, 84
　　外枝　29, 31, 32, 35, 36, 45, 84
　　内枝　28, 29, 31, 32, 33, 34, 35, 45, 47, 49, 50, 84
小後頭直筋　10
上喉頭動脈　29, 30, 31, 32, 33, 34, 35
上行部（十二指腸の）　245
上行部（僧帽筋の）　105, 106, 107
上行腰静脈　224
踵骨　293, 318, 321, 354, 359, 362, 364
　　外側面　355
　　後距骨関節面　321, 358
　　後面　321, 348, 355
　　載距突起　318, 320, 321, 364
　　前距骨関節面　321, 358
　　中距骨関節面　321, 358
　　長母趾屈筋腱溝　318, 321
　　内側面　320
　　腓骨筋滑車　320
踵骨結節　318, 320
踵骨腱：Achilles腱　319, 321, 348, 350, 351, 352, 353, 354, 355, 356, 357, 358, 359
　　滑液包　321
踵骨溝　321

踵骨隆起外側突起　318, 320
踵骨隆起内側突起　318, 320, 321
上根　29, 31, 33, 35
小坐骨孔　284
小坐骨切痕　294, 296, 300, 334
掌枝（尺骨神経の）　159, 167
掌枝（正中神経の）　159, 166, 167, 168
小指：第五指
　　基節骨　128
小指外転筋　130, 162, 163, 166, 167, 168, 169, 171, 174, 176
小趾外転筋　319, 355, 359, 360, 361, 362, 364
上矢状静脈洞　47, 60, 61, 62
上矢状洞溝　8, 11, 27
小指伸筋　162, 163, 168, 174, 175, 177
小指対立筋　130, 169, 171
小趾対立筋　319, 362
上斜筋　51, 52, 53, 54, 80
上尺側側副動脈　151, 153, 158
上縦隔　194, 195
踵舟靱帯　319, 321, 358, 359
上小脳動脈　59, 66, 67, 78
上唇　260
上唇挙筋　2, 6, 39
上伸筋支帯　355
上神経幹　28, 31, 32, 37, 147, 148, 190, 191, 192, 193, 194, 218, 219
小心臓静脈　196, 197
上唇動脈　40
小腎杯　265, 269
上唇鼻翼挙筋　2, 6, 39
上錐体静脈洞　59
小錐体神経　44, 57, 84, 85
小錐体神経管裂孔　11, 23, 59
小錐体神経溝　11, 23
上錐体洞溝　11, 17, 23
上髄帆　70, 71
[虫部]小節　70
[左肺の]小舌　192, 216
上舌区　210, 211, 213
上舌枝　209, 213
上前区動脈　265
上前腸骨棘　96, 231, 276, 277, 284, 294, 296, 298, 300, 331, 333, 336
上前頭回　62, 63
上前頭溝　63
小泉門　14
上双子筋　295, 301, 303, 305, 325
上束：前斜走靱帯　154
掌側骨間筋　171, 176
掌側指神経　171
掌側尺骨手根靱帯　172
掌側靱帯　172
掌側中手動脈　170, 171
上側頭回　63
上側頭溝　63
掌側橈骨手根靱帯　172
上側頭線　4, 20, 24, 40
上大静脈　190, 191, 192, 196, 197, 199, 201, 203, 204, 205, 208, 214, 217, 218, 219, 222, 224, 366, 369
上大脳静脈　62
上唾液核　85
小腸　237, 238, 241, 242, 250, 262, 267, 286
　　腸間膜　242, 260

和文索引

上腸間膜静脈　245, 246, 248, 253, 258, 279
上腸間膜動脈　245, 248, 252, 253, 258, 264, 266, 267, 268, 273, 274, 279
上腸間膜動脈神経節　252, 274
小腸ループ　262, 279
上直筋　51, 52, 53, 54, 80
上直腸静脈　249, 281
上直腸動脈　249, 281
上椎切痕　90, 92
小殿筋　295, 303, 305, 325, 333, 335
小転子　302, 304, 306, 333, 336
上殿静脈　325, 326
上殿動脈　281, 282, 283, 289, 325, 326, 333
上殿皮神経　324
上頭　10, 42
上頭斜筋　10, 109
上橈尺関節　154, 156
上頭頂小葉　63
小内転筋　327
小脳　60, 68, 70, 77
　脚間裂：水平裂　70
　片葉　66
小脳窩　11, 27
小脳後葉　70
小脳前葉　70
小脳テント　44, 59, 60, 61
小脳半球　62, 84
小脳扁桃：腹側傍片葉　66, 70
上鼻甲介　16, 26, 55, 56
上腓骨筋支帯　351, 355
踵腓靱帯　317, 321, 359
上鼻道　26, 55
上腹　29, 30, 31, 32, 33, 35, 147, 148
小伏在静脈　344, 345, 348, 350, 352, 354, 356, 357, 358
上副腎動脈　252
上膀胱動脈　280, 281, 283, 285, 288, 373
漿膜性心膜　196
　壁側板　191, 192, 193, 194
静脈管索裂　251, 255, 256
静脈間隆起　199
静脈弁　349
小網　240, 243, 244, 251
上葉（右肺の）　209, 210, 211, 212, 366
上葉（左肺の）　209, 210, 211, 213
上葉気管支　194, 213
　下舌枝　213
　上舌枝　213
　舌枝　213
小腰筋　274, 297, 299, 301, 375
上葉動脈　204, 205, 208, 215
小翼　1, 3, 11, 12, 16, 25, 43
踵立方靱帯　319, 321, 359
小菱形筋　88, 106, 107, 117, 138, 139, 140, 141
小菱形骨　128, 129, 168, 173, 178
上肋横突靱帯　181, 223
上肋骨窩　90, 91, 181
小弯　240, 243, 244, 247, 251, 252, 372
上腕　115, 151, 152
上腕回旋静脈　142
上腕回旋動脈　142
上腕筋　121, 123, 127, 139, 151, 156, 159, 160
上腕骨　120, 121, 122, 123, 126, 142,

151, 154, 156
外側上顆　126, 153, 154
肘頭窩　154
内側上顆　126, 153, 154, 156, 160, 371
上腕骨滑車　122, 126, 154, 156
上腕骨小頭　122, 126, 153, 154, 156, 161
上腕骨頭　120, 142, 143
上腕三頭筋　127, 139, 144, 145, 151, 153
　外側頭　121, 133, 139, 143, 150, 152
　長頭　106, 107, 117, 119, 136, 137, 139, 140, 149, 150, 151, 152
　内側頭　121, 123, 150, 156
上腕尺骨頭　127, 160
上腕静脈　151, 217
上腕深静脈　143, 151
上腕深動脈　143, 151, 152
上腕頭　123, 160
上腕動脈　151, 153, 157, 158, 159, 160
上腕二頭筋　127, 132, 139, 144, 145, 146, 149, 150, 151, 153, 154, 156, 157, 158, 159, 160, 161, 371
　短頭　117, 119, 135, 142, 147, 148, 151, 219
　長頭　119, 133, 135, 142, 143, 151
上腕二頭筋腱膜　153, 158, 159
食道　37, 48, 193, 194, 195, 204, 205, 206, 208, 214, 221, 222, 225, 226, 246, 251, 267, 369
食道圧痕　255
食道枝（下甲状腺動脈の）　37
食道枝（左胃動脈の）　244, 251, 372
食道神経叢　193, 194, 195, 221, 225, 369
食道裂孔　227, 251, 270
鋤骨　7, 17, 25, 43, 79
　後縁　9, 25
鋤骨鞘突管　9
鋤骨翼　25
耳輪　57
耳輪脚　57
心圧痕　216
腎圧痕　255
深陰茎背静脈　279, 280, 291
腎盂：腎盤　264, 265, 269, 274
腎盂尿管移行部　269
深横中手靱帯　172, 176
深外陰部動脈　280
心外膜：臓側板　191
心筋架橋　197, 198
伸筋支帯　161, 162, 163, 174, 175
神経幹　135
神経根囊胞　286
神経束　142
深枝（外側足底神経の）　361
深枝（尺骨神経の）　168, 169, 171
深指屈筋　127, 130, 158, 159, 160, 167, 168, 169, 171, 177
深指屈筋腱　167
深膝蓋下包　342
心室中隔　208
　筋性部　200
　膜性部　200
深掌枝　168, 169, 170, 171
深掌動脈弓　169, 170, 171
腎静脈　245, 249, 252, 264, 266, 267, 268, 270, 272, 273, 274
[腎] 髄質　265
腎錐体　265

[左肺の] 心切痕　216
心尖　184, 198, 208, 216, 227
心臓　84, 184, 196, 197, 198, 200, 201, 203
腎臓　84, 249, 260, 263, 264, 265, 266, 267, 268, 272, 273, 274
　下端　261, 264, 270
　上端　240, 243, 252, 264
心臓枝　84
心臓神経叢　194, 195
深足底動脈弓　362
深側頭神経　42, 81, 82
深鼠径輪　231, 232, 233, 234, 235, 281
深鼠径リンパ節　374
人中　38
腎柱　265
深腸骨回旋動脈　271
深頭　10, 42, 43
腎動脈　245, 249, 252, 264, 265, 266, 267, 268, 270, 272, 273, 274
　後枝　265
　前枝　265
腎乳頭　265
真の声帯　49, 50
深腓骨神経　346, 357, 358
　反回枝　346
[腎] 皮質　265
腎被膜　267
心房枝　202
心房中隔　201
心膜　196, 204, 205, 206, 207, 222, 240
心膜横隔静脈　206, 207
心膜横隔動脈　206, 207
心膜横洞　196
心膜腔　207
　後壁　196
心膜斜洞　196
腎面　259
腎門　227, 264, 265
深葉：前葉　267

【ス】

髄核　103
膵管　246, 257, 258
膵頸　253
[腎] 髄質　265
膵十二指腸静脈　258
膵十二指腸動脈　258
水晶体　60
膵臓　84, 247, 253, 372
　鈎状突起　245, 253
膵体　245, 257, 270
錐体筋　228, 234, 299, 301
錐体交叉　70
錐体鼓室裂　9, 23
錐体尖　9
錐体突起　7, 9, 22
錐体乳突部：岩様部　11, 23, 56
錐体鱗裂　9, 23
垂直板　22, 26
垂直板（口蓋骨の）　12, 26
垂直板（篩骨の）　17, 55
垂直稜　307
膵頭　227, 245, 253, 257
膵尾　245, 253, 257, 259, 260
水平板　7, 9, 12, 17, 22, 26
水平部：横行部（十二指腸の）　245, 253

水平部：横行部（僧帽筋の） 105, 106
水平裂 216
水平裂：脚間裂（小脳の） 70
髄膜鞘 111
髄膜嚢 101, 260

【セ】

正円孔 3, 11, 25, 58, 81, 85
精管 230, 233, 234, 235, 271, 278, 279, 280, 281, 282
精管動脈 278
精丘 279, 281
精索 230, 234, 271, 278, 280, 328, 330
星状神経節：頸胸神経節 207, 220
性腺動脈 103
精巣 232, 278, 279
精巣挙筋 234
精巣挙筋膜 234, 278
精巣上体 278
精巣上体垂 278
[精巣上体] 体 278
[精巣上体] 頭 278
[精巣上体] 尾 278
精巣鞘膜
　臓側板 278, 279
　嚢 278
　壁側板 278, 279
精巣静脈 233, 235, 261, 271, 281, 375
精巣動脈 233, 235, 261, 271, 272, 273, 274, 278, 281
精巣動脈神経叢 274
声帯突起 48
声帯ヒダ 49, 50
正中弓状靱帯 270
正中溝 71, 77, 105
正中口蓋縫合：上顎間縫合 9
正中臍索 232, 285
正中臍ヒダ 233, 235
正中神経 135, 144, 145, 146, 147, 148, 149, 150, 151, 153, 156, 157, 158, 159, 160, 163, 166, 167, 168, 169, 171, 177, 219, 371
　筋枝 160
　掌枝 159, 166, 167, 168
　総掌側指神経 168
　反回枝 166, 167, 168, 169
正中神経外側根 150, 371
正中神経内側根 150, 371
正中舌喉頭蓋ヒダ 49
正中仙骨動脈 333
正中仙骨稜 94
正中動脈 153, 158
正中隆起 66, 68
正中輪状甲状靱帯 48
精嚢 279, 280, 281, 282
赤核 77
脊髄 60, 61, 67, 98, 99, 100, 101, 225, 270
脊髄円錐 101
脊髄根 37, 61, 66, 67, 71, 78, 84, 85, 100, 138, 147, 148
脊髄神経
　後根 98
　前根 98
脊髄神経節 71, 99, 100, 101, 110, 111
　硬膜鞘 98
脊柱 98, 100, 101, 102, 103, 113, 334

脊柱起立筋 95, 104, 105, 106, 107, 138, 139, 140, 141, 181, 267, 270, 297
舌 43, 49, 50, 56, 60, 84
舌咽神経［IX］ 29, 35, 37, 44, 45, 47, 61, 70, 71, 78, 84
　咽頭枝 45
　鼓室神経 57
舌下神経［XII］ 28, 29, 31, 32, 33, 34, 35, 36, 44, 45, 47, 56, 61, 66, 78, 85, 98
舌下神経管 9, 11, 17, 27, 85, 98
舌下神経三角 71
舌下神経伴行静脈 31
舌下腺 29, 35
舌下腺窩 18
舌顔面動脈幹 29
舌骨 29, 31, 33, 48, 60, 84, 113
　体 28, 30, 32, 48, 50, 56
　大角 28, 31, 32, 33, 34, 49, 50
　大角の先端 45, 47
舌骨下筋 190, 192, 193, 195
舌骨喉頭蓋靱帯 50
舌骨上枝 31, 32
舌骨舌筋 29, 32, 35, 48, 56
舌根 226
舌枝 213
切歯窩 9, 21
切歯管 12, 17, 21
切歯孔 55
切歯骨 55
舌状回 64, 68
舌静脈 31, 32
舌神経 29, 35, 42, 44, 56, 81, 82
舌深動脈 29
舌動脈 31, 32, 34, 35, 56
　舌骨上枝 31, 32
舌背 47, 49
［披裂軟骨］尖 48, 50
線維鞘 172
線維鞘（趾の） 360, 361
線維鞘（指の） 167, 171
線維性心膜 190, 191, 192, 193, 219, 225, 366
線維被膜 267
線維輪 103, 279
浅陰茎背静脈 278
浅陰茎背動脈 278
前陰唇交連 289
浅会陰横筋 289, 290, 291, 292, 297
前［腋窩］リンパ節 79, 370
前縁（右肺の） 216
前縁（下顎枝の） 18
前縁（脛骨の） 310, 311, 312, 314
前縁（咬筋の） 28, 38
前縁（左肺の） 216
前縁（尺骨の） 125
前縁（橈骨の） 124, 155
前縁（腓骨の） 311, 316
浅横中手靱帯 166
浅横中足靱帯 360
浅外陰部静脈 328, 376
浅外陰部動脈 330, 376
前外果動脈 357
前顆間区 312
前角（外側半月の） 313, 340
前角（内側半月の） 313, 340
前下行枝：前室間枝 196, 202, 203

前下小脳動脈 66, 67
［内包］前脚 74, 75, 76
前弓 55, 60, 79, 89, 112, 113
前鋸筋 106, 107, 117, 119, 132, 133, 144, 145, 146, 147, 148, 149, 181, 228, 371
前鋸筋粗面 181
仙棘靱帯 282, 284, 297, 333, 334
前距骨関節面 321, 358
前距腓靱帯 317, 359
前脛骨筋 311, 313, 319, 346, 354, 355, 357, 358, 363, 364
前脛骨静脈 349, 357
前脛骨動脈 345, 346, 353, 357
　筋枝 353
前脛骨反回静脈 346
前脛骨反回動脈 346
浅頸静脈 32
前頸静脈 28, 32, 33
浅頸動脈 29, 31, 32, 36, 37, 218, 367
前結節 89, 90, 98, 99
仙結節靱帯 284, 289, 290, 292, 297, 325, 334
　鎌状突起 284, 297, 334
前交通動脈 51, 67
前交連 68, 75
仙骨 87, 88, 93, 94, 95, 96, 105, 289, 336
　外側部 101, 102
　岬角 96, 260, 277, 279, 282, 284, 285, 336
仙骨角 94
仙骨管 93, 94, 95, 277
前骨間神経 160
前骨間動脈 158, 160, 176
前骨間動脈の枝 170, 176
仙骨神経叢 276, 284
仙骨尖 94
前骨半規管 14, 57, 58
仙骨底 93
仙骨裂孔 94
前枝（外側溝の） 63
前枝（胸神経の） 99
前枝（頸神経の） 29, 31, 36, 37, 71, 98, 99, 100, 220
前枝（左胃動脈の） 244
前枝（尺側反回動脈の） 160
浅枝（尺骨神経の） 171
前枝（腎動脈の） 265
前枝（仙骨神経の） 275, 281, 282, 333
浅枝（橈骨神経の） 158, 160, 174, 175
前枝（閉鎖神経の） 330, 333
前枝（腰神経の） 102, 275, 333
浅指屈筋 130, 159, 167, 168, 169, 171, 177
　上腕尺骨頭 127, 160
　橈骨頭 127, 160
前視交叉溝 11, 25
前篩骨孔 12, 20
前篩骨溝 26
前篩骨神経 51, 52, 53, 81
前篩骨洞 55
前篩骨動脈 51, 52, 53
前室間枝：前下行枝 191, 196, 197, 198, 200, 202, 203
前斜角筋 29, 30, 31, 32, 33, 35, 36, 37, 71, 98, 144, 145, 146, 181, 192, 193,

194, 195, 218, 367
前斜角筋結節　181
前斜線　124
前斜走靱帯：上束　154
前十字靱帯　309, 313, 339, 340, 341, 342
前縦靱帯　37, 98, 102, 274, 275, 284
前障　74, 75, 77
舟状窩　9, 25, 57
前踵骨関節面（距骨の）　321
浅掌枝（橈骨動脈の）　169, 170
浅掌動脈弓　166, 167, 169
前床突起　25
前床突起（蝶形骨の）　11, 58, 59
前上葉区　210, 211, 212, 213
前上葉枝　209, 213
前上葉静脈　213
前上腕回旋動脈　135, 147, 148
前心臓静脈　196
浅心臓神経叢　194
前深側頭動脈　42
前脊髄静脈　100
前脊髄動脈　67, 100, 224
前尖（三尖弁の）　199, 200, 201
前尖（僧帽弁の）　200, 201
浅側頭静脈　38, 39, 40, 57
前側頭泉門　14
浅側頭動脈　29, 38, 39, 40, 57
　前頭枝　39
　頭頂枝　5
浅鼠径静脈　228
浅鼠径輪　228, 231, 234, 275, 278, 328
浅鼠径リンパ節　228, 229, 230, 374, 376
前大脳動脈　47, 51, 59, 60, 66, 67, 68, 73
前中心傍回　64
浅中大脳静脈　62
仙腸関節　96, 336
浅腸骨回旋静脈　280, 328, 376
浅腸骨回旋動脈　330
前庭　58
前庭蝸牛神経：内耳神経［Ⅷ］　58, 59, 61, 66, 70, 78, 83
前庭神経　58, 83
　上部　58
前庭神経野　71
前庭水管　23
前庭窓　58
[喉頭] 前庭ヒダ　49, 50
前殿筋線　294
浅頭（側頭筋の）　43
浅頭（内側翼突筋の）　10
前頭縁　24
前頭蓋窩　59
前［頭］角（側脳室の）　72, 74, 75, 76
前頭角（頭頂骨の）　24
前頭頬骨縫合　4
前頭極　62, 63
前頭筋　5, 39
前頭結節　14, 20
前頭孔：前頭切痕　1, 12, 38
前頭骨　1, 4, 8, 12, 14, 20
　眼窩部　11, 12, 17
　鼻棘　12
前頭枝　39
前頭神経　44, 51, 52, 53, 81
前頭直筋　10
前頭洞　3, 11, 12, 16, 17, 20, 55, 60

前頭突起　1, 4, 12, 21, 24, 26
前頭弁蓋：弁蓋部　63
前頭縫合　14
前頭葉　63
前頭稜　8, 11, 16, 20
前頭鱗　17
前乳頭筋　199, 200
前肺底区　210, 211, 212, 213
前肺底枝　209
前半月大腿靱帯　339
前半月弁　201
仙尾関節　282
前鼻棘　1, 4, 21
浅腓骨神経　346, 347, 357
　中間足背枝　355
　中間足背皮神経　346
　内側足背皮神経　346
前腓骨頭靱帯　346
前部（脳弓柱の）　74
前部（腟円蓋の）　285, 288, 373
前腹　19, 29, 30, 32, 33, 34, 35, 43
浅腹壁静脈　328, 376
浅腹壁動脈　330
前脈絡叢動脈　67, 73
前迷走神経幹　222, 225, 251, 267, 372
前有孔質　66, 79
浅葉：後葉　267, 324
前葉（下垂体の）　60
前葉：深葉（胸腰筋膜の）　267
前葉（胸腰筋膜の）　103
前葉（腹直筋鞘の）　133, 228, 229, 230, 299
前立腺　279, 281
　後面　281
前立腺静脈叢　279, 281
[前立腺] 底　280
前立腺部　279, 281
浅リンパ節　147, 148
前涙嚢稜　4, 12, 21
前肋間静脈　189
前腕　115, 159, 160, 161, 162
前弯　87
前腕骨間膜　154, 155, 161
前腕伸筋群　153
前腕正中皮静脈　157, 159, 371

【ソ】

総肝管　255, 256, 257
総肝動脈　244, 246, 255, 267, 268
総頸動脈　29, 30, 31, 32, 33, 34, 35, 36, 37, 45, 47, 144, 148, 190, 191, 192, 193, 194, 195, 207, 208, 214, 218, 219, 224, 366, 367, 368
総骨間動脈　158, 160
[総] 指伸筋　161, 163, 174, 176, 177
総掌側指神経　166, 168, 169
総掌側指動脈　166, 169, 170, 171
臓側胸膜：肺胸膜　219
臓側板：心外膜（心膜の）　191
臓側板（精巣鞘膜の）　278, 279
臓側腹膜　233, 244
総胆管　247, 255, 256, 257, 258
総腸骨静脈　271, 272, 273, 274
総腸骨動脈　249, 271, 272, 273, 274, 279, 280, 281, 375
総腸骨リンパ管　368
総腸骨リンパ節　374, 375

総底側趾神経　360, 361
総腓骨神経　337, 338, 344, 345, 346, 347, 352
　関節枝　346
　反回枝　346
僧帽筋　10, 29, 30, 32, 33, 34, 85, 88, 104, 108, 117, 119, 132, 134, 135, 136, 137, 138, 139, 140, 141, 179, 186, 208
　横行部：水平部　105, 106
　下行部　105, 106
　上行部　105, 106, 107
僧帽弁：左房室弁　184, 200, 201
　後尖　200, 201
　前尖　200, 201
総涙小管　51
足根　354, 355, 356, 357
側索　176
側切歯　13, 16
足底　360, 362, 363
足底筋　309, 319, 321, 344, 345, 351, 352, 353, 355, 356
足底腱膜　359, 360
足底動脈弓　362
足底方形筋　319, 359, 361, 362
側頭縁　24
側頭窩　41
側頭下窩　42
側頭角：下角　74
側頭下面（上顎骨の）　7, 21
側頭下面（大翼の）　7, 25
側頭下稜　7, 9, 25
側頭極　62, 63, 64, 73
側頭筋　2, 5, 6, 19, 29, 39, 40, 42, 43
　深頭　42, 43
　浅頭　43
側頭筋膜　5, 40
側頭骨　5, 12, 23, 43, 57
　外耳道　4
　岩様部：錐体乳突部　11, 56
　頬骨突起　4
　茎状突起　4, 9, 57
　鼓室部　4, 9, 37
　錐体尖　9
　乳様突起　4
　鱗部　4, 9, 11, 17
側頭枝　83
側頭枝（顔面神経［Ⅶ］の）　39
側頭突起　24
側頭面（頬骨の）　24
側頭面（大翼の）　25
側頭葉　43, 60, 63
　側頭極　73
側脳室　47, 60, 77
　下角　72
　下角：側頭角　74
　後［頭］角　72, 74, 75
　前［頭］角　72, 74, 75, 76
　中心部　72, 74, 76
[側] 脳室房　72
側脳室脈絡叢　75, 76, 77
足背　358
足背静脈　357, 358
足背静脈弓　354, 356, 358
足背動脈　354, 357, 358
側副溝　64, 66
側副三角　73
側副靱帯（指節間関節の）　172

側副靱帯（中足趾節関節の） 363
側腹部 227
側副隆起 73
鼠径鎌：結合腱 234, 235, 299, 301
鼠径三角 232, 233
鼠径靱帯 234, 235, 271, 275, 276, 277, 280, 282, 284, 293, 295, 297, 299, 301, 328, 330, 331, 333, 376
鼠径部 227
咀嚼筋 43
疎性結合組織 5
粗線 304, 306
足根洞 320, 357, 359, 364

【タ】

[精巣上体] 体 278
体（舌骨の） 28, 30, 32, 48, 50, 56
第一貫通動脈 327
第一白歯 13
第一胸椎 183
　棘突起 112
　椎弓根 99
　椎体 99, 100
第一胸肋関節 183
第一頸神経 34, 71, 99
　後枝 99
　根糸 67
第一頸椎：環椎 87
　横突起 28, 37, 44, 57, 71, 98, 99
　外側塊 3, 71, 98, 99, 112, 113
　下関節面 112
　後弓 60, 61, 98, 99, 100, 109, 110, 111
　後弓 71, 112
　前弓 55, 60, 79, 89, 112, 113
第一後仙骨孔 95
第一趾
　基節骨 318
　末節骨 318
第一指：母指 167
　基節骨 128, 129, 178
　末節骨 128, 129, 178
第一小臼歯 13
第一掌側骨間筋 130
第一仙骨神経
　前枝 275, 282, 333
第一前仙骨孔 95
第一仙椎
　椎体 93
第一足根中足関節 359
第一大臼歯 13
第一中手骨 173
第一中手骨体 128, 129
第一中手骨底 128, 129, 168, 172, 178
第一中手骨頭 128, 129, 178
第一中足趾節関節 358, 359
第一中足骨 320, 359, 364
第一中足骨体 318
第一中足骨底 318, 363
第一中足骨頭 318, 354
第一虫様筋 167, 168, 169, 171, 362
第一底側骨間筋 319, 362
第一背側骨間筋 130, 162, 163, 168, 174, 176, 319, 358, 362
第一背側中手動脈 174, 176
第一背側中足動脈 358
第一尾椎 87, 94, 95, 336

第一腰神経 102, 268, 270
　後枝 102
　前枝 102
第一腰椎 102
　下関節突起 113
　棘突起 263
　椎体 101
第一裂：山腹前裂 70
第一肋軟骨 183
第一肋間神経 220
第一肋骨 36, 99, 113, 135, 148, 190, 191, 192, 193, 205, 218, 219, 220
　肋骨頭関節 98
第一肋骨頸 183, 205, 220
第一肋骨結節 99
第一肋骨体 183, 204
第一肋骨頭 183
第一肋骨の軟骨結合 183
第二貫通動脈 327
第二白歯 13
第二胸神経
　硬膜鞘 99
　脊髄神経節 99
第二胸肋関節 183
第二頸神経
　後根 71
　脊髄神経節 110, 111
　前枝 31
第二頸椎：軸椎 87, 89, 98, 110, 111
　外側部 112
　棘突起 99, 100, 110, 112
　歯突起 55, 60, 61, 112, 113
　上関節面 98, 112
　椎弓根 98
　椎体 112
第二指：示指 167, 172
　基節骨 128
第二趾
　基節骨 318
　中節骨 318
　末節骨 318
第二小臼歯 13
第二掌側骨間筋 130
第二仙骨神経 284
　前枝 281, 282, 333
第二前仙骨孔 94
第二仙椎 101
第二大臼歯 13
第二中手骨体 128
第二中手骨底 173
第二中手骨頭 172
第二中足骨頭 363
第二虫様筋 168, 362
第二底側骨間筋 319, 362
第二背側骨間筋 130, 162, 174, 176, 319, 358, 362
第二背側中手動脈 176
第二背側中足動脈 358
第二腰神経
　後枝 102
　前枝 102
第二腰椎
　関節間部 113
　棘突起 102, 103, 113
　上関節突起 113
　椎弓板 103
　肋骨突起 263

第二肋軟骨 183, 184, 187, 217
第二肋間神経 220
第二肋骨 179, 183, 187, 189, 220
第三貫通動脈 327
第三胸神経 144, 145, 146
第三胸椎 214
　棘突起 186
　後枝 71
　前枝 31, 37, 71
第三頸椎 110, 111
　棘突起 112
　椎体 99
第三後頭神経 108, 109, 110, 111
第三後仙骨孔 94
第三指：中指
　基節骨 129, 178
　中節骨 129, 178
　中節骨体 128
　中節骨底 128
　中節骨頭 128
　末節骨 129, 178
第三掌側骨間筋 130
第三仙骨神経 284
　前枝 282
第三大臼歯 7, 13, 21
第三中手骨 129
第三中手骨底 173, 178
第三中手骨頭 178
第三虫様筋 362
第三底側骨間筋 319, 362
第三脳室 72, 74, 76, 77
　視索上陥凹 72
　松果体上陥凹 72
　漏斗陥凹 72
第三脳室脈絡叢 70, 76
第三脳室脈絡組織 76
第三背側骨間筋 130, 162, 174, 319, 358, 362
第三腓骨筋 317, 319, 355, 357, 358
第三腰椎 275
　上関節突起 101
　椎弓根 113
　椎弓板 103
　肋骨突起 103, 113
第三腰動脈 274
第三肋軟骨 184
第四貫通動脈 327
第四胸神経 144
第四頸神経
　後根 71
　後枝の皮枝 110, 111
　後皮枝 111
　脊髄神経節 71
　前根の根糸 71
　前枝 31, 98
第四頸椎 111
第四指：薬指
　基節骨 128
　基節骨底 128
　基節骨頭 128
　末節骨 128
第四掌側骨間筋 130
第四仙骨神経 284
第四仙骨神経の枝 277
第四中手骨底 173
第四虫様筋 169, 362
第四脳室 60, 68, 70, 72

正中溝　77
内側隆起　77
第四脳室外側陥凹　72
第四脳室髄条　71
第四脳室正中口　68，70
第四脳室底：菱形窩　71，76
第四脳室脈絡叢　70
第四背側骨間筋　130，162，174，319，358，362
第四腰神経
　前枝　275，333
第四腰椎
　棘突起　263
　椎体　102
第四腰動脈　271，274
第四肋軟骨　184，217
第四肋間動脈　207
第四肋骨　188
第五胸神経
　後枝　99
　前枝　99
第五胸椎
　椎弓根　101
第五頚神経
　後根　100
　後枝　100
　脊髄神経節　100
　前根　100
　前枝　29，36，100
第五頚椎　111
　横突起の結節間板　99
　横突起の後結節　99
　横突起の前結節　99
　椎体　98
第五指：小指
　基節骨　128
第五仙骨神経　284
第五中手骨　129，173
第五中手骨体　128
第五中手骨底　128
第五中手骨頭　128
第五中足骨粗面　318，320，354，358，363，364
第五中足骨体　318
第五中足骨底　318
第五中足骨頭　318
第五腰神経
　後根　101
　脊髄神経節　101
　前枝　102，275
第五腰椎　285
　下関節突起　334
　棘突起　95
　上関節突起　95，334
　椎体　95，102
　肋骨突起　334，336
第五肋間隙　186
第五肋間静脈　188，207
第五肋間神経　188
第五肋間動脈　188
第五肋骨　188
第六頚神経
　後根　100
　後枝　110
　前枝　99
第六頚椎
　椎弓板　71，113

第六肋軟骨　184，187
第六肋間静脈　204，205，224
第六肋間神経　188
第六肋間動脈　204，205，224
第六肋骨　188，189
第七頚椎：隆椎　90
　棘突起　71，99，100，113
　椎体　99
第七肋軟骨　225
第七肋骨　188
第八頚神経　99
　後根　99
　脊髄神経節　99，100
　前枝　220
第八肋軟骨
　肋骨弓　184
第八肋間静脈　222
第八肋間神経　222
　腹前皮枝　228
第八肋間動脈　222
第八肋骨　188，189，222，229
第九胸椎
　椎体　222
第九肋骨　260
第九肋骨頭　225
第十胸神経
　脊髄神経節　101
第十胸椎
　棘突起　101
第十肋間神経
　腹前皮枝　228，229
第十肋骨　260
第十一肋間神経
　腹前皮枝　230
第十一肋骨　263
第十二肋骨　102，179，189，263
大陰唇　234，289
　後陰唇交連　289
　前陰唇交連　289
大円筋　105，106，107，117，119，121，136，137，138，139，140，141，143，150，152，186
大角　28，31，32，33，34，45，47，48，49，50
対角枝：外側枝　198，202，203
大鉗子　75
大胸筋　28，30，119，121，132，135，139，142，144，145，146，149，183，185，186，190，192，208，366，370，371
　胸骨部　133
　胸肋部　134
　鎖骨部　133，134
　腹部　133，228
大頬骨筋　2，6，39，40
大結節　120，142，143
大結節稜　120
体鈎：鈎状突起　90，91
大口蓋孔　9
大口蓋溝　21，22
大口蓋神経　44，55
大後頭孔：大孔　9，11，17，27，60，61，71，85，100
大後頭神経　108，109，110，111
大後頭直筋　10，109，110
大坐骨孔　284
大鎖骨上窩　132，217
大坐骨切痕　294，296，334

大耳介神経　29，30，31，32，33，35，39，40，108
対珠　57
大十二指腸乳頭　253
帯状回　64，68
帯状回峡　64
帯状溝　64
　縁溝：縁枝　64
　中心傍枝　64
大静脈孔　227，270
大心臓静脈　196，197，198，200，203
大腎杯　265，269
大錐体神経　44，58，85
大錐体神経管裂孔　11，23，59
大錐体神経溝　11，23，57
体性求心性線維　85
大泉門　14
大槽：後小脳延髄槽　60
大腿　326，327，332
大腿管　231
大腿筋膜　234，328，331，338，342，376
大腿筋膜張筋　276，295，328，330，331
大腿骨　293，302，303，304，305，306，307，308，309，332，341，343
　外側顆　337，339，341，343
　外側上顆　343
　小転子　336
　大転子　324，325，336
　内側顆　339，341，343，347，351
　内側上顆　343
大腿骨距　306
大腿骨頚　302，304，335，336
大腿骨体　302，335
大腿骨頭　302，304，335，336
大腿骨頭窩　302
大腿骨頭靭帯　303，334，336
大腿三角　331
大腿枝　233，271，272，273，274，280，283
大腿四頭筋　293，332，341，342
　外側広筋　307
　大腿直筋　307
　中間広筋　307
　内側広筋　307
大腿静脈　230，231，271，276，277，280，328，330，332，349，376
大腿神経　230，231，233，271，273，274，275，276，280，328，330，331，375，376
　筋枝　376
　前皮枝　376
大腿深静脈　332，335
大腿深動脈　327，330，332，335
　貫通枝　328
大腿直筋　276，307，328，330，332，333
　直頭　284，295，297，299，301，334
　反転頭　295，301，334
大腿動脈　230，231，271，276，280，327，328，330，331，332，376
大腿二頭筋　293，311，317，326，337，338，339，340，344，345，346，347，351，352
　短頭　306，309，327，332
　長頭　289，290，295，301，326，327，332
大大脳静脈　60，68
大腿部膝屈筋　293，333
大腿方形筋　289，295，301，303，305，306，325，327，334

大腿輪　235
大腸　250
大殿筋　88, 95, 104, 105, 289, 290, 292, 293, 295, 305, 306, 324, 325, 326, 327
大転子　302, 304, 324, 325, 333, 335, 336
大動脈　103, 224, 245, 266, 270
大動脈弓　192, 194, 206, 207, 208, 214, 215, 219, 224, 226, 368, 369
大動脈腎動脈神経節　252, 274
大動脈前リンパ管　368
大動脈前リンパ節　245, 268, 274
大動脈大静脈間リンパ節　375
大動脈洞　197, 202, 203
大動脈分岐部　231
大動脈弁　184, 197, 201
　右半月弁　200, 201
　後半月弁　200, 201
　左半月弁　200, 201
大動脈傍リンパ管　368
大動脈傍リンパ節　245, 268, 270
大動脈裂孔　227
大内臓神経　101, 207, 221, 222, 223, 225
大内転筋　277, 290, 292, 295, 301, 305, 306, 309, 324, 326, 327, 332, 334, 345
大脳　64, 65
　側頭葉　43
大脳窩　27
大脳鎌　47, 59, 60, 61, 62
大脳脚　66, 70, 78, 79
大脳縦裂　62, 64
大脳上外側面　62
大脳半球　74, 76
大脳半球内側面　60
大脳面　25
大脳葉　63
大伏在静脈　230, 234, 280, 328, 332, 338, 347, 348, 349, 352, 354, 356, 357, 359, 376
大［腹膜］嚢　260
大網　230, 237, 238, 239, 241, 242, 243, 244, 247, 248, 249, 251, 254, 270
大腰筋　103, 261, 263, 267, 268, 270, 271, 273, 274, 276, 277, 280, 303, 305, 306, 331, 335, 375
大翼　1, 3, 4, 11, 12, 16, 43
　眼窩面　25
　側頭下面　25
　側頭下稜　25
　側頭面　25
　大脳面　25
大菱形筋　88, 105, 106, 107, 117, 138, 139, 140, 141
大菱形骨　128, 129, 168, 172, 173, 178
大菱形骨結節　128, 172
対輪　57
対輪脚
　下脚　57
　上脚　57
大弯　238, 241, 243, 244, 247, 251, 252, 372
多裂筋　107
短趾屈筋　319, 359, 360, 361, 362, 364
短趾伸筋　319, 321, 354, 355, 357, 358
短掌筋　163, 166, 167, 168, 169
短小指屈筋　130, 163, 166, 167, 168, 171
短小趾屈筋　319, 360, 361, 362

胆膵管膨大部　246
淡蒼球：古線条体　74, 75, 76, 77
短足底靱帯：底側踵立方靱帯　319, 359, 363
短頭（上腕二頭筋の）　135, 142, 147, 148, 151, 219
短頭（大腿二頭筋の）　306, 309, 327, 332
短橈側手根伸筋　130, 156, 159, 160, 161, 162, 168, 174, 175, 176, 177
短内転筋　276, 295, 301, 305, 306, 330, 334
胆嚢　240, 241, 243, 244, 246, 253, 255, 257, 372
胆嚢管　246, 247, 255, 256, 257
胆嚢頸　256
胆嚢静脈　256
胆嚢体　255, 256
胆嚢底　227, 245, 247, 254, 255, 256
胆嚢動脈　246, 255, 256
短腓骨筋　293, 317, 319, 351, 354, 355, 357, 358, 362, 363, 364
短腓骨筋腱溝　359
短母指外転筋　130, 163, 166, 167, 168, 169, 171
短母指屈筋　130, 163, 166, 167, 168, 169, 171
短母趾屈筋　319, 359, 360, 361, 362
短母指伸筋　127, 130, 161, 162, 163, 168, 174, 175, 176
短母趾伸筋　319, 358
短毛様体神経　53, 54, 81
短毛様体動脈　54

【チ】

恥丘　228, 229, 289
恥骨下枝　282, 291, 294, 296, 300, 336
恥骨筋　276, 280, 299, 301, 305, 306, 328, 330, 331, 334, 335, 376
恥骨筋線　302, 306
恥骨結合　96, 231, 260, 277, 279, 281, 282, 284, 285, 290, 291, 297, 336
恥骨結節　96, 231, 294, 296, 298, 300, 331, 336
恥骨後隙　285, 286
恥骨枝　235
恥骨櫛　96, 296, 298, 300, 336
恥骨櫛靱帯　271, 284, 299, 301
恥骨上枝　235, 294, 296, 336
恥骨上部：下腹部　227
恥骨体　235, 294, 296, 300
恥骨大腿靱帯　301, 333
恥骨直腸筋　281
恥骨尾骨筋　277
恥骨稜　296, 298, 300
腟　285, 286, 288, 373
腟円蓋
　後部　285, 286, 288, 373
　前部　285, 288, 373
腟口　289
腟前庭　285, 289, 290
腟動脈　283, 288
腟壁　286
肘　153, 154, 156, 157, 158, 161
中咽頭収縮筋　45, 47, 48
肘窩　160, 371
中隔縁柱：調節帯　199
中隔尖　200, 201

中隔乳頭筋　199
中間楔状骨　318, 320, 364
中間広筋　303, 305, 306, 307, 309, 330, 332
中間質：視床間橋　68, 70
中間神経　61, 85
肘関節　115, 156
中関節上腕靱帯　143
中間仙骨稜　94
中間足背枝　355
中間足背皮神経　346
中間大腿皮神経　376
中距骨関節面　321, 358
肘筋　123, 127, 139, 153, 156
中頸神経節　35, 37
中結腸静脈　258
中結腸動脈　248, 253, 258
中甲状腺静脈　29, 36
中硬膜静脈　59
中硬膜動脈　42, 47, 56, 59, 82
中硬膜動脈溝　8, 11, 17, 23, 24, 57
中指：第三指
　基節骨　129, 178
　中節骨　129, 178
　中節骨体　128
　中節骨底　128
　中節骨頭　128
　末節骨　129, 178
中耳　58, 84
中膝動脈　345
中斜角筋　29, 30, 31, 32, 34, 36, 37, 135, 181
中手骨底　164
中手骨頭　163, 164
中手指節関節　164, 172
　掌側靱帯　172
中踵骨関節面　321
中小脳脚　70, 83
中心［腋窩］リンパ節　185, 370
中心窩　53
中神経幹　147, 148
中心溝　62, 63, 68
中心後回　62, 63, 68
中心後溝　62, 63
中心前回　62, 63, 68
中心前溝　62, 63
中心臓静脈　197, 203
中心部（側脳室の）　72, 74, 76
中心傍枝（帯状溝の）　64
中心傍小葉　64
虫垂　242, 248, 261
虫垂間膜　242, 261
虫垂動脈　248, 261
肘正中皮静脈　157, 159, 371
中節骨（足の）　318
中節骨（手の）　129, 178
中節骨体（手の）　128
中節骨底（手の）　128, 164
中節骨頭　164
中節骨頭（手の）　128
中切歯　13, 16
中前頭回　63
中足骨　293
中足骨体　364
中足骨底　362, 364
中足趾節関節
　側副靱帯　363

中側頭回　63
中側頭動脈溝　23
中大脳動脈　51, 59, 66, 67, 68, 73
中直腸動脈　281, 283, 288
中手首皮線　163
中殿筋　289, 295, 303, 305, 324, 325, 335
中殿皮神経　324
肘頭　125, 126, 153, 154, 155, 156
肘頭窩　122, 123, 154, 156
中頭蓋窩　59
肘頭皮下包　153
中脳　59, 60
　下丘　68
　上丘　68
中脳蓋　70, 79
中脳水道　68, 70, 72, 77, 79
中脳被蓋　68, 70, 79
中鼻甲介　1, 16, 26, 55, 56, 79
中鼻道　21, 55
［虫部］小節　70
中葉（右肺の）　209, 210, 211, 212
中葉（胸腰筋膜の）　267
虫様筋　166, 171, 176, 360, 361, 362
肘リンパ節　371
蝶下顎筋　42, 43
蝶下顎靱帯　19, 56
腸間膜　241, 242, 248, 260, 261
腸間膜動脈間神経叢　274
長脚　57
鳥距　72, 74, 75
長胸神経　135, 144, 145, 146, 147, 148, 149
鳥距溝　64, 68
蝶形骨　12, 25
　後床突起　11, 59
　小翼　1, 3, 11, 12, 16, 43
　前床突起　11, 58, 59
　大翼　1, 3, 4, 11, 12, 16, 43
　大翼の側頭下面　7
　大翼の側頭下稜　9
蝶形骨角　24
蝶形骨棘　7, 9, 25, 37
蝶形骨体　3, 12, 25
蝶形骨洞　12, 17, 43, 47, 55, 60, 61, 79
蝶形骨洞口　25
蝶形［骨］頭頂静脈洞　59, 61
蝶形骨突起　22
蝶形骨吻　25
蝶形骨隆起　11, 25
腸脛靱帯　228, 293, 311, 313, 326, 327, 328, 331, 332, 337, 338, 340, 342, 346, 347, 376
蝶口蓋孔　12
蝶口蓋切痕　22
腸骨
　弓状線　282
腸骨窩　96, 284, 296, 298, 300
腸骨下腹神経　234, 263, 270, 271, 272, 273, 274, 275
腸骨筋　95, 230, 233, 271, 272, 273, 274, 275, 276, 277, 280, 297, 299, 303, 305, 306, 328, 330, 331, 333, 335, 375
腸骨結節　231, 294, 298, 300
腸骨鼠径神経　228, 229, 230, 234, 263, 270, 271, 272, 273, 274, 275, 278
腸骨粗面　296

腸骨体　294
腸骨大腿靱帯　295, 299, 301, 303, 333
　横部　305
腸骨尾骨筋　277
腸骨稜　88, 96, 104, 105, 231, 272, 274, 294, 296, 298, 324, 333, 334, 335
蝶篩陥凹　55
長趾屈筋　311, 319, 351, 353, 355, 356, 357, 358, 361, 362
長趾伸筋　313, 317, 319, 346, 347, 354, 355, 357, 358
長掌筋　159, 163, 167, 177
聴診三角　105, 106, 137
調節帯：中隔縁柱　199
長足底靱帯　319, 359, 363
腸恥包　333
腸恥隆起　294, 296, 298, 300, 333
長頭（上腕三頭筋の）　106, 107, 117, 119, 136, 137, 139, 140, 149, 150, 151, 152
長頭（上腕二頭筋の）　119, 133, 135, 142, 143, 151
長頭（大腿二頭筋の）　289, 326, 327, 332
長橈側手根伸筋　123, 130, 153, 156, 158, 159, 160, 161, 162, 168, 174, 175, 176, 177
長内転筋　276, 277, 280, 290, 292, 295, 301, 306, 328, 330, 331, 334, 335, 376
長腓骨筋　293, 313, 317, 319, 346, 347, 350, 351, 353, 354, 355, 357, 358, 362, 363
長腓骨筋腱溝　318, 363
長母指外転筋　127, 130, 159, 161, 162, 163, 168, 169, 170, 171, 175, 176
長母指屈筋　127, 130, 159, 160, 161, 167, 168, 169, 171
長母趾屈筋　317, 319, 351, 353, 355, 356, 357, 358, 359, 360, 361, 362, 363
長母趾屈筋腱溝（距骨の）　318, 321
長母趾屈筋腱溝（脛骨の）　359
長母趾屈筋腱溝（載距突起の）　359, 363
長母趾屈筋腱溝（踵骨の）　318, 321
長母指伸筋　127, 130, 161, 162, 163, 168, 174, 175, 176
長母趾伸筋　317, 319, 346, 354, 355, 357, 358, 359
長毛様体神経　53, 54, 81
腸腰筋　331, 333
　大腰筋　306
　腸骨筋　306
腸腰静脈　273, 375
腸腰靱帯　271, 275, 297, 299, 333, 334, 375
腸腰動脈　272, 273, 283
腸肋筋　105, 106, 107
直回　64, 66
直静脈洞　59, 60, 61
直腸　250, 260, 271, 274, 277, 280, 281, 282, 285, 288
直腸前立腺筋膜：直腸膀胱中隔　281
直腸膀胱窩　279
直頭　295, 297, 299, 301, 334
直動脈　248

【ツ】

椎間円板　60, 98, 99, 101, 102, 103, 223, 225, 260, 270, 276, 280
椎間関節　99, 102, 103, 113

椎間孔　99, 102
椎弓根（胸椎の）　90, 91, 99, 101, 102
椎弓根（頸椎の）　89, 90, 98
椎弓根（腰椎の）　92, 113
椎弓板（胸椎の）　90, 91, 223
椎弓板（頸椎の）　71, 89, 90, 113
椎弓板（仙椎の）　93
椎弓板（腰椎の）　92, 95, 103
椎孔（胸椎の）　90, 91
椎孔（頸椎の）　89, 90
椎孔（腰椎の）　92
椎骨静脈　36, 37, 217, 218, 220, 224, 367
椎骨動脈　37, 61, 62, 66, 67, 71, 78, 98, 99, 109, 110, 111, 208, 368
椎骨動脈溝　89
椎前葉（頸筋膜の）　367
椎体（胸椎の）　90, 91, 99, 100, 102, 222
椎体（頸椎の）　89, 90, 98, 99, 112
椎体（仙椎の）　93
椎体（腰椎の）　92, 95, 101, 102
ツチ骨　57, 58
　外側突起　57
蔓状静脈叢　278

【テ】

手　115
［前立腺］底　280
底側楔舟靱帯　363
底側骨間筋　361
底側踵舟靱帯：ばね靱帯　319, 321, 358, 359, 363
底側踵立方靱帯：短足底靱帯　319, 359, 363
底側中足靱帯　363
底側中足動脈　362
底側立方舟靱帯　363
底部　3, 27, 112
殿筋筋膜　324, 326
殿筋粗面　304, 306
殿溝　324
転子窩　302, 304
転子間線　302, 304, 333
転子間稜　304
　方形結節　302
殿裂　105, 324

【ト】

［精巣上体］頭　278
島［葉］　63, 74, 75, 76, 77
頭蓋　2, 3, 4, 5, 6, 7, 8, 9, 10, 11, 12, 16, 17
頭蓋窩　59
頭蓋冠　62
動眼神経［Ⅲ］　44, 52, 56, 59, 61, 66, 67, 70, 78, 80
　下枝　54
動眼神経副核　85
島限　63
瞳孔　51
豆鈎靱帯　130, 172
橈骨　154, 161, 173
　茎状突起　124, 126, 127, 129, 155, 163, 173, 177, 178
　前縁　155
　前面　155
橈骨窩　122, 123

橈骨頸　124, 126, 154, 155
橈骨手根関節　115, 177
橈骨神経　139, 143, 145, 147, 148, 150, 151, 152, 156, 219
　後前腕皮神経　139
　浅枝　158, 160, 174, 175
　浅枝の皮枝　174
橈骨神経溝　120
橈骨切痕　125, 126
橈骨粗面　124, 126, 154, 155
橈骨頭　124, 126, 127, 153, 154, 155, 156, 160
橈骨動脈　156, 158, 159, 160, 163, 166, 167, 168, 169, 170, 171, 176, 177
　浅掌枝　169, 170
　背側手根枝　174
橈骨輪状靱帯　156, 161
頭最長筋　10
導出静脈孔　11
豆状骨　128, 163, 167, 169, 170, 171, 172, 178
道上小窩　23
橈側滑液鞘　167
橈側手根屈筋　130, 159, 163, 166, 167, 168, 169, 170, 171, 177
橈側正中皮静脈　156, 157
橈側反回動脈　158, 160
橈側皮静脈　28, 132, 133, 134, 135, 139, 142, 151, 156, 157, 159, 174, 175, 217, 370, 371
島短回　63
豆中手靱帯　130, 172
島中心溝　63
島長回　63
頭長筋　10, 37, 71
頭頂結節　8, 14, 24
頭頂孔　7, 8, 24
頭頂後頭溝　62, 63, 64, 68
頭頂骨　4, 7, 8, 11, 17, 24
　乳突角　17
頭頂枝　5
頭頂切痕　23
頭頂内溝：頭頂間溝　63
頭頂葉　63
頭半棘筋　10, 109, 110, 111
頭板状筋　10, 29, 108, 109, 110, 111, 138, 139, 141
頭皮　5
洞房結節枝　197, 200, 202
動脈円錐　197, 198, 199, 201
動脈管索　193, 194, 207, 369
透明中隔　68, 72, 75, 76, 77
島［葉］　63, 74, 75, 76, 77
島輪状溝　63
トルコ鞍　14
　下垂体窩　4, 11, 12, 17, 25
鈍［角］縁枝：左縁枝　197, 198, 200, 202, 203

【ナ】

内陰部静脈　290, 326
内陰部動脈　281, 282, 283, 289, 290, 292, 326
内果　311, 314, 315, 348, 351, 354, 355, 356, 357, 359, 364
内果関節面　315
内果面　320

内胸静脈　36, 189, 207, 217, 218, 220, 366
内胸動脈　36, 37, 144, 145, 189, 192, 193, 194, 195, 205, 207, 208, 218, 219, 220, 225, 368
内頸静脈　29, 30, 31, 33, 35, 36, 37, 44, 45, 71, 135, 144, 147, 148, 190, 191, 217, 218, 219, 367, 368
内頸動脈　31, 32, 34, 35, 36, 37, 44, 45, 47, 51, 53, 56, 58, 59, 60, 61, 66, 67, 68, 71, 78
内頸動脈神経　37
内後頭隆起　11, 17, 27
内後頭稜　27
内枝　28, 29, 31, 32, 33, 34, 35, 45, 47, 49, 50, 84
内耳
　蝸牛　58
　前庭　58
内子宮口　285
内耳神経：前庭蝸牛神経［Ⅷ］　58, 59, 61, 66, 70, 78, 83
内耳道　3, 11, 17, 23, 58, 71, 83
内精筋膜　278
内舌筋　85
内側縁（脛骨）　310, 312
内側縁（肩甲骨）　88, 116, 136, 138, 139, 140, 141, 186
内側顆（脛骨の）　310, 311, 312, 339, 340, 343
内側顆（大腿骨の）　304, 307, 308, 339, 341, 343, 347, 351
内側顆間結節　310, 312, 343
内側下膝動脈　345, 353
内側顆上線　306, 308
内側顆上稜　122
内側眼瞼靱帯　38, 51
内側胸筋神経　135, 144, 145, 147, 148, 149
内側距踵靱帯　321
内側楔状骨　318, 320, 359, 363, 364
内側結節　318, 320, 364
内側広筋　303, 305, 306, 307, 309, 311, 313, 328, 330, 332, 335, 337, 338
内側臍索　232, 235, 281, 285, 373
内側臍ヒダ　233, 235
内側膝蓋支帯　332
内側膝状体　70, 79
内側手根側副靱帯　172
内側上顆　122, 126, 153, 154, 156, 157, 159, 160, 308, 343, 371
内側踵骨枝　348, 355, 356
内側上膝動脈　345, 353
内側上腕筋間中隔　151
内側上腕皮神経　149, 150, 157, 158, 371
内側神経束　145, 150, 219, 371
内側靱帯：三角靱帯　311, 314, 358, 359, 363
　脛踵部　321, 359
　後脛距部　359
内側前頭回　64
内側前腕皮神経　144, 145, 147, 148, 149, 150, 151, 156, 157, 371
内側足底神経　358, 361, 362
　固有底側趾神経　360
　総底側趾神経　361
内側足底動脈　359, 361, 362

内側足背皮神経　346, 355
内側側副靱帯　309, 311, 313, 339, 340, 341, 342, 347, 351
　横走靱帯：斜束　154
　後斜走靱帯：後束　154
　上束：前斜走靱帯　154
内側足根動脈　358
内側大腿回旋静脈　335
内側大腿回旋動脈　327, 330, 335
内側大腿皮神経　338
内側中葉区　210, 211, 212
内側中葉枝　209
内側直筋　44, 51, 52, 53, 80
内側頭（上腕三頭筋の）　121, 123, 150, 156
内側頭（腓腹筋の）　309, 338, 344, 345, 347, 350, 351, 352
内側肺底区　210, 211, 212, 213
内側肺底枝　209
内側板　7, 9, 12, 17, 25
内側半月　339, 340, 341, 342, 343
　後角　313, 340
　前角　313, 340
内側腓腹皮神経　344, 352
内側面（下鼻甲介の）　26
内側面（脛骨の）　310, 311, 312, 314, 347, 355
内側面（尺骨の）　125
内側面（踵骨の）　320
内側面（腓骨の）　316
内側面（披裂軟骨の）　50
内側翼突筋　19, 42, 43, 44, 47, 56
　深頭　10
　浅頭　10
内側翼突筋神経　56
内側隆起　71, 77
内側稜　316
内大脳静脈　76
内腸骨静脈　288
内腸骨動脈　271, 272, 280, 281, 282, 283, 288
　後幹　282, 283
　前幹　282, 283
内転筋群　293
内転筋結節　304, 308
内転筋腱裂孔　327, 332
内尿道口　280, 281
内腹斜筋　229, 230, 232, 234, 267, 275, 280, 299, 301
　腱膜　229
　腱膜の後葉　228
　腱膜の前葉　228, 229
内閉鎖筋　276, 277, 282, 284, 289, 297, 303, 305, 325, 333
内包　76, 77
内包膝　75
［内包］後脚　74, 75, 76
［内包］前脚　74, 75, 76
内肋間筋　145, 181, 187, 188, 189
内肋間膜　189
長いヒモ　167
中指：第三指
　基節骨　129, 178
　中節骨　129, 178
　中節骨体　128
　中節骨底　128
　中節骨頭　128

末節骨　129, 178
ナジオン　1, 4
軟口蓋　43, 47, 60, 84

【ニ】

肉様膜　278
二頭筋橈骨包　154
二腹筋窩　18
二分靱帯
　踵舟靱帯　319, 321, 358, 359
　踵立方靱帯　319, 321, 359
乳管　185
乳管洞　185
乳歯
　犬歯　13
　側切歯　13
　第一臼歯　13
　第二臼歯　13
　中切歯　13
乳腺後隙　185
乳頭　132, 184, 185
乳頭体　66, 68, 70, 79
乳頭突起　92
乳突縁　27
乳突角　17, 24
乳突孔　9
乳突小管　23
乳突切痕　7, 9, 23
乳突洞　57, 58
乳突洞口　57, 58
乳突蜂巣　57, 58
乳び槽　368, 372
乳房　185
乳房脂肪体　185
乳房堤靱帯　185
乳様突起　3, 4, 7, 9, 16, 23, 28, 37, 57, 84
乳輪　132, 184
乳輪腺　184
尿管　103, 245, 261, 264, 265, 267, 268, 269, 270, 271, 272, 273, 274, 280, 281, 283, 285, 288, 373, 375
尿管口　280, 281
尿生殖隔膜　281
尿道　286, 291
　海綿体部　279, 281
　隔膜部　281
　前立腺部　279, 281
尿道海綿体　291, 292
尿道球　281
尿道球動脈　292
尿膜管　232

【ノ】

脳幹　70, 71
脳弓　73, 77
脳弓脚　75
脳弓体　68, 74, 76
脳弓柱　68
　前部　74
脳硬膜　61
脳室　72, 73
[側] 脳室房　72
囊状陥凹　172, 173
脳神経　80
脳底動脈　60, 62, 66, 68, 78, 84
　橋枝　67

脳梁　60, 74, 76, 77
　小鉗子　74
脳梁幹　68
脳梁膝　68, 75
脳梁吻　68
脳梁放線
　小鉗子　75
　大鉗子　75
　壁板　73, 75, 77
脳梁膨大　64, 68, 70, 75, 79

【ハ】

肺　84
肺間膜　216
肺胸膜：臓側胸膜　219
肺根　204, 206, 214
肺静脈　190
肺舌静脈
　下舌枝　213
　上舌枝　213
肺尖　36, 216, 217
肺尖区　210, 211, 212
肺尖後区　210, 211, 213
肺尖後枝　209, 213
肺尖後静脈　213
肺尖枝　209
背側結節　124, 126, 155
背側骨間筋　171, 176, 364
背側指静脈　174
背側指動脈　174
背側趾動脈　358
背側手根枝　174
背側手根動脈網　174, 176
背側中手動脈　174
背側橈骨手根靱帯　173
肺動脈 [幹]　192, 193, 194, 195, 196, 197, 198, 199, 200, 201, 203, 208, 214, 215, 369
肺動脈弁　184, 200, 201
　右半月弁　201
　左半月弁　201
　前半月弁　201
肺門リンパ節：気管支肺リンパ節　216
歯茎　43
薄筋　276, 277, 289, 290, 292, 295, 301, 311, 313, 324, 327, 328, 330, 332, 334, 338, 344, 345, 347, 351, 352
白交通枝　221
白線　193, 228, 229, 230
薄束結節　71
白膜　278, 279
ばね靱帯：底側踵舟靱帯　321, 358
馬尾　101, 260, 270
ハムストリング　293, 333
破裂孔　9, 11
反回枝 (深腓骨神経の)　346
反回枝 (正中神経の)　166, 167, 168, 169
反回枝 (総腓骨神経の)　346
反回神経　35, 37, 47, 49, 84, 190, 191, 194, 195, 207, 214, 218, 220, 369
　神経枝　50
板間層　11
半規管　83
半奇静脈　207, 208, 224, 225, 270
半棘筋　107
半月神経節　80
半月線　228, 230, 232

半月裂孔　12, 55
半腱様筋　289, 290, 295, 301, 311, 313, 324, 326, 327, 332, 337, 338, 340, 344, 345, 347, 351, 352
反転頭　295, 301, 334
半膜様筋　289, 295, 301, 311, 313, 327, 332, 337, 340, 341, 342, 344, 345, 347, 351, 352
半膜様筋の滑液包　342

【ヒ】

[精巣上体] 尾　278
鼻咽頭：[咽頭] 鼻部　79
被殻　74, 75, 76, 77
皮下組織　5
眉弓　20
脾曲：左結腸曲　250, 259, 372
鼻棘　12, 20
鼻筋　2, 6, 39
鼻腔　12, 55
鼻腔面　21
鼻甲介稜　21, 22
腓骨　293, 311, 315, 316, 317, 364
　外果　357, 364
　外果関節面　316
　外側面　311
　後面　351, 352, 353
　前縁　311
尾骨　87, 88, 94, 96, 260, 277, 279, 289, 324, 334
鼻骨　1, 4, 12, 17, 21
尾骨角　94
腓骨関節面　310, 312
[坐骨] 尾骨筋　95, 276, 277, 282, 297
尾骨筋　282
腓骨筋滑車　320
腓骨頸　311, 316
腓骨静脈　352
腓骨切痕　314
腓骨頭　315, 316, 337, 338, 342, 343, 346, 347
腓骨頭関節面　315, 316
腓骨頭尖　315, 316, 339, 343
腓骨動脈　353
　貫通枝　357
鼻根　38
鼻根筋　2, 6, 39
肘　153, 154, 156, 157, 158, 161
皮枝　108, 110, 111, 174
[腎] 皮質　265
尾状核　77
尾状核体　68, 74, 76
尾状核頭　74, 75, 76
尾状核尾　76
尾状突起　255, 256
脾静脈　245, 258, 259, 260, 270, 372
尾状葉　244, 246, 247, 251, 255, 256
鼻唇溝　38
脾腎ヒダ　260
鼻切痕　21
鼻尖　38
鼻前庭　55
脾臓　84, 245, 249, 260, 270, 372
　下縁　259
　下極　251
　上縁　259
鼻中隔　1, 3, 16, 38, 43, 56, 60, 61

脾動脈　244, 245, 258, 259, 260, 267, 268, 274, 372
鼻背　38
鼻背動脈　51
皮膚　5
［咽頭］鼻部：鼻咽頭　60, 79
腓腹　350, 351, 352
腓腹筋　293, 353
　外側頭　309, 337, 338, 341, 344, 345, 346, 347, 350, 351, 352
　内側頭　309, 338, 344, 345, 347, 350, 351, 352
腓腹神経　344, 345, 348, 350, 352, 355, 357, 358
鼻毛様体神経　44, 51, 52, 53, 54, 81
脾門　372
鼻翼　38
ヒラメ筋　311, 313, 317, 338, 341, 345, 347, 350, 351, 352, 353, 355, 359
ヒラメ筋線　310, 312
鼻稜　21, 22
鼻涙管　12, 51, 55
披裂関節面　48
披裂喉頭蓋筋　49
披裂喉頭蓋ヒダ　49, 50
披裂軟骨　48
　前外側面　50
　内側面　50
［披裂軟骨］尖　48, 50

【フ】

ファベラ　343
副-腎動脈　266
副横隔神経　36
腹横筋　229, 232, 233, 249, 267, 270, 275, 297, 299, 301
腹腔神経節　84, 252, 267, 274
腹腔神経叢　267
腹腔動脈　224, 244, 246, 252, 258, 260, 264, 266, 267, 268, 272, 274
腹腔リンパ節　244, 274
伏在枝　332
伏在神経　328, 330, 332, 338, 347, 348, 352, 356, 357, 376
　膝蓋下枝　338, 347
伏在裂孔　234
副耳下腺　39
副尺側皮静脈　157
副腎　252, 260, 264, 267, 268, 270, 272, 273, 274
副腎圧痕　255
副神経［XI］　28, 29, 30, 31, 32, 35, 44, 45, 61, 70, 85, 134
　延髄根　71
　脊髄根　37, 61, 66, 67, 71, 78, 84, 100, 138, 147, 148
副腎動脈　264
副膵管　257
腹前皮枝　228, 229, 230
腹側淡蒼球　77
腹側傍片葉：小脳扁桃　66
腹大動脈　249, 260, 264, 267, 268, 270, 271, 272, 274
腹大動脈神経叢　268, 270, 271
腹直筋　183, 191, 193, 228, 229, 230, 232, 234, 235, 237, 238, 239, 241, 242, 271, 279, 285, 286, 299, 301, 373, 375

腱画　228
腹直筋鞘　229, 301
　弓状線　375
　後葉　229, 232, 233
　前葉　133, 228, 229, 230, 299
副突起　92
副半奇静脈　224
副鼻腔　999
　上顎洞　43
腹部（大胸筋の）　133, 228
副閉鎖静脈　281
副閉鎖動脈　233
腹膜　103, 236, 241, 243, 260, 261, 267, 288
　直腸膀胱窩　279
腹膜外脂肪　103
腹膜外組織　263
腹膜垂　237, 238, 239, 241, 242
プテリオン　4, 17
ブレグマ　8
分界溝　49
分界稜　199, 201
噴門　372

【ヘ】

閉鎖筋膜　277, 282, 284, 289
閉鎖孔　96, 284, 294, 296, 300, 336
閉鎖溝　294, 296, 300
閉鎖静脈　235, 271, 283, 285, 288, 333, 373
閉鎖神経　235, 271, 273, 274, 275, 276, 280, 281, 282, 283, 284, 285, 288, 331, 373
　後枝　333
　前枝　330, 333
閉鎖動脈　235, 271, 280, 281, 282, 283, 285, 288, 333, 373
閉鎖膜　284
閉鎖稜　294, 300
壁側胸膜　193, 194, 195, 218, 219, 369
壁側板（漿膜性心膜の）　191, 192, 193, 194
壁側板（精巣鞘膜の）　278, 279
壁側腹膜　233, 237, 241, 242, 247, 279
壁板（脳梁放線の）　73, 75, 77
臍　228, 229, 230, 232
弁蓋部：前頭弁蓋　63
片葉　66, 70

【ホ】

方形回内筋　127, 159, 160, 171
方形結節　302, 304
方形葉　240, 244, 255, 256
膀胱　232, 233, 235, 260, 269, 271, 279, 281, 283, 286, 287, 375
縫工筋　230, 276, 277, 295, 297, 301, 311, 313, 328, 330, 331, 332, 338, 347, 351, 352, 376
縫工筋下筋膜　328
膀胱頸　285, 373
膀胱三角　280, 281, 285, 286, 373
膀胱子宮窩　260, 285, 286, 287, 288, 373
膀胱静脈叢　281
膀胱底　281
房室結節枝　197, 200, 202, 203
房室溝：冠状溝　191
紡錘状回：外側後頭側頭回　64

［会陰］縫線　290, 291
放線状肋骨頭靱帯　223
包皮　278
母指：第一指　165, 167
　基節骨　128, 129, 178
　末節骨　128, 129, 178
母趾：第一趾
　基節骨　318
　末節骨　318
母趾外転筋　319, 355, 358, 359, 360, 361, 362, 364
母指球　163
母指主動脈　167, 169, 170
母指主動脈の枝　176
母指対立筋　130, 171
母指内転筋　163, 166, 168, 171, 176
　横頭　130, 171
　斜頭　130, 171
母趾内転筋　319
　横頭　361, 362
　斜頭　361, 362

【マ】

膜性部　200
末節骨（足の）　318, 359
末節骨（手の）　128, 129, 178
末節骨底（手の）　164

【ミ】

眉間　1, 4, 20, 38
短いヒモ　167
脈絡糸球　72, 77
脈絡叢　66, 68, 71, 72, 73, 74
脈絡裂　76

【ム】

無漿膜野　255

【メ】

迷走神経［X］　29, 30, 34, 35, 36, 37, 45, 47, 61, 70, 71, 78, 84, 190, 191, 192, 193, 194, 195, 204, 205, 206, 207, 214, 218, 219, 220, 367, 368
　咽頭枝　45
　下頸心臓枝　205
　下神経節　37, 45
　頸動脈小体枝　45
　上咽頭枝　47
　上喉頭神経　45
迷走神経三角：灰白翼　71

【モ】

盲孔　11, 20, 49
盲腸　230, 242, 248, 250, 260, 261
盲腸後陥凹　261
網嚢　241, 253, 260
網嚢孔　240, 243, 244
網膜中心静脈
　下内側静脈　53
　上外側静脈　53
網膜中心動脈　52
　下内側動脈　53
　上外側動脈　53
毛様体神経節　44, 53, 54, 80, 81, 82
毛様体動脈　53
［肝］門脈　246, 255, 256, 258
　右枝　258

左枝　244, 258

【ヤ】

薬指：第四指　176
　基節骨　128
　基節骨底　128
　基節骨頭　128
　末節骨　128

【ユ】

有郭乳頭　49
有鈎骨　128, 129, 168, 173, 177, 178
有鈎骨鈎　128, 163, 168, 172, 178
有頭骨　128, 129, 168, 173, 177, 178
有頭骨頭　172
幽門　246
幽門管　251, 252
幽門洞　251, 252, 253
幽門洞枝　244
幽門平面　227
指の滑液鞘　167
指の腱鞘　168
指（趾）の線維鞘　360, 361
指の線維鞘　167, 171

【ヨ】

葉気管支　209
腰筋筋膜　267
腰三角　105, 106
腰神経
　後枝　106
腰神経叢　275
腰仙骨神経幹　273, 275, 276, 282, 284, 333
腰椎　87
　肋骨突起　269
腰内臓神経　274
腰方形筋　181, 267, 270, 271, 273, 274, 275, 297, 299, 375
翼口蓋窩　7
翼口蓋神経節　44, 55, 81, 82
翼上顎裂　7
翼状腱　176
翼状靱帯　98
翼状突起　25
　外側板　7, 9, 12, 17, 25, 44
　内側板　7, 9, 12, 17, 25
翼突下顎縫線　19
翼突管　25
翼突管神経　44, 55
翼突筋窩　18
翼突筋枝（顎動脈の）　43
翼突筋神経　81
翼突鈎　7, 9, 12, 17, 25
翼突切痕　25

【ラ】

ラムダ　7, 8
ラムダ縁　27
ラムダ［状］縫合　3, 4, 7, 8, 14, 17
卵円窩　199
卵円窩縁　199
卵円孔　9, 11, 25, 58, 81, 85
卵管　286, 373
卵管間膜　287

卵管峡部　287
卵管采　288
卵管端　287
卵管膨大部　287, 288
卵管漏斗　287
卵形嚢　83
卵巣　286
　子宮端　287
　卵管端　287
卵巣間膜　287
卵巣静脈　375
卵巣提靱帯：卵巣提索　287

【リ】

梨状陥凹　47, 226
梨状筋　95, 276, 277, 282, 284, 289, 295, 303, 305, 325, 333
立方骨　318, 320, 362, 364
　長腓骨筋腱溝　318, 363
立方骨粗面　318
隆椎：第七頸椎　90
　棘突起　71, 99, 100, 113
　椎体　99
菱形窩：第四脳室底　71, 76
菱形筋　104
菱形靱帯　117, 119, 142
菱形靱帯線　118
鱗縁　24
輪状咽頭部　45, 47
輪状甲状関節　49
輪状甲状筋　30, 36, 48, 49
輪状甲状枝　34
輪状軟骨　48, 217
　甲状関節面　50
輪状軟骨弓　28, 36, 48, 49, 50, 190, 192, 193, 218
輪状軟骨板　48, 50
輪状ヒダ　250, 260
輪状披裂関節　50
輪帯　335, 336
リンパ管　230, 268, 367, 370, 371, 376
リンパ節　367, 371, 376
鱗部　4, 9, 11, 17, 23

【ル】

涙管カテーテル　51
涙丘　51
涙骨　1, 4, 12, 21
涙骨鈎　21
涙骨突起　26
涙小管　44, 51
涙腺　51, 52, 53, 54
涙腺窩　20
涙腺神経　44, 51, 52, 53, 54, 81
涙腺動脈　51, 53, 54
涙点　51
涙乳頭　51
涙嚢　51
涙嚢窩　4, 12
涙嚢溝　21

【レ】

裂孔靱帯　235, 271, 277, 282, 284, 299, 301
レンズ核

古線条体：淡蒼球　74, 76
被殻　74, 75, 76

【ロ】

漏斗陥凹　68, 72
肋横突関節　223
肋横突靱帯　181, 223
肋下筋　222
肋下静脈　224, 263
肋下神経　245, 263, 268, 273, 375
　腹前皮枝　230
肋下動脈　224, 263
肋間隙　222, 369
肋頸動脈　207
肋鎖靱帯　119, 181
肋鎖靱帯圧痕　118
肋間筋　181
肋間静脈　194, 195, 221, 369
肋間上腕神経　135, 144, 145, 146, 149, 150, 370, 371
肋間神経　194, 195, 221, 223
肋間動脈　194, 195, 221
肋間膜　181
肋骨　179, 208, 369
肋骨横隔洞　191, 192, 193, 225, 259, 260, 263
肋骨角　181
肋骨弓　179, 184, 186, 270
肋骨胸膜　204
肋骨挙筋　181
肋骨頸　181, 223
肋骨結節　181
肋骨結節関節面　223
肋骨溝　181
肋骨縦隔洞　191, 192, 193, 225
肋骨切痕　182
肋骨体　181
肋骨頭　181
肋骨頭関節　98, 223
肋骨頭関節面　181
肋骨突起　92, 103, 113, 263, 269, 334, 336
肋骨傍リンパ節　185
肋骨肋軟骨連結　183

【ワ】

腕神経叢　36, 145, 146, 147, 148, 149, 150, 370
　外側神経束　144, 145, 146, 371
　下神経幹　147, 148
　後神経束　145, 146
　根　30, 33
　上神経幹　28, 31, 32, 37, 147, 148, 190, 191, 192, 193, 194, 218, 219
　神経幹　135
　神経束　142
　中神経幹　147, 148
　内側神経束　145, 219, 371
腕橈骨筋　123, 127, 133, 139, 151, 153, 156, 157, 158, 159, 160, 162, 168, 176
腕頭静脈　220, 368
腕頭動脈　36, 37, 190, 191, 192, 193, 194, 195, 208, 214, 218, 219, 220, 224, 366

欧文索引

【数字】

1st anterior sacral foramen　95
1st cervical nerve　34, 99
1st cervical vertebra　87
1st coccygeal vertebra　94, 95, 336
1st costal cartilage　183
1st costal notch　182
1st dorsal interosseous　130, 162, 163, 168, 174, 176, 319, 358, 362
1st dorsal metacarpal artery　174, 176
1st dorsal metatarsal artery　358
1st incisor : Central incisor　13, 16
1st intercostal nerve　220
1st lumbar nerve　102, 268, 270
1st lumbar vertebra　102
1st lumbrical　167, 168, 169, 171, 362
1st metacarpal bone　173
1st metatarsal bone　320, 359, 364
1st metatarsophalangeal joint　358, 359
1st molar tooth　13
1st palmar interosseous　130
1st perforating artery　327
1st plantar interosseous　319, 362
1st posterior sacral foramen　95
1st premolar tooth　13
1st rib　36, 99, 113, 135, 148, 190, 191, 192, 193, 205, 218, 219, 220
1st sternocostal joint　183
1st tarsometatarsal joint　359
1st thoracic vertebra　183
2nd anterior sacral foramen　94
2nd cervical vertebra　87, 98, 110, 111
2nd costal cartilage　183, 184, 187, 217
2nd costal notch　182
2nd dorsal interosseous　130, 162, 174, 176, 319, 358, 362
2nd dorsal metacarpal artery　176
2nd dorsal metatarsal artery　358
2nd incisor : Lateral incisor　13
2nd intercostal nerve　220
2nd lumbrical　168, 362
2nd molar tooth　13
2nd palmar interosseous　130
2nd perforating artery　327
2nd plantar interosseous　319, 362
2nd premolar tooth　13
2nd rib　179, 183, 187, 189, 220
2nd sacral nerve　284
2nd sacral vertebra　101
2nd sternocostal joint　183
2nd toe [II]
　Distal phalanx　318
　Middle phalanx　318
　Proximal phalanx　318
3rd cervical vertebra　110, 111
3rd costal cartilage　184
3rd costal notch　182
3rd dorsal interosseous　130, 162, 174, 319, 358, 362
3rd lumbar artery　274
3rd lumbrical　362
3rd metacarpal bone　129
3rd molar tooth　7, 13, 21
3rd occipital nerve　108, 109, 110, 111
3rd palmar interosseous　130
3rd perforating artery　327
3rd plantar interosseous　319, 362
3rd posterior sacral foramen　94
3rd sacral nerve　284
3rd thoracic nerve　144, 145, 146
3rd thoracic vertebra　214
3rd ventricle　72, 74, 76, 77
　Infundibular recess　72
　Supra-optic recess　72
　Suprapineal recess　72
4th cervical vertebra　111
4th costal cartilage　184, 217
4th costal notch　182
4th dorsal interosseous　130, 162, 174, 319, 358, 362
4th lumbar artery　271, 274
4th lumbrical　169, 362
4th palmar interosseous　130
4th perforating artery　327
4th posterior intercostal artery　207
4th rib　188
4th sacral nerve　284
4th thoracic nerve　144
4th ventricle　60, 68, 70, 72
　Medial eminence　77
　Median sulcus　77
5th cervical vertebra　111
5th costal notch　182
5th intercostal nerve　188
5th intercostal space　186
5th lumbar vertebra　285
5th metacarpal bone　129, 173
5th posterior intercostal artery　188
5th posterior intercostal vein　188, 207
5th rib　188
5th sacral nerve　284
6th costal cartilage　184, 187
6th costal notch　182
6th intercostal nerve　188
6th posterior intercostal artery　204, 205, 224
6th posterior intercostal vein　204, 205, 224
6th rib　188, 189
7th costal cartilage　225
7th costal notch　182
7th rib　188
8th cervical nerve　99
8th costal cartilage
　Costal arch　184
8th intercostal nerve　222
　Anterior abdominal cutaneous branch　228
8th posterior intercostal artery　222
8th posterior intercostal vein　222
8th rib　188, 189, 222, 229
9th rib　260
10th intercostal nerve
　Anterior abdominal cutaneous branch　228, 229
10th rib　260
11th intercostal nerve
　Anterior abdominal cutaneous branch　230
11th rib　263
12th rib　102, 179, 189, 263

【A】

Abdominal aorta　249, 260, 264, 267, 268, 270, 271, 272, 274
Abdominal aortic plexus　268, 270, 271
Abdominal part　133, 228
Abducent nerve [VI]　52, 53, 54, 55, 56, 58, 59, 61, 66, 67, 70, 78, 80, 83
Abductor digiti minimi　130, 162, 163, 166, 167, 168, 169, 171, 174, 176, 319, 355, 359, 360, 361, 362, 364
Abductor hallucis　319, 355, 358, 359, 360, 361, 362, 364
Abductor pollicis brevis　130, 163, 166, 167, 168, 169, 171
Abductor pollicis longus　127, 130, 159, 161, 162, 163, 168, 169, 170, 171, 175, 176
Accessory basilic vein　157
Accessory hemi-azygos vein　224
Accessory nerve [XI]　28, 29, 30, 31, 32, 35, 44, 45, 61, 70, 85, 134
　Cranial root　71
　Spinal root　37, 61, 66, 67, 71, 78, 84, 100, 138, 147, 148
Accessory nuclei of oculomotor nerve　85
Accessory obturator artery　233
Accessory obturator vein　281
Accessory pancreatic duct　257
Accessory parotid gland　39
Accessory phrenic nerve　36
Accessory process　92
Accessory renal artery　266
Acetabular fossa　334
Acetabular labrum　334, 335
Acetabular margin　294, 300, 335, 336

Acetabular notch   294, 300
Acetabulum   96, 294, 300, 335
Achilles tendon   319, 321, 348, 350, 351, 352, 353, 354, 355, 356, 357, 358, 359
Acromial angle   116
Acromial branch   148
Acromial end   118, 132, 134, 136
　Acromial facet   118
Acromial facet   118
Acromioclavicular joint   118, 132, 134, 136, 142, 143, 184
　Articular disc   143
Acromion   116, 118, 132, 134, 136, 137, 138, 139, 140, 141, 142, 143, 179
Adductor brevis   276, 295, 301, 305, 306, 330, 334
Adductor hallucis   319
　Oblique head   361, 362
　Transverse head   361, 362
Adductor hiatus   327, 332
Adductor longus   276, 277, 280, 290, 292, 295, 301, 306, 328, 330, 331, 334, 335, 376
Adductor magnus   277, 290, 292, 295, 301, 305, 306, 309, 324, 326, 327, 332, 334, 345
Adductor minimus   327
Adductor muscles   293
Adductor pollicis   163, 166, 168, 171, 176
　Oblique head   130, 171
　Transverse head   130, 171
Adductor tubercle   304, 308
Aditus to mastoid antrum   57, 58
Adrenal gland   252, 260, 264, 267, 268, 270, 272, 273, 274
Ala of crista galli   26
Ala of nose   38
Ala of vomer   25
Alar ligament   98
Alveolar part   18
Alveolar process   17, 21
Alveolar ridge   43
Ambient cistern   60
Ampulla of uterine tube   287, 288
Anal canal   279, 281
Anatomical neck   120
Anatomical snuffbox   163
Anconeus   123, 127, 139, 153, 156
Angle of Louis   183, 187, 189
Angle of mandible   13, 17, 18, 28, 38
Angle of mouth   38
Angle of rib   181
Angular gyrus   63
Ankle joint
　Tibiotalar part   359
Anococcygeal body   289, 291, 292
Anococcygeal ligament   289, 291, 292
Ansa cervicalis   31, 85, 147, 148
　Inferior root   29, 31, 33
　Superior root   29, 31, 32, 33, 35
Ansa subclavia   36, 207, 368
Anterior abdominal cutaneous branch   228, 229, 230
Anterior arch   55, 60, 79, 89, 112, 113
Anterior basal segment   210, 211, 212, 213
Anterior basal segmental bronchus   209

Anterior belly   19, 29, 30, 32, 33, 34, 35, 43
Anterior border   18, 28, 38, 124, 125, 155, 216, 310, 311, 312, 314, 316
Anterior branch   160, 265, 330, 333, 244
Anterior cardiac vein   196
Anterior cerebral artery   47, 51, 59, 60, 66, 67, 68, 73
Anterior choroidal artery   67, 73
Anterior circumflex humeral artery   135, 147, 148
Anterior clinoid process   11, 25, 58, 59
Anterior column   74
Anterior commissure   68, 75, 289
Anterior communicating artery   51, 67
Anterior cranial fossa   59
Anterior cruciate ligament   309, 313, 339, 340, 341, 342
Anterior cusp   199, 200, 201
Anterior cutaneous branches   376
Anterior deep temporal artery   42
Anterior end   26
Anterior ethmoidal artery   51, 52, 53
Anterior ethmoidal cells   55
Anterior ethmoidal foramen   12, 20
Anterior ethmoidal nerve   51, 52, 53, 81
Anterior ethmoidal sulcus   26
Anterior facet for calcaneus   321
Anterior fontanelle   14
Anterior gluteal line   294
Anterior horn   72, 74, 75, 76, 313, 340
Anterior inferior cerebellar artery   66, 67
Anterior inferior iliac spine   96, 284, 294, 296, 298, 300, 333
Anterior inferior segmental artery   265
Anterior intercondylar area   312
Anterior intercostal vein   189
Anterior interosseous artery   158, 160, 176
Anterior interosseous nerve   160
Anterior interventricular branch   191, 196, 197, 198, 200, 202, 203
Anterior jugular vein   28, 32, 33
Anterior lacrimal crest   4, 12, 21
Anterior lateral malleolar artery   357
Anterior layer   103, 133, 228, 229, 230, 267, 299
Anterior layer of aponeurosis   228, 229
Anterior ligament of fibular head   346
Anterior limb   74, 75, 76
Anterior lobe   60
Anterior lobe of cerebellum   70
Anterior longitudinal ligament   37, 98, 102, 274, 275, 284
Anterior meniscofemoral ligament   339
Anterior nasal spine   1, 4, 21
Anterior nodes   79, 370
Anterior oblique ligament   154
Anterior oblique line   124
Anterior papillary muscle   199, 200
Anterior paracentral gyrus   64
Anterior perforated substance   66, 79
Anterior ramus   63
Anterior scalene   29, 30, 31, 32, 33, 35, 36, 37, 71, 98, 144, 145, 146, 181, 192, 193, 194, 195, 218, 367
Anterior segment   210, 211, 212, 213

Anterior segmental bronchus   209, 213
Anterior semicircular canal   14, 57, 58
Anterior semilunar cusp   201
Anterior spinal artery   67, 100, 224
Anterior spinal veins   100
Anterior superior iliac spine   96, 231, 276, 277, 284, 294, 296, 298, 300, 331, 333, 336
Anterior superior segmental artery   265
Anterior surface   21, 122, 124, 125, 155
Anterior talar articular surface   321, 358
Anterior talofibular ligament   317, 359
Anterior tibial artery   345, 346, 353, 357
　Muscular branches   353
Anterior tibial recurrent artery   346
Anterior tibial recurrent vein   346
Anterior tibial vein   349, 357
Anterior trunk   282, 283
Anterior tubercle   89, 90, 98, 99
Anterior vagal trunk   222, 225, 251, 267, 372
Anterior vein   213
Anterolateral surface   50
Antihelix   57
　Lower crus   57
　Upper crus   57
Antitragus   57
Antral branch   244
Antrum   72
Anular ligament of radius   156, 161
Anulus fibrosus   103, 279
Anus   290, 326
Aorta   103, 245, 266, 270
Aortic arch   192, 194, 206, 207, 208, 214, 215, 219, 224, 226, 368, 369
Aortic bifurcation   231
Aortic hiatus   227
Aortic sinus   197, 202, 203
Aortic valve   184, 197
　Left coronary cusp   200, 201
　Left semilunar cusp   200, 201
　Noncoronary cusp   200, 201
　Posterior semilunar cusp   200, 201
　Right coronary cusp   200, 201
　Right semilunar cusp   200, 201
Aorticorenal ganglia   252, 274
Aortocaval node   375
Apex of arytenoid cartilage   48, 50
Apex of head of fibula   315, 316, 339, 343
Apex of heart   184, 198, 208, 216, 227
Apex of lung   36, 216, 217
Apex of nose   38
Apex of patella   307, 341
Apex of petrous part   9
Apex of sacrum   94
Apical nodes   185
　Infraclavicular nodes   370
Apical segment   210, 211, 212
Apical segmental bronchus   209
Apicoposterior segment   210, 211, 213
Apicoposterior segmental bronchus   209, 213
Apicoposterior vein   213
Aponeurosis   5, 51, 228, 229, 230, 234, 275, 280, 328, 342, 350
Appendicular artery   248, 261

Appendix　　242, 248, 261
Appendix of epididymis　　278
Aqueduct of midbrain　　68, 72, 77, 79
Aqueduct of Sylvius　　70
Aqueduct of vestibule　　23
Arachnoid granulations　　60, 61, 62
Arachnoid mater　　71, 98, 100, 111
Arch of aorta　　192, 194, 206, 207, 208,
　　214, 215, 219, 224, 226, 368, 369
Arch of azygos vein　　205, 221
Arch of cricoid cartilage　　28, 36, 48, 49,
　　50, 190, 192, 193, 218
Arcuate artery　　358
Arcuate eminence　　11, 23
Arcuate line　　96, 232, 282, 296, 298, 375
Areola　　132, 184
Areolar glands　　184
Arm　　115
Arterial branch to vastus medialis　　328
Artery of bulb of penis　　292
Artery to ductus deferens　　278
Articular branch　　346
Articular capsule　　29, 40, 42, 142, 143,
　　154, 156, 335, 339, 341, 342, 351
Articular cartilage　　342
Articular cavity　　223
Articular disc　　42, 143, 172, 173, 177, 178
Articular facet　　315, 316
Articular facet of fibula　　315, 316
Articular facet of head of rib　　181
Articular facet of lateral malleolus　　315
Articular facet of tubercle of rib　　223
Articular surface　　48, 50
Articular tubercle　　7, 9, 23
Articularis genu　　309, 342
Ary-epiglottic fold　　49, 50
Ary-epiglotticus　　49
Arytenoid articular surface　　48
Arytenoid cartilage
　　Anterolateral surface　　50
　　Medial surface　　50
Ascending aorta　　191, 192, 193, 194, 195,
　　196, 197, 199, 200, 201, 202, 203, 222
Ascending branch　　330
Ascending cervical artery　　36, 37, 195, 218, 367
Ascending colon　　237, 238, 239, 241, 242,
　　243, 248, 250, 253, 260, 261
Ascending lumbar vein　　224
Ascending palatine artery　　29, 35
Ascending part　　105, 106, 107, 245
Ascending pharyngeal artery　　34, 35, 37, 45
　　Posterior meningeal artery　　37
Ascending ramus　　63
Atlanto-occipital joint　　10, 71, 98
Atlas : C I　　87
　　Anterior arch　　55, 60, 79, 89, 112, 113
　　Inferior articular surface　　112
　　Lateral mass　　3, 71, 98, 99, 112, 113
　　Posterior arch　　60, 61, 71, 98, 99, 100, 109, 110, 111, 112
　　Transverse process　　28, 37, 44, 57, 71, 98, 99
Atrial branches　　202

Atrioventricular nodal branch　　197, 200, 202, 203
Atrioventricular sulcus　　191
Auditory tube : Pharyngotympanic tube
　　56, 58, 84
　　Bony part　　57
Auricular branch　　84
Auricular surface　　93, 296, 298
Auricular tubercle　　57
Auriculotemporal nerve　　29, 38, 39, 40, 42, 56, 57, 81, 82
Auscultatory triangle　　105, 106, 137
Axilla　　186
Axillary artery　　142, 144, 147, 148, 149,
　　190, 191, 192, 193, 194, 195, 208, 219, 371
　　Pectoral branches　　149
Axillary fascial sheath　　370
Axillary lymph nodes　　135
　　Anterior nodes　　370
　　Central nodes　　370
　　Lateral nodes　　370
　　Posterior nodes　　370
Axillary nerve　　136, 142, 145, 146, 147, 148, 149, 150, 152
Axillary process　　184
Axillary tail　　184
Axillary vein　　135, 190, 191, 208, 217, 219, 370, 371
Axis : C II　　87, 98, 110, 111
　　Dens　　55, 60, 61, 112, 113
　　Lateral part　　112
　　Pedicle　　98
　　Spinous process　　99, 100, 110, 112
　　Superior articular facet　　98, 112
　　Vertebral body　　112
Azygos vein　　204, 208, 214, 221, 224, 225, 270, 369

【B】

Bare area　　255
Base of 1st metatarsal bone　　128, 129, 168, 172, 178, 318, 363
Base of 2nd metatarsal bone　　173
Base of 3rd metatarsal bone　　173, 178
Base of 4th metatarsal bone　　173
Base of 5th metacarpal bone　　128
Base of 5th metatarsal bone　　318
Base of distal phalanx　　164
Base of mandible　　18
Base of metacarpal bone　　164
Base of metatarsal bone　　362, 364
Base of middle phalanx　　128, 164
Base of patella　　307
Base of phalanx　　178
Base of prostate　　280
Base of proximal phalanx　　128, 164, 172, 363, 364
Base of stapes　　58
Basilar artery　　60, 62, 66, 68, 78, 84
　　Pontine arteries　　67
Basilar part　　3, 27, 98, 112
Basilic vein　　151, 156, 157, 158, 159, 217, 371
Basilic vein of forearm　　156, 157
Biceps brachii　　127, 132, 139, 144, 145, 146, 149, 150, 151, 153, 154, 156, 157,
158, 159, 160, 161, 371
　　Long head　　119, 133, 135, 142, 143, 151
　　Short head　　117, 119, 135, 142, 147, 148, 151, 219
Biceps femoris　　293, 301, 311, 317, 326, 337, 338, 339, 340, 344, 345, 346, 347, 351, 352
　　Long head　　289, 290, 295, 301, 326, 327, 332
　　Short head　　306, 309, 327, 332
Bicipital aponeurosis　　153, 158, 159
Bicipital groove　　120
Bicipitoradial bursa　　154
Bifurcate ligament
　　Calcaneocuboid ligament　　319, 321, 359
　　Calcaneonavicular ligament　　319, 321, 358, 359
Bile duct　　247, 255, 256, 257, 258
Biliaropancreatic ampulla　　246
Body　　72, 74, 76
Body of 1st metacarpal bone　　128, 129
Body of 1st metatarsal bone　　318
Body of 1st rib　　183, 204
Body of 2nd metacarpal bone　　128
Body of 5th metacarpal bone　　128
Body of 5th metatarsal bone　　318
Body of Caudate nucleus　　68
Body of caudate nucleus　　74, 76
Body of clavicle　　118
Body of corpus callosum　　68
Body of epididymis　　278
Body of femur　　302, 335
Body of fornix　　68, 74, 76
Body of gallbladder　　255, 256
Body of hyoid bone　　28, 30, 32, 48, 50, 56
Body of ilium　　294
Body of ischium　　294, 296
Body of mandible　　1, 4, 13, 16, 17, 18, 32, 39, 40, 42
　　Inferior border　　38
Body of metatarsal bone　　364
Body of middle phalanx　　128
Body of pancreas　　245, 257, 270
Body of penis　　278
Body of phalanx　　178
Body of proximal phalanx　　128
Body of pubis　　235, 294, 296, 300
Body of rib　　181
Body of sphenoid　　3, 12, 25
Body of sternum　　179, 182, 183, 189
Body of stomach　　251, 252, 253
Body of uterus　　288
Bony canal of cochlea　　58
Bony part　　57
Border of oval fossa　　199
Brachial artery　　151, 153, 157, 158, 159, 160
Brachial plexus　　36, 370
　　Cords　　142
　　Inferior trunk　　147, 148
　　Lateral cord　　144, 145, 146, 371
　　Lower trunk　　147, 148
　　Medial cord　　145, 219, 371
　　Middle trunk　　147, 148
　　Posterior cord　　145, 146

Roots　30, 33
　Superior trunk　28, 31, 32, 37, 147, 148, 190, 191, 192, 193, 194, 218, 219
　Trunks　135
　Upper trunk　28, 31, 32, 37, 147, 148, 190, 191, 192, 193, 194, 218, 219
Brachial vein　151, 217
Brachialis　121, 123, 127, 139, 151, 156, 159, 160
Brachiocephalic trunk　36, 37, 190, 191, 192, 193, 194, 195, 208, 214, 218, 219, 220, 224, 366
Brachiocephalic vein　220, 368
Brachioradialis　123, 127, 133, 139, 151, 153, 156, 157, 158, 159, 160, 162, 168, 176
Brachium of inferior colliculus　70
Branch of Anterior interosseous artery　170, 176
Branch of Inferior rectal nerve　290
Branch of Posterior interosseous artery　161
Branch of Princeps pollicis artery　176
Branch of S4　277
Branch of Saphenous branch　347
Branch to carotid body　45
Branches of 3rd occipital nerve　110
Branches of Cervical plexus　34
Branches of Circumflex scapular artery　137, 138, 139, 140, 141
Branches of Deep branch　362
Branches of Lateral pectoral nerve　135
Branches of Medial femoral cutaneous nerve　338
Branches of Medial pectoral nerve　135
Branches of Radial nerve　150
Branches of Superior medial genicular artery　347
Bregma　8
Broad ligament of uterus　287
Bronchial branch　192, 193, 195, 214, 215, 216
Bronchomediastinal trunk　37
Bronchopulmonary nodes　216
Buccal branches　83
Buccal fat pad　32, 40
Buccal nerve　40, 42, 81
Buccinator　2, 6, 19, 29, 33, 39, 40, 42, 43
Bulb of duodenum　252
Bulb of occipital horn　74
Bulb of penis　281
Bulbospongiosus　281, 290, 291, 292
Bursa of achilles tendon　321
Bursa of calcaneal tendon　321

【C】

C1　71
　Dorsal ramus　99
　Rootlets　67
C2
　Dorsal rootlets　71
　Spinal ganglion　110, 111
　Ventral ramus　31
C3
　Dorsal ramus　71
　Ventral ramus　31, 37, 71

C4
　Dorsal root　71
　Dorsal root ganglion　71
　Posterior cutaneous branches　111
　Spinal ganglion　71
　Ventral ramus　31, 98
　Ventral rootlets　71
C5
　Dorsal ramus　100
　Spinal ganglion　100
　Ventral ramus　29, 36, 100
　Ventral root　100
C6
　Dorsal root　100
　Ventral ramus　99
C8
　Spinal ganglion　99, 100
　Ventral ramus　220
C I : Atlas
　Anterior arch　113, 55, 60, 79, 89, 112
　Inferior articular surface　112
　Lateral mass　3, 71, 98, 99, 112, 113
　Posterior arch　60, 61, 71, 98, 99, 100, 109, 110, 111, 112
　Transverse process　28, 37, 44, 57, 71, 98, 99
C II : Axis
　Dens　55, 60, 61, 112, 113
　Lateral part　112
　Pedicle　98
　Spinous process　99, 100, 110, 112
　Superior articular facet　98, 112
　Vertebral body　112
C III
　Spinous process　112
　Vertebral body　99
C V
　Vertebral body　98
C VI
　Lamina　71, 113
C VII : Vertebra prominens
　Spinous process　71, 99, 100, 113
　Vertebral body　99
Calcaneal sulcus　321
Calcaneal tendon　319, 321, 348, 350, 351, 352, 353, 354, 355, 356, 357, 358, 359
Calcaneal tubercle　318, 320
Calcaneocuboid ligament　319, 321, 359
Calcaneofibular ligament　317, 321, 359
Calcaneonavicular ligament　319, 321, 358, 359
Calcaneus　293, 318, 354, 359, 362, 364
　Anterior talar articular surface　321, 358
　Fibular (Peroneal) trochlea　320
　Groove for tendon of flexor hallucis longus　318, 321
　Lateral surface　355
　Medial surface　320
　Middle talar articular surface　321, 358
　Posterior surface　321, 348, 355
　Posterior talar articular surface　321, 358
　Sustentaculum tali　318, 320, 321, 364
Calcar femorale　306
Calcarine spur　72, 74, 75

Calcarine sulcus　64, 68
Calf venous plexus　349
Canal for auditory tube　23
Canal for tensor tympani　23
Canine eminence　21
Canine fossa　21
Canine tooth　13
Capitate　128, 129, 168, 173, 177, 178
Capitulum of humerus　122, 126, 153, 154, 156, 161
Capsule of distal radio-ulnar joint　172
Cardia　372
Cardiac branches　84
Cardiac impression　216
Cardiac notch of left lung　216
Cardiac plexus　195
Carina of trachea　193, 195, 212
Carotid branch　34, 84
Carotid canal　9, 23, 57
Carotid sinus　35, 45
Carotid sulcus　11, 25
Carpal tunnel　171
Carpometacarpal joint of thumb
　Lateral ligament　172
　Palmar ligament　172
Cauda equina　101, 260, 270
Caudate lobe　244, 246, 247, 251, 255, 256
Caudate nucleus　77
Caudate process　255, 256
Caval opening　227, 270
Cavernous sinus　47, 59
Cecum　230, 242, 248, 250, 260, 261
Celiac ganglia　252, 267, 274
Celiac nodes　244, 274
Celiac plexus　267
Celiac trunk　224, 244, 252, 258, 260, 264, 266, 267, 268, 272, 274
Central incisor : 1st incisor　13, 16
Central nodes　185, 370
Central retinal artery　52
　Inferior nasal retinal arteriole　53
　Superior temporal arteriole　53
Central retinal vein
　Inferior nasal retinal venule　53
　Superior temporal venule　53
Central sulcus　62, 63, 68
Central sulcus of insula　63
Central tendon　225, 270
Cephalic vein　28, 132, 133, 134, 135, 139, 142, 151, 156, 157, 159, 174, 175, 217, 370, 371
Cephalic vein of forearm　156, 157
Cerebellar fossa　11, 27
Cerebellum　60, 68, 77
　Flocculus　66
　Horizontal fissure　70
　Intercrural fissure　70
Cerebral aqueduct　68, 70, 72, 77, 79
Cerebral crus　66, 78, 79
Cerebral falx　47, 59, 60, 61, 62
Cerebral fossa　27
Cerebral peduncle　70
　Cerebral crus　66
Cerebral surface　25
Cerebrum
　Temporal lobe　43

Cervical branch 32, 42, 83
Cervical fascia
　Prevertebral layer 367
Cervical ligament 321, 358, 359
Cervical plexus 85
Cervical vertebrae 87
Cervicothoracic ganglion 207, 220
Cervix of uterus 285, 286, 288, 373
Chiasmatic cistern 60
Choanae 9, 17, 60, 61
Chorda tympani 42, 44, 56, 57, 58, 82, 85
Chordae tendineae 199, 200
Choroid enlargement 72, 77
Choroid plexus 66, 68, 71, 72, 73, 74
Choroid plexus of 3rd ventricle 70, 76
Choroid plexus of 4th ventricle 70
Choroid plexus of lateral ventricle 75, 76, 77
Choroidal fissure 76
Chyle cistern 368
Ciliary arteries 53
Ciliary ganglion 44, 53, 54, 80, 81, 82
Cingulate gyrus 64, 68
Cingulate sulcus 64
　Marginal branch 64
　Marginal sulcus 64
　Paracentral rami 64
Circular fold 250, 260
Circular sulcus of insula 63
Circumflex branch 197, 198, 200, 202, 203
Circumflex humeral artery 142
Circumflex humeral vein 142
Circumflex scapular artery 143, 146, 147, 148, 149, 152
Circumflex scapular vein 143
Cisterna chyli 368, 372
Cisterna magna 60
Claustrum 74, 75, 77
Clavicle 28, 30, 48, 133, 134, 135, 142, 143, 147, 148, 149, 179, 184, 208, 217, 219, 367, 370, 371
　Acromial end 118, 132, 134, 136
　Sternal end 118, 183
Clavicular branch 367, 370
Clavicular head 133, 134, 28, 30, 32, 134, 217
Clavicular notch 182
Clavipectoral fascia 119, 134, 370
Clitoris 285, 289, 290
Clivus 11, 12, 17, 55, 60, 61, 79, 84
Coccygeal cornu 94
Coccygeal vertebrae 87
Coccygeus 95, 276, 277, 282, 297
Coccyx 87, 88, 96, 260, 277, 279, 289, 324, 334
Cochlea 58, 83
　Osseous spiral lamina 58
Cochlear canaliculus 23
Cochlear cupula 58
Cochlear nerve 58, 83
Coeliac ganglia 84
Colic impression 255, 259
Collateral eminence 73
Collateral ligament 172, 363
Collateral sulcus 64, 66

Collateral trigone 73
Column of fornix 68
Common bony limb 58
Common carotid artery 29, 30, 31, 32, 33, 34, 35, 36, 37, 45, 47, 144, 148, 190, 191, 192, 193, 194, 195, 207, 208, 214, 218, 219, 224, 366, 367, 368
Common fibular (peroneal) nerve 337, 338, 344, 345, 346, 347, 352
　Articular branch 346
　Lateral sural cutaneous nerve 344
　Recurrent branch 346
Common flexor sheath 167
Common hepatic artery 244, 246, 255, 267, 268
Common hepatic duct 255, 256, 257
Common iliac artery 249, 271, 272, 273, 274, 279, 280, 281, 375
Common iliac nodes 374, 375
Common iliac vein 271, 272, 273, 274
Common iliac vessels 368
Common interosseous artery 158, 160
Common lacrimal canaliculus 51
Common palmar digital artery 166, 169, 170, 171
Common palmar digital nerve 166, 168, 169
Common plantar digital nerve 360, 361
Communicating branch of Internal branch 49, 50
Concha 57
Conchal crest 21, 22
Condylar canal 9
Condylar fossa 27
Cone of light 57
Conjoint tendon 234, 235, 299, 301
Conoid ligament 117, 119, 142
Conoid tubercle 118
Conus arteriosus 197, 198, 199, 201
Conus branch 197, 200, 202, 203
Conus medullaris 101
Coraco-acromial ligament 117, 119, 142
Coracobrachialis 117, 119, 121, 135, 142, 145, 146, 147, 148, 149, 150, 151, 370, 371
Coracoclavicular ligament
　Conoid ligament 117
　Trapezoid ligament 117
Coracohumeral ligament 119
Coracoid process 116, 118, 135, 143
Cord of umbilical artery 232, 235, 281, 283, 285, 288, 373
Cords 142
Corneal limbus 51
Corneoscleral junction 51
Corniculate cartilage 49, 50
Corona of glans 278, 328
Coronal suture 4, 8, 14, 17
Coronary ligament 255
Coronary sinus 197, 198, 203
Coronary sulcus 191
Coronoid fossa 122, 123
Coronoid process 4, 18, 125, 126, 154, 155, 156
Corpus callosum 60, 74, 76, 77
　Minor forceps 74
　Occipital forceps 74

Corpus cavernosum penis 279, 291, 292
Corpus luteum 286
Corpus spongiosum of penis 291, 292
Corrugator supercilii 2, 6
Costal arch 179, 184, 186, 270
Costal groove 181
Costal margin 179, 186, 270
Costal pleura 204
Costal process 92, 103, 113, 263, 269, 334, 336
Costocervical trunk 207
Costochondral joint 183
Costoclavicular ligament 119, 181
Costodiaphragmatic recess 191, 192, 193, 225, 259, 260, 263
Costomediastinal recess 191, 192, 193, 225
Costotransverse ligament 181, 223
Coxal bone 293
Cranial nerves 80
Cranial root 71, 85
Cremaster 234
Cremasteric fascia 234, 278
Crest of greater tubercle 120
Crest of lesser tubercle 120
Cribriform fascia 234
Cribriform plate 11, 12, 26, 51, 53, 55, 59, 79
Crico-arytenoid joint 50
Cricoid cartilage 48, 217
　Thyroid articular surface 50
Cricopharyngeal part 45, 47
Cricothyroid 30, 36, 48, 49
Cricothyroid branch 34
Cricothyroid joint 49
Crista galli 3, 11, 16, 17, 26, 53
Crista terminalis 199, 201
Cruciate ligament of atlas
　Longitudinal bands 98
　Transverse ligament of atlas 98
Crus of clitoris 285, 290
Crus of fornix 75
Crus of helix 57
Cubital lymph nodes 371
Cuboid 318, 320, 362, 364
　Groove for tendon of fibularis (peroneus) longus 318, 363
Cuneate tubercle 71
Cuneiform cartilage 49
Cuneonavicular joint 359
Cuneus 64
Cutaneous branch 108, 110, 111, 174
Cystic artery 246, 255, 256
Cystic duct 246, 247, 255, 256, 257
Cystic vein 256

【D】

Dartos fascia 278
Deciduous teeth
　1st incisor : Central incisor 13
　1st molar tooth 13
　2nd incisor : Lateral incisor 13
　2nd molar tooth 13
　Canine tooth 13
Decussation of pyramids 70
Deep artery of thigh 327, 330, 332, 335
Deep branch 168, 169, 171, 361

Deep circumflex iliac artery　271
Deep dorsal vein of penis　279, 280, 291
Deep external pudendal artery　280
Deep fascia of leg　338, 346, 347, 348, 350, 351, 356, 357
Deep fibular (peroneal) nerve　346, 357, 358
　　Branch to Tibialis anterior　346
　　Recurrent branch　346
Deep head　10, 42, 43
Deep infrapatellar bursa　342
Deep inguinal nodes　374
Deep inguinal ring　231, 232, 233, 234, 235, 281
Deep lingual artery　29
Deep palmar arch　169, 170, 171
Deep palmar branch　168, 169, 170, 171
Deep plantar arch　362
Deep temporal nerves　42, 81, 82
Deep transverse metacarpal ligament　172, 176
Deep vein of thigh　332, 335
Deltoid　28, 88, 105, 106, 107, 115, 117, 119, 121, 132, 133, 134, 135, 136, 137, 138, 139, 140, 141, 142, 143, 147, 148, 150, 152, 186, 219, 370, 371
Deltoid branch　370
Deltoid ligament : Medial ligament　311, 314, 358, 359, 363
　　Posterior tibiotalar part　359
　　Tibiocalcaneal part　321, 359
Deltoid tuberosity　120
Deltopectoral groove　132, 179
Dens　55, 60, 61, 89, 112, 113
Denticulate ligament　71, 98, 100, 111
Depressor anguli oris　2, 6, 19, 33, 39, 40
Depressor labii inferioris　2, 6, 19, 39
Descending aorta　208
　　Thoracic aorta　189, 194, 206
Descending branch　330
Descending colon　237, 238, 239, 249, 250
Descending genicular artery
　　Branch of Saphenous branch　347
　　Saphenous branch　332
Descending part　105, 106, 240, 245, 250, 261
Diaphragm　181, 183, 191, 192, 193, 194, 196, 204, 205, 206, 225, 226, 230, 232, 240, 252, 254, 255, 259, 260, 268, 270, 372
　　Aortic hiatus　227
　　Caval opening　227
　　Central tendon　225, 270
　　Esophageal hiatus　227, 251, 270
　　Left crus　267
　　Right crus　252, 268, 273, 372
Diaphragmatic surface　216, 259
Digastric
　　Anterior belly　19, 29, 30, 32, 33, 34, 35, 43
　　Posterior belly　10, 29, 31, 32, 33, 35, 37, 42, 47, 56
Digastric fossa　18
Digital branches　171
Diploe　11

Distal interphalangeal joint (DIPJ)　164, 172
Distal palmar crease　163
Distal phalanx　128, 129, 178, 318, 359
Distal radio-ulnar joint　155
　　Articular disc　172
　　Sacciform recess　173
Distal wrist crease　163
Dome of pleura　217
Dorsal artery of penis　280, 291, 292
Dorsal branch　174
Dorsal carpal arch　174, 176
Dorsal carpal branch　174
Dorsal digital artery　174, 358
Dorsal digital vein　174
Dorsal interossei　171, 176, 364
Dorsal median sulcus　71
Dorsal metacarpal artery　174
Dorsal nasal artery　51
Dorsal nerve of penis　278, 280, 291, 292
Dorsal radiocarpal ligament　173
Dorsal ramus　71, 99, 100, 102, 106, 107, 108, 110, 111, 223
Dorsal root　71, 98, 99, 100, 101
Dorsal root ganglion　71
Dorsal scapular artery　37, 138, 367
Dorsal scapular nerve　31, 32
Dorsal tubercle　124, 126, 155
Dorsal venous arch of foot　354, 356, 358
Dorsal venous network of hand　168
Dorsalis pedis artery　354, 357, 358
Dorsalis pedis vein　357, 358
Dorsum of nose　38
Dorsum of tongue　47, 49
Dorsum sellae　11, 12, 17, 25, 60
Ductus deferens　230, 233, 234, 235, 271, 278, 279, 280, 281, 282
Duodenal impression　255
Duodenojejunal flexure　241
Duodenum　245, 246
　　Ascending part　245
　　Descending part　240, 245, 250, 261
　　Horizontal part　245, 253
　　Superior part　240, 241, 243, 251
　　Transverse part　245, 248, 253
Dura mater　5, 62, 71, 82, 98, 99, 100, 101, 110, 111
Dural sheath　98, 99, 101
Dural sheath of optic nerve　52

【E】

Edge of Tegmen tympani　9
Edinger-Westphal nucleus　85
Ejaculatory duct　281
Elbow joint　115
Emissary foramen　11
Epicardium　191
Epigastric fold　232, 233
Epigastric region　227
Epiglottic vallecula　47, 49, 50, 60, 226
Epiglottis　47, 49, 50, 60
Epiphysial line　143, 343
Epitympanic recess　57
Erector spinae　95, 104, 105, 106, 107, 138, 139, 140, 141, 181, 267, 270, 297
Esophageal branch　37, 244, 251, 372
Esophageal hiatus　227, 251, 270

Esophageal impression　255
Esophageal plexus　193, 194, 195, 221, 225, 369
Esophagus　37, 48, 193, 194, 195, 204, 205, 206, 208, 214, 221, 222, 225, 226, 246, 251, 267, 369
Ethmoid　12
　　Cribriform plate　11, 12, 51, 53, 55, 59
　　Crista galli　17
　　Orbital plate　4, 12
　　Perpendicular plate　17, 55
　　Uncinate process　12
Ethmoidal bulla　12, 26, 55
Ethmoidal cells　3, 12, 16, 60
　　Roof　20
Ethmoidal crest　21, 22
Ethmoidal infundibulum　55
Ethmoidal labyrinth　26
Ethmoidal notch　20
Ethmoidal process　26
Ethmoidal spine　25
Eustachian tube　23
Eustachian valve　199
Extensor aponeurosis　130, 176, 355
Extensor carpi radialis brevis　130, 156, 159, 160, 161, 162, 168, 174, 175, 176, 177
Extensor carpi radialis longus　123, 130, 153, 156, 158, 159, 160, 161, 162, 168, 174, 175, 176, 177
Extensor carpi ulnaris　127, 130, 161, 162, 168, 174, 175, 176, 177
Extensor digiti minimi　162, 163, 168, 174, 175, 177
Extensor digitorum　161, 162, 163, 168, 174, 175, 176, 177
Extensor digitorum brevis　319, 321, 354, 355, 357, 358
Extensor digitorum longus　313, 317, 319, 346, 347, 354, 355, 357, 358
Extensor hallucis brevis　319, 358
Extensor hallucis longus　317, 319, 346, 354, 355, 357, 358, 359
Extensor hood　176
Extensor indicis　127, 161, 162, 163, 174, 175
Extensor muscles　153
Extensor pollicis brevis　127, 130, 161, 162, 163, 168, 174, 175, 176
Extensor pollicis longus　127, 130, 161, 162, 163, 168, 174, 175, 176
Extensor retinaculum　161, 162, 163, 174, 175
External acoustic meatus　4, 7, 9, 14, 23, 47, 57, 58
External anal sphincter　281, 289, 290, 291, 326
External branch　29, 31, 32, 35, 36, 45, 84
External capsule　75, 77
External carotid artery　29, 30, 31, 32, 33, 34, 35, 36, 44, 56, 71
External iliac artery　233, 235, 271, 272, 276, 280, 281, 282, 283, 285, 335, 373
External iliac nodes　283, 373, 374, 375

External iliac vein 233, 235, 271, 281, 283, 285, 373
External intercostal membrane 187
External intercostal muscle 106, 107, 145, 146, 181, 187, 188
External jugular vein 28, 32, 33, 190, 191, 217
External oblique 88, 105, 106, 107, 181, 186, 228, 229, 232, 267, 275, 295, 299, 301
　Aponeurosis 228, 229, 230, 234, 275, 328
External occipital crest 9, 27, 110, 111
External occipital protuberance 4, 7, 9, 17, 27, 110, 111
External os of uterus 285
External pudendal veins 230
External spermatic fascia 278
External talocalcaneal ligament 321, 358, 359
External urethral orifice 278, 289
External urethral sphincter 297
Extraperitoneal fat 103
Extraperitoneal tissue 263
Extreme capsule 75, 77
Extrinsic muscles of tongue 85
Eyeball 51, 53, 54, 60

【F】

Fabella 343
Facet for dens 89
Facial artery 28, 29, 30, 31, 32, 33, 34, 35, 38, 39, 40, 42, 47
Facial canal 57, 58
Facial colliculus 71
Facial nerve 33
Facial nerve〔Ⅶ〕 39, 40, 44, 58, 59, 66, 70, 78, 83, 84
　Buccal branches 39
　Cervical branch 32, 42
　Geniculate ganglion 44, 58
　Intermediate nerve 61
　Marginal mandibular branch 31, 32, 34, 39
　Motor root 61
　Temporal branch 39
　Zygomatic branch 39
Facial vein 30, 31, 32, 33, 38, 39, 40, 42
Falciform ligament 230, 232, 237, 239, 240, 243, 245, 254, 255, 274
Falciform process 284, 297, 334
Fallopian tube 286, 373
Falx cerebri 47, 59, 60, 61, 62
Fascia lata 234, 328, 331, 338, 342, 376
Fat pad 359
Fatty appendices of colon 237, 238, 239, 241, 242
Femoral artery 230, 231, 271, 276, 280, 327, 328, 330, 331, 332, 376
Femoral branch 233, 271, 272, 273, 274, 280, 283
Femoral canal 231
Femoral nerve 230, 231, 233, 271, 273, 274, 275, 276, 280, 328, 330, 331, 375, 376
　Anterior cutaneous branches 376

Muscular branches 376
Femoral ring 235
Femoral vein 230, 231, 271, 276, 277, 280, 328, 330, 332, 349, 376
　Muscular tributary 349
Femur 293, 332, 341, 343
　Greater trochanter 324, 325, 336
　Lateral condyle 337, 339, 341, 343
　Lateral epicondyle 343
　Lesser trochanter 336
　Medial condyle 339, 341, 343, 347, 351
　Medial epicondyle 343
Fibrous capsule 267
Fibrous pericardium 190, 191, 192, 193, 219, 225, 366
Fibrous sheath 172
Fibrous sheaths of digits of hand 167, 171
Fibrous sheaths of toes 360, 361
Fibula 293, 311, 364
　Anterior border 311
　Articular facet 316
　Lateral malleolus 357, 364
　Lateral surface 311
　Posterior surface 351, 352, 353
Fibular articular facet 310, 312
Fibular collateral ligament 309, 311, 317, 339, 340, 342, 347, 351
Fibular notch 314
Fibularis (Peroneus) brevis 317, 319, 351, 354, 355, 357, 358, 362, 363, 364
Fibularis (Peroneus) longus 313, 317, 319, 346, 347, 350, 351, 353, 354, 355, 357, 358, 362, 363
Fibularis (Peroneus) tertius 317, 319, 355, 357, 358
Fibularis (Peroneus) brevis 358
Fibular (Peroneal) artery 353
　Perforating branch 357
Fibular (Peroneal) trochlea 320
Fibular (Peroneal) vein 352
Filum terminale 101
Fimbria 73
Fimbriae of uterine tube 288
Fissure for ligamentum teres 255, 256
Fissure for ligamentum venosum 251, 255, 256
Fissure for round ligament 255, 256
Flank 227
Flexor accessorius 319, 359, 361, 362
Flexor carpi radialis 130, 159, 163, 166, 167, 168, 169, 170, 171, 177
Flexor carpi ulnaris 127, 130, 153, 156, 158, 159, 160, 163, 166, 167, 168, 169, 170, 171, 177
Flexor digiti minimi brevis 130, 163, 166, 167, 168, 171, 319, 360, 361, 362
Flexor digitorum brevis 319, 359, 360, 361, 362, 364
Flexor digitorum longus 311, 319, 351, 353, 355, 356, 357, 358, 361, 362
Flexor digitorum profundus 127, 130, 158, 159, 160, 167, 168, 169, 171, 177
Flexor digitorum superficialis 130, 159, 167, 168, 169, 171, 177
　Humero-ulnar head 127, 160
　Radial head 127, 160

Vinculum longum 167
Flexor hallucis brevis 319, 359, 360, 361, 362
Flexor hallucis longus 317, 319, 351, 353, 355, 356, 357, 358, 359, 360, 361, 362, 363
Flexor pollicis brevis 130, 163, 166, 167, 168, 169, 171
Flexor pollicis longus 127, 130, 159, 160, 161, 167, 168, 169, 171
Flexor retinaculum 159, 166, 167, 168, 169, 171, 351, 355, 356
Flocculus 66, 70
Floor of 4th ventricle 71, 76
Floor of maxillary sinus 3
Foramen cecum 11, 20, 49
Foramen lacerum 9, 11
Foramen magnum 9, 11, 17, 27, 60, 61, 71, 85, 100
Foramen of Magendie 70
Foramen of Winslow 240, 243, 244
Foramen ovale 9, 11, 25, 58, 81, 85
Foramen rotundum 3, 11, 25, 58, 81, 85
Foramen spinosum 9, 11, 25, 58
Foramen transversarium 89, 90
Forearm 115
Foreskin 278
Fornix 73, 77
　Anterior column 74
Fossa for lacrimal sac 4, 12
Fossa ovalis 199
Fovea centralis 53
Fovea for ligament of head 302
Free coli 261
Frontal angle 24
Frontal belly 5, 39
Frontal bone 1, 4, 8, 12, 14
　Nasal spine 12
　Orbital part 11, 12, 17
Frontal border 24
Frontal branch 39
Frontal crest 8, 11, 16, 20
Frontal foramen 1, 12
Frontal forceps 75
Frontal horn 72, 74, 75, 76
Frontal lobe 63
Frontal nerve 44, 51, 52, 53, 81
Frontal notch 1, 12, 38
Frontal pole 62, 63
Frontal process 1, 4, 12, 21, 24, 26
Frontal sinus 3, 11, 12, 16, 17, 20, 55, 60
Frontal suture 14
Frontal tuber 14, 20
Frontozygomatic suture 4
Fundus of bladder 281
Fundus of gallbladder 227, 245, 247, 254, 255, 256
Fundus of stomach 251
Fundus of uterus 285, 286, 287, 288, 373
Fungiform papilla 49
Fusiform gyrus 64

【G】

Galen's anastomosis 49

Gallbladder　240，241，243，244，246，253，255，257，372
Ganglion of sympathetic trunk　101，102，195
Gastric impression　255，259
Gastrocnemius　293，353
　Lateral head　309，337，338，341，344，345，346，347，350，351，352
　Medial head　309，338，344，345，347，350，351，352
Gastroduodenal artery　244，246，247，255
Gastrosplenic ligament　259，260
Gemellus inferior　289，297，301，303，305，325，333
Gemellus superior　295，301，303，305，325
Geniculate ganglion　44，58
Geniculocalcarine fibers　74，75
Genioglossus　19，43，48
Geniohyoid　19，29，48，56，85
Genital branch　233，271，272，273，274，280，283
Genitofemoral nerve　261，271，272，273，274，275，375
　Femoral branch　233，271，272，273，274，280，283
　Genital branch　233，271，272，273，274，280，283
Genu　75
Genu of corpus callosum　68，75
Genu of internal capsule　74，76
Gerdy's tubercle　311
Glabella　1，4，20，38
Glans penis　278
Glenohumeral joint：Shoulder joint　115，142
　Articular capsule　142
Glenoid cavity　116，118，142，143
Glenoid labrum　142，143
Glossopharyngeal nerve [IX]　29，35，37，44，45，47，61，70，71，78，84
　Pharyngeal branches　45
　Tympanic nerve　57
Gluteal fascia　324，326
Gluteal fold　324
Gluteal sulcus　324
Gluteal tuberosity　304，306
Gluteus maximus　88，95，104，105，289，290，292，293，295，305，306，324，325，326，327
Gluteus medius　289，295，303，305，324，325，335
Gluteus minimus　295，303，305，325，333，335
Gonadal artery　103
Gracile tubercle　71
Gracilis　276，277，289，290，292，295，301，311，313，324，327，328，330，332，334，338，344，345，347，351，352
Granular foveolae　8
Gray ramus communicans　221
Great auricular nerve　29，30，31，32，33，35，39，40，108
Great cardiac vein　196，197，198，200，203
Great cerebral vein　60，68
Great saphenous vein　230，234，280，328，332，338，347，348，349，352，354，356，357，359，376
Great toe [I]
　Distal phalanx　318
　Proximal phalanx　318
Greater curvature　238，241，243，244，247，251，252，372
Greater horn　28，31，32，33，34，48，49，50
Greater occipital nerve　108，109，110，111
Greater omentum　230，237，238，239，241，242，243，244，247，248，249，251，254，270
Greater palatine foramen　9
Greater palatine groove　21，22
Greater palatine nerve　44，55
Greater petrosal nerve　44，58，85
Greater sac　260
Greater sciatic foramen　284
Greater sciatic notch　294，296，334
Greater splanchnic nerve　101，207，221，222，223，225
Greater supraclavicular fossa　132，217
Greater trochanter　302，304，324，325，333，335，336
Greater tubercle　120，142，143
Greater wing　1，3，4，11，12，16，43
　Cerebral surface　25
　Infratemporal crest　9，25
　Infratemporal surface　7，25
　Orbital surface　25
　Temporal surface　25
Groin　227
Groove for anterior ethmoidal nerve　21
Groove for fibularis (peroneus) brevis　359
Groove for greater petrosal nerve　11，23，57
Groove for inferior petrosal sinus　11，27
Groove for lesser petrosal nerve　11，23
Groove for middle meningeal artery　8，11，17，23，24，57
Groove for middle temporal artery　23
Groove for popliteus　308
Groove for radial nerve　120
Groove for sigmoid sinus　11，17，23，24，27
Groove for subclavian artery　181
Groove for subclavian vein　181
Groove for subclavius　118
Groove for superior petrosal sinus　11，17，23
Groove for superior sagittal sinus　8，11，27
Groove for tendon of fibularis (peroneus) longus　318，363
Groove for tendon of flexor hallucis longus　318，321，359，363
Groove for tibialis posterior　359
Groove for transverse sinus　11，17，27
Groove for vertebral artery　89

【H】

Hamate　128，129，168，173，177，178
Hamstrings　293，333
Hand　115
Hard palate　43，51，60

Haustra of colon　250
Head of 1st metatarsal bone　128，129，178，318，354
Head of 1st rib　183
Head of 2nd metatarsal bone　172，363
Head of 3rd metatarsal bone　178
Head of 5th metatarsal bone　128，318
Head of 9th rib　225
Head of capitate　172
Head of caudate nucleus　74，75，76
Head of epididymis　278
Head of femur　302，304，335，336
Head of fibula　315，316，337，338，342，343，346，347
Head of humerus　120，142，143
Head of mandible　4，18，38
Head of metacarpal bone　163，164
Head of middle phalanx　128，164
Head of pancreas　227，245，253，257
Head of phalanx　178
Head of proximal phalanx　128，164
Head of Radius　156
Head of radius　124，126，153，154，155，156
Head of rib　181
Head of talus　318，320，321，364
Head of ulna　125，163，170，173，178
Heart　84
Heel　356
Helix　57
Hemi-azygos vein　207，208，224，225，270
Hemisphere of cerebellum　62，84
Hepatic artery proper　244，246，247，255，256，274
　Left branch　246，247，255，256，258
　Right branch　246，247，255，256，258
Hepatic flexure　243，250
Hepatic portal vein　246，255，256，258
　Left branch　244，258
　Right branch　258
Hepatopancreatic ampulla　246
Hepatorenal recess　243
Hesselbach's triangle　232，233
Hiatus for greater petrosal nerve　11，23，59
Hiatus for lesser petrosal nerve　11，23，59
Higest nasal concha　56
Highest nuchal line　7，27
Hilar lymph nodes　216
Hilum of kidney　227，264，265
Hip bone　293
Hip joint　250
　Articular capsule　335
Hippocampus　72，73，76，77
　Pes　73
Hoffa　341，342，347
Hook of hamate　128，163，168，172，178
Horizontal fissure　70，216
Horizontal part　245，253
Horizontal plate　7，9，12，17，22，26
Humeral head　123，160
Humero-ulnar head　127，160
Humerus　142，151，154，156
　Lateral epicondyle　126，153，154

Medial epicondyle　126, 153, 154, 156, 160, 371
　Olecranon fossa　154
Hyo-epiglottic ligament　50
Hyoglossus　29, 32, 35, 48, 56
Hyoid bone　29, 31, 33, 60, 84, 113
　Greater horn　28, 31, 32, 33, 34, 49, 50
　Tip of greater horn　45, 47
Hypochondrium　227
Hypogastric nerve　271
Hypogastrium　227
Hypoglossal canal　9, 11, 17, 27, 85, 98
Hypoglossal nerve [XII]　28, 29, 31, 32, 33, 34, 35, 36, 44, 45, 47, 56, 61, 66, 78, 85, 98
Hypoglossal trigone　71
Hypopharynx　60
Hypophysial fossa　4, 11, 12, 17, 25
Hypothalamic sulcus　68, 70
Hypothalamus　68, 70

【I】

Ileal arteries　279
Ileal orifice : Orifice of ileal papilla　250
　Inferior lip　260
　Superior lip　260
Ileal veins　279
Ileocolic artery　248, 253, 258, 261
Ileocolic vein　248, 258
Ileum　230, 239, 248, 249, 250, 261
Iliac crest　88, 96, 104, 105, 231, 272, 274, 294, 296, 298, 324, 333, 334, 335
Iliac fossa　96, 284, 296, 298, 300
Iliac tuberosity　296
Iliacus　95, 230, 233, 271, 272, 273, 274, 275, 276, 277, 280, 297, 299, 303, 305, 306, 328, 330, 331, 333, 335, 375
Ilio-inguinal nerve　228, 229, 230, 234, 263, 270, 271, 272, 273, 274, 275, 278
Iliococcygeus　277
Iliocostalis　105, 106, 107
Iliofemoral ligament　295, 299, 301, 303, 333
　Transverse part　305
Iliohypogastric nerve　234, 263, 270, 271, 272, 273, 274, 275
Iliolumbar artery　272, 273, 283
Iliolumbar ligament　271, 275, 297, 299, 333, 334, 375
Iliolumbar vein　273, 375
Iliopectineal bursa　333
Iliopsoas　306, 331, 333
Iliopubic eminence　294, 296, 298, 300, 333
Iliotibial tract　228, 293, 311, 313, 326, 327, 328, 331, 332, 337, 338, 340, 342, 346, 347, 376
Ilium　282
Impression for costoclavicular ligament　118
Incisive bone　55
Incisive canal　12, 17, 21
Incisive foramina　55
Incisive fossa　9, 21
Incudomallealar joint　58
Incudostapedial joint　58

Incus　57, 58
　Long limb　57
Index finger
　Proximal phalanx　128
Inferior alveolar artery　42
Inferior alveolar nerve　29, 42, 56, 81, 82
Inferior angle　116, 118, 136, 186
Inferior articular facet　89
Inferior articular process　90, 91, 92, 112, 113, 334
Inferior articular surface　89, 112, 311, 315
Inferior belly　28, 29, 30, 31, 32, 117, 119, 135, 146, 195
Inferior border　18, 38, 216, 259
Inferior branch　54
Inferior cerebral veins　62
Inferior cervical cardiac branches　205
Inferior cervical ganglion　37
Inferior clunial nerves　324
Inferior colliculus　68, 70, 71, 76
Inferior concha　79
Inferior constrictor　31, 32, 35, 45, 47, 48
　Cricopharyngeal part　45, 47
　Thyropharyngeal part　45
Inferior costal facet　90, 91
Inferior epigastric artery　229, 231, 232, 233, 235, 276, 280, 281, 282, 285, 373, 375, 376
　Pubic branch　235
Inferior epigastric vein　229, 231, 232, 233, 235, 281, 285, 373, 375, 376
Inferior extensor retinaculum　321, 355, 357, 358
Inferior extremity　261, 264, 270
Inferior eyelid　51
Inferior fibular (peroneal) retinaculum　355
Inferior frontal gyrus　63
　Opercular part　63
　Orbital part　63
　Triangular part　63
Inferior frontal sulcus　63
Inferior ganglion　37, 45
Inferior gemellus　289, 297, 301, 303, 305, 325, 333
Inferior glenohumeral ligament　143
Inferior gluteal artery　281, 282, 283, 289, 325
Inferior gluteal line　294
Inferior gluteal vein　325
Inferior head　42, 44
Inferior horn : Temporal horn　48, 72, 74, 76
Inferior hypogastric plexus　271, 282
Inferior ileocaecal recess　261
Inferior lateral genicular artery　345, 353
Inferior lingular bronchus　209, 213
Inferior lingular segment　210, 211, 213
Inferior lip　260
Inferior lobar arteries　214
Inferior lobar bronchus　213
Inferior lobe　209, 210, 211, 212, 213, 254
Inferior medial genicular artery　345, 353
Inferior mental (genial) spine　18

Inferior mesenteric artery　245, 249, 258, 271, 272, 274, 375
Inferior mesenteric ganglion　274
Inferior mesenteric nodes　274
Inferior mesenteric plexus　271
Inferior mesenteric vein　245, 258, 270, 375
Inferior nasal concha　1, 12, 16, 43, 55, 56
　Anterior end　26
　Ethmoidal process　26
　Lacrimal process　26
　Posterior end　26
Inferior nasal meatus　12, 21, 55
Inferior nasal retinal arteriole　53
Inferior nasal retinal venule　53
Inferior nuchal line　7, 9, 27
Inferior oblique　51, 52, 54, 80
Inferior olive　66, 76, 78
Inferior orbital fissure　1, 7, 9, 12
Inferior pancreaticoduodenal artery　272
Inferior parietal lobule　63
Inferior phrenic artery　252, 264, 267, 268, 270, 274
Inferior phrenic vein　267, 268, 270
Inferior pole　261, 264, 270, 251
Inferior pubic ramus　282, 291, 294, 296, 336
Inferior ramus of pubis　300
Inferior rectal artery　291, 292, 326
Inferior rectal nerves　289, 291, 292
Inferior rectal veins　291, 292, 326
Inferior rectus　44, 52, 54, 80
Inferior root　29, 31, 33
Inferior sagittal sinus　61
Inferior salivatory nucleus　85
Inferior segmental artery　265
Inferior suprarenal artery　252
Inferior temporal gyrus　63, 64
Inferior temporal line　4, 20, 24, 40
Inferior temporal sulcus　63, 64
Inferior thyroid artery　31, 35, 36, 37, 192, 194, 195, 218, 367, 368
　Branches to longus colli　367
　Esophageal branch　37
Inferior thyroid tubercle　48
Inferior thyroid vein　30, 32, 36, 190, 191, 192, 193, 194, 217, 218, 366
Inferior tibiofibular joint　315, 364
Inferior tracheobronchial nodes　369
Inferior transverse ligament　314, 359
Inferior trunk　147, 148
Inferior tubercle　91
Inferior vena cava　103, 192, 193, 194, 196, 197, 199, 200, 203, 204, 208, 222, 225, 231, 240, 243, 245, 252, 255, 256, 261, 264, 266, 268, 270, 271, 272, 279
Inferior vertebral notch　90, 91, 92
Inferior vesical artery　280, 281, 283
Infra-orbital artery　38, 52, 54
Infra-orbital canal　21
Infra-orbital foramen　1, 12, 21, 38, 54
Infra-orbital groove　12, 21
Infra-orbital margin　1, 16, 21, 38
Infra-orbital nerve　38, 40, 51, 52, 53, 54, 81, 82
Infra-orbital vein　38

Infraclavicular fossa 28, 132, 217
Infraclavicular nodes 185, 370
Infraglenoid tubercle 118
Infrahyoid muscles 190, 192, 193, 195
Infrapatellar branch 338, 347
Infrapatellar fat pad 341, 342, 347
Infraspinatus 104, 105, 106, 117, 119, 121, 136, 138, 139, 140, 141, 142, 152
Infraspinous fascia 105, 137
Infraspinous fossa 116, 118, 139, 141
Infratemporal crest 7, 9, 25
Infratemporal surface 7, 21, 25
Infratrochlear nerve 51, 52, 81
Infundibular recess 68, 72
Infundibulum 197, 198, 199, 201
Infundibulum of uterine tube 287
Inguinal falx 234, 235, 299, 301
Inguinal ligament 234, 235, 271, 275, 276, 277, 280, 282, 284, 293, 295, 297, 299, 301, 328, 330, 331, 333, 376
Inguinal region 227
Inguinal triangle 232, 233
Inion 4, 7
Inner ear 58
Innermost intercostal muscle 188, 189, 194, 195
Insula 63, 74, 75, 76, 77
Insular 63
Insular lobe 63, 74, 75, 76, 77
Interatrial septum 201
Intercondylar eminence 310, 312, 341, 343
Intercondylar fossa 308, 343
Intercostal membranes 181
Intercostal muscles 181
Intercostal nerve 194, 195, 221, 223
Intercostal space 369
Intercostobrachial nerves 135, 144, 145, 146, 149, 150, 370, 371
Intercrural fissure 70
Intergluteal cleft 105, 324
Intermaxillary suture 9
Intermediate cuneiform 318, 320, 364
Intermediate dorsal cutameous nerve 346
Intermediate nerve 61, 85
Intermediate sacral crest 94
Intermesenteric plexus 274
Internal acoustic meatus 3, 11, 17, 23, 58, 71, 83
Internal branch 28, 29, 31, 32, 33, 34, 35, 45, 47, 49, 50, 84
Internal capsule 76, 77
　Anterior limb 74, 75, 76
　Genu 75
　Posterior limb 74, 75, 76
Internal carotid artery 31, 32, 34, 35, 36, 37, 44, 45, 47, 51, 53, 56, 58, 59, 60, 61, 66, 67, 68, 71, 78
Internal carotid nerve 37
Internal cerebral veins 76
Internal iliac artery 271, 272, 280, 281, 282, 283, 288
　Anterior trunk 282, 283
　Posterior trunk 282, 283
Internal iliac vein 288
Internal intercostal membrane 189
Internal intercostal muscle 145, 181, 187, 188, 189
Internal jugular vein 29, 30, 31, 33, 35, 36, 37, 44, 45, 71, 135, 144, 147, 148, 190, 191, 217, 218, 219, 367, 368
Internal oblique 229, 230, 232, 234, 267, 275, 280, 299, 301
　Anterior layer of aponeurosis 228, 229
　Aponeurosis 229
　Posterior layer of aponeurosis 228
Internal occipital crest 27
Internal occipital protuberance 11, 17, 27
Internal os of uterus 285
Internal pudendal artery 281, 282, 283, 289, 290, 292, 326
Internal pudendal vein 290, 326
Internal spermatic fascia 278
Internal thoracic artery 36, 37, 144, 145, 189, 192, 193, 194, 195, 205, 207, 208, 218, 219, 220, 225, 368
Internal thoracic vein 36, 207, 217, 218, 220, 366
Internal thoracic veins 189
Internal urethral orifice 280, 281
Interosseous border 124, 125, 155, 310, 312, 314, 316
Interosseous ligament 314, 316, 317
Interosseous membrane of forearm 154, 155, 161
Interosseous membrane of leg 311, 313, 314, 317, 346
Interosseous metacarpal ligament 172
Interosseous sacro-iliac ligament 297, 299
Interpectoral nodes 185
Interpeduncular cistern 76
Interphalangeal joint of foot 359
Interphalangeal joint of hand 115
　Collateral ligament 172
Interspinous ligament 101, 102, 103
Interthalamic adhesion 68, 70
Intertragic incisure 57
Intertragic notch 57
Intertrochanteric crest 304
　Quadrate tubercle 302
Intertrochanteric line 302, 304, 333
Intertubercular lamella 90, 98, 99
Intertubercular sulcus 120
Intervenous tubercle 199
Interventricular foramen 68, 72, 74
Interventricular septum 208
　Membranous part 200
　Muscular part 200
Intervertebral disc 60, 98, 99, 101, 102, 223, 225, 260, 270, 276, 280
Intervertebral disc space 113
Intervertebral foramen 99, 102
Intrinsic muscles of tongue 85
Iris 51
Ischial spine 96, 277, 282, 284, 294, 296, 298, 300, 334
Ischial tuberosity 282, 284, 289, 290, 294, 296, 300, 324, 325, 326, 327, 333, 334, 336
　Longitudinal ridge 300
　Lower part 300
　Transverse ridge 300
　Upper part 300
Ischio-anal fossa 282, 289, 290, 324, 326

Ischiocavernosus 290, 291, 292, 297
Ischiococcygeus 95, 276, 277, 282, 297
Ischiofemoral ligament 295, 301
Ischiorectal fossa 282, 289, 290, 326
Ischium 336
Isthmus of cingulate gyrus 64
Isthmus of thyroid gland 28, 36, 48, 50, 190, 192, 193, 194, 195, 217, 218
Isthmus of uterine tube 287

【J】
Jejunal artery 248, 253, 279
Jejunal vein 248, 279
Jejunum 239, 241, 242, 245, 248, 249, 250, 261
Joint of head of rib 98
Jugular foramen 9, 11, 71, 84, 85
Jugular fossa 23
Jugular notch 27, 28, 179, 182, 183, 184, 217
Jugular process 27
Jugular surface 23
Jugular trunk 36, 37, 367
Jugular tubercle 27
Jugulodigastric nodes 32, 148
Jugum sphenoidale 11, 25

【K】
Kidney 84, 249, 260, 263, 267, 268, 272, 273, 274
　Inferior extremity 261, 264, 270
　Inferior pole 261, 264, 270
　Superior extremity 240, 243, 252, 264
　Superior pole 240, 243, 252, 264
Knee joint 351
Kyphosis 87

【L】
L1
　Dorsal ramus 102
　Ventral ramus 102
L2
　Dorsal ramus 102
　Ventral ramus 102
L4
　Ventral ramus 275, 333
L5
　Spinal ganglion 101
　Ventral ramus 102, 275
L I
　Inferior articular process 113
　Spinous process 263
　Vertebral body 101
L II
　Costal process 263
　Lamina 103
　Pars interarticularis 113
　Spinous process 102, 103, 113
　Superior articular process 113
L III 275
　Costal process 103, 113
　Lamina 103
　Pedicle 113
　Superior articular process 101
L IV
　Spinous process 263
　Vertebral body 102

L V
　Costal process　334, 336
　Inferior articular process　334
　Spinous process　95
　Superior articular process　95, 334
　Vertebral body　95, 102
Labium majus　234, 289
　Anterior commissure　289
　Posterior commissure　289
Labium minus　285, 289, 290
Lacrimal artery　51, 53, 54
Lacrimal bone　1, 4, 12
Lacrimal canaliculus　44, 51, 51
Lacrimal caruncle　51
Lacrimal catheters　51
Lacrimal fossa　20
Lacrimal gland　51, 52, 53, 54
Lacrimal groove　21
Lacrimal hamulus　21
Lacrimal nerve　44, 51, 52, 53, 54, 81
Lacrimal papilla　51
Lacrimal process　26
Lacrimal punctum　51
Lacrimal sac　51
Lactiferous duct　185
Lactiferous sinus　185
Lacunar ligament　235, 271, 277, 282, 284, 299, 301
Lambda　7, 8
Lambdoid border　27
Lambdoid suture　3, 4, 7, 8, 14, 17
Lamina　71, 89, 90, 91, 92, 93, 95, 103, 113, 223
Lamina of cricoid cartilage　48, 50
Lamina terminalis　68
Laryngeal inlet　50, 60
Laryngeal prominence　28, 30, 48, 217
Laryngeal ventricle　50
Laryngeal vestibule　50
Laryngopharynx　60
Larynx　113
Lateral angle　27
Lateral antebrachial cutaneous nerve　151, 156, 157, 158, 160
Lateral atlanto-axial joint　71, 98, 99, 112, 113
Lateral band　176
Lateral basal segment　210, 211, 212, 213
Lateral basal segmental bronchus　209
Lateral bony ampulla　58
Lateral border　116, 118, 143
Lateral branch　198, 202, 203
Lateral caval nodes　375
Lateral cervical nodes
　Superficial nodes　147, 148
Lateral circumflex calf vein　349
Lateral circumflex femoral artery　230, 327, 330
　Ascending branch　330
　Descending branch　330
　Transverse branch　330
Lateral condyle　304, 307, 308, 310, 312, 315, 337, 339, 340, 341, 343
Lateral cord　144, 145, 146, 150, 371
Lateral costotransverse ligament　181, 223
Lateral crico-arytenoid　49
Lateral cuneiform　318, 320, 364

Lateral cutaneous branches　137
Lateral cutaneous nerve of forearm　151, 156, 157, 158, 160
Lateral epicondyle　122, 126, 153, 154, 156, 157, 161, 308, 343
Lateral femoral cutaneous nerve　233, 271, 272, 273, 274, 275, 330, 373, 375, 376
Lateral femoral intermuscular septum　332
Lateral geniculate body　70, 79
Lateral glosso-epiglottic fold　49
Lateral head　121, 133, 139, 143, 150, 152, 309, 337, 338, 341, 344, 345, 346, 347, 350, 351, 352
Lateral incisor : 2nd incisor　13
Lateral intercondylar tubercle　310, 312, 343
Lateral ligament　172
Lateral lip　120
Lateral malleolar facet　320
Lateral malleolus　311, 315, 316, 348, 351, 354, 355, 357, 359, 364
　Groove for fibularis (peroneus) brevis　359
Lateral mass　3, 71, 98, 99, 112, 113
　Inferior articular surface　89
　Superior articular surface　89
Lateral meniscus　339, 340, 341, 342, 347
　Anterior horn　313, 340
　Posterior horn　313, 340
Lateral nodes　185, 370
Lateral occipito-temporal gyrus　64
Lateral part　27, 93, 94, 101, 102, 112
Lateral pectoral nerve　144, 145, 146, 150, 371
Lateral plantar artery　359, 360, 361, 362
Lateral plantar nerve　358, 359, 360, 361
　Branches of Deep branch　362
　Common plantar digital nerve　361
　Deep branch　361
　Proper plantar digital nerve　360
Lateral plantar vein　359
Lateral plate　7, 9, 12, 17, 25, 44
Lateral process　57
Lateral process of calcaneal tuberosity　318, 320
Lateral pterygoid　19, 43
　Inferior head　42, 44
　Upper head　10, 42
Lateral recess　72
Lateral rectus　43, 51, 52, 53, 54, 80
Lateral region　227
Lateral root of median nerve　150, 371
Lateral sacral artery　281, 282, 283
Lateral sacral crest　94
Lateral segment　210, 211, 212
Lateral segmental bronchus　209
Lateral semicircular canal　57, 58
Lateral sulcus　63
　Anterior ramus　63
　Ascending ramus　63
　Posterior ramus　63
Lateral superficial dorsal vein of penis　278
Lateral supracondylar line　306, 308
Lateral supracondylar ridge　122
Lateral sural cutaneous nerve　338, 344, 347, 350, 352

Lateral surface　124, 310, 311, 312, 316, 21, 355
Lateral talocalcaneal ligament　321
Lateral thoracic artery　135, 145, 146, 147, 148, 370, 371
Lateral tubercle　318, 320, 91
Lateral umbilical fold　232, 233
Lateral ventricle　47, 60, 77
　Anterior horn　72, 74, 75, 76
　Antrum　72
　Body　72, 74, 76
　Central part　72, 74, 76
　Frontal horn　72, 74, 75, 76
　Inferior horn　72, 74
　Occipital horn　72, 74, 75
　Posterior horn　72, 74, 75
　Tempolal horn　72, 74
　Trigone area　72
Latissimus dorsi　88, 105, 106, 107, 117, 121, 133, 136, 137, 138, 139, 140, 141, 144, 145, 146, 147, 148, 149, 150, 152, 181, 186, 190, 191, 371
Left atrioventricular orifice　200
Left atrioventricular valve　184, 200
Left atrium　197, 198, 200, 201, 203, 214
Left auricle　196, 197, 198, 203
Left brachiocephalic vein　36, 37, 190, 191, 207, 208, 217, 218, 219, 224, 366
Left branch　244, 246, 255, 256, 258
Left bundle　200
Left colic artery　249, 258
　Sigmoid branches　375
Left colic flexure　250, 259, 372
Left colic vein　258, 270
Left coronary artery　198, 200, 202, 203
　Anterior interventricular branch　196, 202, 203
　Circumflex branch　197, 198, 200, 203
　Marginal branch　198, 203
Left coronary artery branches　200
Left coronary cusp　200, 201
Left crus　267, 270
Left fibrous ring　200, 201
Left fibrous trigone　200, 201
Left gastric artery　244, 246, 247, 251, 258, 260, 267, 372
　Anterior branch　244
　Esophageal branch　244, 251, 372
　Posterior branch　244
Left gastric vein　251, 256, 258
Left gastro-epiploic artery　244, 246, 251
Left gastro-epiploic vein　241, 246, 251
Left gastro-omental artery　244, 246, 251
Left gastro-omental vein　241, 246, 251
Left hepatic duct　246, 247, 256, 257
Left hepatic vein　256
Left inferior lobar bronchus　193, 194, 209, 212, 215
Left inferior pulmonary vein　192, 193, 196, 197, 198, 206, 207, 213, 214, 216, 222
Left lamina　47, 49, 50
Left lobe　30, 32, 34, 36, 190, 193, 194, 218
Left lobe of liver　238, 240, 243, 244, 245, 253, 254, 255, 256, 260

Left lobes　48
Left lung　190, 191, 192, 193, 209, 210, 212
Left main bronchus　195, 206, 207, 209, 212, 213, 214, 215, 216, 222, 369
Left marginal artery　197, 198, 200, 202, 203
Left marginal vein　198
Left ovarian vein　103, 245, 267, 268, 270
Left pulmonary artery　193, 194, 206, 207, 213, 214, 215, 216, 222, 369
　Superior lobar artery　208
Left pulmonary veins　203
Left semilunar cusp　200, 201
Left superior intercostal vein　206, 207
Left superior lobar bronchus　209, 212, 215
Left superior pulmonary vein　193, 196, 197, 198, 206, 207, 213, 216, 222
Left suprarenal vein　264, 266, 267, 268, 270
Left testicular vein　103, 245, 267, 268, 272
Left triangular ligament　255
Left ventricle　191, 196, 197, 198, 200, 203, 207, 208
Lens　60
Lentiform nucleus
　Pallidum：Paleostriatum　74, 76
　Putamen　74, 75, 76
Lesser curvature　240, 243, 244, 247, 251, 252, 372
Lesser horn　48
Lesser occipital nerve　29, 31, 32, 33, 108
Lesser omentum　240, 243, 244, 251
Lesser palatine canals　22
Lesser palatine foramina　9
Lesser palatine nerves　44, 55
Lesser petrosal nerve　44, 57, 84, 85
Lesser sac　241, 253, 260
Lesser sciatic foramen　284
Lesser sciatic notch　294, 296, 300, 334
Lesser trochanter　302, 304, 306, 333, 336
Lesser tubercle　120, 142
Lesser wing　1, 3, 11, 12, 16, 25, 43
Levator anguli oris　2, 6, 39
Levator ani　235, 282, 284, 286, 289, 290, 292, 297, 324, 326
　Iliococcygeus　277
　Pubococcygeus　277
　Puborectalis　281
Levator labii superioris　2, 6, 39
Levator labii superioris alaeque nasi　2, 6, 39
Levator palpebrae superioris　51, 52, 53, 54, 80
　Aponeurosis　51
Levator scapulae　29, 31, 33, 37, 106, 117, 119, 138, 139, 140, 141
Levator veli palatini　10, 47
Levatores costarum　181
Lienorenal ligament　260
Ligament of head of femur　303, 334, 336
Ligament of ovary　285, 287

Ligamentum arteriosum　193, 194, 207, 369
Ligamentum flava　103
Limbus fossae ovali　199
Limen insulae　63
Linea alba　193, 228, 229, 230
Linea aspera　304, 306
Linea semilunaris　228, 230, 232
Lingual artery　31, 32, 34, 35, 56
　Suprahyoid branch　31, 32
Lingual gyrus　64, 68
Lingual nerve　29, 35, 42, 44, 56, 81, 82
Lingual vein　31, 32
Lingula　17, 18
Lingula of left lung　192, 216
Lingular bronchus　213
Lingular vein
　Inferior part　213
　Superior part　213
Linguofacial trunk　29
Lister's tubercle　124, 126, 155
Little finger
　Proximal phalanx　128
Liver　84, 237, 242, 247, 270, 372
　Caudate lobe　244, 246, 247, 251
　Quadrate lobe　240, 244
　Riedel's lobe　245
Llight reflex　57
lntraparietal sulcus　63
Lobar bronchi　209
Lobule of auricle　57
Long ciliary nerves　53, 54, 81
Long gyrus of insula　63
Long head　106, 107, 117, 119, 133, 135, 136, 137, 139, 140, 142, 143, 149, 150, 151, 152, 289, 290, 326, 327, 332
Long limb　57
Long plantar ligament　319, 359, 363
Long saphenous vein　230, 234, 280, 328, 332, 338, 347, 348, 349, 352, 354, 356, 357, 359, 376
Long thoracic nerve　135, 144, 145, 146, 147, 148, 149
Longissimus　105, 106, 107
Longissimus capitis　10
Longitudinal bands　98
Longitudinal cerebral fissure　62, 64
Longitudinal crease　163
Longitudinal ridge　300
Longus capitis　10, 37, 71
Longus colli　37, 207, 368
Loose connective tissue　5
Lordosis　87
Lower crus　57
Lower edge　263
Lower lateral incisor　16
Lower part　300
Lower subscapular nerves　147, 148, 149, 150
Lower trunk　147, 148
Lumbar nerves　106
Lumbar splanchnic nerves　274
Lumbar triangle　105, 106
Lumbar vertebrae　87
　Costal process　269
Lumbosacral trunk　273, 275, 276, 282,

284, 333
Lumbrical　166, 171, 176, 360, 361, 362
Lunate　128, 129, 172, 173, 177, 178
Lunate sulcus　74
Lunate surface　334
Lung　84
Luschka's joint　112
Lymph node　367, 371, 376
Lymphatic vessel　230, 268, 367, 370, 371, 376

【M】

Macula
　Fovea centralis　53
Magendie 孔　68
Main pancreatic duct　257
Major calyx　265, 269
Major duodenal papilla　253
Major forceps　75
Malleolar fossa　315, 316
Malleus　57, 58
　Lateral process　57
Mamillary body　66, 68, 79
Mamillary process　92
Mammary fat pad　185
Mammillary body　70
Mandible　12, 30, 33, 43, 60
　Coronoid process　4
　Ramus of mandible　4, 16
Mandibular canal　42
Mandibular foramen　17, 18
Mandibular fossa　7, 9, 23
Mandibular nerve [V₃]　42, 44, 47, 56, 59, 82
　Buccal nerve　40, 42
　Muscular branches　44
Mandibular notch　18
Mandibular symphysis　14
Manubriosternal joint　182, 183, 184, 217
Manubrium of sternum　36, 48, 179, 182, 183, 217
Margin of anus　289, 291, 292
Marginal arcade　249
Marginal artery　249
Marginal branch　64, 198, 203
Marginal mandibular branch　31, 32, 34, 39, 83
Marginal sulcus　64
Marginal tubercle　12, 24
Massa intermedia　68, 70
Masseter　2, 6, 10, 19, 32, 33, 34, 39, 40, 43
　Anterior border　28, 38
Masseteric nerve　81, 82
Mastoid angle　17, 24
Mastoid antrum　57, 58
Mastoid border　27
Mastoid canaliculus　23
Mastoid cells　57, 58
Mastoid fontanelle　14
Mastoid foramen　9
Mastoid notch　7, 9, 23
Mastoid process　3, 4, 7, 9, 16, 23, 28, 37, 57, 84
Maxilla　1, 4, 12, 14, 43
　Alveolar process　17
　Alveolarridge　43

Frontal process　　1, 4, 12, 26
　Infratemporal surface　　7
　Palatine process　　9, 12, 17, 22, 26
Maxillary air sinus　　82
Maxillary artery　　42, 47, 56, 82
　Pterygoid branches　　43
Maxillary border　　24
Maxillary hiatus　　21
Maxillary nerve [V₂]　　44, 54, 56, 59, 82
Maxillary process　　22, 26
Maxillary sinus　　16, 21, 43, 44, 55
Maxillary tuberosity　　7, 9, 21
McBurney's point　　231
MCPJ　　172
Medial antebrachial cutaneous nerve　　144, 145, 147, 148, 149, 150, 151, 156, 157, 371
Medial basal segment　　210, 211, 212, 213
Medial basal segmental bronchus　　209
Medial border　　88, 116, 136, 138, 139, 140, 141, 186, 310, 312
Medial brachial cutaneous nerve　　149, 150, 157, 158, 371
Medial calcaneal branches　　348, 355, 356
Medial circumflex femoral artery　　327, 330, 335
Medial circumflex femoral veins　　335
Medial clunial nerves　　324
Medial condyle　　304, 307, 308, 310, 311, 312, 339, 340, 341, 343, 347, 351
Medial cord　　145, 150, 219, 371
Medial crest　　316
Medial cuneiform　　318, 320, 359, 363, 364
Medial cutaneous nerve of arm　　149, 150, 157, 158, 371
Medial cutaneous nerve of forearm　　144, 145, 147, 148, 149, 150, 151, 156, 157, 371
Medial dorsal cutaneous nerve　　346, 355
Medial eminence　　71, 77
Medial epicondyle　　122, 126, 153, 154, 156, 157, 159, 160, 308, 343, 371
Medial frontal gyrus　　64
Medial geniculate body　　70, 79
Medial head　　121, 123, 150, 156, 309, 338, 344, 345, 347, 350, 351, 352
Medial intercondylar tubercle　　310, 312, 343
Medial intermuscular septum of arm　　151
Medial ligament：Deltoid ligament　　311, 314, 358, 359, 363
　Posterior tibiotalar part　　359
　Tibiocalcaneal part　　321, 359
Medial lip　　120
Medial malleolar facet　　320
Medial malleolus　　311, 314, 315, 348, 351, 354, 355, 356, 357, 359, 364
　Groove for tibialis posterior　　359
Medial meniscus　　339, 340, 341, 342, 343
　Anterior horn　　313, 340
　Posterior horn　　313, 340
Medial palpebral ligament　　38, 51
Medial patellar retinaculum　　332
Medial pectoral nerve　　144, 145, 147, 148, 149
Medial plantar artery　　359, 361, 362

Medial plantar nerve　　358, 361, 362
　Common plantar digital nerve　　361
　Proper plantar digital nerve　　360
Medial plate　　7, 9, 12, 17, 25
Medial process of calcaneal tuberosity　　318, 320, 321
Medial pterygoid　　19, 42, 43, 44, 47, 56
　Deep head　　10
　Superficial head　　10
Medial rectus　　44, 51, 52, 53, 80
Medial root of median nerve　　150, 371
Medial segment　　210, 211, 212
Medial segmental bronchus　　209
Medial supracondylar line　　306, 308
Medial supracondylar ridge　　122
Medial sural cutaneous nerve　　344, 352
Medial surface　　50, 125, 310, 311, 312, 314, 316, 347, 348, 355
Medial surface of cerebral hemisphere　　60, 26, 320
Medial talocalcaneal ligament　　321
Medial tarsal arteries　　358
Medial tubercle　　318, 320, 364
Medial umbilical fold　　233, 235
Medial umbilical ligament　　232, 235, 373, 285
Medial wall　　44
Medial wall of Orbit　　44
Median antebrachial vein　　157, 159, 371
Median aperture of 4th ventricle　　68, 70
Median arcuate ligament　　270
Median artery　　153, 158
Median cricothyroid ligament　　48
Median cubital vein　　157, 159, 371
Median eminence　　66, 68
Median furrow　　105
Median glosso-epiglottic fold　　49
Median nerve　　135, 144, 145, 146, 147, 148, 149, 150, 151, 153, 156, 157, 158, 159, 160, 163, 166, 167, 168, 169, 171, 177, 219, 371
　Common palmar digital nerves　　168
　Muscular branches　　160
　Palmar branch　　159, 166, 167, 168
　Recurrent branch　　166, 167, 168, 169
Median palatine suture　　9
Median sacral artery　　333
Median sacral crest　　94
Median sulcus　　71, 77
Median umbilical fold　　233, 235
Median umbilical ligament　　232, 285
Mediastinal pleura　　206
Medulla　　84
Medulla oblongata：Myelencephalon　　60, 61, 62, 66, 67, 68, 70, 100
　Inferior olive　　66, 76, 78
Medullary cone　　101
Medullary striae of fourth ventricle　　71
Membranous part　　200, 281
Meningeal branch　　81
Meningeal sheath　　111
Mental artery　　38
Mental foramen　　1, 4, 13, 16, 18, 38
Mental nerve　　38, 40, 81, 82
Mental protuberance　　1, 4, 17, 18
Mental tubercle　　18
Mental vein　　38

Mentalis　　2, 19, 40
Mesencephalon　　59, 60
Mesentery　　241, 242, 248, 260, 261
Meso-appendix　　242, 261
Mesosalpinx　　287
Mesovarium　　287
Metacarpophalangeal joint (MCPJ)　　164, 172
　Palmar ligament　　172
Metatarsals　　293
　Collateral ligaments　　363
Metopic suture　　14
Meyer's loop　　79
Midbrain　　59, 60
　Inferior colliculus　　68
　Superior colliculus　　68
Middle cardiac vein　　197, 203
Middle cerebellar peduncle　　70, 83
Middle cerebral artery　　51, 59, 66, 67, 68, 73
Middle cervical ganglion　　35, 37
Middle colic artery　　248, 253, 258
Middle colic vein　　258
Middle concha　　79
Middle constrictor　　45, 47, 48
Middle cranial fossa　　59
Middle ear　　58, 84
Middle facet for calcaneus　　321
Middle finger
　Base of middle phalanx　　128
　Body of middle phalanx　　128
　Distal phalanx　　129, 178
　Head of middle phalanx　　128
　Middle phalanx　　129, 178
　Proximal phalanx　　129, 178
　Shaft of Middle phalanx　　128
Middle frontal gyrus　　63
Middle genicular artery　　345
Middle glenohumeral ligament　　143
Middle layer　　267
Middle lobar bronchus　　193, 195, 214, 215, 216
Middle lobe　　209, 210, 211, 212
Middle lobe bronchus　　209
Middle meningeal artery　　42, 47, 56, 59, 82
Middle meningeal veins　　59
Middle nasal concha　　1, 16, 26, 55, 56
Middle nasal meatus　　21, 55
Middle phalanx　　129, 178, 318
Middle rectal artery　　281, 283, 288
Middle scalene　　29, 30, 31, 32, 34, 36, 37, 135, 181
Middle talar articular surface　　321, 358
Middle temporal gyrus　　63
Middle thyroid vein　　29, 36
Middle trunk　　147, 148
Middle wrist crease　　163
Minor calyx　　265, 269
Minor forceps　　74, 75, 76
Mitral valve　　184, 200
　Anterior cusp　　200, 201
　Posterior cusp　　200, 201
Moderator band　　199
Modiolus　　58
Molar salivary glands　　29
Mons pubis　　228, 229, 289

Morrison's pouch   243
Motor decussat10n   70
Motor root   56, 61
Multifidus   107
Muscular process   48
Muscular tributary   349
Musculi pectinati   199, 201
Musculocutaneous nerve   135, 142, 144, 145, 146, 147, 148, 150, 151, 219, 371
Musculophrenic artery   225
Musculus uvulae   10
Myelencephalon : Medulla oblongata   66, 76, 78
Mylohyoid   19, 29, 30, 32, 33, 34, 35, 42, 48, 56
Mylohyoid groove   17, 18
Mylohyoid line   17, 18
Myocardial bridge   197, 198
Myometrium   286

【N】

Nares   38
Nasal bone   1, 4, 12, 17
Nasal crest   21, 22
Nasal notch   21
Nasal septum   1, 3, 16, 38, 43, 56, 60, 61
Nasal spine   12, 20
Nasal surface   21
Nasal vestibule   55
Nasalis   2, 6, 39
Nasion   1, 4
Nasociliary nerve   44, 51, 52, 53, 54, 81
Nasolabial sulcus   38
Nasolacrimal duct   12, 51, 55
Nasopharynx   60, 79
Natal cleft   105, 324
Navicular   318, 320, 358, 359, 364
Neck of 1st rib   183, 205, 220
Neck of bladder   285, 373
Neck of femur   302, 304, 335, 336
Neck of fibula   311, 316
Neck of gallbladder   256
Neck of mandible   18, 47
Neck of pancreas   253
Neck of radius   124, 126, 154, 155
Neck of rib   181, 223
Neck of scapula   116
Neck of talus   318, 320, 359, 364
Nerve of pterygoid canal   44, 55
Nerve to lateral pterygoid   82
Nerve to medial pterygoid   56
Nerve to mylohyoid   29, 42, 56, 81
Nerve to stapedius   58
Nerves to levator ani   282, 284
Nerves to pterygoids   81
Nipple   132, 184, 185
Nodule [X]   70
Noncoronary cusp   200, 201
Nostrils   38
Nuchal ligament   108, 109
Nucleus pulposus   103

【O】

Obex   71
Oblique arytenoid   47, 49
Oblique band   154

Oblique cord   154
Oblique fissure   213, 216
Oblique head   130, 171, 361, 362
Oblique line   18, 33
Oblique pericardial sinus   196
Oblique vein of left atrium   203
Obliquus capitis inferior   109, 110
Obliquus capitis superior   10, 109
Obturator artery   235, 271, 280, 281, 282, 283, 285, 288, 333, 373
Obturator crest   294, 300
Obturator externus   295, 301, 303, 305, 333, 334
Obturator fascia   277, 282, 284, 289
Obturator foramen   96, 284, 294, 296, 300, 336
Obturator groove   294, 296, 300
Obturator internus   276, 277, 282, 284, 289, 297, 303, 305, 325, 333
Obturator membrane   284
Obturator nerve   235, 271, 273, 274, 275, 276, 280, 281, 282, 283, 284, 285, 288, 331, 373
　Anterior branch   330, 333
　Posterior branch   333
Obturator vein   235, 271, 283, 285, 288, 333, 373
Occipital angle   24
Occipital artery   29, 34, 35, 37, 44, 108, 109, 110, 111
　Sternocleidomastoid branches   29
Occipital belly   6, 10, 108, 110, 111
Occipital bone   4, 7, 8, 14, 17, 100, 109
　Basilar part   3, 98, 112
　Cerebellar fossa   11
Occipital border   24
Occipital condyle   7, 9, 17, 27
Occipital forceps   74, 75, 76
Occipital groove   7, 9, 23
Occipital horn   72, 74, 75
Occipital lobe   63
Occipital pole   62, 63
Occipitofrontalis
　Aponeurosis   5
　Frontal belly   5, 39
　Occipital belly   6, 10, 108, 110, 111
Occiptal lobe   79
Oculomotor nerve [III]   44, 52, 56, 59, 61, 66, 67, 70, 78, 80
　Inferior branch   54
Odontoid peg   89
Olecranon   125, 126, 153, 154, 155, 156
Olecranon fossa   122, 123, 154, 156
Olfactory bulb   59, 66, 78
Olfactory nerves   55
Olfactory sulcus   64
Olfactory tract   59, 61, 66, 67, 79
Olive   67, 70
Omental appendices   237, 238, 239, 241, 242
Omental bursa   241, 253, 260
Omental foramen   240, 243, 244
Omohyoid   31, 34, 48, 85, 139, 141, 144, 145
　Inferior belly   28, 29, 30, 31, 32, 117, 119, 135, 146, 195
　Superior belly   29, 30, 31, 32, 33, 35,

147, 148
Opening for left coronary artery   197, 201
Opening for right coronary artery   200, 201
Opening of coronary sinus   199, 200
Opening of inferior vena cava   197, 199
Opening of maxillary sinus   12
Openings of sphenoidal sinuses   25
Opercular part   63
Ophthalmic artery   51, 53, 54, 60
Ophthalmic nerve [V₁]   44, 56, 59, 81
Opponens digiti minimi   130, 169, 171, 319, 362
Opponens pollicis   130, 171
Optic canal   11, 12, 25
Optic chiasm   47, 51, 59, 60, 66, 68, 70, 79
Optic chiasma   47, 51, 59, 60, 66, 68, 70, 79
Optic disc   53
Optic nerve [II]   43, 44, 51, 52, 53, 54, 55, 56, 59, 60, 61, 66, 67, 70, 73, 78, 79, 81
Optic radiation   74, 75, 79
Optic tract   59, 66, 70, 76, 79
Oral cavity   43
Oral vestibule   43
Orbicularis oculi   2, 6, 39, 40
Orbicularis oris   39, 40
Orbit   1
　Medial wall   44
Orbital border   24
Orbital cavity   1
Orbital fat body   51
Orbital gyri   64
Orbital margin   12
Orbital part   11, 12, 17, 20, 63
Orbital plate   4, 12, 26
Orbital process   12, 22
Orbital septum   51
Orbital sulci   64, 66
Orbital surface   21, 24, 25, 21
Orifice of ileal papilla : Ileal orifice   250
　Inferior lip   260
　Superior lip   260
Oropharynx   60, 226
Osseous spiral lamina   58
Otic ganglion   44, 82, 84
Outer sheath   52
Oval window   58
Ovarian vein   375
Ovary   286
　Tubal extremity   287
　Uterine extremity   287

【P】

Palate   43
Palatine bone   12, 16
　Horizontal plate   7, 9, 12, 17, 22, 26
　Maxillary process   22
　Orbital process   12
　Perpendicular plate   12, 26
　Pyramidal process   7, 9
Palatine grooves   9
Palatine process   9, 12, 17, 21, 22, 26
Palatine spines   9
Palatine tonsil   84

Palatomaxillary suture 9
Palatopharyngeus 10, 47
Palatovaginal canal 9
Paleostriatum 74, 75, 76, 77
Pallidum 74, 75, 76, 77
Palmar aponeurosis 166
Palmar branch 159, 166, 167, 168
Palmar interossei 171, 176
Palmar ligament 172, 172
Palmar metacarpal artery 170, 171
Palmar radiocarpal ligament 172
Palmar ulnocarpal ligament 172
Palmaris brevis 163, 166, 167, 168, 169
Palmaris longus 159, 163, 167, 177
Pampiniform plexus 278
Pancreas 84, 247, 253, 372
   Uncinate process 245, 253
Pancreatic duct 246, 257, 258
Pancreaticoduodenal arteries 258
Pancreaticoduodenal veins 258
Para-aortic nodes 245, 268, 270
Para-aortic vessels 368
Paracentral lobule
   Anterior paracentral gyrus 64
   Posterior paracentral gyrus 64
Paracentral rami 64
Parahippocampal gyrus 64, 66
Paranasal sinuses
   Maxillary sinus 43
Parasternal nodes 185
Parietal bone 4, 7, 8, 11, 17
   Mastoid angle 17
Parietal branch 5
Parietal foramen 7, 8, 24
Parietal layer 191, 192, 193, 194, 278, 279
Parietal lobe 63
Parietal notch 23
Parietal peritoneum 233, 237, 241, 242, 247, 279
Parietal pleura 193, 194, 195, 218, 219, 369
Parietal tuber 8, 14, 24
Parieto-occipital sulcus 62, 63, 64, 68
Parotid branch 81
Parotid duct 29, 38, 40
Parotid gland 28, 30, 32, 33, 34, 39, 40, 43, 47, 56, 81, 82, 84
Parotid plexus 83
Pars flaccida 57
Pars interarticularis 113
Pars tensa 57
Patella 293, 332, 337, 338, 341, 342, 343
Patellar ligament 307, 311, 313, 337, 340, 341, 342, 346, 347
Patellar surface 308
Pecten pubis 96, 296, 298, 300, 336
Pectinate muscles 199, 201
Pectineal ligament 271, 284, 299, 301
Pectineal line 302, 306
Pectineus 276, 280, 299, 301, 305, 306, 328, 330, 331, 334, 335, 376
Pectoral branches 135, 144, 145, 149, 190, 191, 192, 370
Pectoral fascia 185
Pectoralis major 28, 30, 119, 121, 132, 135, 139, 142, 144, 145, 146, 149, 183, 185, 186, 190, 192, 208, 366, 370, 371
   Abdominal part 133, 228
   Clavicular head 133, 134
   Sternal head 133
   Sternocostal head 134
Pectoralis minor 117, 135, 144, 145, 146, 147, 148, 149, 150, 187, 190, 191, 192, 193, 208, 370, 371
Pedicle 89, 90, 91, 92, 98, 99, 101, 102, 113
Pelvic brim 233
Pelvic plexus 271, 282
Pelvic splanchnic nerves 271, 282
Pelvic surface 93
Pelviureteric junction 269
Penis 278, 331
   Corona of glans 328
Perforating artery 327, 328
Perforating branch 357
Perforating cutaneous nerve 292, 324
Pericardiacophrenic artery 206, 207
Pericardiacophrenic veins 206, 207
Pericardial cavity 207
Pericardium 196, 204, 205, 206, 207, 222, 240
Perineal artery 292
Perineal body 289, 290, 291
Perineal branches 289, 292
Perineal muscles 286
Perineal nerve 292
Perineal raphe 290, 291
Perinephric fat 267
Perineural cyst 286
Periosteum 5, 51
Perirenal fat capsule 267
Peritoneum 103, 241, 260, 261, 267, 288
   Recto-vesical pouch 279
Permanent teeth
   1st incisor：Central incisor 13
   1st molar tooth 13
   1st premolar tooth 13
   2nd incisor：Lateral incisor 13
   2nd molar tooth 13
   2nd premolar tooth 13
   Canine tooth 13
Peroneus (fibularis) brevis 293
Peroneus (fibularis) longus 293
Perpendicular plate 12, 17, 22, 26, 55
Pes 73
Petit's triangle 105
Petrosquamous fissure 9, 23
Petrotympanic fissure 9, 23
Petrous part 11, 23, 56
   Arcuate eminence 11
Phalanges 293
Pharyngeal branch 45, 84
Pharyngeal nerve 55
Pharyngeal opening of auditory tube 55, 60
Pharyngeal plexus 84
Pharyngeal plexus of veins 47
Pharyngeal raphe 10, 45
Pharyngeal tonsil 60
Pharyngeal tubercle 9, 27
Pharyngeal veins 45
Pharyngobasilar fascia 45
Pharyngotympanic tube：Auditory tube 56, 58
   Bony part 57
Philtrum 38
Phrenic nerve 29, 30, 31, 32, 35, 36, 37, 135, 144, 145, 190, 191, 192, 193, 194, 195, 204, 205, 206, 207, 218, 219, 221, 225, 368, 369
Pineal body 68, 75
Pineal gland 68, 75
PIPJ 172
Piriform fossa 47, 226
Piriform recess 47, 226
Piriformis 95, 276, 277, 282, 284, 289, 295, 303, 305, 325, 333
Pisiform 128, 163, 167, 169, 170, 171, 172, 178
Pisohamate ligament 130, 172
Pisometacarpal ligament 130, 172
Pituitary gland 55, 60, 61
   Anterior lobe 60
   Posterior lobe 60
Pituitary stalk 59, 60, 66, 70, 78, 79
Plantar aponeurosis 359, 360
Plantar calcaneocuboid ligament 319, 359, 363
Plantar calcaneonavicular ligament 319, 321, 358, 359, 363
Plantar cuboideonavicular ligament 363
Plantar cuneonavicular ligament 363
Plantar digital arteries proper 362
Plantar digital nerve of great toe 362
Plantar interossei 361
Plantar metatarsal artery 362
Plantar metatarsal ligament 363
Plantaris 309, 319, 321, 344, 345, 351, 352, 353, 355, 356
Platysma 2, 6, 19, 30, 33, 40, 43
Pleura 98, 188, 205, 207, 225, 263, 267, 366, 368
   Lower edge 263
Pleural cavity 366
Pleural cupula 217
Pleural recesses
   Costodiaphragmatic recess 260, 263
Plica semilunaris 51
Pons 56, 60, 62, 66, 67, 68, 70, 76, 77, 78, 83
Pontine arteries 67
Popliteal artery 327, 344, 345, 352, 353
   Branches to Gastrocnemius 344
Popliteal fossa 337
Popliteal surface 308
Popliteal vein 327, 344, 349, 352
   Branches to Gastrocnemius 344
Popliteus 309, 311, 313, 339, 340, 341, 342, 345, 347, 351, 353
Postcentral gyrus 62, 63, 68
Postcentral sulcus 62, 63
Posterior antebrachial cutaneous nerve 139
Posterior arch 60, 61, 71, 89, 98, 99, 100, 109, 110, 111, 112
Posterior arch vein 348, 356
Posterior atlanto-occipital membrane 110, 111
Posterior auricular artery 29

Posterior auricular nerve 83
Posterior auricular vein 32, 217
Posterior band 154
Posterior basal segment 210, 211, 212, 213
Posterior basal segmental bronchus 209
Posterior belly 10, 29, 31, 32, 33, 35, 37, 42, 47, 56
Posterior border 9, 18, 25, 124, 125, 153, 316
Posterior brachial cutaneous nerve 137, 139, 140
Posterior branch 153, 158, 160, 265, 333, 244
Posterior calcaneal articluar facet 321
Posterior cerebellomedullary cistern 60
Posterior cerebral artery 59, 66, 67, 76, 78
Posterior ciliary artery 51, 53
Posterior circumflex humeral artery 143, 145, 146, 147, 148, 152
Posterior circumflex humeral vein 143
Posterior clinoid process 11, 25, 59
Posterior commissure 68, 289
Posterior communicating artery 59, 66, 67, 78
Posterior cord 145, 146, 150
Posterior crico-arytenoid 47, 48, 49
Posterior cruciate ligament 309, 311, 313, 339, 340, 341, 342
Posterior cusp 200, 201
Posterior cutaneous branches 111
Posterior cutaneous nerve of arm 137, 139, 140
Posterior cutaneous nerve of forearm 139
Posterior cutaneous nerve of thigh 325
Posterior end 26
Posterior ethmoidal foramen 12, 20
Posterior ethmoidal nerve 81
Posterior ethmoidal sulcus 26
Posterior femoral cutaneous nerve 325
　Inferior clunial nerves 324
　Perineal branches 289, 292
Posterior fontanelle 14
Posterior gluteal line 294
Posterior horn 72, 73, 74, 75, 313, 340
Posterior inferior cerebellar artery 66, 67, 71
Posterior inferior iliac spine 294, 296, 298
Posterior intercondylar area 312
Posterior intercostal artery 194, 195, 221
Posterior intercostal vein 194, 195, 221, 369
Posterior interosseous artery 176
Posterior interosseous nerve 156, 161
Posterior interventricular branch 197, 200, 202, 203
Posterior labial nerve 289
Posterior lacrimal crest 4, 12, 21
Posterior layer 229, 232, 233, 267, 324
Posterior layer of aponeurosis 228
Posterior limb 74, 75, 76
Posterior lobe 60
Posterior lobe of cerebellum 70
Posterior longitudinal ligament 98
Posterior meningeal artery 37, 45
Posterior meniscofemoral ligament 339, 341
Posterior nasal aperture 9, 17, 60, 61
Posterior nasal spine 9, 22
Posterior nodes 185, 370
Posterior papillary muscle 199, 200
Posterior paracentral gyrus 64
Posterior perforated substance 66, 68, 70, 79
Posterior process 364
Posterior ramus 63, 107, 223
Posterior rectus sheath 375
Posterior sacro-iliac ligament 334
Posterior scalene 34, 181
Posterior scrotal arteries 292
Posterior scrotal nerves 292
Posterior scrotal veins 292
Posterior segment 210, 211, 212
Posterior segmental bronchus 209
Posterior semicircular canal 58
Posterior semilunar cusp 200, 201
Posterior spinal artery 71, 98, 99
Posterior spinal veins 99
Posteiror superior alveolar branch 81
Posteiror superior alveolar nerves 82
Posterior superior iliac spine 104, 105, 294, 296, 298, 324, 334
Posterior surface 122, 124, 125, 281, 310, 312, 314, 316, 351, 352, 353, 321, 348, 355
Posterior talar articular surface 321, 358
Posterior talofibular ligament 317, 351, 357, 359
Posterior tibial artery 345, 352, 353, 354, 355, 356, 357, 358
Posterior tibial vein 349, 352, 355, 356, 357, 358
Posterior tibiofibular ligament 314, 317, 359
Posterior tibiotalar part 359
Posterior trunk 282, 283
Posterior tubercle 89, 90, 98, 99
Posterior vagal trunk 251, 267, 372
Posterior vein of left ventricle 203
Posterior wall of pericardial cavity 196
Posteriorobique ligament 154
Postglenoid tubercle 23
Pouch of Douglas 260, 285, 286, 287, 288, 373
Pre-aortic nodes 245, 268, 274
Pre-aortic vessels 368
Pre-olivary groove 70
Precentral gyrus 62, 63, 68
Precentral sulcus 62, 63
Prechiasmatic sulcus 11, 25
Preclival fissure 70
Precuneus 64
Premaxilla 55
Preoccipital notch 63
Prepontine cistern 60
Prepuce 278
Prepuce of clitoris 289
Prevertebral layer 367
Primary fissure 70
Primary visual area 79
Princeps pollicis artery 167, 169, 170
Procerus 2, 6, 39
Profunda brachii artery 143, 151, 152
Profunda brachii vein 143, 151
Promontory 57, 93, 94, 96, 260, 277, 279, 282, 284, 285, 336
Pronator quadratus 127, 159, 160, 171
Pronator teres 127, 151, 156, 157, 158, 159, 160, 161
　Humeral head 123, 160
　Ulnar head 127, 160
Pronator tuberosity 124
Proper palmar digital artery 167, 169, 170
Proper palmar digital nerves 167, 169, 171
Proper plantar digital nerve 360
Prostate 279, 281
　Posterior surface 281
Prostatic urethra 279, 281
Prostatic venous plexus 279, 281
Proximal interphalangeal joint 164
Proximal interphalangeal joint（PIPJ） 172
Proximal palmer crease 163
Proximal phalanx 128, 129, 178, 318, 359
Proximal radio-ulnar joint 154, 156
Proximal wrist crease 163
Psoas fascia 267
Psoas major 103, 261, 263, 267, 268, 270, 271, 273, 274, 276, 277, 280, 303, 305, 306, 331, 335, 375
Psoas minor 274, 297, 299, 301, 375
Pterion 4, 17
Pterygoid branches 43
Pterygoid canal 25
Pterygoid fovea 18
Pterygoid hamulus 7, 9, 12, 17, 25
Pterygoid notch 25
Pterygoid process 25
　Lateral plate 7, 9, 12, 17, 25, 44
　Medial plate 7, 9, 12, 17, 25
Pterygomandibular raphe 19
Pterygomaxillary fissure 7
Pterygopalatine fossa 7
Pterygopalatine ganglion 44, 55, 81, 82
Pubic branch 235
Pubic crest 296, 298, 300
Pubic symphysis 96, 231, 260, 277, 279, 281, 282, 284, 285, 290, 291, 297, 336
Pubic tubercle 96, 231, 294, 296, 298, 300, 331, 336
Pubococcygeus 277
Pubofemoral ligament 301, 333
Puborectalis 281
Pudendal nerve 284, 289, 290, 326, 333
Pulmonary ligament 216
Pulmonary pleura 219
Pulmonary trunk 192, 193, 194, 195, 196, 197, 198, 199, 200, 201, 203, 208, 214, 215, 369
Pulmonary valve 184, 200
　Anterior semilunar cusp 201
　Left semilunar cusp 201
　Right semilunar cusp 201
Pulmonary vein 190
Pulvinar 79
Pupil 51
Putamen 74, 75, 76, 77
Pyloric antrum 251, 252, 253

Pyloric canal 251, 252
Pylorus 246
Pyramid 66, 67, 70, 76, 78
Pyramidal process 7, 9, 22
Pyramidalis 228, 234, 299, 301

【Q】

Quadrangular membrane 49, 50
Quadrangular space 152
Quadrate lobe 240, 244, 255, 256
Quadrate tubercle 302, 304
Quadratus femoris 289, 295, 301, 303, 305, 306, 325, 327, 334
Quadratus lumborum 181, 267, 270, 271, 273, 274, 275, 297, 299, 375
Quadratus plantae 319, 359, 361, 362
Quadriceps femoris 293, 332, 341, 342
 Rectus femoris 307
 Vastus intermedius 307
 Vastus lateralis 307
 Vastus medialis 307

【R】

Radial artery 156, 158, 159, 160, 163, 166, 167, 168, 169, 170, 171, 176, 177
 Dorsal carpal branch 174
 Superficial palmar branch 169, 170
Radial bursa 167
Radial collateral ligament 154, 161
Radial collateral ligament of wrist joint 173
Radial fossa 122, 123
Radial head 127, 160
Radial nerve 139, 143, 145, 147, 148, 150, 151, 152, 156, 219
 Posterior antebrachial cutaneous nerve 139
 Posterior cutaneous nerve of forearm 139
 Superficial branch 158, 160, 174, 175
Radial notch 125, 126
Radial recurrent artery 158, 160
Radial styloid process 124, 126, 129, 155, 163, 173, 177, 178
Radial tuberosity 124, 126, 154, 155
Radialis indicis artery 167, 169, 170, 174
Radiate ligament of head of rib 223
Radiation of corpus callosum
 Frontal forceps 75
 Major forceps 75
 Minor forceps 75
 Occipital forceps 75
 Tapetum 73, 75, 77
Radicular artery 98, 100
Radicular vein 100
Radius 154, 161, 173
 Anterior border 155
 Anterior surface 155
Rami communicantes 101, 102, 205, 207, 223, 275
Ramus of ischium 282, 291, 294, 296, 300
Ramus of mandible 1, 4, 13, 14, 16, 17, 18, 29
 Anterior border 18
 Inferior border 18, 38
 Posterior border 18

Recto-uterine pouch 260, 285, 286, 287, 288, 373
Recto-vesical pouch 279
Rectoprostatic fascia 281
Rectovesical septum 281
Rectum 250, 260, 271, 274, 277, 280, 281, 282, 285, 288
Rectus abdominis 183, 191, 193, 228, 229, 230, 232, 234, 235, 237, 238, 239, 241, 242, 271, 279, 285, 286, 299, 301, 373, 375
 Tendinous intersection 228
Rectus capitis anterior 10
Rectus capitis lateralis 10, 37, 44, 71
Rectus capitis posterior major 10, 109, 110
Rectus capitis posterior minor 10
Rectus femoris 276, 307, 328, 330, 332, 333
 Reflected head 295, 301, 334
 Straight head 284, 295, 297, 299, 301, 334
Rectus sheath 301
 Anterior layer 133, 228, 229, 230, 299
 Posterior layer 229, 232, 233
Recurrent branch 166, 167, 168, 169, 346
Recurrent laryngeal nerve 35, 37, 47, 49, 84, 190, 191, 194, 195, 207, 214, 218, 220, 369
Red nucleus 77
Reflected head 295, 301, 334
Renal artery 245, 249, 252, 264, 265, 266, 267, 268, 270, 272, 273, 274
 Anterior branch 265
 Posterior branch 265
Renal column 265
Renal cortex 265
Renal fascia 267
Renal impression 255, 259
Renal medulla 265
Renal papilla 265
Renal pelvis 264, 265, 269, 274
Renal pyramid 265
Renal vein 245, 249, 252, 264, 266, 267, 268, 270, 272, 273, 274
Retinacular ligament 176
Retro-olivary groove 70
Retrobulbar fat 51
Retrocaecal recess 261
Retrocalcaneal bursa 321
Retromammary space 185
Retromandibular vein 32, 33, 40, 42, 82, 217
Retropubic space 285, 286
Rhinal sulcus 64
Rhomboid fossa 71, 76
Rhomboid major 88, 105, 106, 107, 117, 138, 139, 140, 141
Rhomboid minor 88, 106, 107, 117, 138, 139, 140, 141
Rhomboids 104
Rib 179, 208, 369
Rib I 36, 99, 113, 135, 148, 190, 191, 192, 193, 205, 218, 219, 220
 Joint of head of rib 98
Rib II 179, 183, 187, 189, 220

Rib IV 188
Rib V 188
Rib VI 188, 189
Rib VII 188
Rib VIII 188, 189, 222, 229
Rib IX 260
Rib X 260
Rib XI 263
Rib XII 102, 179, 189, 263
Riedel's lobe 245
Right atrial branches 197
Right atrioventricular orifice
 Right fibrous ring 200
Right atrioventricular valve 184, 199
Right atrium 196, 197, 199, 200, 201, 203, 208
Right auricle 191, 196, 197, 198, 199, 201
Right brachiocephalic vein 30, 36, 37, 190, 191, 208, 217, 218, 219, 224, 366
Right branch 246, 255, 256, 258
Right colic artery 248, 253, 258, 261
Right colic flexure 243, 250
Right colic vein 258
Right coronary artery 196, 197, 200, 202, 203
 Atrioventricular nodal branch 197
 Conus branch 197, 200, 202, 203
 Posterior interventricular branch 197, 200, 202, 203
 Right atrial branches 197
 Right marginal branch 196, 202
 Right ventricular branches 197, 198, 200, 203
Right coronary cusp 200, 201
Right crus 252, 268, 270, 273, 372
Right fibrous ring 200, 201
Right fibrous trigone 200, 201
Right gastric artery 246, 251
 Antral branch 244
Right gastric vein 256
Right gastro-epiploic artery 247, 251, 253
Right gastro-epiploic vein 241, 247, 251, 253
Right gastro-omental artery 247, 251, 253
Right gastro-omental vein 241, 247, 251, 253
Right hepatic duct 246, 247, 257
Right inferior lobar bronchus 193, 195, 209, 214, 215
Right inferior pulmonary vein 192, 193, 196, 197, 198, 204, 205, 214, 216, 222
Right lamina 48, 50
Right lobe 29, 30, 33, 35, 36, 45, 192, 195
Right lobe of liver 230, 239, 240, 241, 243, 244, 245, 251, 253, 254, 255, 256, 267
Right lobes 48
Right lung 190, 191, 192, 193, 209, 210, 212
 Inferior lobe 254
 Superior lobe 366
Right lymphatic duct 31, 37
Right main bronchus 193, 195, 204, 205, 209, 212, 214, 215, 220, 369
Right marginal branch 196, 197, 202

Right ovarian vein 245, 268
Right pulmonary artery 190, 193, 194, 195, 204, 205, 208, 214, 215, 216, 222
　Superior lobar artery 204, 205
Right pulmonary vein 203
Right semilunar cusp 200, 201
Right superior intercostal vein 205, 220
Right superior lobar bronchus 193, 195, 204, 205, 209, 212, 214, 215, 216
Right superior pulmonary vein 192, 196, 197, 198, 204, 205, 216, 222
Right suprarenal vein 266
Right supreme intercostal vein 224
Right testicular vein 245, 268, 273
Right ventricle 196, 197, 198, 200
　Conus arteriosus 201
　Infundibulum 201
Right ventricular branch 197, 198, 200, 202, 203
Ring finger
　Base of proximal phalanx 128
　Body of proximal phalanx 128
　Distal phalanx 128
　Head of proximal phalanx 128
　Shaft of proximal phalanx 128
Risorius 40
Root of nose 38
Root of tongue 226
Rostrum of corpus callosum 68
Round ligament of liver 237, 238, 239, 241, 244, 255, 274
Round ligament of uterus 228, 229, 234, 283, 285, 287, 288, 373

【S】

S1
　Ventral ramus 275, 282, 333
S2
　Ventral ramus 281, 282, 333
S3
　Ventral ramus 282
S I
　Vertebral body 93
Sac of tunica vaginalis 278
Sacciform recess 172, 173
Saccule 83
Sacral canal 93, 94, 95, 277
Sacral cornu 94
Sacral hiatus 94
Sacral horn 94
Sacral plexus 276
Sacro-iliac joint 96, 336
Sacrococcygeal joint 282
Sacrospinous ligament 282, 284, 297, 333, 334
Sacrotuberous ligament 284, 289, 290, 292, 297, 325, 334
　Falciform process 284, 297, 334
Sacrum 87, 88, 96, 105, 289, 336
　Lateral part 101, 102
　Promontory 96, 260, 277, 279, 282, 284, 285, 336
Sagittal border 24
Sagittal crest 20
Sagittal suture 7, 8, 14
Santorini's duct 257
Saphena varix 376

Saphenous branch 332
Saphenous nerve 328, 330, 332, 338, 347, 348, 352, 356, 357, 376
　Infrapatellar branch 338, 347
Saphenous opening 234
Sartorius 230, 276, 277, 295, 297, 301, 311, 313, 328, 330, 331, 332, 338, 347, 351, 352, 376
Scalene tubercle 181
Scalenus anterior 30
Scaphoid 128, 129, 173, 177, 178
　Tubercle 128, 172
　Waist 128
Scaphoid fossa 9, 25, 57
Scapula 115, 208
　Inferior angle 136, 186
　Lateral border 143
　Medial border 88, 136, 138, 139, 140, 141, 186
Sciatic nerve 289, 324, 325, 326, 327, 332
Sclera 51
Scrotum 278, 291, 326, 331
Segmental bronchi 209
Sella turcica 14
　Hypophysial fossa 4, 11, 12, 17, 25
Semicircular canals 83
Semilunar ganglion 80
Semilunar hiatus 12, 55
Semimembranosus 289, 295, 301, 311, 313, 327, 332, 337, 340, 341, 342, 344, 345, 347, 351, 352
Semimembranosus bursa 342
Seminal colliculus 279, 281
Seminal vesicle 279, 280, 281, 282
Semispinalis 107
Semispinalis capitis 10, 109, 110, 111
Semispinalis cervicis 109, 110
Semitendinosus 289, 295, 301, 311, 313, 324, 326, 327, 332, 337, 338, 340, 344, 345, 347, 351, 352
Septal cusp 200, 201
Septal papillary muscle 199
Septomarginal trabeculum 199
Septum pellucidum 68, 72, 75, 76, 77
Serous pericardium 196
　parietal layer 191, 192, 193, 194
Serratus anterior 106, 107, 117, 119, 132, 133, 144, 145, 146, 147, 148, 149, 181, 228, 371
Serratus posterior inferior 181
Serratus posterior superior 139, 141, 181
Sesamoid bone 363
Shaft of 1st metacarpal bone 128, 129
Shaft of 1st metatarsal bone 318
Shaft of 1st rib 183, 204
Shaft of 2nd metacarpal bone 128
Shaft of 5th metacarpal bone 128
Shaft of 5th metatarsal bone 318
Shaft of femur 302, 335
Shaft of metatarsal bone 364
Shaft of Middle phalanx 128
Shaft of proximal phalanx 128
Shaft of rib 181
Sheath of styloid process 7, 23
Short ciliary artery 54
Short ciliary nerves 53, 54, 81

Short gyri of insula 63
Short head 135, 142, 147, 148, 151, 219, 306, 309, 327, 332
Short plantar ligament 319, 359, 363
Short saphenous vein 344, 345, 348, 350, 352, 354, 356, 357, 358
Shoulder joint : Glenohumeral joint 115, 142
　Articular capsule 142
Sigmoid arteries 249, 258
Sigmoid branches 375
Sigmoid colon 250, 260, 273, 274, 279, 280, 285, 286, 375
Sigmoid mesocolon 288
Sigmoid sinus 71
Sigmoid veins 258
Sinu-atrial nodal branch 197, 200, 202
Sinus of Valsalva 197, 202, 203
Skin 5
Small cardiac vein 196, 197
Small intestine 237, 238, 241, 242, 267, 279, 286
　Ileum 239
　Jejunum 239
　Mesentery 242, 260
Small saphenous vein 344, 345, 348, 350, 352, 354, 356, 357, 358
Soft palate 43, 47, 60, 84
Soleal line 310, 312
Soleus 311, 313, 317, 338, 341, 345, 347, 350, 351, 352, 353, 355, 359
Somatic afferent fiber 85
Space of Retzius 285, 286
Spermatic cord 230, 234, 271, 278, 280, 328, 330
Spheno-ethmoidal recess 55
Sphenoid 12
　Anterior clinoid process 11, 58, 59
　Greater wing 1, 3, 4, 11, 12, 16, 43
　Lesser wing 1, 3, 11, 12, 16, 43
　Posterior clinoid process 11, 59
Sphenoidal angle 24
Sphenoidal fontanelle 14
Sphenoidal process 22
Sphenoidal rostrum 25
Sphenoidal sinus 12, 17, 43, 47, 55, 60, 61, 79
Sphenoidal yoke 11, 25
Sphenomandibular ligament 19, 56
Sphenomandibularis 42, 43
Sphenopalatine foramen 12
Sphenopalatine notch 22
Sphenoparietal sinus 59, 61
Spinal cord 60, 61, 67, 98, 99, 100, 101, 225, 270
Spinal ganglion 71, 99, 100, 101, 110, 111
　Dural sheath 98
Spinal root 37, 61, 66, 67, 71, 78, 84, 85, 100, 138, 147, 148
Spinalis 105, 106, 107
Spinalis cervicis 109
Spine of scapula 104, 105, 106, 116, 118, 136, 138, 139, 141, 186
Spine of sphenoid 7, 9, 25, 37
Spinous process 71, 89, 90, 91, 92, 95, 99, 100, 101, 102, 103, 110, 112, 113,

186, 223, 263
Spinous tubercle 93
Spleen 84, 245, 249, 260, 270, 372
   Inferior border 259
   Inferior pole 251
   Superior border 259
Splenic artery 244, 245, 258, 259, 260, 267, 268, 274, 372
Splenic flexure 250, 259, 372
Splenic hilum 372
Splenic hilum with Splenic artery 372
Splenic notch 259
Splenic vein 245, 258, 259, 260, 270, 372
Splenium of corpus callosum 64, 68, 70, 75, 79
Splenius capitis 10, 29, 108, 109, 110, 111, 138, 139, 141
Splenorenal ligament 260
Spongy urethra 279, 281
Spring ligament 319, 321, 358, 359, 363
Squamosal border 24
Squamous part 4, 9, 11, 17, 23
Squamous part of frontal bone 17
Squamous part of occipital bone 27
Stapedius 57, 58
Stapes 57, 58
Stellate ganglion 207, 220
Sternal angle 182, 187, 189
Sternal end 118, 183
   Sternal facet 118
Sternal facet 118
Sternal head 28, 133, 30, 32, 134, 217
Sternoclavicular joint 28, 36, 183, 184, 208, 217
Sternocleidomastoid 6, 10, 28, 29, 31, 32, 33, 34, 35, 37, 39, 48, 85, 110, 119, 147, 148, 183, 184, 195, 367
   Clavicular head 28, 30, 32, 134, 217
   Sternal head 30, 32, 134, 217, 28
Sternocleidomastoid branches 29
Sternocostal head 134
Sternohyoid 29, 30, 31, 32, 33, 34, 35, 36, 48, 85, 119, 135, 144, 147, 148, 183
Sternothyroid 29, 31, 32, 33, 35, 48, 85, 135, 147, 148, 183
Sternum 193, 208
Stomach 84, 226, 238, 241, 246, 250, 254, 259, 260, 270, 372
   Cardia 372
   Greater curvature 238, 241, 243, 244, 247, 251, 252, 372
   Lesser curvature 240, 243, 244, 247, 251, 252, 372
Straight arteries 248
Straight gyrus 64, 66
Straight head 295, 297, 299, 301, 334
Straight sinus 59, 60, 61
Styloglossus 10, 29, 35, 47
Stylohyoid 10, 29, 31, 32, 34, 35, 47, 48
Stylohyoid branch 83
Stylohyoid ligament 29, 35, 48
Styloid process 4, 7, 9, 23, 57
Stylomandibular ligament 19
Stylomastoid foramen 9, 14, 23, 57

Stylopharyngeus 10, 35, 45, 47, 84
Subacromial bursa 142
Subarachnoid space 52
Subarcuate fossa 23
Subclavian artery 30, 36, 37, 144, 145, 146, 192, 193, 194, 195, 204, 205, 207, 208, 214, 218, 219, 220, 224, 368
Subclavian vein 30, 31, 36, 37, 135, 149, 190, 191, 205, 207, 208, 217, 218, 219, 220, 224, 367, 368
Subclavius 30, 119, 135, 147, 149, 181, 370
Subcostal artery 224, 263
Subcostal nerve 245, 263, 268, 273, 375
   Anterior abdominal cutaneous branch 230
Subcostal vein 224, 263
Subcostales 222
Subcutaneous olecranon bursa 153
Subcutaneous tissue 5
Sublingual fossa 18
Sublingual gland 29, 35
Submandibular duct 29, 35, 56
Submandibular fossa 18
Submandibular ganglion 35, 56
Submandibular gland 28, 29, 30, 32, 33, 36, 40, 42, 43, 47
Submental artery 31, 32, 34
Submental vein 32
Suboccipital nerve 109
Subpopliteal recess 342
Subsartorial fascia 328
Subscapular artery 145, 146, 147, 148, 149, 370
Subscapular fossa 116
Subscapular vein 370
Subscapularis 117, 119, 121, 135, 142, 143, 145, 146, 147, 148, 149, 150, 371
Substantia nigra 76, 79
Subtalar joint 359
Subtendinous bursa of subscapularis 142
Sulcus limitans 71
Sulcus tali 321
Superciliary arch 20
Superficial cardiac plexus 194
Superficial cervical artery 29, 31, 32, 36, 37, 218, 367
Superficial cervical vein 32
Superficial circumflex iliac artery 330
Superficial circumflex iliac vein 280, 328, 376
Superficial dorsal artery of penis 278
Superficial dorsal vein of penis 278
Superficial epigastric artery 330
Superficial epigastric vein 328, 376
Superficial external pudendal artery 330, 376
Superficial external pudendal vein 328, 376
Superficial fascia of scrotum 278
Superficial fibular (peroneal) nerve 346, 347, 357
   Intermediate dorsal cutaneous nerve 346
   Medial dorsal cutaneous nerve 346
   Middle dorsal cutaneous nerve 355
Superficial inguinal nodes 228, 229, 230,

374, 376
Superficial inguinal ring 228, 231, 234, 275, 278, 328
Superficial inguinal veins 228
Superficial middle cerebral vein 62
Superficial nodes 147, 148
Superficial palmar arch 166, 167, 169
Superficial palmar branch 169, 170
Superficial temporal artery 29, 38, 39, 40, 57
   Frontal branch 39
   Parietal branch 5
Superficial temporal veins 38, 39, 40, 57
Superficial transverse metacarpal ligament 166
Superficial transverse metatarsal ligament 360
Superficial transverse perineal muscle 289, 290, 291, 292, 297
Superior angle 27, 116
Superior articular facet 89, 98, 112
Superior articular process 90, 91, 92, 93, 94, 95, 101, 112, 113, 334
Superior articular surface 89
Superior belly 29, 30, 31, 32, 33, 35, 147, 148
Superior border 116, 259
Superior bulb of jugular vein 56, 57
Superior cerebellar artery 59, 66, 67, 78
Superior cerebral veins 62
Superior cervical ganglion 37, 45, 47, 85
Superior clunial nerves 324
Superior colliculus 68, 70
Superior constrictor 10, 19, 45, 47
Superior costal facet 90, 91, 181
Superior costotransverse ligament 181, 223
Superior extensor retinaculum 355
Superior extremity 240, 243, 252, 264
Superior eyelid 51
Superior facet 318
Superior fibular (peroneal) retinaculum 351, 355
Superior fovea 71
Superior frontal gyrus 62, 63
Superior frontal sulcus 63
Superior gemellus 295, 301, 303, 305, 325
Superior glenohumeral ligament 143
Superior gluteal artery 281, 282, 283, 289, 325, 326, 333
Superior gluteal vein 325, 326
Superior horn 48
Superior hypogastric plexus 249, 270, 271, 274, 375
Superior ileocaecal recess 261
Superior labial branch 40
Superior laryngeal artery 29, 30, 31, 32, 33, 34, 35
Superior laryngeal nerve 45, 84
   External branch 29, 31, 32, 35, 36, 45, 84
   Internal branch 28, 29, 31, 32, 33, 34, 35, 45, 47, 49, 50, 84
Superior lateral genicular artery 345, 353
Superior left pulmonary vein 214
Superior lingular bronchus 209, 213

Superior lingular segment 210, 211, 213
Superior lip 260
Superior lobar artery 204, 205, 208, 215
Superior lobar bronchus 194, 213
　　Inferior lingular bronchus 213
　　Lingular bronchus 213
　　Superior lingular bronchus 213
Superior lobe 209, 210, 211, 212, 213, 366
Superior medial genicular artery 345, 353
Superior medullary velum 70, 71
Superior mental (genial) spine 18
Superior mesenteric artery 245, 252, 253, 258, 264, 266, 267, 268, 273, 274
　　Ileal arteries 279
　　Jejunal arteries 253, 279
Superior mesenteric ganglion 252, 274
Superior mesenteric vein 245, 246, 248, 253, 258
　　Ileal veins 279
　　Jejunal veins 279
Superior nasal concha 16, 26, 55, 56
Superior nasal meatus 26, 55
Superior nuchal line 7, 9, 27, 110, 111
Superior oblique 51, 52, 53, 54, 80
Superior orbital fissure 1, 11, 12, 16, 25, 80, 81, 85
Superior parietal lobule 63
Superior petrosal sinus 59
Superior pharyngeal branch 47
Superior pole 240, 243, 252, 264
Superior pubic ramus 235, 294, 296, 336
Superior rectal artery 249, 281
Superior rectal vein 249, 281
Superior rectus 51, 52, 53, 54, 80
Superior right pulmonary vein 193, 214
Superior root 29, 31, 33, 35
Superior sagittal sinus 47, 60, 61, 62
Superior salivatory nucleus 85
Superior segment 210, 211, 212, 213
Superior segmental artery 265
Superior segmental bronchus 209
Superior suprarenal arteries 252
Superior temporal arteriole 53
Superior temporal gyrus 63
Superior temporal line 4, 20, 24, 40
Superior temporal sulcus 63
Superior temporal venule 53
Superior thoracic artery 145, 146, 149
Superior thyroid artery 29, 30, 31, 32, 33, 34, 35, 36, 45
Superior thyroid notch 48
Superior thyroid tubercle 48
Superior thyroid vein 29, 30, 36
Superior tibiofibular joint : Tibiofibular joint 315
　　Articular capsule 339
Superior tracheobronchial nodes 369
Superior transverse scapular ligament 117, 119, 139, 141, 142
Superior trunk 28, 31, 32, 37, 147, 148, 190, 191, 192, 193, 194, 218, 219
Superior tubercle 91
Superior ulnar collateral artery 151, 153, 158
Superior vena cava 190, 191, 192, 196, 197, 199, 201, 203, 204, 205, 208, 214, 217, 218, 219, 222, 224, 366, 369
Superior vertebral notch 90, 92
Superior vesical artery 280, 281, 283, 285, 288, 373
Superolateral face of cerebral hemisphere 62
Supinator 127, 159, 161, 162
Supinator crest 125, 154, 161
Supra-optic recess 68, 72
Supra-orbital artery 38, 51, 52
Supra-orbital foramen 1, 12, 20, 38
Supra-orbital margin 1, 16, 20, 38
Supra-orbital nerve 38, 39, 40, 51, 52, 53, 54, 82
Supra-orbital notch 1, 12, 20, 38
Supra-orbital vein 38
Supraclavicular nerve 30, 32, 134
Supraclavicular node 185, 367
Supraglenoid tubercle 118
Suprahyoid branch 31, 32
Supramarginal gyrus 63
Suprameatal triangle 23
Suprapatellar bursa 342
Suprapatellar fat pad 342
Suprapineal recess 68, 72
Suprapleural membrane 181
Suprapubic region 227
Suprarenal arteries 264
Suprarenal gland 252, 260, 264, 267, 268, 270, 272, 273, 274
Suprarenal impression 255
Suprascapular artery 30, 31, 32, 33, 36, 37, 139, 140, 141, 142, 143, 144, 145, 146, 147, 148, 192, 193, 194, 195, 218, 219, 367
Suprascapular nerve 31, 32, 135, 139, 140, 141, 142, 143, 144, 219
Suprascapular notch 116
Suprascapular vein 30, 142, 143, 217
Suprasellar cistern 60
Supraspinatus 117, 119, 121, 138, 139, 140, 141, 142, 143
Supraspinous fossa 116, 118, 139, 141
Supraspinous ligament 101, 102, 103
Suprasternal notch 179, 182, 183, 184, 217
Supratrochlear artery 38, 51, 53
Supratrochlear nerve 38, 39, 40, 51, 52, 53, 54, 81, 82
Supratrochlear vein 38
Supreme intercostal artery 207, 220
Supreme intercostal vein 205, 220, 224
Supura-orbital nerve 81
Sural nerve 344, 345, 348, 350, 352, 355, 357, 358
Surgical neck 120
Suspensory ligament of ovary 287
Suspensory ligament of penis 230
Suspensory ligament of breast 185
Suspensory retinaculum of breast 185
Sustentaculum tali 318, 320, 321, 364
　　Groove for tendon of flexor hallucis longus 359, 363
Sympathetic ganglion 204, 205, 207, 221, 222, 271, 274, 275
Sympathetic part 45, 205, 207
Sympathetic trunk 37, 45, 100, 101, 194, 195, 204, 205, 207, 218, 220, 221, 222, 223, 225, 267, 271, 274, 275, 282, 368
　　Branches to Greater splanchnic nerve 204, 205
　　Thoracic cardiac branches 194
Synovial membrane 336
Synovial sheaths of digits of hand 167

【T】

T2
　　Dural sheath 99
　　Spinal ganglion 99
T5
　　Dorsal ramus 99
　　Ventral ramus 99
T10
　　Spinal ganglion 101
T I
　　Pedicle 99
　　Spinous process 112
　　Vertebral body 99, 100
T III
　　Spinous process 186
T V
　　Pedicle 101
T IX
　　Vertebral body 222
T X
　　Spinous process 101
Taenia coli 261
Tail of caudate nucleus 76
Tail of epididymis 278
Tail of pancreas 245, 253, 257, 259, 260
Talocalcaneal cervical ligament 364
Talocalcaneal interosseous ligament 321, 358, 359
Talocalcanean joint 359
Talocalcaneonavicular joint 359
　　Talonavicular part 359
Talus 357, 359, 364
　　Anterior facet for calcaneus 321
　　Groove for tendon of flexor hallucis longus 318, 321
　　Lateral malleolar facet 320
　　Lateral tubercle 318, 320
　　Medial malleolar facet 320
　　Medial tubercle 318, 320, 364
　　Middle facet for calcaneus 321
　　Posterior calcaneal articluar facet 321
　　Posterior process 364
Tapetum 73, 75, 77
Tarlov's cyst 286
Tarsal sinus 320, 357, 359, 364
Tectorial membrane 98
Tectum of midbrain 70, 79
Tegmen tympani 11, 23, 57
Tegmentum of midbrain 68, 70, 79
Tegmentum of pons 60
Tela choroidea of 3rd ventricle 76
Tempolal horn 72, 74
Temporal bone 5, 12, 43
　　Apex of petrous part 9
　　External acoustic meatus 4
　　Mastoid process 4
　　Petrous part 11, 56
　　Squamous part 4, 9, 11, 17
　　Styloid process 4, 9, 57

Tympanic part 4, 9, 37
　Zygomatic process 4
Temporal border 24
Temporal branch 39, 83
Temporal fascia 5, 40
Temporal horn：Inferior horn 76
Temporal lobe 43, 60, 63
　Temporal pole 73
Temporal pole 62, 63, 64, 73
Temporal process 24
Temporal surface 24, 25
Temporalis 2, 5, 6, 19, 29, 39, 40, 42, 43
　Deep head 42, 43
　Superficial head 43
Temporomandibular joint 6, 10
　Articular capsule 29, 40, 42
　Articular disc 42
Tendinous arch of levator ani 276, 277, 284
Tendinous cords 199, 200
Tendinous intersection 228, 229
Tendon of Flexor digitorum profundus 167
Tendon of Triceps brachii 139
Tendon sheath
　Fibrous sheath 172
Tendon sheath of digits of hand 168
Tendon sheath of Flexor tendons 166, 171
Tensor fasciae latae 276, 295, 328, 330, 331
Tensor tympani 10, 57
Tensor veli palatini 10, 44, 56
Tentorium cerebelli 44, 59, 60, 61
Teres major 105, 106, 107, 117, 119, 121, 136, 137, 138, 139, 140, 141, 143, 150, 152, 186
Teres minor 106, 117, 119, 121, 137, 138, 139, 140, 141, 152
Terminal filum 101
Terminal ileum 242, 250, 261
Terminal sulcus of tongue 49
Testicular artery 233, 235, 261, 271, 272, 273, 274, 278, 281
Testicular plexus 274
Testicular vein 233, 235, 261, 271, 281, 375
Testis 232, 278, 279
TFCC 173, 178
Thalamostriate vein 74, 76
Thalamus 60, 68, 70, 73, 74, 75, 76, 77
Thebesian valve 199
Thecal sac 101, 260
Thenar eminence 163
Thoracic aorta 189, 194, 206, 207, 215, 224, 225, 267
Thoracic cardiac branches 193, 194, 195
Thoracic duct 37, 214, 218, 221, 225, 367, 368
Thoracic nerve
　Dorsal ramus 107, 223
　Posterior ramus 107, 223
Thoracic vertebra 87, 179
Thoracic wall 259
Thoraco-acromial artery 370, 371
　Acromial branch 135, 148, 135
　Clavicular branch 367, 370
　Deltoid branch 370
　Pectoral branches 135, 144, 145, 190, 191, 192, 370
Thoraco-acromial vein 217, 371
Thoracodorsal artery 145, 146, 147, 148, 149, 191, 371
Thoracodorsal nerve 144, 146, 147, 148, 149, 150, 371
Thoracodorsal vein 191, 217, 219
Thoracolumbar fascia 88, 105, 106, 107, 138, 139, 140, 267, 270, 271
　Anterior layer 103, 267
　Middle layer 267
　Posterior layer 267, 324
Thumb 167
　Distal phalanx 128, 129, 178
　Proximal phalanx 128, 129, 178
Thymic artery 218
Thymic veins 207, 217, 218, 366
Thymus 218, 366
Thyro-arytenoid 49
Thyro-epiglotticus 49
Thyrocervical trunk 31, 36, 37, 147, 148, 192, 193, 195, 218
Thyrohyoid 29, 30, 31, 32, 33, 34, 35, 48, 85, 144
Thyrohyoid branch 29, 31, 32, 35
Thyrohyoid membrane 29, 32, 33, 49, 50
Thyroid articular surface 48, 50
Thyroid cartilage 60
　Laryngeal prominence 48, 217
　Left lamina 47, 49, 50
　Oblique line 33
　Right lamina 50
Thyroid gland 144
　Left lobe 30, 32, 34, 36, 48, 190, 193, 194, 218
　Right lobe 29, 30, 33, 35, 36, 45, 48, 192, 195
Thyropharyngeal part 45
Tibia 293, 311, 341, 343, 359, 364
　Anterior border 311
　Articular facet 315
　Groove for tendon of flexor hallucis longus 359
　Inferior articular surface 315
　Lateral condyle 315, 337, 339, 340, 341, 343
　Lateral surface 311
　Medial condyle 339, 340, 343
　Medial malleolus 356, 357, 364
　Medial surface 311, 347, 348, 355
　Posterior surface 353
Tibial collateral ligament 309, 311, 313, 339, 340, 341, 342, 347, 351
Tibial nerve 344, 345, 352, 353, 355, 356, 357
　Branches to lateral head of gastrocnemius 352
　Branches to medial head of gastrocnemius 352
　Branches to soleus 352
　Medial calcaneal branches 348, 355, 356
　Medial sural cutaneous nerve 344
　Muscular branches 344
Tibial tuberosity 310, 311, 312, 337, 341, 342, 343, 346
Tibialis anterior 311, 313, 319, 346, 354, 355, 357, 358, 363, 364
Tibialis posterior 311, 313, 317, 319, 351, 354, 355, 356, 357, 358, 359, 363
Tibiocalcaneal part 321, 359
Tibiofibular joint：Superior tibiofibular joint 315
　Articular capsule 339
Tibiofibular syndesmosis 315, 364
Tibiofibular trunk 353
　Muscular branches 353
Tibiotalar part 359
Tip of greater horn 45, 47
Tongue 43, 50, 56, 60, 84
Tonsil of cerebellum 66, 70
Trachea 28, 36, 37, 49, 50, 112, 113, 190, 191, 193, 195, 205, 208, 214, 215, 218, 220, 226, 366
Tracheal cartilages 48
Tracheobronchial nodes 369
Tragus 38, 40, 42, 57
Transpyloric plane 227
Transversalis fascia 235
Transverse acetabular ligament 295, 301, 334, 336
Transverse arytenoid 49, 50
Transverse branch 330
Transverse cervical artery 147, 148, 192, 193, 194, 195, 219, 367
　Dorsal scapular artery 138
　Superficial cervical artery 29, 31, 32, 36, 218
Transverse cervical vein 217
　Superficial cervical vein 32
Transverse colon 230, 237, 238, 239, 241, 242, 243, 246, 247, 248, 249, 250, 253, 254
Transverse costal facet 90, 91, 181, 223
Transverse facial artery 40
Transverse head 130, 171, 361, 362
Transverse ligament 154
Transverse ligament of atlas 98
Transverse ligament of knee 340, 341
Transverse mesocolon 241
Transverse palatine 9
Transverse part 105, 106, 245, 248, 253, 305
Transverse pericardial sinus 196
Transverse process 89, 90, 91, 94, 102, 223, 28, 37, 44, 57, 71, 98, 99
　Anterior tubercle 90, 98
　Intertubercular lamella 90, 98
　Posterior tubercle 90, 98
　Transverse costal facet 91
Transverse ridge 94, 300
Transverse sinus 59, 61
Transversus abdominis 229, 232, 233, 249, 267, 270, 275, 297, 299, 301
Transversus thoracis 183, 189
Trapezium 128, 129, 168, 172, 173, 178
Trapezius 10, 29, 30, 32, 33, 34, 85, 88, 104, 108, 117, 119, 132, 134, 135, 136, 137, 138, 139, 140, 141, 179, 186, 208
　Ascending part 105, 106, 107

Descending part　　105, 106
Inferior part　　105, 106, 107
Middle part　　105, 106
Superior part　　105, 106
Transverse part　　105, 106
Trapezoid　　128, 129, 168, 173, 178
Trapezoid ligament　　117, 119, 142
Trapezoid line　　118
Triangle of auscultation　　137
Triangular fibrocartilage complex　　173, 178
Triangular fossa　　57
Triangular interval　　152
Triangular ligament　　176
Triangular part　　63
Triceps brachii　　127, 144, 145, 151, 153
　Lateral head　　121, 133, 139, 143, 150, 152
　Long head　　106, 107, 117, 119, 136, 137, 139, 140, 149, 150, 151, 152
　Medial head　　121, 123, 150, 156
Tricuspid valve　　184, 199
　Anterior cusp　　199, 200, 201
　Posterior cusp　　200, 201
　Septal cusp　　200, 201
Trigeminal ganglion　　44, 56, 59, 80
Trigeminal impression　　11, 23
Trigeminal nerve [V]　　55, 56, 59, 61, 66, 67, 70, 78
　Motor root　　56
Trigone area　　72
Trigone of bladder　　280, 281, 285, 286, 373
Trigone of hypoglossal nerve　　71
Trigone of vagus nerve　　71
Triquetrum　　128, 129, 173, 177, 178
Trochanteric fossa　　302, 304
Trochlea　　51, 52
Trochlea of humerus　　122, 126, 154, 156
Trochlea of talus　　318
Trochlear fovea　　20
Trochlear nerve [IV]　　51, 52, 53, 54, 56, 59, 61, 66, 70, 76, 78, 80
Trochlear notch　　125, 126, 154, 155, 156
Trunk of corpus callosum　　68
Trunks　　135
Tubal extremity　　287
Tuber cinereum　　66, 68, 79
Tubercle　　128, 172
Tubercle of 1st rib　　99
Tubercle of Lower　　199
Tubercle of rib　　181
Tubercle of trapezium　　128, 172
Tuberculum of iliac crest　　231, 294, 298, 300
Tuberculum sellae　　11, 25
Tuberosity for serratus anterior　　181
Tuberosity of 5th metatarsal bone　　318, 320, 354, 358, 363, 364
Tuberosity of cuboid　　318
Tuberosity of navicular　　318, 320, 354, 359, 362, 363
Tuberosity of ulna　　125, 126, 154, 155
Tumor　　369
Tunica albuginea　　278, 279
Tunica vaginalis
　Parietal layer　　278, 279
　Visceral layer　　278, 279
Tympanic canaliculus　　23
Tympanic membrane　　57, 58
Tympanic nerve　　57, 84
Tympanic part　　4, 9, 23, 37
Tympanic ring　　14
Tympanosquamous fissure　　9, 23

【U】

Ulna　　154, 155
　Coronoid process　　126, 154, 155, 156
　Olecranon　　126, 153, 154, 155, 156
　Posterior border　　153
　Radial notch　　126
　Supinator crest　　154, 161
　Trochlear notch　　126, 154, 155, 156
Ulnar artery　　153, 156, 158, 159, 160, 163, 166, 167, 168, 169, 170, 171, 177
　Deep palmar branch　　168, 169, 170, 171
Ulnar collateral ligament　　154
　Oblique band　　154
　Posterior band　　154
　Posterioroblique ligament　　154
　Transverse ligament　　154
　Upper band　　154
Ulnar collateral ligament of wrist joint　　172
Ulnar head　　127, 160
Ulnar nerve　　145, 146, 147, 148, 149, 150, 151, 152, 153, 156, 158, 159, 160, 163, 166, 167, 168, 169, 171, 219, 371
　Branch to flexor carpi ulnaris　　158
　Common palmar digital nerve　　168, 169
　Deep branch　　168, 169, 171
　Digital branches　　171
　Dorsal branch　　174
　Muscular branch　　168
　Palmar branch　　159, 167
　Superficial branch　　171
Ulnar notch　　124
Ulnar recurrent artery
　Anterior branch　　160
　Posterior branch　　153, 158, 160
Ulnar styloid process　　125, 126, 129, 155, 162, 173, 177, 178
Umbilical artery　　232
Umbilical region　　227
Umbilical vein　　232
Umbilicus　　228, 229, 230, 232
Umbo of tympanic membrane　　57
Uncinate process　　12, 26, 90, 91, 245, 253
Uncovertebral joint　　112
Uncus　　64, 66, 77
Uncus of body　　90, 91
Upper band　　154
Upper crus　　57
Upper head　　10, 42
Upper subscapular nerves　　147, 148, 149, 150
Upper trunk　　28, 31, 32, 37, 147, 148, 190, 191, 192, 193, 194, 218, 219
Urachus　　232
Ureter　　103, 245, 261, 264, 265, 267, 268, 269, 270, 271, 272, 273, 274, 280, 281, 283, 285, 288, 373, 375
Ureteric orifice　　280, 281
Urethra　　286, 291
Urinary bladder　　232, 233, 235, 260, 269, 271, 279, 283, 286, 287, 375
Urogenital diaphragm　　281
Uterine artery　　283, 288
Uterine cavity　　260, 285, 286, 373
Uterine extremity　　287
Uterine tube　　286, 373
Uterosacral ligament　　288
Utricle　　83
Uvula　　47

【V】

Vagal trigone　　71
Vagina　　285, 286, 288, 373
Vaginal artery　　283, 288
Vaginal fornix
　Anterior part　　285, 288, 373
　Posterior part　　285, 286, 288, 373
Vaginal orifice　　289
Vaginal process　　25
Vaginal wall　　286
Vagus nerve [X]　　29, 30, 34, 35, 36, 37, 45, 47, 61, 70, 71, 78, 84, 190, 191, 192, 193, 194, 195, 204, 205, 206, 207, 214, 218, 219, 220, 367, 368
　Branch to carotid body　　45
　Inferior cervical cardiac branches　　205
　Inferior ganglion　　37, 45
　Pharyngeal branch　　45
　Superior laryngeal nerve　　45
　Superior pharyngeal branch　　47
Vallate papillae　　49
Valve of coronary sinus　　199
Valve of inferior vena cava　　199
Valvulae conniventes　　250, 260
Vastus intermedius　　303, 305, 306, 307, 309, 330, 332
Vastus lateralis　　276, 303, 305, 306, 307, 328, 332, 335
　Aponeurosis　　342
Vastus medialis　　303, 305, 306, 307, 309, 311, 313, 328, 330, 332, 335, 337, 338
Vein of Galen　　60, 68
Vena comitans of Brachial artery　　151
Vena comitans of hypoglossal nerve　　31
Venous foramen　　11
Venous valve　　349
Ventral pallidum　　77
Ventral paraflocculus　　66
Ventral ramus　　29, 31, 36, 37, 71, 98, 99, 100, 102, 220, 275, 281, 282, 333
Ventral root　　100
Vermiform appendix　　242, 248, 261
Vertebra prominens : C VII
　Spinous process　　71, 99, 100, 113
　Vertebral body　　99
Vertebral artery　　37, 61, 62, 66, 67, 71, 78, 98, 99, 109, 110, 111, 208, 368
Vertebral body　　89, 90, 91, 92, 93, 95, 98, 99, 100, 101, 102, 112, 222, 223
　Superior costal facet　　181
Vertebral foramen　　89, 90, 91, 92
Vertebral vein　　36, 37, 217, 218, 220, 224, 367
Vertical ridge　　307
Vesical venous plexus　　281

Vesico-uterine pouch　260, 285, 286, 287, 288, 373
Vestibular area　71
Vestibular fold　49, 50
Vestibular nerve　58, 83
　Superior part　58
Vestibule　58
Vestibule of vagina　285, 289, 290
Vestibulocochlear nerve [VIII]　58, 59, 61, 66, 70, 78, 83
Vinculum breve　167
Vinculum longum　167
Virchow node　185, 367
Visceral layer　191, 278, 279
Visceral peritoneum　233, 244
Visceral pleura　219
Visual cortex　74

Vocal fold　49, 50
Vocal process　48
Vomer　7, 17, 43, 79
　Posterior border　9, 25
Vomerovaginal canal　9

【W】

Waist　128
White ramus communicans　221
Wing tendon　176
Wirsung's canal　257
Wrist joint　115

【X】

Xiphisternal joint　182, 184
Xiphoid process　179, 182, 187, 189, 227

【Z】

Zona orbicularis　335, 336
Zygapophysial joint　99, 102, 103, 113
Zygomatic arch　4, 7, 9, 16, 29, 38, 40, 42, 43
Zygomatic bone　1, 4, 12, 43
　Orbital margin　12
Zygomatic branch　39, 83
Zygomatic nerve　81
Zygomatic process　4, 20, 21, 23
Zygomatico-orbital foramen　12, 24
Zygomaticofacial foramen　24
Zygomaticotemporal foramen　24
Zygomaticus major　2, 6, 39, 40
Zygomaticus minor　2, 6, 39

訳者略歴

佐藤　達夫
1963 年	東京医科歯科大学医学部医学科卒業
1968 年	東京医科歯科大学医学研究科形態学系・解剖学修了，医学博士
1968 年	福島県立医科大学講師
1970 年	東北大学医学部助教授
1974 年	東京医科歯科大学教授
1983 年	東京医科歯科大学学生部長
1995 年	東京医科歯科大学医学部長
2001 年	東京医科歯科大学副学長
2002 年	東京医科歯科大学医歯学教育研究センター長
2003 年	東京医科歯科大学名誉教授
2009 年	東京有明医療大学学長
2017 年	東京有明医療大学名誉学長・名誉教授

秋田　恵一
1987 年	札幌医科大学医学部卒業
1991 年	東京医科歯科大学大学院医学研究科博士課程修了
同　年	東京医科歯科大学医学部助手
1993〜95 年	University College London 解剖学・発生生物学講座研究員
1996 年	東京医科歯科大学医学部講師
1999 年	東京医科歯科大学大学院助教授
2010 年	東京医科歯科大学大学院教授（臨床解剖学分野）

人体解剖カラーアトラス 原書第 8 版（電子書籍付）

2021 年 1 月 20 日　第 1 刷発行
2023 年 8 月 15 日　第 2 刷発行

著　者　Peter H. Abrahams, Jonathan D. Spratt, Marios Loukas, Albert N. van Schoor
訳　者　佐藤達夫・秋田恵一
発行所　エルゼビア・ジャパン株式会社
　　　　☎（編集）03-3589-5024
発売元　株式会社　南江堂
　　　　〒113-8410　東京都文京区本郷三丁目 42 番 6 号
　　　　☎（出版）03-3811-7235（営業）03-3811-7239
　　　　ホームページ https://www.nankodo.co.jp/
　　　　印刷・製本　小宮山印刷工業

Abrahams' & McMinn's Clinical Atlas of Human Anatomy, 8th Edition
©2021 Elsevier Japan KK

定価はカバーに表示してあります．
落丁・乱丁の場合はお取り替えいたします．
本書の無断複製を禁じます．

Printed and Bound in Japan
ISBN978-4-524-22764-8

JCOPY〈出版者著作権管理機構　委託出版物〉

本書の無断複製は，著作権法上での例外を除き禁じられています．複製される場合は，そのつど事前に，出版者著作権管理機構（TEL 03-5244-5088，FAX 03-5244-5089，e-mail：info@jcopy.or.jp）の許諾を得てください．

本書のコピー，スキャン，デジタル化等の無断複製は著作権法上の例外を除き禁じられています．違法ダウンロードはもとより，代行業者等の第三者によるスキャンやデジタル化はたとえ個人や家庭内での利用でも一切認められていません．著作権者の許諾を得ないで無断で複製した場合や違法ダウンロードした場合は，著作権侵害として刑事告発，損害賠償請求などの法的措置をとることがあります．〈発行所：エルゼビア・ジャパン株式会社〉